A History of Engineering and Science in the Bell System

Communications Sciences
(1925-1980)

Prepared by Members of the Technical Staff, AT&T Bell Laboratories.

S. Millman, Editor.

AT&T Bell Laboratories

Credits for figures taken from
other than Bell System sources
appear on page 487.

Inquiries may be made to the following address:

AT&T Technologies
Commercial Sales Clerk
Select Code 500-471
PO Box 19901
Indianapolis, Indiana 46219
1-800-432-6600

First Printing, 1984

International Standard Book Number: 0-932764-06-1

Library of Congress Catalog Card Number: 84-72181

Printed in the United States of America

Contents

eration, Propagation, and Reverberation, 119. Signal Processing in the Auditory System, 123. Linguistic Studies, 124. Research in Psychoacoustics and Perception, 125. Electroacoustic Systems and Transducers, 126. Human-Machine Communication, 129. **References, 134.**

3. Picture Communication Research 141

I. Early Explorations—Picture Scanning, Color Television, PICTURE-PHONE* Visual Telephone Service, 141. Picture Scanning, 142. Color Television, 146. Early Research into PICTUREPHONE Visual Telephone Service, 147. **Bandwidth Compression—Bit-Rate Reduction, 147.** Redundancy in Television Transmission, 147. Application of Digital Processing to Picture Communication, 150. **III. Further Advances in Picture Communications, 160.** Scanned Graphics, 160. Video Conferencing, 162. Network Quality Television, 165. **References, 166.**

4. Vacuum Tube Electronics Research 169

I. Electron Beams, 169. The Pierce Electron Gun, 170. The Reflex Klystron, 171. **II. Multicavity Magnetron Research, 173.** Magnetron Research During World War II, 173. Postwar Magnetron Research, 174. **III. Traveling Wave Tubes, 175.** The Helix Traveling Wave Tube Amplifier, 178. The Spatial Harmonic Amplifier, 182. Backward-Wave Voltage-Tunable Oscillator, 184. The Karp Space-Harmonic Oscillator at Millimeter Waves, 185. The Easitron Amplifier, 185. Double-Stream Amplification, 186. **IV. Noise in Microwave Amplifiers and Detectors, 187.** Noise Studies in Traveling Wave Tubes, 187. Noise and Parametric Amplification, 188. **V. Concluding Comment on Vacuum Tube Electronics Research, 189.** References, 189.

5. Radio Systems Research 193

I. Research at Short and Ultrashort Wavelengths, 193. Shortwave Propagation and Detection, 194. Beyond-the-Horizon Tropospheric Propagation, 197. Early Antenna Research—The Rhombic Antenna, 198. Angle of Arrival of Radio Waves, 200. Overcoming the Effects of Fading, 202. Receiving System Noise, 203. Shortwave Radio Multiplex, 204. Ultra-Shortwave Studies, 204. **II. Microwave Radio-Relay Systems, 207.** Microwave Propagation Studies, 208. New York-Boston TDX and the TD-2 Radio Systems, 209. Detectors, Modulators, Converters, and Other Components, 211. Experimental 11-GHz Short-Hop Radio System, 212. Microwave Short-Haul Radio Systems, 212. **III. Propagation Studies at Millimeter Waves, 214.** Effect of Rain, 214. Earth-Space Propagation, 214. Space Diversity, 216. Cross Polarization, 217. Satellite Beacon Measurements, 217. **IV. Antenna Research at Microwave Frequen-**

---

* Registered service mark of AT&T Co.

10. Digital Communications 399

11. Behavioral Science 431

---

* Trademark of AT&T Bell Laboratories.

Acknowledgments

Communications Sciences is the second of two volumes on research at Bell Laboratories; the first, *Physical Sciences*, was published in 1983. Like *Physical Sciences*, this volume covers the period from 1925 to roughly 1980. It records research accomplishments by Bell Labs scientists and engineers, with appropriate references to pioneering contributions by researchers in other institutions. The two research volumes are part of the series entitled *A History of Engineering and Science in the Bell System*. As in the case of *Physical Sciences*, the manuscript for *Communications Sciences* was prepared from material contributed by many authors—about 30 in this volume—who have themselves carried out research and published in the fields of communications they write about. In addition to the principal authors, who are listed at the bottom of the first page of each chapter, many other scientists made contributions, either by writing about their own research or by commenting on drafts of chapters in various stages of preparation. These comments contributed immeasurably to the accuracy, balance, and readability of these chronicles. These contributors are listed below:

M. R. Aaron, J. B. Allen, A. Ashkin, E. E. Bailey, A. C. Beck, E. F. Brown, C. A. Burrus, J. D. Carroll, T. S. Chu, A. B. Crawford, W. H. Doherty, G. R. Faulhaber, M. R. Garey, R. L. Graham, D. W. Hagelbarger, R. W. Hamming, G. J. Hansen, B. G. Haskell, W. C. Jakes, H. M. Jenkins, B. W. Kernighan, H. Kogelnik, W. D. Lewis, J. O. Limb, E. A. J. Marcatili, D. Marcuse, M. V. Mathews, S. E. Miller, F. W. Mounts, M. B. Panish, A. A. Penzias, J. R. Pierce, H. O. Pollak, S. Pruzansky, H. E. Rowe, I. W. Sandberg, S. A. Schelkunoff, M. R. Schroeder, R. N. Shepard, D. Slepian, G. Sperling, D. A. Spicer, S. Sternberg, P. K. Tien, J. E. Tschirgi, V. A. Vyssotsky, W. D. Warters, R. W. Wilson.

Special recognition is due to W. E. Evans and D. M. Solomon, who prepared this volume and saw it through the press, and to C. Biczak, who checked and completed the numerous references. The coordination of their efforts was in the capable hands of S. Annunziata. G. E. Schindler, Jr., of the AT&T Bell Laboratories Publication Center played a crucial role by his involvement in many aspects of the publication process, from discussions with some authors about technical content of manuscripts and publication deadlines to the final review of chapter manuscripts and illustrations. The preparation of the various drafts for each chapter was greatly facilitated by the use of the UNIX* operating system for text processing, guided by P. A. Harrison and G. A. Wallace.

S. Millman
Editor

---

* Trademark of AT&T Bell Laboratories.

Overview—
Research in Communications

This is the second of two volumes on the history of research at Bell Laboratories* from 1925 to about 1980. The first, subtitled *Physical Sciences* and published in 1983, recorded the important achievements of Bell Labs scientists in physics and in materials research. The present volume describes research in communications.

Designing and building a telecommunications network for the nation has been a task of almost overwhelming complexity. It has occupied many thousands of engineers and scientists at Bell Laboratories, as well as their associates at AT&T, Western Electric, and the various operating telephone companies. By contrast, the number of people involved in communications studies and experiments in the research organization of Bell Laboratories has been very small. Nonetheless, the work chronicled in this volume testifies to the profound impact of these researchers on the course of communications history. Included are a number of brilliant individual achievements, such as the conception of information theory by C. E. Shannon, as well as a number of extended efforts embroidered by a succession of researchers, such as the evolution of pulse-code-modulation transmission.

Communications research in the Bell System predated the formation of Bell Laboratories in 1925. By that time, many of the mathematical foundations for communications had already been firmly laid. Mathematical techniques had been applied successfully to the study of the stability of vacuum-tube amplifiers, the understanding of sidebands in amplitude-modulated carrier waves, the investigation of the properties of the ionosphere for radio communication, and to other communications studies. Acoustics research was also well under way at that time. Theories had been advanced on the nature of hearing, and mathematical relationships had been derived linking electromechanical and electroacoustical systems. These and other research contributions from this early period are described in Chapter 10 of the first volume of this series, called *The Early Years (1875-1925)*.

The present volume is divided into 12 chapters, each representing a particular broad topic within communications sciences. Some of the chapters describe research areas, such as vacuum-tube electronics and waveguides, that are no longer active. Other chapters deal with areas that are as active

---

* As of January 1, 1984, Bell Laboratories adopted the designation AT&T Bell Laboratories in order to clearly show its relationship with AT&T.

today as they have been in previous decades, and represent enduring commitments to research in the constituent branches of communications. Such areas include mathematics, acoustics, visual communications, switching, and computer science.

The first chapter covers mathematical research, work that predated the formal founding of Bell Laboratories. One of the early problems that concerned mathematicians was the study of the properties of modulation. The existence of lower-frequency and higher-frequency sidebands when a voice band is impressed on a carrier frequency by amplitude modulation had been established before 1925. The case of frequency modulation was more complicated, particularly because of its interrelation with noise. Studies by H. Nyquist, with the aim of finding the maximum signaling rate that could be used over a telegraph channel of a given bandwidth, led him to derive the version of the sampling theorem for which he is famous—that reconstruction of a band-limited signal requires sampling at a rate at least twice the highest frequency component of the signal.

The need to maximize the number of channels that can be used in a carrier transmission system brought about fundamental investigations of networks and filters, and of oscillators with frequency stability of one part in a billion. This led W. P. Mason to the study of crystal vibrations and the theory of fabrication and control of crystal oscillators. Sophisticated network synthesis methods were developed by S. Darlington. The stability and feedback problems encountered in multistage amplifiers for very long-distance transmission with many such repeating amplifiers were solved by H. S. Black with his invention of the negative feedback amplifier and by H. W. Bode with his fundamental mathematical techniques.

The noise problems encountered in multiplexed-carrier telephony, when wideband amplifiers with inherent nonlinearities serve many channels, were solved first by fundamental understanding of Johnson noise, present in any electrical resistor, and by S. O. Rice's classical analysis of the properties of noise in transmissions signals.

The most celebrated result of communications mathematics research came in 1948 with C. E. Shannon's formulation of information theory. Shannon related the information content of a message to the probability of its occurrence. Building on this conceptual foundation, Shannon derived his famous equation for the capacity of a band-limited communication channel—the capacity in bits per second being equal to the bandwidth times the logarithm (base two) of the signal-to-noise ratio plus one. Shannon's work began an active field of research for mathematicians and engineers around the world; it had a profound impact on the philosophy of communications. Shannon's capacity equation represents both a goal and an unreachable barrier, and it still motivates engineers more than three decades after its derivation.

One field of communications systems research stimulated by Shannon's work was error-correcting coding. The first error-detecting and -correcting codes were credited to R. W. Hamming. A mathematical framework for the analysis and synthesis of codes was laid by D. Slepian in his conception of linear codes. Later, error-correcting codes were made more practical by the invention by E. R. Berlekamp of an efficient decoding algorithm for the most important known class of codes.

Mathematical research was also conducted in statistics. This proved important in guiding experimental programs on quality control in the Bell System. When modern computers became available in the 1950s, the statistical methods became especially useful in the analysis of large masses of data, such as the measurement of high-energy protons gathered by instruments in the Telstar satellite.

Although most of the research in computer science is described in Chapter 9 of this volume, some important work in the theory of computational complexity appears in the initial chapter devoted to mathematics. Numerous contributions to the development of a branch of mathematics treating the study of inherently intractable problems—NP-complete problems—were made by the mathematical research group, particularly by M. R. Garey and D. S. Johnson.

Acoustics research has long been a strength of Bell Laboratories. The early work on speech and hearing was led by H. Fletcher. The well-known Fletcher-Munson curves summarized the measurements of subjective loudness as a function of frequency for various magnitudes of loudness level. This relationship formed the basis for frequency equalization in high-fidelity sound systems, and later in stereophonic sound. Studies in speech analysis led to the development of a speech analyzer, called the vocoder, with the subsequent development of the sound spectrograph, which gave a graphic representation of speech spectra in a form that exhibited temporal as well as spectral properties of speech components. Following that, H. Dudley developed the electrical speech synthesizer, named the voder, which was operated from a keyboard to produce reasonably intelligible artificial speech. The voder used a bandwidth of 300 hertz, thus giving a bandwidth reduction of ten compared to ordinary speech transmission. Electrical transmission-line analog models of the vocal tract and the inner ear were also developed to give a more quantitative understanding of the mechanisms of speech and hearing.

Acoustics research after 1950 was strongly influenced by the increasing availability of solid-state digital computers and the development of techniques for simulating and studying physical systems by numerical methods. The use of analog-to-digital converters facilitated the study of many problems in acoustics, such as reverberation and stereophonic sound, bandwidth reduction, and the design of digital equivalents of classical wave filters.

Computer simulation became an attractive means for rapidly implementing and testing new ideas in speech transmission. Using that method, J. L. Flanagan invented in 1965 the phase vocoder for achieving moderate bandwidth conservation with good quality transmission, and, in 1967, the linear predictive coding (LPC) algorithm was invented by a group of researchers in his department. The LPC algorithm has since provided an efficient means for low bit rate coding and synthesis of speech in both transmission and computer systems. Digital simulation also greatly facilitated acoustic studies in underwater sound, room acoustics, musical acoustics, human-machine communication, and automatic speech recognition.

Picture communication has been another long-standing interest in research at Bell Laboratories. There was a small effort in the field even before the formation of Bell Laboratories itself, and, in 1927, H. E. Ives demonstrated a television system that stimulated research throughout the industry. Successful experiments on television transmission over coaxial cables and other lines were performed. M. W. Baldwin's research on the perceived sharpness of images as a function of several factors helped to establish scanning standards and criteria for transmission of color images. These research results were also very useful in the various stages of development of the PICTUREPHONE* visual telephone service.

The large bandwidth required for high-fidelity television transmission stimulated research effort on bandwidth compression systems. In the mid-1940s, the interest in pulse-code modulation (PCM) led to C. C. Cutler's invention of differential PCM, which provided a relatively simple and powerful way of coding pictures with fewer bits per picture element. The next significant steps in picture coding occurred with the selective replenishment and conditional replenishment coding algorithms, in which only portions of television frames with significant change from previous frames need be transmitted. In the 1970s, A. N. Netravali introduced the motion compensation algorithm, which provided even more bandwidth compression by estimating the movement of shaded areas in the picture and transmitting only the differences from these anticipated values. It was then possible to transmit conference-quality video using as little as 375 kilobits per second.

Fundamental investigations of the interaction of electron streams in vacuum tubes with electromagnetic waves started in the mid-1930s. Such explorations became increasingly important for meeting the needs of electronic amplifiers at higher and higher frequencies. The time of flight of the electrons between the vacuum-tube electrodes, space charge, and velocity distribution of the electrons and its effect on noise had to be taken

---

* Registered service mark of AT&T.

into account. J. R. Pierce's research on electron guns and the reflex klystron was an outgrowth of such a fundamental approach. During the war years, the work of J. B. Fisk and his group in advancing the understanding of the operation of the magnetron, and the design and development of magnetrons, stood out as important contributions to the radar program centered at the Massachusetts Institute of Technology. The magnetron activities decreased after the war, and the researchers in the vacuum-tube electronics department concentrated on the traveling wave tube of R. Kompfner and J. R. Pierce for the amplification of microwaves. The invention by S. Millman of the spatial harmonic traveling wave amplifier and his contribution to the understanding of backward-wave amplification opened the way for millimeter-wave amplifiers and voltage-tunable oscillators. Interest in research on vacuum-tube electronics decreased rapidly in the late 1950s with the development of solid-state amplifiers for millimeter waves.

Radio research at Bell Laboratories, centered at Holmdel, New Jersey, was motivated by the need to provide communications systems over long distances and with increasingly greater capacity. This naturally led to the exploration of the potentials of higher and higher frequencies where large bandwidths were expected to come more easily. Research interests concentrated on antennas and related receiver noise and on propagation studies, ranging from the shortwave region of the electromagnetic spectrum to microwaves and the visible region. The antenna studies led to the design of the rhombic antenna for shortwaves and to the horn antenna for microwaves, as well as to heterodyne techniques for detection of radiofrequency radiation. Propagation studies led to better understanding of the effect of various ionized layers in the atmosphere on radio transmission at different frequencies; they determined the effect of rain and fog on propagation of different portions of the electromagnetic spectrum and helped in the design of appropriate diversity techniques to overcome fading at shortwaves.

An outgrowth of these fundamental studies was the experimental TDX microwave relay system of the mid-1940s for the 4-gigahertz (GHz) frequency region. This prototype system was the forerunner of the popular TD microwave system, which was to evolve into a nationwide radio network system. The TDX system connected New York and Boston with a pair of 10-megahertz wideband channels. It went into service on an experimental basis in 1947. The first commercial TD system was installed in 1950; by 1983, 72 percent of the long-haul facilities of the Bell System were provided by microwave radio-relay systems.

Bell Laboratories researchers were also pioneers in satellite communications. The first satellite transmission experiment, Project Echo, occurred as a result of a suggestion by J. R. Pierce and R. Kompfner to the National Aeronautics and Space Administration. The Echo balloon was placed in orbit on August 12, 1960, and the first message relayed from space was a recorded statement by President Eisenhower, which was transmitted from the Jet Propulsion Laboratories to Bell Laboratories. This experiment was followed in 1962 by an experimental active satellite system, Telstar, which was a large project involving scientists and engineers from research and development organizations of Bell Laboratories. The world's first transatlantic television transmission was carried on Telstar. It was an exciting time at Bell Labs as a new era in communications was begun.

In mobile communications, propagation studies at microwave frequencies were conducted in the early 1950s. A more intensive research program, starting in the early 1960s, led to the development of the highly successful cellular mobile radio system. Techniques were devised for dynamic channel assignment and efficient use of allotted frequency bands to take care of short-term statistical fluctuations in communication demands.

Waveguide research began in 1931 with experiments by G. C. Southworth, who was then in the research department of the AT&T Company. At that time there was skepticism about whether electromagnetic waves could pass through hollow metal tubes and dielectric rods, and whether there was any practical use for them even if they could. Southworth's initial experiments showed promise, and he transferred to Bell Laboratories to continue his investigations. Collaborations with J. R. Carson and S. A. Schelkunoff laid an experimental and mathematical foundation for modes of propagation in guided media. One of their findings was that certain modes could have unusually low losses, with the attenuation of a circular waveguide approaching zero in some circumstances as the frequency was increased. This high-frequency characteristic was particularly attractive to researchers interested in very large bandwidths at frequencies unfavorable for propagation in the open atmosphere. For the more commonly used waveguide (i.e., rectangular), where only one electromagnetic mode could propagate, the contributions by Bell Labs scientists and engineers were used principally in components for radar and microwave radio-relay systems.

The potential of circular waveguide for large bandwidth fascinated researchers. For exploiting the intriguing properties of this medium, a considerable research effort grew. It was necessary to find a way of propagating only a single desirable mode in a waveguide configuration capable of propagating more than a hundred modes. Eventually, researchers successfully demonstrated the engineering and commercial feasibility of this ultrabroadband system for long-distance transmission. By this time lightwave transmission via optical fibers appeared to be a more promising alternative, and the work on circular systems was terminated. A study of history offers some perspective on the pathways of research; not every project ends in changing the face of the world. As this volume attests, however, Bell Laboratories can point with pride to the large number that have done just that.

The history of lightwave communications is of more recent vintage than any other chapter in this volume. Early studies in the 1940s and 1950s considered optical transmission, but it was not until the proposal by A. L. Schawlow and C. H. Townes for an optical maser in 1958 that interest built in this field. The potential increase in frequency by a factor of 10,000 over microwave sources was enormously exciting. Even before the excellent propagation properties of glass fibers were realized, Bell Labs scientists began to explore the uses of glass lenses and gas lenses for guided optical transmission. Work in this area was given a tremendous boost by the fabrication of low-loss glass fibers by R. D. Maurer at the Corning Glass Company.

Bell Laboratories research on sources for optical emission resulted in the invention of the injection semiconductor heterostructure laser by I. Hayashi and M. B. Panish and a light-emitting diode especially tailored for optical fiber application by C. A. Burrus. These sources were used with optical fibers in both single-mode and multimode applications. Techniques for splicing and connecting fibers had to be invented, as well as a family of components for lightwave systems, including photodetectors, filters, amplifiers, and regenerators. The field of integrated optics was originated, and research began on miniature forms of the modulators, switches, filters, and directional couplers required in optical systems.

Although lightwave transmission is still a small percent of the long-haul telecommunications network, it is clear as this volume goes to press that the future belongs to optics. Major optical links have been installed on both coasts of the nation, and plans for a nationwide optical system are well underway. Optical fibers are prevalent in metropolitan area transmission systems and on subscriber loop carrier systems. Research is extremely active in optics, and major discoveries seem to occur monthly. Thus the present history ends abruptly in midstream with this publication. Clearly, a more complete history of lightwave communications is yet to come.

The impact of research activities on the field of switching is probably not as profound as in transmission. Nonetheless, a series of experimental telephone switching systems was constructed in the research area, particularly during the late 1940s and the 1950s, which influenced future generations of commercial switches. The advantages to be derived from the application of electronic techniques to switching systems were explored in the electronically controlled automatic switching system using vacuum tubes and high-speed relays. The most famous research system, the experimental solid-state exchange (ESSEX) system, was constructed in 1959 by W. A. Malthaner, H. E. Vaughan, and associates. ESSEX used PCM to implement time-division switching. Articles about the ESSEX system are among the most quoted in switching literature. Eventually the technology begun in ESSEX resulted in the first commercial time-division switch, the 4ESS* switch, which began service in 1976.

The fascinating evolution of PCM as a transmission philosophy is the principal component of the chapter on digital communication. It is not so well known that PCM was the essence of a 1926 patent by P. M. Rainey of the Western Electric Company. The credit for the invention of PCM is generally given to the 1942 patent of A. H. Reeves of the International Telephone and Telegraph Company. Bell Labs early involvement with PCM centered about wartime projects, which provided a need for what was then an expensive methodology. After World War II, Bell Labs researchers built up a theoretical foundation for PCM. Much of this work was credited to W. R. Bennett, while its antecedents were laid in a famous telegraph paper by H. Nyquist in 1928.

In the period from 1944 to 1948 several experimental PCM systems were constructed in research. Speech signals were sent from Murray Hill, New Jersey to New York City using a 4-GHz radio link carrying 96 PCM channels. The technology had been demonstrated, and a theory had been elucidated, but, for some years afterwards, the researchers were in the position of having a solution without a needful problem. Eventually, it was realized that an ideal application for PCM was in providing multiple channels on a wire pair, and the development of the T-1 carrier system was begun. Today such systems are the main intracity links, and digital communication is the basis of the information age. Even in a book of history, it is hard to realize that at one time the world was all analog, and no one could find a use for PCM!

Though Bell Laboratories is naturally associated with communications technology, the contributions to computer science are preeminent. The greatest contribution that Bell Labs made to computer technology was, of course, the invention of the junction transistor. But that story was more properly placed in the companion *Physical Sciences* volume of this series. A pioneering analog computer, designed by Bell Labs scientists for the control of antiaircraft guns during World War II, used precision wire-wound potentiometers and vacuum-tube amplifiers to perform standard arithmetic operations. The first binary-relay calculator was designed in 1937 by G. R. Stibitz. Standard telephone relays were used in the Stibitz calculator for binary-to-decimal conversion and for memory. The need for calculating complex numbers was met by using two computers, one for the real parts of the complex numbers, the other for their imaginary parts. Relay computers were also used for applications during World War II and for telephone accounting.

---

* Trademark of AT&T Technologies, Inc.

The rapid increase in the use of computers in the 1950s by Bell Labs scientists and engineers brought about the need for acquiring large commercial computers. It also became necessary to get involved in critical examination of available software for optimal use of these computers. Not surprisingly, Bell Labs computer scientists began developing new programming languages suitable for their applications, such as the higher-level languages called L1 and L2. Disenchantment with the time-sharing environment then current led K. Thompson and D. M. Ritchie to invent an entirely new computer operating system and a language more adaptable to the needs of the great majority of Bell Labs personnel: the UNIX* system and the C language. By the 1980s, UNIX systems had become ubiquitous throughout the computing world on thousands of machines from dozens of manufacturers ranging in size from mainframes to microcomputers.

Behavioral science research began in Bell Laboratories in 1956; eventually it grew into a sizeable departmental effort that attracted outstanding psychologists interested in carrying out research of relevance to Bell System needs. Some of the first achievements were in the area of programmed instruction and in the basic mechanisms of learning. A notable achievement occurred in the early 1960s with R. N. Shepard's development of multidimensional scaling, which was originally motivated by Shepard's desire to understand better how people perceive various qualities, or "subjective dimensions," of the world around them. Today the techniques Shepard and his associates originated are standard approaches in the field of psychology. Other noteworthy contributions from the behavioral science group include the invention by B. Julesz of the random-dot stereogram and the studies of memory by S. Sternberg and his coworkers.

The final chapter in this volume describes the history and role of economics research at Bell Laboratories. The economics research effort was motivated initially by the need to support increasing regulatory activities at both federal and state levels. New theories were developed for the natural monopoly and for the multiproduct firm. Extensive empirical studies were also conducted on both the cost of and demand for Bell System products and services. Financial theories were extended to include the estimation of risk and return in the financial market, equilibria conditions when supply and demand are unequal and may result in unemployment, and the economics of innovation in a regulated industry.

From this wealth of achievements it is not difficult to choose highlights, although any such list must be a personal one. For the systems work, one might choose the evolution of PCM or the development of the long-haul microwave radio-relay system as singular accomplishments of worldwide importance. The origin of satellite communications, through the Echo and

---

* Trademark of AT&T Bell Laboratories.

Telstar experiments, and the first electronic switching experiment, ESSEX, are also achievements of the first magnitude that are detailed in this volume.

In the category of individual contributions of lasting influence, in addition to C. E. Shannon's brilliant insight in creating information theory, one might begin with the telegraph theory of H. Nyquist, or the discovery of negative feedback by H. S. Black, or G. R. Stibitz's implementation of the first binary computer. The acoustics field was foreshadowed by H. Fletcher's fundamental investigations on speech and hearing and by H. Dudley's vocoder, while microwave communications has long been in debt to the traveling wave tube work of R. Kompfner and J. R. Pierce. In the more modern era of computer science, the creation of the UNIX operating system and the C language by K. Thompson and D. M. Ritchie gains more in influence with the perspective of each passing day. These are some of the great ideas which have shaped the philosophy and technology of communications detailed in this volume.

R. W. Lucky
Executive Director—Research
Communications Sciences Division
AT&T Bell Laboratories
July, 1984

Chapter 1

Mathematical Foundations
of Communications

The Bell System was a pioneer in industrial mathematics even before its mathematics center was created in 1922. That center, comprising initially a consulting group working on problems posed by engineers and scientists, brought mathematicians together for the first time in an industrial setting. Eventually it established its own research programs, initiating studies in many areas of telecommunications. Starting with the limited mathematical tools of early telephony, Bell System mathematicians dealt with basic problems in transmission and in switching and forged new tools for dealing with them. New methods developed around applications of probability and statistics. As new techniques were invented, new fields of study opened up. As modern telecommunications evolved, merging with the technology of digital computation and supported by advances in a broad range of sciences, mathematicians continued to play an important role in the solution of new problems.

I. BACKGROUND

1.1 Early Industrial Mathematics—The Mathematics Department at Bell Labs

Industrial mathematics can trace its origins to the earliest days of industrial research. In 1878, Thomas Edison needed mathematical assistance and hired F. R. Upton.[1] In 1897, the Bell System also employed one mathematician, G. A. Campbell, and, over the next few decades, built up a staff that included a large share of all the mathematicians employed in industry at that time.

Early industrial mathematicians were hired primarily as consultants for individual engineering groups. Then, in May 1922, the Engineering Department at Western Electric created a small, separate mathematics section

Principal authors: E. N. Gilbert, C. L. Mallows, B. McMillan, and A. D. Wyner.

to serve the many engineering sections that could not afford full-time mathematicians of their own. This mathematics section initially consisted of one mathematician, T. C. Fry, with a small staff to assist in computations. [Fig. 1-1] In 1925, Fry's section became part of the newly formed Bell Laboratories.

Possibly because the separate mathematics department was an innovation, the organization's function was described in the first issue of the *Bell Laboratories Record:*

> Our Mathematical Research Department is therefore primarily a consulting organization, its chief function being to furnish expert advice regarding the mathematical phases of the investigations carried on in the laboratories. As part of the research organization, it is available to other branches of the company as well, and a considerable portion of its activities is devoted to the mathematical phases of development problems such as filter design, circuit theory, and the apportionment of apparatus in automatic telephone installations.[2]

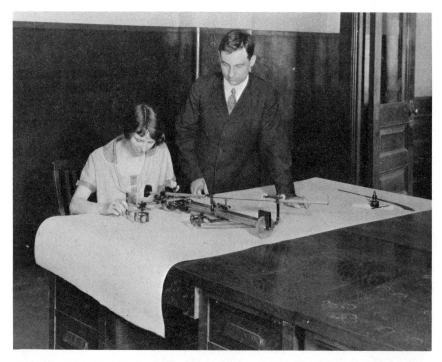

Fig. 1-1.   T. C. Fry (right) watches as J. Smith, one of the five assistants comprising the Mathematics Consulting Department in 1925, uses the Coradi Datagraph, an elaborate analog mechanism for evaluating an integral numerically. The small department that Fry created in 1922 and directed through 1943 evolved into the Mathematics and Statistics Research Center of the early 1980s, with 55 mathematicians.

In 1925, there were Bell System mathematicians in departments other than Fry's, notably Campbell, J. R. Carson, H. Nyquist, E. C. Molina, O. J. Zobel, L. A. MacColl, and R. M. Foster. Soon thereafter Fry began to enroll other mathematicians, including some from other areas of the Bell System.

In the 1930s, another important innovation occurred—Fry's department was no longer exclusively a consulting organization. The change resulted from a change in the department's funding. Although part of its funds came from departments receiving mathematical consulting services, the mathematics department also acquired direct control of a fund of its own. Its purpose was explained by Fry in his 1934 annual work authorization.

> The purpose of this case [fund] is to provide for a certain class of mathematical activities which are of considerable value in the aggregate, but which individually involve such small sums of money or are so definitely exploratory in character that it is inconvenient to handle them as separate cases. It is proposed to develop more powerful and more economical mathematical methods for the study of communications problems and to furnish mathematical advice and consultation.

Fry used the adjective "exploratory" to describe mathematical research that was not dictated or guided by an engineering department. Many such explorations had been performed earlier—Campbell's wave filter resulted from one—but this 1934 document finally gave them official recognition. As more exploratory efforts succeeded, the mathematics department became less a consulting group and more an autonomous research unit. At no time, however, were a majority of the mathematicians at Bell Labs members of the mathematics department. Fry's department evolved to become the Mathematics and Statistics Research Center, with about 55 mathematicians in the early 1980s.

1.2 Mathematicians and Engineering

Mathematicians in the past suffered from an image of impracticality. A typical unverified story had two of Edison's mathematicians working all night without success to calculate the volume of a light bulb, only to watch the next morning as Edison himself solved the problem by measuring the volume of water needed to fill it.[3]

As their training prepared them to use sophisticated mathematics themselves and provided a common language for discussions with mathematical consultants, later generations of engineers gained more confidence in mathematics as a practical tool. But this training had evolved because of the successes of engineering mathematics at earlier times, when mathematicians and engineers received different training and spoke different technical languages. These differences (well illustrated by the early history of Campbell's wave filter, as discussed in section 3.1) posed formidable barriers to communication.

Academic credentials are not necessarily good criteria for success in industrial mathematics because some of the best mathematics has been done by people not trained as specialists in mathematics. Molina, to cite a notable example, had only a high school diploma. He became a self-taught expert in probability theory and, after a brilliant Bell System career, a professor of mathematics.

In 1941, Fry tried to identify mathematicians entirely by the way they think:

> The typical mathematician feels great confidence in a conclusion reached by careful reasoning. He is not convinced to the same degree by experimental evidence. . . . Confronted by a carefully thought-out theory which predicts a certain result, and a carefully performed experiment which fails to produce it, the typical mathematician asks first, "What is wrong with the experiment?" and the typical engineer, "What is wrong with the argument?" . . .
>
> A second characteristic . . . is his highly critical attitude toward the details of a demonstration. For the mathematician, an argument is either perfect in every detail or else it is wrong. He calls this "rigorous thinking." . . . The typical engineer calls it "hair-splitting." . . .
>
> The mathematician also tends to idealize any situation with which he is confronted. His gases are "ideal," his conductors "perfect," his surfaces "smooth." He calls this "getting down to essentials." . . . The engineer or physicist is likely to dub it . . . "ignoring the facts."
>
> A fourth and closely related characteristic is the desire for generality. Confronted with the problem of solving the simple equation $x^3 - 1 = 0$, he solves $x^n - 1 = 0$. He calls this "conserving energy." . . . The engineer calls it "wasting time."[4]

Fry's definition still agrees well with usage at Bell Laboratories and will serve for the purposes of this chapter.

1.3 Early Mathematics

Before discussing specific examples of Bell System mathematics, it may help to survey briefly the mathematical tools of early telephony. A typical switching problem might concern the blocking that occurs when all wires between two central offices are in use and no more conversations can be established between them. An analysis of the problem would require the theory of probability. The mathematical theory as presented by Laplace (1812) was usually adequate, but the limiting formula of Poisson (1837) was also frequently required. Fry reviewed these telephone applications of probability in a textbook, published in 1928.[5] The modern theory of queues[6] is a direct descendant of early work done on telephone switching.

Most other mathematical problems concerned transmission of signals. The problems were usually reduced to finding the effect of sending a sinusoidal signal through a circuit. One could think of speech as being decomposed into a sum of sinusoids, and could deduce the effect of a linear circuit on speech from its effect on the sinusoidal components. This decomposition was implicit even in Bell's early work on harmonic telegraphy. Sinusoidal speech components resembled the waves that appeared in ac power engineering and were analyzed by the same means, that is, by linear algebraic equations involving complex numbers. The use of complex numbers stemmed from Lord Rayleigh's early studies of mechanical vibrations.[7] By 1911, Campbell was able to include sophisticated circuit theorems in his definitive paper on complex methods in telephony.[8]

Complex equations describing transmission of a sinusoid were extended immediately for more general signals or transients. This extension was accomplished by O. Heaviside's operational calculus, in which each frequency term $i\omega$ was replaced by a mysterious operator p. Although T. J. I'A. Bromwich in England and later J. R. Carson at AT&T managed to give rigorous proofs of Heaviside's theorems, operational calculus has been supplanted by equivalent techniques using Fourier or Laplace transforms.[9]

By modern standards, early research was handicapped by the absence of large-scale computing equipment. Mechanical analog integrating devices existed. There were also some digital desk calculators, which were at best the equal of a modern four-function pocket calculator. Some mathematical interest in computing for its own sake is evidenced by a mechanism patented by Fry.[10] Later, the first large electrical digital computer was designed in Fry's department, but that story belongs to another chapter. (See Chapter 9 of this volume.)

II. MODULATION

2.1 Amplitude Modulation

The idea of modulating the amplitude of an electromagnetic wave in accordance with a speech signal originated with Alexander Graham Bell. He transmitted speech over a beam of light using his photophone, which he patented in 1880. Radio waves, however, offered more promise since they are absorbed less in the atmosphere than light waves. By 1915, many experimenters had produced speech-modulated radio signals. At AT&T, experiments were being conducted on transatlantic radiotelephony and on multiplexed-carrier telephony, or wired wireless as it was often called.[11]

Most radio experts, including J. S. Stone of AT&T and J. A. Fleming, thought of an amplitude-modulated (AM) signal as a kind of pure sinusoid,

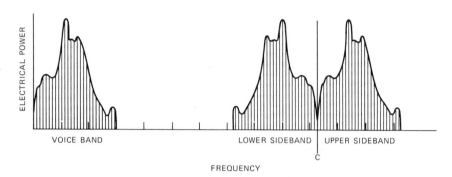

Fig. 1-2.   When the voiceband of frequencies (left) is used to amplitude-modulate a carrier frequency (C), the double sideband frequency spectrum shown (right) is produced, since each sinusoudal speech component frequency, f_n, generates two additional components in the transmitted signal, $C - f_n$ and $C + f_n$.

occupying only a single frequency in the radio spectrum.[12] That view made multiplexing seem very attractive; it suggested that multiplexed speech channels could be given carriers differing only slightly in frequency without causing interference. Actually, carrier frequencies must not be too close because modulation spreads radio signals over a band of frequencies. For each sinusoidal component of the speech wave, the modulated radio wave contains two sideband components, one above the carrier frequency and one below it. [Fig. 1-2] The earliest known record of this discovery is a notebook entry made in 1914 by C. R. Englund of Western Electric. Englund's conclusion follows directly from a simple trigonometric identity. Nevertheless, looking back from 1956, the radio pioneer A. A. Oswald wrote, "For more than a decade thereafter the physical reality of sidebands continued to be argued vigorously in some quarters; it was alleged that sidebands were merely a mathematical fiction."[13]

2.1.1 Single-Sideband Transmission

In 1915, H. D. Arnold demonstrated experimentally that an ordinary radio receiver could reproduce the voice signal even after the lower sideband was removed from the radio signal by filtering. At the same time, Carson reached the same conclusion analytically. He realized further that the carrier, too, could be removed if an oscillator were built into the receiver to generate the missing carrier locally. Carson filed a patent showing how to produce a single-sideband wave and receive it by homodyne detection.[14] Using only one sideband reduced the radio bandwidth by a factor of two and saved the power formerly wasted in the carrier.[15] [Fig. 1-3]

Filtering was the most obvious way to remove the carrier. Carson's patent, however, contained a more clever and effective device, a balanced

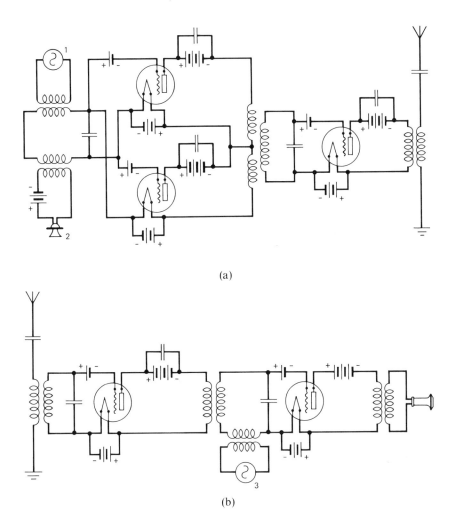

(a)

(b)

Fig. 1-3. Single-sideband circuits for transmitter (a) and receiver (b) as adapted from J. R. Carson's patent. To conserve power and bandwidth, the balanced modulator mixes speech (2) and carrier (1) signals in a way that cancels the carrier and one set of sidebands. A local oscillator (3) in the receiver (b) supplies the carrier frequency that was not transmitted.

modulator in which carrier components canceled out by symmetry. R. V. L. Hartley contributed still another way to generate and receive single-sideband transmission by using a phasing modulator.[16] It employed two balanced modulators and networks to shift the phases of the carrier and all voice components by 90 degrees. Signals from these two modulators were combined to cancel one set of sidebands. Single-sideband transmission was adopted in the earliest multiplexed-carrier telephone system of 1918.[17]

For more than half a century it has remained the most commonly used method of transmitting speech over a narrow band.

2.2 Frequency Modulation

The hope of reducing bandwidth still further prompted suggestions for several frequency-modulation (FM) systems. These resembled modern FM systems, but the frequency deviations were to be much smaller, on the assumption that the bandwidth would then be small. However, in 1922, Carson showed that frequency modulation produces sidebands, not only at the frequencies obtained with amplitude modulation, but also at frequencies even farther from the carrier.[18] Strictly, FM requires infinite bandwidth. Around 1939, Carson gave a rough rule of thumb for estimating the bandwidth needed for the most important sidebands. According to Carson's rule as described by S. O. Rice,[19] this bandwidth is $2(f_m + \Delta F)$, where f_m is the highest frequency present in the modulating speech and ΔF is the peak frequency deviation.

Although Carson's 1922 paper correctly criticized FM as a way of reducing bandwidth, it unfortunately convinced many engineers and Carson, too, that FM had little promise. In 1936, when E. H. Armstrong of Columbia University developed a wideband FM system with great immunity to noise, it came as a surprise.[20,21]

Shortly after Armstrong's development, R. Bown produced a simple phasor diagram that seemed to show that noise has only a slight effect on the zeros of an FM wave. These zeros, which survive the action of the FM limiter circuit, are the main features used in FM detection. Bown showed his diagram to Fry and asked for a more exact analysis. The result was a theoretical paper, published by Carson and Fry in 1937, which supported Armstrong's contention that the signal-to-noise ratio in the output of an FM receiver increases as the frequency deviation, and consequently the bandwidth, of the FM signal increases.[22]

The first studies of noise in FM reception were adequate as long as the received noise was weak enough to be considered a small perturbation. These studies could not explain a curious threshold effect that was observed experimentally. When the input noise power exceeded a certain threshold, the output signal suddenly disappeared into the noise. In 1963, Rice developed a new kind of FM noise analysis that was more appropriate for noise levels near the threshold.[23] According to Rice, the main part of the output noise occurred in isolated short clicks. The receiver, designed to follow the phase of the incoming signal, would emit a click each time noise made it slip out of phase by 360 degrees.

In 1962, D. Slepian showed that this threshold effect, as exhibited by FM, is indeed a universal property of modulation schemes that are effective in reducing noise.[24] His paper is set within the framework of C. E. Shannon's general theory of communication in the presence of noise, as discussed in section VIII of this chapter.

2.3 Nyquist's Fundamental Transmission Formula

Telegraphy is a form of amplitude modulation in which the amplitude is restricted to two values (corresponding to key on and key off). Consequently, telegraphy generates sidebands. They occupy wider bandwidths for faster signaling rates. In the mid-1920s, H. Nyquist studied telegraph signaling with the aim of finding the maximum signaling rate that could be used over a telegraph channel of given bandwidth.[25,26] He adopted a generalized model of a telegraph system that has come to be called a pulse transmission system. A typical transmitted signal could be any function $s(t)$ of the form:

$$s(t) = \sum_k a_k f(t - kT) . \tag{1}$$

Here $f(t)$ represented a basic pulse shape, a_k was the amplitude of the kth pulse, and T was the time between pulses. Ordinary dc telegraphy fit this description if the basic pulse shape $f(t)$ was a rectangular pulse lasting T seconds and a_k equaled 0 or 1, according to whether the key was up or down for the duration of the kth pulse. However, Nyquist would allow $f(t)$ to have other shapes; indeed, his problem was to design $f(t)$ so that T could be as small as possible. Only pulses that occupied the band from 0 to W cycles per second, hertz (Hz), were allowed. Because of that restriction, arbitrarily narrow pulses could not be achieved. With a given pulse $f(t)$, T could be reduced only to the point that successive pulses overlapped and caused serious intersymbol interference.

Nyquist concluded that the pulse rate $1/T$ could not be increased beyond $2W$ pulses per second, a rate now called the Nyquist rate. Moreover, the Nyquist rate could be achieved by using a pulse with the shape $f(t)$ = $(\sin 2\pi Wt)/(2\pi Wt)$. With this pulse, errors from intersymbol interference could be avoided completely by using a new system of detection based on measuring samples of the received waveform $s(t)$ at the discrete times $t = k/(2W)$. These conclusions contradicted a prevailing opinion that an ideal telegraph wave should approximate a sinusoid of frequency somewhat less than W. Since 1900, that idea had led to proposals for sine-wave telegraph systems.[27] Nyquist was able to show that they had no special merit. They were included in his theory by taking $f(t)$ to be a half cycle of a sine wave.

Nyquist's analysis applied to an ideal channel, producing infinite attenuation at all frequencies outside a band of width W. It was presumed also to apply approximately to real channels, producing merely large finite attenuation outside a nominal band of width W. However, using the ideal channel as a model for real channels introduces some subtle difficulties. These were reviewed in a 1976 paper by D. Slepian.[28] L. A. MacColl seems to have been the first to suspect trouble. In 1936, he invented a signaling system that, in principle, sent pulses over a real channel much faster than the Nyquist rate without errors from intersymbol interference.[29,30] MacColl's system would work as long as the pulse $f(t)$ had even a tiny amount of energy at frequencies out of the band. The system was not practical because very slight interference from other channels or from noise would render detection impossible. Thus, although Nyquist's rate remained useful as a working guide, there was some doubt about its logical basis.

Shannon helped to clarify the problem. In 1949, he studied signals $s(t)$ that were strictly band limited, that is, with zero energy outside a band 0 to W Hz.[31] Shannon considered arbitrary signals $s(t)$, not just pulse trains of the special form described by equation (1). Nevertheless, he found that $s(t)$ satisfied an identity:

$$s(t) = \sum_k s(k/(2W)) \frac{\sin 2\pi W(t - k/(2W))}{2\pi W(t - k/(2W))} \tag{2}$$

which is equation (1) with $f(t)$ equal to (sin $2\pi Wt/(2\pi Wt)$, a_k equal to $s(k/(2W))$, and T equal to $1/(2W)$. Even an analog signal, such as band-limited speech, is expressed by equation (2) as a sum of pulses, but with pulse amplitudes that may be distributed continuously, instead of discretely as in telegraphy. The Nyquist rate 2W appears in equation (2) as the rate at which sample values $s(k/(2W))$ must be measured in order to determine $s(t)$. Equation (2) already existed in the mathematical literature and was known as the sampling theorem, a formula for interpolating a function from sample values.[32] Of course, the connection with signal transmission was not apparent in that context.

The sampling theorem has the defect that no physical signal has all its energy confined to a finite band of frequencies. For example, any signal $s(t)$ that turns on at some time t_0 and vanishes at all earlier times is sure to have energy distributed to arbitrarily high frequencies. MacColl's signaling system showed that one can reach radically different conclusions depending on whether signals are assumed to be exactly or only approximately band limited. H. J. Landau, H. O. Pollak [Fig. 1-4], and Slepian in 1961 tried to find a precise meaning for the Nyquist rate, even for approximately band-limited functions. They considered signals $s(t)$ that had all but a prescribed small fraction of their energy contained within a frequency band W-Hz wide and also had all but a fraction of their energy contained within a time interval τ-seconds long. Very roughly, the conclusion was that for large τ, these signals can be specified by $2W\tau$ independent parameters.[33] That number is just the number of Nyquist samples in a τ-second interval, although the appropriate parameters are no longer the samples $s(k/(2W))$.

Fig. 1-4. H. O. Pollak, who served as director of the Mathematics and Statistics Center at Bell Labs for over 20 years. He is a mathematical analyst with a variety of contributions to probability and signal theory.

In 1967, Landau returned to the sampling theorem for functions strictly limited to frequencies in a band of width W. He showed that in order for such functions to be reconstructable from their samples so that small errors in the samples produce only small errors in the reconstruction, the sampling instants must be distributed with a rate at least $2W$ per unit time. This work formed the basis for understanding the fundamental limits in analog-to-digital conversion.[34,35]

III. NETWORKS

A wave filter is an electrical circuit designed to pass signals of desired frequencies and reject others. Its use dates from around 1915 and the beginnings of frequency-multiplexed telephony, in which a single radio channel carries many simultaneous amplitude-modulated speech signals. To receive one multiplexed speech signal, a wave filter is used to pass one set of sidebands and reject those of the other speakers, in somewhat the same way that a radio receiver tunes in a single radio station. Because telephone wave filters are often complicated as well as very useful, much of the research on electrical networks has been concerned with wave filters.

The early history of the wave filter illustrates the communications gap, mentioned in section 1.2, that once existed between engineers and mathematicians. G. A. Campbell invented the wave filter before 1910, but its patent was delayed several years because Campbell's mathematics did not convince his patent attorney that the idea was novel, useful, or even correct. The attorney, T. D. Lockwood, was general patent attorney of AT&T and a well-known inventor, author, and lecturer on engineering.[36] Even J. J. Carty, chief engineer of AT&T, who agreed that the wave filter would work, wrote (in a letter to Lockwood) in 1913 that the patent application "should be dropped on account of its slender novelty and doubtful patentability." Two years later the need for wave filters in multiplexing became apparent and two patents were filed.[37,38] They were granted in 1917 and were indispensable for the development of long-distance telephony. The problem of making wave-filter theory understandable was solved with some help from J. Mills, an engineer with a flair for writing. Mills, who later became the first director of publications at Bell Laboratories, managed to assimilate Campbell's mathematics and rewrite it into a memorandum that was more understandable to the other engineers who were developing the multiplex system.

3.1 Electrical and Mechanical Filters

In the 19th century, Lord Kelvin and Lord Rayleigh both noted an electromechanical analogy, that is, a correspondence between the equations for mechanical vibrations and those for electrical oscillations.[39,40] When electrical theory was in its infancy, the electromechanical analogy was used to reinterpret well-known mechanical results as statements about electrical networks. By the 1920s, however, electrical theory had long outgrown its dependence on mechanics. It contained many new ideas that had originated in a purely electrical setting. The electromechanical analogy could now be used in reverse to make mechanical applications of new electrical theory. The electrical device that found the most mechanical applications was Campbell's wave filter.

The mechanical phonograph contained a speech transmission channel between the vibrating needle and the horn radiator. As early as 1915, H. D. Arnold recognized that phonographs resembled telephone transmission circuits and suggested that electrical theory might be applied, using the electromechanical analogy, to improve the mechanical phonograph. This task was later undertaken by J. P. Maxfield and H. C. Harrison and completed by 1926.[41] Using an electrical filter as the model for the mechanical pickup design, they obtained a response that was constant within a few dB from 120 to 4000 Hz, a radical improvement over existing phonographs. [Fig. 1-5] Their design was licensed to the Victor Talking Machine Company and manufactured under the name Orthophonic Victrola.

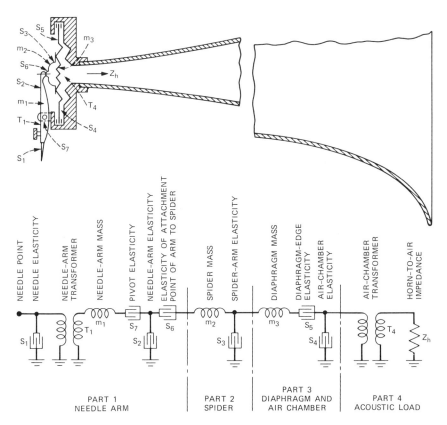

Fig. 1-5. Electrical circuit equivalents of acoustical components of a phonograph and exponentially tapered horn. Since mechanical and electrical oscillations satisfy similar differential equations, telephone engineers could analyze mechanical problems in terms of equivalent electrical circuits.

The good bass response of the Orthophonic Victrola resulted from using a long, exponentially tapered horn, which was cleverly folded to fit inside a cabinet of reasonable size. [Fig. 1-6] P. B. Flanders solved the mathematical problems of horn design, including estimation of the effect of folds in the horn.

An electrical record-cutting head was designed as part of the same phonograph study. Again, an electrical wave filter served as a model for designing the moving parts of the record cutter. While working on phonograph problems, E. L. Norton discovered his well-known theorem that shows that an electrical network with internal sources can be replaced by an equivalent current generator. A record groove driving a phonograph pickup was analogous to a current generator.

In 1924, R. L. Wegel and C. E. Lane constructed a theory of hearing using a tapered electrical transmission line as a model of the cochlea in

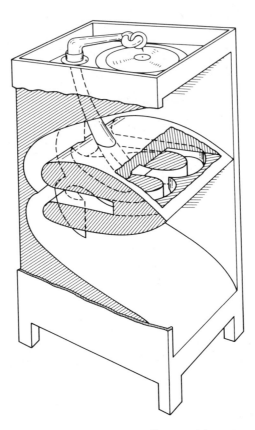

Fig. 1-6. A long, exponentially tapered horn, intricately folded into a cabinet of reasonable size. This horn was a feature of the 120- to 4000-Hz Orthophonic Victrola phonograph.

the human ear. In 1950, following their model, L. C. Peterson and B. P. Bogert built a 175-section electrical filter as an artificial cochlea for use in hearing studies.[42] [Fig. 1-7]

Wave filters became linked with mechanical vibrations in an entirely different way in 1926, following L. Espenschied's suggestion of using piezoelectric crystals as filter components.[43,44] Piezoelectric crystals vibrate mechanically in response to electrical signals. As electrical elements, piezoelectric crystals are resonant circuits with extremely small damping. Because of their small damping, crystals can be used to build bandpass filters with unusually sharp cutoff characteristics. After 1930, an important part of filter research was directed toward incorporating crystals and other electromechanical elements into filter structures. W. P. Mason [Fig. 1-8] and his associates pioneered in the application of specially cut quartz

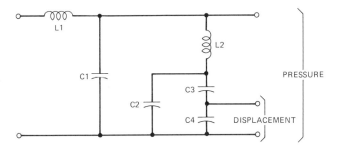

Fig. 1-7.   One section of a multisection electrical wave filter connected in tandem, representing the electrical equivalent of the cochlea in the human ear.

crystals for wave filters with highly selective frequency responses and for oscillators with frequency stability of 1 part in 10^9.[45,46] One mathematical problem involved studying crystal vibrations to obtain ways of controlling a crystal's electrical properties through control of its physical and geometrical parameters. Another problem arose because routine filter design

Fig. 1-8.   W. P. Mason, who invented special-cut quartz crystals for wave filters and frequency standards. He also conducted fundamental investigations of losses in organic crystals.

would not ordinarily lead to element values suitable for crystals; new filter structures were found that were more appropriate.

3.2 Network Synthesis

The earliest network theorems described the action of a given network in mathematical terms; that is, they were results about *network analysis*. Doing the reverse, finding some network that acts in accordance with a given mathematical description, is called *network synthesis*. The wave filter was useful for certain synthesis problems because there was a large selection of standard filters that produced delay, resonance peaks, or attenuation bands. These filters could be connected in tandem to synthesize more complicated behavior. In 1924, R. M. Foster considered a much more general kind of synthesis and proved what is now called Foster's reactance theorem.[47] In this theorem, the mathematical description prescribes a reactance as a desired function of frequency, $X(\omega)$. The theorem gives a condition for determining whether it is possible to construct a two-terminal network, entirely from lossless inductors and capacitors, with the given $X(\omega)$ as its reactance. The condition requires $X(\omega)$ to be a rational function—that is, a quotient of two polynomials—satisfying further restrictions on its zeros and poles. If the condition is satisfied, a partial fraction expansion of $X(\omega)$ leads to a network realization containing several parallel-tuned circuits connected in series. Alternatively, Foster expanded the susceptance $-1/X(\omega)$ to obtain series-tuned circuits connected in parallel. Related work had appeared earlier in publications of Campbell and O. J. Zobel.[48,49] In 1929, T. C. Fry found another method of synthesizing the reactance function. He expanded $X(\omega)$ into a continued fraction to obtain a ladder network.[50]

Later research generalized Foster's theorem in two directions. First, other kinds of elements, such as resistors and transformers, were allowed in addition to inductors and capacitors. Second, networks with several pairs of accessible terminals were considered; Foster's reactance function was then generalized to an impedance matrix. A network synthesis method then became a general-purpose procedure to design a network, using only the allowed elements and having a prescribed impedance function or matrix. Important methods of network synthesis were devised by S. Darlington [Fig. 1-9] and B. McMillan at Bell Labs, and by many others elsewhere.[51] Most synthesis methods make free use of the ideal transformer, a fictitious element that is only roughly approximated by a real transformer with closely coupled windings. R. Bott and R. J. Duffin, at the Carnegie Institute of Technology, succeeded in avoiding ideal transformers, but only for two-terminal networks.[52]

Network synthesis methods were typically applied to equalizers or to networks for miscellaneous uses, such as the 90-degree phase-shifting

Fig. 1-9. S. Darlington, who pioneered in the application of mathematical techniques to network synthesis.

networks used in single sideband. Also, new kinds of wave filters could be synthesized as individual large networks instead of tandem chains of small networks. Like Foster's reactance theorem, the later synthesis theorems always imposed conditions on the desired network function. If these conditions were not satisfied, no solution (that is, no network) would exist. There was always one condition—the network function must be a rational function. Networks were often needed, however, to have network functions that were not rational. In these instances, the irrational function had to be approximated by a rational one. For example, suppose one wanted a network to compensate for losses in a cable. Cable attenuation in decibels varies in proportion to the square root of the frequency. A perfect compensator for such a cable would insert gain, in decibels, proportional to the square root of the frequency. That gain is unrealizable. However, over any finite frequency band of interest, the desired gain can be approximated by a realizable gain. Then an approximating network can be synthesized.

Some of the classical mathematical literature about approximating functions by polynomials was applicable to the network problem of approximating by realizable rational functions. For example, the Tchebycheff polynomials are particularly convenient for network approximation problems. They were studied in that connection by Darlington.[53]

One novel approximation method used a mathematical analogy between the gain function of a network and the two-dimensional potential function produced by point charges located at the network's poles and zeros in the complex ω plane. H. W. Bode used this idea in the late 1930s to design phase-compensating networks. The same analogy was used independently by W. Cauer in Germany.[54] This potential analog method could immediately suggest good approximations for some networks, such as delay networks, just from physical intuition about electrostatics. More complicated network functions, such as the cable attenuation compensator function mentioned previously, could be approximated using an extended theory that Darlington developed in 1951.[55]

3.3 Digital Filters

Because linear equations describe how resistors, capacitors, and inductors behave, a filter constructed from these elements performs a linear operation on an input signal $S(t)$ to produce an output signal $r(t)$. In general, this linear operation can be expressed as a kind of weighted average

$$r(t) = \int_0^\infty S(t - \tau)\, k(\tau) d\tau .$$

The weight function $k(t)$, which characterizes the filter in question, is called the filter's impulse response because the output signal is just $k(t)$ when the input signal is a sharp impulse.

Instead of synthesizing a network to have a prescribed frequency response, one can equally well formulate the network synthesis problem in terms of finding a network with a desired impulse response $k(t)$. One solution approximates the integral for $r(t)$ by a sum

$$r(t) = h \sum_n S(t - nh)a_n$$

where $a_n = k(nh)$. This sum may be realized by using a delay line, with taps at delays $0, h, 2h, \ldots, nh$ to produce the delayed signal terms $S(t - nh)$ that appear in the sum. Those delayed signals are then attenuated by amounts ha_n and superimposed to create $r(t)$. A filter, using a delay line in this way, is called a transversal filter, an idea patented in 1935 by N. Wiener and Y. W. Lee of the Massachusetts Institute of Technology (MIT).[56]

These filters came into widespread use only after improvements in vacuum tube and transistor amplifiers made transversal filters convenient to build. One of their attractive features is the ease with which the coefficients a_n can be changed to control the filter characteristics. As early as 1950, C. E. Shannon had observed the possibility of dynamically varying the coefficients a_n in the transversal filter to improve performance of the filter during its operation, and experimental adaptive transversal filters were constructed to perform simple filtering tasks. At about that time, following a suggestion of Fry, Shannon and McMillan analyzed an adaptive filter that would equalize a transmission line on the basis of the receipt of a single, standardized signal pulse. An experimental equalizer was built and tested. Other versions of this idea have appeared in quite different contexts.

The maturing of solid-state technology and the high-speed digital computing that it supports brought the transversal filter into prominence because it permits the filtering function to be performed arithmetically. The input and output signals are now considered to be discrete sequences of sample values $S(nh)$ and $r(nh)$, while the filter action is merely described by a linear recurrence equation relating these samples. In this way, a computer can act as a digital filter.

If the output sample $r(nh)$ depends on earlier outputs $r(mh)$ as well as inputs $S(mh)$, there is the possibility that this feedback can cause instability (see section IV). Also, any digital filtering operation uses computations that are subject to round-off error. More serious errors may be caused by overload, when some quantity exceeds the range of significant figures allowed to the computation.

It was discovered experimentally that digital filters sometimes developed catastrophic round-off and overload errors, even when designed to represent systems that were stable when idealized to purely analog devices (i.e., with arithmetic of infinite precision). I. W. Sandberg,[57] D. Mitra, J. E. Mazo, and A. N. Willson showed that this undersirable behavior could be avoided by designing the arithmetic devices to behave suitably under overload.

The coefficients of a digital filter can often be regarded simply as parameters in a computer program. As such, they can be varied by some additional computation using other data (such as the amount of noise measured in the filter output, or some other measured departure of the filtered output from a previous specified condition). Examples of such adaptive filters were analyzed by M. M. Sondhi and Mitra[58,59] in a series of papers. By 1981, adaptive digital filters for telephone application—e.g., echo cancellers—had become standard items of commerce.

3.4 Graphs

A graph is a diagram consisting of some vertices and some lines drawn between certain pairs of vertices. The circuit diagram of an electrical network becomes a graph if each resistor, inductor, and capacitor is simply replaced by a line. Indeed, for this reason, G. Kirchhoff, who first gave the laws commonly used to analyze resistance networks, also proved many fundamental theorems about graphs.[60]

Campbell encountered a graph-theoretical problem in his work on antisidetone telephone subscriber sets (see Chapter 3, section 3.1 of the first

volume of this series, subtitled *The Early Years (1875-1925)).* He patented
a number of anti-sidetone circuits[61] and with Foster published a complete
set of such circuits in 1920.[62] To include every possibility, Campbell and
Foster had to prepare a catalog of all possible circuit configurations containing the elements of the subscriber's set—that is, the receiver, transmitter,
incoming line, various transformer windings, and a side-tone balancing
resistor. The circuit diagram for each configuration could be simplified to
a graph by showing each two-terminal element simply as a line. Then a
basic part of Campbell and Foster's problem was to count and catalog
graphs.

Foster continued cataloging graphs according to special properties of
interest in circuit theory. In a paper published in 1932,[63] he arranged the
graphs according to rank and nullity (the numbers of equations needed
to analyze a circuit in terms of voltages or currents). [Fig. 1-10] Another
interesting kind of graph, constructed entirely by combining elements in
series or parallel, was studied by J. Riordan [Fig. 1-11] and Shannon in
1942 and by Foster in 1952.[64,65] Riordan's book on combinatorial analysis
includes a large number of other graph enumerations.[66]

Graphs are used in the solution of many different telecommunications
problems. These problems usually require something other than a catalog.
Instead of representing simple two-terminal elements, the lines of a graph

NULLITY	RANK			
	3	4	5	6
3	△			
4		▨	⬗⬗ ⊟	
5			△ ⬡ ▱ ◇ ◇	▨ ◇ ◻ ⬠
6			⬟ ◇ △ ◇ ▨	18 GRAPHS

Fig. 1-10. One of Foster's tables of graphs. The graphs are arranged according to rank and
nullity—i.e., the number of equations required to analyze a network of electrical circuits in
terms of voltages or currents. [Foster, *Trans. Amer. Inst. Elect. Eng.* **51** (1932): 315.]

Fig. 1-11. J. Riordan, an expert in combinatorial analysis—a subject that includes techniques for counting configurations that arise in telephone probability problems. Riordan authored widely used books on combinatorial analysis and queueing theory.

may stand for trunks connecting different telephone offices. In 1959, E. F. Moore viewed this graph of trunks as a kind of road map or maze and gave algorithms for finding a shortest path between two given points of a maze.[67]

Graphs also enter into billing problems. A customer who leases private lines to interconnect stations in several cities is charged for these lines on a per-mile basis. However, this charge is not figured from the actual lines physically supplied. Instead, the tariff for this service requires the telephone company to draw a kind of road map using minimal total length to interconnect the cities. This graph (called the minimal tree for the given cities) becomes the basis for billing. In 1957, R. C. Prim found minimal trees by a simple algorithm that is especially convenient for machine computation.[68] Earlier algorithms were given by O. Borůvka in Czechoslovakia and J. B. Kruskal at Bell Labs.[69,70] [Fig. 1-12]

The minimal tree has the curious property that adding an extra city can sometimes produce a shorter minimal tree. For instance, the minimal tree for four cities at the corners of a unit square has length 3.0; if a fifth city is added at the center of the square, the length of the minimal tree for the five cities is only 2.828. The ability to reduce tree lengths further by adding vertices is useful in designing routing or wiring layouts of various

Fig. 1-12. "Minimal tree" for interconnecting 48 state capitals, using lines of the minimum total length, as required by tariff regulations. J. B. Kruskal and R. C. Prim developed efficient algorithms for finding minimal trees.

kinds. Methods of constructing a minimal length tree when extra vertices are allowed were obtained by Z. A. Melzak in Canada and by E. N. Gilbert, Pollak, and F. K. Hwang at Bell Labs.[71] However, these constructions can be very complicated because of the large number of interconnection patterns that are possible with extra vertices.

IV. FEEDBACK

Feedback is any form of coupling from the output of a power amplifying device back to its input. Shortly after telephony began, feedback was used to produce test tones. A telephone set with its receiver acoustically coupled to its transmitter produces a hum or howl. [Fig. 1-13] The humming occurs, in part, because the telephone transmitter is an amplifier; it produces a large amount of electrical power for a small amount of acoustical power in the mouthpiece. D. E. Hughes described the humming telephone in 1883. H. Fletcher at Bell Labs explained it mathematically in 1926.[72,73]

4.1 Feedback Amplifier

Soon after its invention, the vacuum tube was used not only as an amplifier, but also as a generator of electrical oscillations. In fact, high-

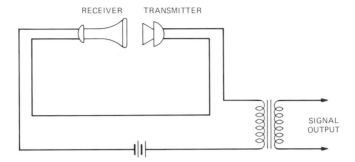

Fig. 1-13. A laboratory signal generator used in early telephony. This electromechanical feedback arrangement produces telephone howl or hum because the transmitter amplifies. [Adapted from Wright and Puchstein, *Telephone Communication* (1925): 402.]

Fig. 1-14. H. S. Black, who invented the negative-feedback amplifier, which greatly reduced distortion of signals in transmission applications.

gain vacuum tube circuits often oscillated unintentionally because of un-
wanted feedback paths caused by stray capacitive or inductive coupling.
Feedback in telephone amplifiers was a nuisance until 1927, when H. S.
Black [Fig. 1-14] discovered that deliberate feedback, with proper phase,

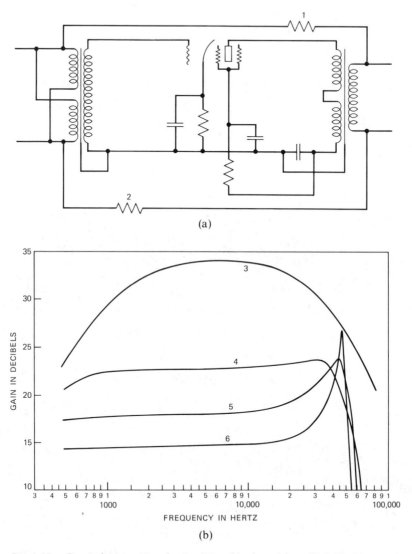

Fig. 1-15. Circuit diagram (a) and gain curves (b) adapted from H. S. Black's patent
on the negative-feedback vacuum-tube amplifier. Part of the output signal is returned
to the input through resistors 1 and 2. Decreasing their resistance increases the feedback
and improves the frequency response from that shown in curve 3 to the flat curve 4.
Further increases in feedback produce curves 5 and 6 that peak at a high frequency;
with still further increases in feedback the amplifier becomes unstable.

could flatten the frequency response and reduce the effects of nonlinear distortion.[74] In presenting Black with the American Institute of Electrical Engineers 1957 Lamme medal, the then president of Bell Laboratories M. J. Kelly said of Black's discovery, "It easily ranks coordinate with de Forest's invention of the audion as one of the two inventions of broadest scope and significance in electronics and communications of the past 50 years." [Fig. 1-15]

4.1.1 Nyquist's Diagram and Cauchy's Theorem

Early feedback amplifiers required careful design if they were to remain stable. Until the early 1930s, however, stability was not well understood. In a fundamental paper published in 1932, H. Nyquist produced an analysis of stability.[75,76] He showed that the net gain of a stable feedback amplifier is $\mu/(1 - \mu\beta)$, where μ is the voltage gain of the amplifier and β is the network gain of the feedback. [Fig. 1-16] Stability is determined by the denominator $1 - \mu\beta$, which is a function of frequency. Here "frequency" is a complex number; complex frequencies are associated with oscillations that either grow or decay exponentially with time. If all the roots of $1 - \mu\beta = 0$ are at complex frequencies of decaying oscillations, the amplifier is stable. Otherwise, it is unstable. To avoid the problem of actually computing these complex roots, Nyquist devised a graphical test based on what came to be called the Nyquist diagram, which is a plot, in the complex plane, of the path followed by $\mu\beta$ as the frequency ω varies from $-\infty$ to $+\infty$. In Nyquist's test, instability or stability is determined merely by observing whether the path encloses the point 1. This test answers the stability question entirely from the behavior of $\mu\beta$ at real frequencies, without solving for roots of $\mu\beta = 1$. [Fig. 1-17]

Before the advent of the Nyquist diagram, H. J. Van der Bijl had analyzed some simple vacuum-tube oscillator circuits and determined how much tube gain they required.[77] Much earlier, E. J. Routh in England gave a

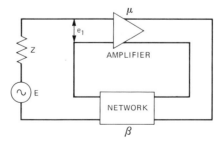

Fig. 1-16. A basic form of feedback amplifier. The gain of this feedback arrangement is $\mu e_1/E = \mu/(1 + \mu\beta)$, where μ is the amplifier gain and β is the network gain.

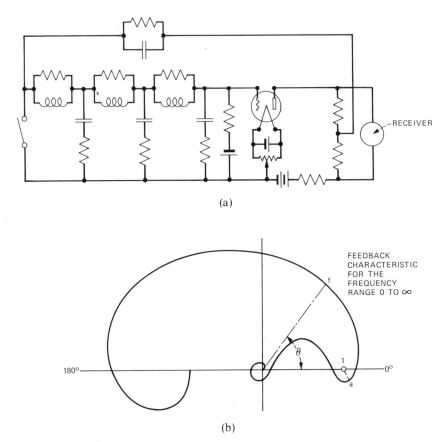

(a)

(b)

Fig. 1-17. Nyquist's amplifier. (a) An adaptation of one of H. Nyquist's patent diagrams of a feedback amplifier. (b) The amplifier's related diagram. The diagram is a plot, in the complex plane, of the path traced out by the complex loop gain $\mu\beta$ as the frequency is varied. The path encircles the point 1, showing that the amplifier is unstable. The amplifier is unusual because it becomes stable if the vacuum tube is replaced by one of higher gain.

stability analysis for mechanical systems and also studied complex roots.[78,79] Routh mentioned a diagram like Nyquist's, but only briefly. He used it as a step toward deriving an algebraic test for stability.

For amplifier designers, Nyquist's diagram has a particular advantage over algebraic tests. The amplifier gain enters the Nyquist diagram as a simple scale factor. Thus, a single Nyquist diagram suffices to display the stability behavior of a feedback amplifier for all values of the gain.

For example, it is possible to design an unstable feedback amplifier having the property that if the tube gain, μ, is increased enough, the curve of $\mu\beta$ becomes magnified until it no longer encircles 1. With enough gain, μ, the amplifier stabilizes. Such an amplifier was considered so paradoxical that, in 1934, E. Peterson, J. G. Kreer, and L. A. Ware built one just to demonstrate that it really worked as predicted.[80]

One of the earliest and most basic theorems in the theory of functions of a complex variable is Baron A. L. Cauchy's "principle of the argument," which provides a way of counting zeros and poles of an analytic function. The Nyquist diagram can be derived directly from Cauchy's principle. Routh was familiar with Cauchy's principle but Nyquist, who was not a mathematician by training, essentially rediscovered it.

In 1937, T. C. Fry used Cauchy's principle of the argument again to invent the isograph, a mechanical analog computer that found zeros of polynomials. One such instrument was built by R. L. Dietzold.[81,82] [Fig. 1-18] It plotted curves, like Nyquist diagrams, from which the number of zeros contained within given circles in the complex plane could be deduced.

Fig. 1-18. The isograph, an invention of T. C. Fry, built in 1937 to locate complex roots of polynomials. At the top of the machine a pen plotted a curve, like a Nyquist diagram, from which one could deduce the number of zeros contained within a given circle in the complex plane.

In practice, this was rather awkward and the isograph became obsolete after G. R. Stibitz invented a general-purpose relay computer (see Chapter 9 of this volume).

4.2 Applications of the Feedback Amplifier

The feedback amplifier was used in network synthesis. As the gain formula $g = \mu /(1 - \mu\beta)$ shows, a desired gain function g could be obtained by synthesizing a feedback network with suitable β instead of synthesizing g directly. For example, if μ is large, g is approximately equal to $-1/\beta$. Then one way to equalize a circuit with transfer function F was to use a feedback amplifier, designing the feedback path to have $\beta = F$. With simple capacitive feedback networks, feedback amplifiers became devices to perform integration and differentiation, and they were used in electronic analog computers. In addition, they could simulate inductors or circuits containing inductors, an important usage after transistors and integrated circuits made amplifiers more compact and less expensive than inductors.

In some applications, feedback was obtained mechanically, by having the amplifier drive a motor and taking the feedback voltage from a potentiometer on the motor shaft. These electromechanical feedback amplifiers were useful because simple electrical networks could be inserted into the feedback loop to obtain desired mechanical behavior.[83] [Fig. 1-19] Elec-

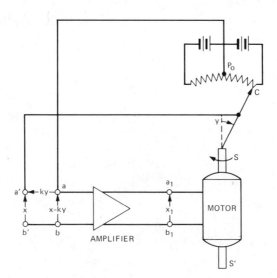

Fig. 1-19. Servomechanism producing an electromechanical feedback for controlling the angle y of a motor shaft from an input voltage signal x. The potentiometer produces a feedback signal ky, and the amplifier drives the motor to make $x - ky = 0$. [MacColl, *Fundamental Theory of Servomechanisms* (1945): 6.]

tromechanical gun directors, designed on feedback principles, were a major contribution of Bell Labs to the World War II effort. (See Chapter 3 of another volume of this series, subtitled *National Service in War and Peace (1925-1975)*.)

4.3 Gain-Phase Integral

A feedback amplifier ordinarily has large gain around the feedback loop in the frequency band of interest. (Otherwise, it would behave essentially as an ordinary amplifier.) Outside this band, the designer would like to make $|\mu\beta|$ fall off sharply in order to arrive quickly at the part of the Nyquist diagram where $|\mu\beta| < 1$ and the danger of encircling 1 is past. Unfortunately, there is a fundamental limitation on how sharply $|\mu\beta|$ can diminish. If the loop gain $|\mu\beta|$ drops abruptly, the phase of $\mu\beta$ must change so much that the $\mu\beta$ curve encircles 1 before reaching values $|\mu\beta| < 1$. Typically, the frequencies requiring close attention (that is, where $|\mu\beta| > 1$) extend above the frequencies of actual interest by a large factor. The mathematical connection between the gain and phase of $\mu\beta$ was discovered by H. W. Bode [Fig. 1-20], who followed Fry as head of the Mathematics Department in 1944.

Fig. 1-20. H. W. Bode, who pioneered in mathematical studies of feedback and stability in amplifiers.

Bode derived an integral that gives the phase angle of a certain realizable network having the prescribed gain $|\mu\beta|$ as a function of frequency.[84] Actually, many network functions $\mu\beta$ can have the same gain. Indeed, given any one of these functions, another can be obtained by multiplying it by a network function with constant gain (representing an all-pass network of the sort commonly used for phase equalizing). The particular network function $\mu\beta$ obtained by using Bode's gain-phase integral had also been discovered earlier by Y. W. Lee, at MIT, who had characterized it in terms of its zeros in the complex frequency plane.[85] However, Bode recognized that this particular network function was the one with the smallest phase. If Bode's minimum phase function had too large a phase shift, other network functions with the given $|\mu\beta|$ would be even worse and there would be no satisfactory amplifier design. Developed originally in the study of feedback, Bode's gain-phase inequalities have important implications for the design of amplifiers more generally and for transducers, such as loudspeakers, that must deliver power efficiently to a reactive load over a wide band of frequencies. [Fig. 1-21]

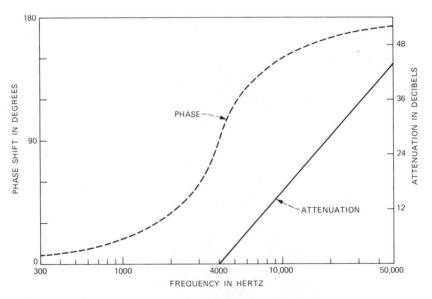

Fig. 1-21.   Attenuation and phase-shift characteristics for a low-pass network filter, as derived from H. W. Bode's gain-phase integral, expressing the minimum phase function in terms of the given attenuation function. The example shown is for a filter having zero attenuation below 4000 Hz and an attenuation that increases at 12 dB per octave above 4000 Hz. Understanding the connection between attenuation and phase was a crucial help to designers of stable feedback amplifiers. [Bode, *Network Analysis and Feedback Amplifier Design* (1945): 316.]

4.4 Stability of General Systems

Directed specifically at the problem of designing stable feedback amplifiers, the work on stability by Nyquist, Bode, and others stood in its time somewhat outside of a considerable body of literature on stability that had been developing since the mid-19th century. The work of Routh, cited in section 4.1.1, is only one example of early work; physicists and astronomers had long been concerned with the stability of general dynamic systems and mathematicians with the stability or boundedness of solutions of systems of differential equations. A generally linear theory associated with feedback in electrical circuits burgeoned during the period after 1945, stimulated at least in part by the exposure during World War II of many workers to the kinds of feedback problems treated by Nyquist and Bode, and to the work of these pioneers. Generalizations were made to feedback systems with many inputs and outputs, with some nods toward circuits having time-varying or mildly nonlinear elements. With few exceptions, however, the users of linear theory, when faced with the presence of a nonlinear element, were forced either to fall back on the classical technique of analyzing the stability of the system only under small perturbations, or else to treat the nonlinearity itself as a small perturbation. In a seminal sequence of papers beginning in 1963, I. W. Sandberg[86] at Bell Labs set forth a full analysis, not limited to small perturbations, of the stability of feedback systems containing nonlinear elements of a precisely specified kind.

Sandberg's results can be described briefly by thinking of them as an extension of the work of Nyquist and Bode. To do so simplifies discussion but omits some significant mathematical innovations concerning function-space formulation and study of the equations of a very general class of feedback systems. His main results include tool theorems of two types: small-gain theorems and passivity theorems, from which a variety of stability criteria have been obtained. With regard to specific applications, one extension relative to the work of Nyquist and Bode is of a kind common to much work in the field—an extension to systems with many inputs and outputs; scalars are replaced by vectors and scalar operators by matrix operators. More basic is Sandberg's way of dealing with nonlinear elements. He allows a time-varying distortion in the amplifying path, one that takes an input signal $f(t)$ and distorts it into $g(t) = \psi[f(t), t]$, where $\psi(\cdot, \cdot)$ is a function of two variables that is bounded by two linear functions via the inequalities

$$a \leq \frac{\psi[f(t), t]}{f(t)} \leq b .$$

The numbers a and b here can be thought of as specifying two different linear amplifiers.

In their simplest form (and assuming now that $a > 0$), Sandberg's results extend Nyquist's criterion. The latter requires that the trace of $\mu\beta$, for real frequencies, not encircle the point $+1$ in the complex plane. Sandberg's elegant circle criterion requires that the trace of $\mu\beta$, where now $\mu\beta$ is the loop gain of the linear, nondistorting part of the amplifier, not encircle or meet a certain region of the complex plane. That region is itself a circle having size and location specified by two numbers a and b above. This "forbidden" circle is centered on the real axis, and its two extreme points on that axis correspond to Nyquist's criterion applied to the two limiting amplifiers described by a and b.

V. TRANSMISSION LINES

5.1 Wire Pairs and Coaxial Cable

The original transmission lines of electrical communication were pairs of wires or single wires with ground return. Because they were used only at telegraph or voice frequencies (i.e., for signals having wavelengths on the line that, typically, were much longer than the cross-sectional dimensions of the line itself), they could be studied by static methods. The theory of lumped-element electrical networks is also a static theory in the sense that it is correct only in the limit of low frequencies. It ignores high-frequency effects, in particular radiation. High-frequency electrical problems must be formulated in terms of partial differential equations for the electric and magnetic field components. These equations, developed by Maxwell, contain a displacement current term that does not enter into the simpler static theory.

In 1855, Lord Kelvin explained the severe wave distortion on submarine telegraph cables by taking account of distributed capacitance between the conductors.[87] G. Kirchhoff (1857), O. Heaviside (1876), and H. Poincaré (1893) included the effect of self-inductance of the wires.[88] By observing that the inductance somewhat offset the bad effects of the capacitance, they set the stage for the invention of inductive loading by M. I. Pupin of Columbia University[89] and independently by G. A. Campbell.[90] (For a discussion of the patent award to Pupin, who filed two weeks prior to Campbell, see Chapter 4, section 4.1.3 of an earlier volume of this series, subtitled *The Early Years (1875-1925)*.)

All these authors regarded a transmission line as a limit of a recurrent lumped-element network, with each section representing a piece of the line of length Δ. By going to the limit of many short pieces ($\Delta \rightarrow 0$), equations governing the propagation of voltage and current along the line were obtained. [Fig. 1-22] The older literature derived the telegrapher's equation in that way; it was equivalent to what later came to be called the transmission-line equations.

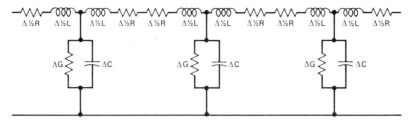

Fig. 1-22. Electrical filter representation of part of a continuous transmission line. The line of length l is approximated by many (n) electrical filter sections connected in tandem, each section representing a small piece of line of length $\Delta(=l/n)$. R, L, G, and C are the series resistance, series inductance, shunt conductance, and shunt capacitance, respectively, per unit length of the line. [Johnson, *Transmission Circuits for Telephonic Communication* (1924): 144.]

An example of a static transmission line analysis was the generalization of the transmission line equations to systems of many wires. In a many-wire problem, one pair of wires might be a telephone line and the other wires might be power lines or other telephone lines producing hum or crosstalk in the first line by capacitative and inductive coupling. The multiwire form of the transmission line equations was obtained in 1927 by J. R. Carson and R. S. Hoyt.[91]

5.1.1 Transmission Line Losses—Skin Effect

The inadequacy of static methods became evident in connection with transmission line losses. Although the resistance per mile might be precisely measured using a dc ohmmeter, the transmission line equations with that measured resistance might give inaccurate results even at voice frequencies. The difficulty lies in the way electric current flows through a resistive wire. At high frequencies, the current becomes concentrated near the surface of the wire (skin effect), thus reducing the effective cross-sectional area of the conductor and causing more power loss than at low frequencies.

In 1921, Carson and J. J. Gilbert gave a skin-effect analysis to treat losses in a submarine telephone cable.[92] The cable used the ocean as a ground-return path. Instead of spreading uniformly over the ocean, the return current was concentrated near the cable by skin effect. A large part of the return current flowed in the resistive iron-armor wires that were wound around the cable for mechanical strength. The practical conclusion was that cable attenuation and distortion could be greatly reduced by adding a thin copper sheath, just under the armor wires, to carry the return current. In effect, Carson and Gilbert were advocating use of a coaxial cable.

In the early 1930s, a carrier telephony system was developed, using coaxial cable to obtain a wide bandwidth, small attenuation, and good shielding between circuits. S. A. Schelkunoff and T. M. Odarenko gave the quantitative analysis of these benefits.[93,94] While crosstalk effects in the old balanced-pair cables increased with frequency, they decreased in coaxial cable.

In 1951, A. M. Clogston proposed a scheme for alleviating the skin-effect problem in a transmission line by the use of a conductor composed of many insulated thin conducting strips, running parallel to the direction of current flow.[95] For lamina thickness small in comparison with the theoretical skin depth of the metal used, the electromagnetic wave can penetrate a distance great enough to include a thickness of conducting material many skin depths deep. S. P. Morgan extended the calculations to include the case of the coaxial conductor.[96,97] The calculations were confirmed experimentally, but the cable structure and precision required for such a transmission turned out to be too expensive and too difficult to fabricate to play a role in Bell System transmission systems.

During the 1920s, Carson applied Maxwell's equations to study losses in such transmission lines as wire pairs, overhead or underground wires with ground return, and some multiple-wire combinations.[98] These structures all propagated what was called a principal wave. In the special case of perfectly conducting wires and perfectly lossless dielectrics, a principal wave could be derived from Maxwell's equations by looking for a solution with no electric- or magnetic-field components in the direction of propagation. The problem then simplified to a static problem. Apart from perturbing effects of losses in conductors and dielectrics, a principal wave behaved very much like the waves in the old transmission line theory.

5.2 Waveguides

In the late 19th century, J. J. Thomson and Lord Rayleigh showed mathematically that electromagnetic waves can propagate inside a hollow conducting tube.[99,100] These waves were not widely known, and Carson seems to have rediscovered them independently in a memorandum of 1924. Around 1932, G. C. Southworth at AT&T built hollow tubes, or waveguides, and produced these waves experimentally.

At that time, the shortwave spectrum was already becoming crowded. Southworth foresaw the coming of microwave communication, in which the waveguide could serve as a new kind of transmission line. In reply to the memorandum in which Southworth first described his ideas and experiments, however, one of the leading mathematicians of the company wrote an evaluation that stated, "I have arrived therefore at the tentative conclusion that Southworth's proposed system of transmission is not practicable."[101] Fortunately, the unnamed mathematician, whose opinion was highly regarded by Southworth's supervision, discovered an error in his analysis and issued a retraction. Thereafter, Southworth received mathematical support, both from Carson and S. P. Mead at AT&T and from Schelkunoff at Bell Labs.

Unlike the earlier wire and coaxial transmission lines, the waveguide had no principal wave that propagated at low frequencies. It was more like a high-pass filter, propagating only at frequencies above some cutoff frequency.

One of the first mathematical problems connected with waveguides was the study of modes. These are field configurations that can propagate without changing shape. Each mode has its own cutoff frequency, propagation speed, and attenuation. The mathematical analysis of waveguide modes proceeded independently at AT&T and Bell Labs, each producing internal memoranda in 1933. This work formed the basis for Carson's, Mead's, and Schelkunoff's joint paper of 1936, a mathematical companion to Southworth's experimental paper.[102] By then, waveguide research had also been carried on at MIT by W. L. Barrow and L. J. Chu.[103,104]

In later papers, Schelkunoff found that certain field parameters, for a given mode, behaved mathematically like such things as the voltages, currents, and impedances of earlier transmission lines.[105,106] Most engineering waveguide calculations could then be made using well-understood formulas related to the old telegrapher's equation. These calculations were more important than ever because even a few inches of waveguide could be long in terms of wavelength; pieces of waveguide had replaced inductors and capacitors as resonators and as impedance-matching devices.

Waveguide calculations were further simplified in 1939 when P. H. Smith published his chart, a nomogram based on the traditional transmission-line formulas for calculating impedances.[107,108] In his autobiography, Southworth stated, "Few pieces of apparatus have proven more useful to the practical engineer than the Smith diagram."[109]

5.2.1 The TE_{01} Waveguide

Most modes have high attenuations near the cutoff frequency and also at high frequencies. One exceptional mode, TE_{01}, having concentric circular electric field lines, has attenuation decreasing steadily to zero at high frequencies, a fact that makes this mode especially suited for low-loss transmission. However, L. Brillouin in France suggested that the TE_{01} mode might be unstable, changing to a mode with high attenuation if the waveguide were deformed even slightly from a perfectly circular shape.[110] To answer this objection, Schelkunoff analyzed a deformed circular guide and showed that a small deformation did not increase the attenuation significantly until very large frequencies were attained.[111] By studying elliptical waveguides, Chu obtained a similar result.[112] The TE_{01} mode is a difficult one to work with experimentally, but the millimeter-wavelength research effort at Bell Labs solved this problem and established the technical feasibility of the predicted low attenuation of this mode for a practical carrier telephony system (see Chapter 6 of this volume).

VI. ANTENNAS AND ELECTROMAGNETIC RADIATION

The earliest triumph of electromagnetic theory was its success in explaining light as a form of electromagnetic radiation. The same theory applied to radio waves, but there were new problems of analyzing the production of radiation by currents in antennas.

In Germany, the fundamental problem of radiation from a dipole antenna near an imperfectly conducting earth was analyzed both by A. Sommerfeld (1909) and by H. Weyl (1919), but with conflicting results.[113,114] Sommerfeld's answer contained a surface wave term that was absent in Weyl's. For 18 years, these two theories remained in conflict. Both were so complicated that errors were not easily detected. In 1937, C. R. Burrows at Bell Labs performed experiments to decide between the two theories. When he compared his experimental results against elaborate series expansions that W. H. Wise and S. O. Rice had made from the Sommerfeld and Weyl formulas, Burrows's data confirmed Weyl's theory.[115] Soon afterward K. F. Niessen in Germany and Rice at Bell Labs discovered that Sommerfeld had chosen the wrong sign when taking a square root.[116]

Because H. Hertz performed his original experiments at ultrahigh frequencies, he found it relatively easy to produce directive antennas using reflectors. At the long wavelengths first used in wireless communication, however, antennas could not easily be built large enough to have much directivity. After the discovery of long-distance shortwave propagation, interest revived in directive antennas, many wavelengths across, as a way of concentrating radiated power in the direction of the receiving station. For a discussion of antenna research at short waves and of microwave frequencies, see Chapter 5, sections 1.3 and IV in this volume.

One early form of directive antenna was the wave antenna, an invention of H. H. Beverage at RCA.[117] The wave antenna was a wire, many wavelengths long, arranged as a transmission line with ground return. As a receiving antenna, it extracted power from the incident wave in the same way that one transmission line received crosstalk from another. Carson's papers on wire transmission lines were motivated in part by the wave antenna and included formulas useful in wave-antenna design.[118,119]

Another interest of Carson's was a reciprocity theorem that Lord Rayleigh had given for acoustic waves. Carson generalized this theorem to a form applicable to antennas. A useful consequence of this generalized theorem is that an antenna has the same directivity pattern for receiving as for transmitting.[120,121]

6.1 Antenna Arrays

The idea of combining several small antennas into one directive structure was a natural extension of the diffraction grating in optics.[122] Antennas composed of two elements were described as early as 1899.[123] G. A. Campbell studied more complicated antenna arrays in 1919. They contained larger numbers of elements, regularly spaced in a line, circle, or rectangle.[124] Campbell's table of array patterns was extended by R. M. Foster in 1926 and by Southworth in 1930.[125,126]

In these arrays, all elements were excited with currents of the same magnitude; the phase of the excitation varied linearly across the array. Arrays of that kind could produce a pattern with a single, narrow lobe, such as might be used in transatlantic shortwave radiotelephony. In World War II, there were radar applications for more complicated patterns, such as the cosecant squared pattern that produced constant radar response from a ground target at any range. By allowing currents of unequal magnitude and general phases, S. A. Schelkunoff developed techniques of pattern synthesis by which one could find the currents to produce a prescribed pattern.[127,128] For arrays of radiators evenly spaced along a line, Schelkunoff observed that a simple transformation of variables converted the expression for the pattern function into a polynomial. Given a desired pattern, one could then use standard mathematical methods to approximate it by a polynomial, the coefficients of which became the required currents. By using Tchebycheff polynomials for the pattern functions, C. L. Dolph designed linear arrays having maximum gain for a prescribed side-lobe level.[129] Similarly, in the case of radiation from a two-dimensional aperture illuminated by a horn reflector, or lens, Schelkunoff expressed the pattern as a Fourier integral that could be inverted to obtain the required field in the aperture.

E. N. Gilbert and S. P. Morgan[130] considered antennas made up of many discrete radiators disposed arbitrarily in space. They proved general theorems concerning the pattern of radiation from such arrays, directing particular attention to the departures from a desired pattern caused by errors in realizing the design. Errors could be caused by failure of the exciting currents in the radiating elements to match, in phase and amplitude, the currents specified by the design or by departures of the antenna elements from the physical positions specified by the design. One result put into concrete and quantitative terms some of the folklore about so-called hyperdirective antennas—antennas that focused a narrow beam of radiation from an aperture or array having small dimensions. It was shown that hyperdirectivity could be realized only by the imposition of extremely precise control over the position and excitations of the radiators.

The purpose of a directive receiving antenna is to reject signals from sources that are separated in angular position from the source of a desired signal. Generally one thinks of the unwanted signal or signals as originating, like the desired one, from point sources. There are situations, however, in which it is reasonable to consider that the unwanted signals are simply background noise originating from a diffuse cloud of sources, each source radiating at minute power and incoherently from all others. D. Slepian considered the design of an antenna of finite aperture to optimize reception from a desired source in the presence of such spatially distributed background. The problem turns out to be similar to that of detecting a sinusoidal signal in noise, using a sample of data of finite duration. (See section 7.5.)

VII. NOISE

7.1 Crosstalk

The most troublesome noises on early telephone circuits were hum and crosstalk induced by nearby power and telephone lines. In 1879, Alexander Graham Bell invented the twisted-pair cable to reduce this interference.[131,132] J. A. Barrett invented more elaborate wire-transposition schemes in 1888.[133] (See Chapter 4, section 2.2 of the first volume of this series, subtitled *The Early Years (1875-1925)*.)

When many twisted pairs are grouped together into a single cable, crosstalk can be further reduced by cutting the cable into sections spliced together according to rules that prevent any two pairs from lying close together too often. H. P. Lawther, Jr., of Southwestern Bell Telephone Co., first devised splicing rules in 1935; J. Riordan extended them in 1943.[134,135] These rules are mathematically interesting as applications of the theory of numbers.

In multiplexed-carrier telephony, crosstalk arises in another way. A telephone repeater is a wide-band amplifier serving many channels at once. If this amplifier is not perfectly linear, it can produce spurious tones by beating or heterodyne action. If frequencies f_1 and f_2 are present at the input to the repeater, the output can contain frequencies $2f_1$, $f_1 + f_2$, $2f_1 - f_2$, and others. In this way, speech signals on two different telephone channels interact to produce interference on a third. To help control this interference, B. D. Holbrook and J. T. Dixon developed a load rating theory in 1931.[136] Their theory was probabilistic. It took into account random fluctuations in the number of busy channels and the wide variability in loudness of speech. In that way, the theory determined a limit on the traffic level. Below this limit, the amplifier operated in its linear range most of the time.

The amplitudes of the various crosstalk tones that result from nonlinear distortion depend in a complicated way on the amplitudes of the input tones and on the kind of nonlinearity. In 1940, W. R. Bennett developed a technique for finding this dependence and applied it, in 1947, to nonlinear characteristics that occur in repeater amplifiers.[137,138]

7.2 Impulse Noise

Impulse noise is a mathematical model for noise as a sum of many impulses or transients, all of the same shape $F(t)$, but with random amplitudes A_k and arrival times T_k

$$x(t) = \sum_k A_k F(t - T_k) .$$

Vacuum-tube noise, or shot noise, fits the impulse-noise model with the impulses corresponding to the arrival of electrons at the plate of the tube and the shape of each impulse being the output response that an electron produces in the plate circuit.

In 1909, N. R. Campbell in England used the impulse-noise model to study fluctuations of current in a photoelectric cell and proved the Campbell Theorems of noise theory.[139] One of these theorems expresses the power in the noise in terms of the integral of the impulse shape.

In 1925, J. R. Carson used impulse noise as a model for atmospheric noise, or static, in a radio receiver.[140,141] By an extension of Campbell's theorems, Carson showed that impulse noise has a power spectrum proportional to the square of the magnitude of the Fourier transform of the shape of the impulse. Carson used this result to evaluate the effectiveness of filters in reducing noise on radiotelephone channels. He concluded that simple filters achieved about as much reduction as could be obtained. In 1938, W. Shockley and J. R. Pierce developed a theory for noise in electron multipliers.[142] (See Chapter 4, section IV in this volume.)

7.3 Johnson Noise

In 1918, W. Schottky in Germany first analyzed the shot effect in vacuum tubes by an impulse-noise model.[143] In his paper, he suggested a second kind of noise, thermal noise, that would result from random thermal motions of the electrons in a resistor. Schottky concluded that thermal noise in vacuum-tube circuits would be impossible to observe, being masked by the much stronger shot noise. To reach this conclusion, Schottky had to evaluate a complicated integral, as in Campbell's theorem, for the power in the shot noise. In 1920, J. B. Johnson [Fig. 1-23] tried to check Schottky's integration, but after much labor, obtained a smaller shot-noise power. When he showed the integral to L. A. MacColl, MacColl agreed with Johnson's answer. In fact, MacColl used the method of residues to evaluate the integral at sight, a performance that Johnson still remembered as impressive 50 years later.[144] By 1928, Johnson actually observed and measured thermal noise in carefully controlled experiments.[145] To provide a theoretical foundation for Johnson's interpretation of the experimental results, H. Nyquist gave a mathematical analysis of thermal noise, combining transmission line theory with the equipartition theorem of statistical me-

Fig. 1-23.   J. B. Johnson, who discovered that resistors made of diverse materials are always a source of white noise.

chanics.[146] A resistor of R ohms at absolute temperature T is a wide-band noise-voltage source. The noise voltage V that the resistor generates in any frequency band of width Δf has a mean-squared value $\overline{V^2} = 4kTR\Delta f$, where k is the Boltzmann constant of thermodynamics, 1.37×10^{-23} joules per degree Kelvin.

Thermal noise is often called Johnson noise. It becomes important in weak-signal communication systems such as satellite systems, where the expense of eliminating other noise sources is justifiable. Then Nyquist's formula for $\overline{V^2}$ sets an irreducible minimum on the noise power that must be tolerated.

7.4 Gaussian Noise

The mathematical properties of impulse noise simplify greatly in a limiting case in which the rate of arrival of impulses becomes infinite. Fortunately, this limit is often approached in practice, as in the shot effect with many electrons arriving per second. The limiting noise is called Gaussian noise because noise samples have a Gaussian probability distribution.

In 1906, Albert Einstein derived a Gaussian limiting distribution in his study of Brownian motion.[147] As a model of Brownian motion, Einstein used the random walk, which may be regarded as a kind of impulse-noise motion in which the impulse $F(t)$ is a unit step:

$$F(t) = 1 \text{ for } t \geq 0$$
$$= 0 \text{ for } t < 0.$$

Electrical noise problems require impulses $F(t)$ of many other shapes. Nyquist, in an unpublished memorandum in 1932, also obtained a Gaussian limit with a different $F(t)$, making an interesting connection between impulse noise and another representation of noise as a sum of a large number of sinusoids with random amplitudes and phases. This latter model of noise dates back to Lord Rayleigh, who had suggested it for blackbody radiation.[148] In early studies, noise might be modeled as a sum of either independent impulses or independent sinusoids, but the connection between the two models was not clear. Nyquist showed that the sinusoidal components of impulse noise became independent in the limit of Gaussian noise.

In 1944 and 1945, S. O. Rice [Fig. 1-24] published a monumental study of noise,[149,150] generally regarded to be the single most useful source of information about Gaussian noise. Rice derived the Gaussian limiting form of impulse noise and the limiting independence of the sinusoidal components for a general impulse shape. He developed many of the properties of Gaussian noise that have engineering applications. For example, Rice derived the probability distribution for the noise energy received during a given time interval, a result that can be used to predict the rate at which a threshold detector will produce false alarms. Other topics in Rice's paper relate to the zeros, maxima, minima, and envelope of Gaussian noise and to the effect of putting Gaussian noise through a nonlinear device.

One of Rice's results was a formula for the mean number of zeros per second of Gaussian noise.[151] For some spectra, the mean number of zeros per second is infinite, a surprising result indicative of the very jittery appearance of such noises.

Curiously, Rice's original interest was not electrical noise in the usual sense. He started with a transmission problem in which reflections from irregularities, such as mismatched repeaters and loading coils, caused interference and even instability of repeater amplifiers. This was an old probabilistic problem. In 1912, J. Mills had treated the reflecting irregularities as randomly distributed along the line and obtained formulas used in engineering the transcontinental telephone line of 1913 through 1914. G. Crisson extended this work in 1925.[152] Rice's repeater problem turned out to involve the envelope of a Gaussian noise. As Rice's 1944 paper showed, narrow-band Gaussian noise can be represented as a sinusoid with slowly

Fig. 1-24. S. O. Rice, who pioneered in fundamental mathematical analysis of noise in electrical circuits.

varying random envelope and phase. Rice solved his repeater problem by finding the probability distribution function for the envelope. Actually, the same kind of narrow-band noise appears at the output of selective circuits in radio receivers. In a later paper, Rice added this noise to a pure sinusoid, representing a radio signal, to derive results about the effects of noise in AM and FM detection.[153]

Rice's several alternative representations of Gaussian noise have found wide application in engineering problems. E. L. Kaplan, in a basic paper, used the narrow-band envelope form to model the effects of fading or glinting in radar signals and to derive several optimal procedures for extracting data from such signals.[154]

From a time preceding Einstein's paper, properties of the path of the random walk, or of Brownian motion, have been studied for their physical or mathematical interest. Rice's paper represents a comprehensive attack on problems of engineering interest, many of them new.[155] Further contributions to this line of study were made by D. Slepian, by M. Kac of Rockefeller University, by L. A. Shepp, and by Shepp and Slepian during the period from 1959 through 1977.

7.5 Prediction, Estimation, and Detection

During World War II, an unusual noise problem arose in connection with antiaircraft fire control. Targets performed haphazard evasive maneuvers to confuse gun directors. Thus, a target coordinate $x(t)$ had some resemblance to a random noise signal. To allow for the time α that an antiaircraft missile would take to reach the target, a prediction of the future target coordinate $x(t + \alpha)$ was needed. The prediction had to be based on observations of the target up to the present time t only, and even these observations contained inaccuracies or noise. N. Wiener at MIT and A. Kolmogoroff in the USSR independently found the way to estimate the future coordinate $x(t + \alpha)$ with least mean-squared error, assuming that the appropriate spectrum for random target coordinates was known.[156,157] The best estimator had to be obtained by solving an integral equation. Formidable mathematical difficulties, which earned Wiener's original yellow-cover publication the nickname "yellow peril," were neatly sidestepped in a later treatment by R. B. Blackman, H. W. Bode, and C. E. Shannon.[158,159] Engineers preferred this treatment because it used only familiar ideas about filters and impulse noise. The solution of the integral equation was, in effect, found with the help of Bode's loss-phase integral.

The work on antiaircraft gunnery illustrates the propensity toward idealization that T. C. Fry cited as one characteristic of mathematicians (see section 1.2 of this chapter). The mathematical problem differed from the real problem in at least two major respects. First, observations of the target were not available for all past times, but only for the rather short interval from the start of target tracking to the time the gun fired. Second, instead of a minimum mean-squared error prediction, what was really needed was an estimate of where to point the gun to maximize the probability of hitting the target. Indeed, large errors contribute most to the mean-squared error, but misses by an inch or a mile are no different in figuring the hit probability. Nevertheless, the solution of the idealized problem provided insight that could not have been obtained by trying to solve the difficult real problem directly.

In fact, the integral equation solved by Wiener, for the idealized model in which the whole past history of $x(t)$ is known, is a limiting case of the kind of integral equation solved by Slepian in his analysis of the antenna problem mentioned at the end of section 6.1 above. Slepian's solution of the latter equation then solved the prediction problem addressed by Wiener, Kolmogoroff, and Blackman-Bode-Shannon for cases of engineering interest in which only a finite segment of past data is available. Slepian and T. T. Kadota solved several related equations that appear in detection theory when only a finite segment of data is available.[160]

Prediction is just one special member of a class of problems that seek a good estimate of some quantity $Q(t)$ that depends linearly on the signal $x(t)$. For instance, $Q(t)$ might be the output of a filter with input $x(t)$. Or, since only a noisy version of $x(t)$ is observable, $Q(t)$ might be the true value of $x(t)$ (with the noise removed). Although $x(t)$ may be observed throughout an entire interval of past times, it is often convenient to base the estimate of $Q(t)$ on only a finite number of these observations. The estimation problem then simplifies to one that can be handled by standard methods of multivariate statistics. During World War II, multivariate methods solved many estimation problems of radar and fire control, at least to engineering satisfaction. Sometimes the (finite) number of observations could be made to approach infinity to obtain, in the limit, a formal solution to the original continuous-time problem. The mathematical difficulties in making such a passage rigorous are formidable. It was not until about 1950 that a mathematical foundation, which was broad enough to provide convenient and rigorously justifiable solutions to many estimation problems of importance to engineers, had been laid.[161]

Multivariate estimation problems are solved by computing probabilities as integrals over certain volumes in the finite-dimensional space that has the observed signal samples as coordinates. In continuous-time estimation problems, these probabilities become integrals over a function space of infinite dimension. Finding an appropriate notion of volume or measure in function space thus becomes a central problem in estimation theory. Wiener had already introduced an infinite-dimensional measure (Wiener measure) in his study of Brownian motion.

A definitive paper of Shepp established Wiener measure as the proper underlying volume in function space for dealing with problems involving Gaussian noise.[162] This paper provides complete formulas for calculating the density in function space of one Gaussian probability measure with respect to another, or with respect to Wiener measure. These formulas help to provide an interpretation of estimation problem solutions as applications of the method of maximum likelihood, a familiar technique in multivariate statistics. The paper also establishes a large class of equivalent representations for the random-walk (or Wiener) process in terms of countably many independent, identically distributed, random variables; it extends many prior results, including those of Rice.

Detection problems differ from estimation problems only in requiring that the signal information be used to decide between a small number of alternatives. For example, in a radar application the alternatives might be target present and no target. A telegraph application might require the decision between a mark and a space. Again, if only a finite number of signal samples is to be used in making the decision, the detection problem becomes a standard one in multivariate statistics, the problem of hypothesis testing. Beginning around 1945, many examples of detection problems were attacked by multivariate methods. More recently, Kadota has used the results given in the above-mentioned paper by Shepp to solve a number of problems in detection and estimation directly by function-space methods.[163]

7.6 Stochastic Control

A typical problem of stochastic control is encountered in missile guidance. Using noisy data describing the motion of a randomly maneuvering target, one must control the motors that try to steer a missile along a collision course. Although prediction or estimation is involved in this control, there is also an element of feedback; steering done at a given time will affect subsequent missile headings and hence subsequent steering.

One may state the central problem in stochastic control as that of devising a rule or strategy for converting information about such factors as present and past target position, rate, and heading into steering orders that will minimize some cost—average miss distance being one example of a cost. Using the random walk as a model for the target motion, V. E. Beneš formulated this kind of problem in a general setting.[164] His formulation included an explicit description of the information available at each time t, upon which to take control actions. Under weak assumptions about the controllability of the system being controlled, and with the assumption that sufficient information is available to the controller, he showed that for each cost function of a wide class, an optimal (cost minimizing) control strategy exists. No ad hoc restrictions were placed on the admissible control strategies. Exploiting this generality, Beneš later validated a conjecture widely held about a large class of stochastic control problems—essentially, that a steering strategy using only the two rudder positions, hard left and hard right, minimizes final miss distance.[165] In these papers and in other papers applying the same results and methods, Beneš set forth general techniques for stochastic control problems in which the target motion is derived from the random walk.[166] Beneš, L. A. Shepp, and H. S. Witsenhausen gave an explicit solution to the problem of tracking a jinking target under a constraint on the total amount of control effort expended (e.g., a limit to the total amount of energy consumed by induced drag when the rudder is hard over).[167] Applications ranging from vehicle steering to investment strategies were described.

Picturesque terms, such as target and steering as just used, correctly suggest the historical background of problems that have been studied under the general heading of stochastic control, but many other situations fit a similar mathematical mold. The moves of the players of a game, the actions taken by independent dealers in a market, the decisions made by division managers of a dispersed commercial enterprise, and the actions taken by one individual at successive stages of an endeavor can in each case be thought of as control actions taken by agents who, at the time of acting, may have neither complete knowledge of nor complete control over the situation being controlled. Drawing extensively upon prior work in the theory of games, Witsenhausen proposed in 1971 a mathematical framework within which to phrase problems of stochastic control at a basic level of generality.[168,169] Within this framework he developed a taxonomy of control problems (or of information structures), established conditions for the existence of (actionable) control strategies, and isolated some critical unsolved problems.

VIII. INFORMATION THEORY

Probably the most spectacular development in communications mathematics to take place at Bell Laboratories was the formulation in the 1940s of information theory by C. E. Shannon. Information theory is a study of signaling systems from a very general point of view in order to derive theorems and limitations universally applicable to all systems. Perhaps the best succinct description of information theory is the title Shannon chose for his fundamental paper of 1948, "A Mathematical Theory of Communication."[170] In a 1977 monograph on information theory, R. J. McEliece of the California Institute of Technology wrote:

> With many profound scientific discoveries (for example, Einstein's discovery in 1905 of the special theory of relativity) it is possible with the aid of hindsight to see that the times were ripe for the breakthrough. Not so with information theory. While, of course, Shannon was not working in a vacuum in the 1940s, his results were so breathtakingly original that even the communication specialists of the day were at a loss to understand their significance. Gradually, as Shannon's theorems were digested by the mathematical/ engineering community, it became clear that he had created a brand-new science, and others began to make first-rate contributions of their own. Slowly at first, and then more rapidly, the subject grew, until now hundreds of research papers in information theory are published each year.[171]

As viewed from a modern perspective, Shannon's theory can be described by use of the following block diagram:[172]

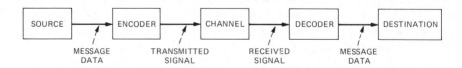

In this diagram the source output is some form of data that must be communicated reliably through the channel to the destination. For example, the source might be a computer and the data a binary sequence of zeros and ones, or the source might be a voice and the data a continuous-time waveform. The channel might be a telephone line or an optical-fiber waveguide. The channel might also be a computer memory. The process shown in the diagram could represent the storing of data into a memory and its subsequent withdrawal.

In general, there are two limitations on the reliability with which we can communicate the data:

1) The channel may introduce noise into the system. Here noise is defined as anything that makes it impossible to determine the exact channel input information by observing the channel output. A well-known example of noise in a radio channel is static. Another example is an imperfectly operating computer memory that occasionally changes bits.

2) There may exist a source-channel mismatch. This situation occurs whenever the data is not in a suitable form to go directly into the channel. Examples of mismatch are a binary data source (say a computer) and a continuous channel (say a radio channel), or a continuous source (say speech) and a digital channel (say a computer memory). Another example of mismatch occurs when a binary source emits data faster than a binary channel can transmit it.

The encoder and decoder in the diagram are processors that have the task of combating these limitations as far as possible. Thus, the encoder processes the data to combat the channel noise (for example, it may use an error-correcting code on a binary channel) and to put the data in a suitable form for transmission over the channel—i.e., overcome source-channel mismatch (for example, it may quantize continuous data for transmission over a digital channel). The decoder must undo the effects of the encoder and the channel and deliver data to the destination, which is, one hopes, close to the data output of the source.

To illustrate the central ideas of Shannon's theory, several important special cases of the system represented by the diagram will be discussed and some conclusions will be stated that can be deduced from the theory.

8.1 Source Coding and the Information Measure

Suppose that the channel in the diagram is the so-called noiseless binary channel that accepts R binary digits per second and transmits them perfectly. The task of the encoder is to transform the source output into a binary stream of R digits per second in such a way that the decoder can recover the source symbols as accurately as possible. Suppose, for example, that the source output is a white Gaussian random process with power P and bandwidth W. Then the encoder is an analog-to-digital (A/D) converter or quantizer. The theory tells us that the mean-squared quantizing error that must inevitably arise when the source output is transmitted over our noiseless channel with rate R must be at least $P2^{-2R/W}$ and, further, that there exists an encoder/decoder (albeit complex) that can achieve this level of distortion.

For an arbitrary source and an arbitrary measure of distortion or error between source output data and data delivered to the destination, the theory gives a function $D(R)$ that is the minimum achievable average distortion D when the source data is transmitted over a noiseless binary channel with rate R. In our example, $D(R) = P2^{-2R/W}$.

Another important example is that of a noiseless binary channel with rate R with the source emitting a sequence of independent letters at say 1 letter each second. Suppose there are M letters possible. Let $p_i = Pr\{$source output $= i\}$, where $0 \leq i \leq M - 1$. Let the distortion measure be the average error rate—i.e., the average number of times per second the destination receives a letter that is different from the corresponding source letter. For this case the theory tells us that $D(R) = 0$, provided R exceeds a quantity H called the entropy, defined by

$$H = - \sum_{i=0}^{M-1} p_i \log_2 p_i.$$

Note that, since the channel accepts R binary symbols per source letter, the entropy is the minimum number of binary digits needed by the encoder to represent the source output without error. Thus the entropy is a measure of the amount of information contained in the source. To give a name to the units in which Shannon measured information, J. W. Tukey coined the word "bits," a contraction of "binary digits" that quickly established itself in engineering. The word information had been used in a technical sense by R. V. L. Hartley in 1928.

Shannon's theory includes two important concepts: the first is the idea of coding, in which the source data is processed by a complex encoder in order to represent it optimally in a binary stream of rate R; the second is the notion of an information source as a statistical process with its information (i.e., its entropy) defined by its probability law. In the case of a noiseless channel with a source emitting a sequence of independent letters, an efficient code must, like Morse code, give the shortest code words to the most frequent letters. However, to exploit this possibility efficiently, large blocks of letters may be involved instead of just single letters.

To treat message sources statistically was somewhat unusual in communications engineering. Section VII of this chapter cites examples of repeater load rating theory and antiaircraft fire control. Earlier examples in cryptography were common. Philosophical objections are sometimes raised against describing human behavior in probabilistic terms. To counter arguments that human messages do not have random origin, Shannon's 1948 paper included random sources that wrote random English approximating real English text. A typical source, a trigram source that chooses each letter at random from a distribution determined by the preceding two letters, wrote "IN NO IST LAT WHEY CRATICT FROURE BIRS GROCID PONDENOME OF DEMONSTURES OF THE REPTAGIN IS

REGOACTIONA OF CRE," which is at least pronounceable and contains some real words. A book by J. R. Pierce quotes more fluent passages written by more complicated random sources. Pierce also credits W. A. Mozart with the idea of writing music at random (Koechel listing 294D).[173]

Random English sources illustrate one of the reasons why ideal transmitters and receivers are complicated and expensive. Because trigram sources do not write very good English, one must conclude that English contains important statistical correlations between letters more than three letters apart. An ideal transmission system would have to use these correlations in an optimal way. In 1951, Shannon gave particular attention to the problem of transmitting written English over a noiseless binary channel.[174] He concluded that, although over 4 (binary) digits per letter are required to transmit English letter by letter, 2.1 digits per letter suffice to transmit entire words and about 1 digit per letter suffices for blocks 100 letters long. To make these numbers somewhat plausible, one may note that most English text remains readable even after the vowels are deleted. Since about half the text letters are vowels, vowel deletion provides one fairly reliable way of speeding transmission by a factor of two.

8.2 Channel and Source Coding

Let us now consider another special case of the communication system of the diagram above (see page 46). Here the source is taken to be a binary source that emits digits at a rate of R per second to be transmitted over a noisy channel and delivered to the destination essentially error free. The gist of Shannon's results as applied to this problem is that each channel has a characteristic information rate C, called the capacity of the channel, that cannot be exceeded in a reliable communication system. Given any high standard of reliability, say an error probability of 10^{-10} at the output of the receiver, one can maintain this reliability and an information rate as close to C as desired by proper design of the transmitter and receiver. The surprising thing about this result is that the channel capacity C is not zero. One obvious way to achieve high reliability is to repeat the messages many times, but that also reduces the information rate. Shannon's theorem shows that high reliability at a fixed information rate is obtainable by encoding the messages more cleverly. Error-correcting codes that provide one way of accomplishing this are described in sections 8.6 and 8.7.

Determining the capacity C of a given channel is often a difficult problem. One channel that Shannon analyzed is particularly appropriate as a model of a radio channel. It transmits signals occupying a band W-Hz wide at average power levels of up to S watts. During transmission, Gaussian noise interference of power N is added to the signal. This channel has capacity

$$C = W \log_2(1 + S/N) .$$

This equation may be interpreted as an exchange relationship, showing how much an increase in bandwidth W is worth in terms of increased signal-to-noise ratio S/N.

Using the source coding procedure described in section 8.1, the source output can be encoded into a binary stream of R binary digits per second with a resulting distortion of $D(R)$. Since the channel can transmit essentially perfectly C binary digits per second, the system can deliver the source data to the destination with a distortion $D(C)$.

A most remarkable consequence of the Shannon theory is that a distortion $D(C)$ is the optimal obtainable. In other words, the process of source coding and channel coding can be decoupled with no loss in the quality of performance.

8.3 The First Two Decades of Information Theory

Much of the early research work on Shannon's theory was devoted to fine-tuning Shannon's original results. One problem of considerable interest (which by the early 1980s had not been completely solved) is the effect of limiting the memory or the complexity of the encoder and decoder in the system represented in the diagram. Rice did the first study of this problem for the band-limited channel with Gaussian noise.[175] Shannon and later Slepian, Wyner, and many others outside Bell Laboratories continued this line of research for many years.

Another interesting version of the system arises when an extra return, or feedback, channel is added. Suppose one only wants to transmit in the forward direction, using the feedback channel for repeat requests or other error-control messages. For a wide class of channels, Shannon showed in 1956 that it is impossible to increase the capacity in the forward direction, although use of a feedback channel can dramatically reduce the complexity required of the encoder/decoder to achieve a given level of performance.[176,177]

In the 1950s and 1960s, much work was done to characterize explicitly and carefully the sources and channels for which Shannon-like coding theorems can be established. A great deal of work was done by Wyner, Kadota, and L. H. Brandenburg to broaden this class as much as possible.[178]

8.4 Multiple-User Theory

In the classical communication setup in the diagram describing Shannon's theory, there is but a single source and a single destination. In multiple-user information theory, systems are studied in which there are more than one source and/or channel and more than one encoder/decoder pair with various constraints placed on collaboration between the encoders and/or decoders.

The earliest work on multiple-user theory was done by Shannon in 1961 when he generalized his theorem about channel capacity to cover the two-way channel.[179] A trade-off exists between rates R_1 and R_2 of information transmission in the two directions. Instead of having a single capacity C, the two-way channel has a curve defining the best achievable pairs of rates (R_1, R_2). Even simple applications of two-way channel theory have surprising results. Suppose, for instance, that a noiseless telegraph line is connected so that a buzzer sounds at each end only when both operators have closed their signaling keys. One operator might keep his key closed, sending no information, in order to receive information from the other operator. The two operators might agree on a schedule in which each spends half the time receiving, so that both achieve an information rate that is half the capacity C of the line as a one-way channel: $R_1 = R_2 = C/2$. They can achieve higher rates, however, by using another signaling code that permits them both to signal at the same time.

Shannon's 1961 results, though surprising, did not create much of a stir in the information-theory community, in part because neither Shannon nor anyone else was able to determine the family of achievable rate pairs (R_1, R_2) exactly. It remained for three papers in the early 1970s to awaken the research community to the potential of multiple-user theory. In the first of these, T. M. Cover of Stanford University studied a broadcast channel in which a single transmitter sends different information to two or more receivers that cannot communicate with each other.[180] Cover showed that significantly improved performance is achievable if the information is cleverly encoded by the transmitter. In 1973, D. Slepian and J. Wolf (then of the Polytechnic Institute of Brooklyn) showed how to separately encode a pair of correlated sources with no performance degradation.[181] Also in 1973, A. Wyner and J. Ziv (a frequent visitor to Bell Labs from the Haifa Technion) published a paper which gave a powerful technique for proving nonexistence or converse coding theorems for multiple-user situations.[182,183] In the ten years that followed publication of these three papers, dozens of multiple-user papers appeared in the literature; they were authored by Wyner, Ziv, Witsenhausen, Ozarow, and many others outside Bell Laboratories.[184]

8.5 Error Control and Coding

An important part of information theory is the study of explicit coding schemes that attempt to realize the ideal performance promised by the Shannon theory. The simplest codes just detect errors, without trying to correct them. An error-detecting code is a list of code words designed so that the received signal can be recognized as erroneous if certain noise

Fig. 1-25. The two-out-of-five code was invented for tone signaling between telephone offices. The ten possible combinations of five basic tones (F, A, C#, E, F#), taken two at a time, represent the ten digits 1, 2, . . . , 0. The code is error-detecting because reception of numbers of tones different from two can only result from a transmission error. More elaborate codes can correct errors as well as detect them.

patterns occur during transmission. Error-detecting codes are most useful in a two-way communication in which the receiver can ask for the erroneous message to be repeated. More complicated codes also correct errors; that is, the receiver can correctly interpret the message without asking for a repeat when certain kinds of errors occur. Error-detecting codes had been used in cable telegraphy since the 19th century, and the principle of error correction had been recognized, although perhaps not used.[185] C. E. Shannon was not aware of these cable codes, but another error-detecting telephone code, the 2-out-of-5 code, may have influenced him. This code is believed to have been invented (but not published or patented) by R. E. Hersey around 1938 for intraoffice signaling of telephone numbers.[186,187] [Fig. 1-25] It encoded each decimal digit of a telephone number into five binary digits, of which two were ones and the other three were zeros. In practice, the five binary digits were associated with five tones of different pitch, a digit 1 or 0 being transmitted as a tone or no tone. If noise caused one of the five binary digits to be received in error, the receiver could detect the error and ask for a repeat.

Although error detection and correction were clearly important for any theory of transmission over a noisy channel, they did not provide Shannon with the clue that led to his coding theorem. That clue came from his World War II work on cryptography. A cryptogram is a message encoded by one of many possible codes. To create confusion, the code is chosen in a way that seems to be random. It occurred to Shannon that signaling codes could be constructed at random, too. Shannon could derive, relatively simply, statistical properties of a random code, such as the expected probability of a decoding error. By this technique, he discovered the channel capacity and its properties. However, instead of finding an explicit code that signaled reliably at a rate close to capacity, Shannon obtained rules for constructing a code at random. He showed that this random code has a high probability of being fast and reliable, and therefore, some fast reliable codes do exist. His proof, however, did not actually exhibit one.

8.6 Algebraic Coding Theory

Shannon's 1948 paper also reported the first development in algebraic coding theory. This was a code R. W. Hamming had devised for controlling errors in binary computers. Hamming had the idea of encoding messages into blocks of binary digits that satisfied certain algebraic equations. These equations were called parity-check equations because they checked whether certain sets of digits contained even or odd numbers of ones (an odd number indicating error). By using properly designed parity-check equations, Hamming could obtain codes for error detection or correction.

Error correction can be illustrated by one of Hamming's simplest codes. The code words are blocks $(x_1, x_2, \ldots, x_7)$ of seven binary digits. Of the 128 possible strings, there are 16 blocks, all satisfying three simultaneous check equations:

$$x_4 + x_5 + x_6 + x_7 = \text{even,}$$

$$x_2 + x_3 \qquad\quad + x_6 + x_7 = \text{even,}$$

$$x_1 \quad + x_3 \quad + x_5 \quad\quad + x_7 = \text{even.}$$

If one digit x_i is received in error, the sums in which x_i appear change from even to odd, indicating an error. Since no two different digits x_i, x_j appear in exactly the same set of sums, the parities of the three sums identify the unique erroneous digit x_i. B. D. Holbrook designed switching equipment to do the checking and correcting operations; he and Hamming obtained a patent in 1951.[188] By using more complicated systems of parity-check equations, many others have invented codes that can correct more than one error per message.

It appears that powerful codes must inevitably be complicated, and coding theory has progressed by building codes that have an ever-increasing mathematical structure. The first main step in this direction occurred in the 1960s, when D. Slepian used group theory to develop linear codes.[189,190] In this work he also introduced the notion of a standard array, which greatly clarified the decoding problem.

The second major step was the introduction, around 1959, by R. C. Bose (at the University of North Carolina) of other algebraic techniques that led to Bose-Chaudhuri-Hocquenghem (or BCH) codes. Although not invented at Bell Laboratories, the subsequent widespread use of these codes is due to the discovery of an efficient decoding procedure for them by E. R. Berlekamp at Bell Labs.[191,192] The Berlekamp decoding algorithm also turned out to have another, apparently unrelated, application. It can be used to find the shortest shift register that generates a given sequence, an important problem in cryptanalysis.[193] Another stage in the decoding process for BCH codes involves factoring polynomials with coefficients from a finite field. To speed up this step, Berlekamp developed a second algorithm, his factoring algorithm, which today is the standard method for factoring polynomials over finite fields.[194] Both algorithms, together with digital circuitry for carrying out the encoding and decoding, are described in his 1968 book *Algebraic Coding Theory*.[195]

Another major theoretical advance was F. J. MacWilliams's discovery in 1962 of a set of fundamental equations (now called the MacWilliams identities) that any linear code must satisfy.[196,197] These identities were the starting point for a considerable amount of research by MacWilliams, C. L. Mallows, N. J. A. Sloane, and others.

Two other decoding techniques from the 1960s should also be mentioned: MacWilliams's permutation decoding,[198] and S. Y. Tong's burst trapping.[199] Many other algebraic coding contributions developed during the 1960s and 1970s can be found in *The Theory of Error Correcting Codes* by MacWilliams and Sloan.[200]

So far the codes mentioned have been block codes for a binary channel. In a block code the message digits are divided into blocks, each block being encoded separately. In recurrent or convolutional codes invented by D. W. Hagelbarger, the message is converted into a stream of binary

Fig. 1-26.   D. Slepian, E. N. Gilbert, and B. McMillan (left to right), who were, at the time this picture was taken in 1952, working on information theory. McMillan also made important contributions to network synthesis (see section 3.2 in this chapter). When these three Murray Hill mathematicians began to study kites and fly them at noontime, they in effect crossed strings with Alexander Graham Bell, who, in addition to inventing the telephone, was a serious student of the aerodynamics of kites.

digits. Check digits are interspersed among the message digits in a regular pattern; each check digit is computed from a parity-check equation that involves only nearby digits.[201]

Codes for a continuous channel have also been extensively studied. Using the sampling theory (section 2.3 of this chapter), a code that encodes quantized messages of duration T seconds on a channel limited to bandwidth W Hz can be thought of as an array of vectors in a space of $2WT$ dimensions, one of which is selected for transmission each T seconds. The transmitted vector is, as received, perturbed by the addition of a noise vector. Idealizing the problem to one in which the noise vector has a distribution in space that carries very little probability outside a sphere of some given radius r, a good code can be thought of as a packing of nonoverlapping spheres of radius r, all packed close to the origin (the zero-signal) to conserve transmitting power. The relation between coding for the channel with additive noise and the packing of spheres in a high-dimensional space has proved a fruitful subject of study in both fields. Systematic codes for a channel of this kind, being orderly arrays of vectors, are natural objects to study by means of group theory or other combinatorial methods. In turn, the study of codes as packings of spheres has enriched these other domains of mathematics. E. N. Gilbert, Slepian, Sloane, and others [Fig. 1-26] have contributed to this work.[202]

8.7 Impact of Information Theory

In the years that followed the publication of Shannon's 1948 paper, the number of research papers on information theory published at Bell Laboratories and elsewhere increased rapidly. In the early 1950s, the Institute of Radio Engineers (which later became the Institute of Electrical and Electronics Engineers (IEEE)) formed a special interest group on information theory that published a quarterly journal devoted to Shannon theory and cognate areas. At Bell Labs the impact of information theory on many aspects of communications has been pervasive, helping scientists and engineers to set realistic goals in their design of a variety of communication systems.

IX. LOGIC CIRCUITS AND COMPUTING

From the beginnings of telephony, switching circuits have been used to interconnect telephone subscribers. With the development of dial systems, large, intricate switching circuits became commonplace. Nevertheless, until 1938, switching circuit designers had to rely on their own intuitions and cleverness because no routine, mathematical-design procedures were available.

9.1 Boolean Algebra

In 1938, Shannon, then a student at MIT, published a master's thesis in which he applied Boolean algebra to switching circuit design.[203] In another paper, in 1949, he enlarged upon the same idea.[204] Boolean algebra, invented by the British logician, George Boole, is a system for representing logical propositions in algebraic terms.[205,206] The formulas of Boolean algebra contain letters, representing simple propositions, joined by addition and multiplication signs (representing the logical connectives "or" and "and") to produce compound propositions. Each formula can be manipulated by

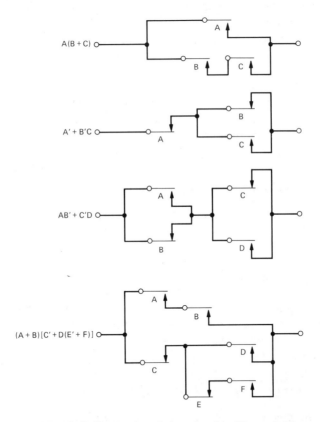

Fig. 1-27. C. E. Shannon's technique for describing switching circuits in algebraic terms. To design a switching circuit, one can first express the desired switching circuit's behavior through an algebraic expression and then combine switches in series and parallel in accordance with the addition and multiplication signs. The figure shows four simple expressions and their corresponding circuits. [Keister, Ritchie, and Washburn, *The Design of Switching Circuits* (1951): 69.]

rules, similar to those of ordinary algebra, to obtain other formulas representing logically equivalent compound propositions.

In Shannon's application, each letter A, B, C, . . . stands for the proposition that a particular relay is turned on. The proposition that a closed path exists between two terminals of a relay contact network can be expressed as a formula involving propositions A, B, C, . . . of the relays controlling the network. Once a desired switching-circuit behavior is expressed in algebraic terms, the formula immediately indicates a circuit design. [Fig. 1-27] (Each addition becomes a series connection, and each multiplication becomes a parallel connection.) Moreover, the rules for manipulating formulas may be applied to derive other circuits with the same behavior. Relay contact networks have lost favor to newer kinds of electronic logic circuits, but Boolean algebra remains applicable. The elementary propositions A, B, C, . . . have merely become statements about the voltage levels on input leads to electronic gates.

Boolean algebra was very useful in changing some aspects of circuit design from an art to a logical process that almost anyone could learn. Moreover, it provided an appropriate language for discussing switching, helping to make a theory of switching possible.

9.2 Minimization

One of the first problems of switching theory was that of economy, that is, using as little equipment as possible to perform a given switching task. Although some Boolean functions could be manipulated algebraically into a compact form that would require little equipment to implement, Shannon's 1949 paper contained a proof showing that most functions were quite complicated. In fact, almost all Boolean functions for two-terminal contact networks operated by n relays required about $2^n/n$ contact pairs, even in the most economical circuit realization. The argument was reminiscent of random coding; it managed to prove the result without ever exhibiting any specific function requiring that many contacts.

For values of n equal to 4 or less, M. Karnaugh represented switching functions as geometrical diagrams from which many ways of economizing were evident on sight.[207] The Karnaugh diagram was a truth table, or Venn diagram, arranged in a particularly convenient way. In 1881, A. Marquand had invented the same arrangement for solving logical puzzles, but it was subsequently forgotten.[208,209]

Although not a visual technique for economizing, the method of "prime implicants," widely used by switching engineers, also deals directly with switching functions in a tabular form. It was invented by the logician W. V. Quine at Harvard University and later adapted by E. J. McCluskey at Bell Labs for use on a computer.[210,211]

In 1952, E. F. Moore made an exhaustive study of relay circuits for functions of up to four variables, tabulating a most economical circuit for each function.[212] Different solutions existed, depending on whether one wanted to economize on contacts or springs. Since there are 2^{24}, or 65,536, different Boolean functions of four variables, one might expect a table like Moore's to require superhuman effort. Fortunately, these 65,536 functions can be classified into 402 types using certain symmetry operations, such as permuting the variables, that do not change a function in an important way. Slepian derived the number of types as a function of the number of variables.[213] For five variables, there are 1,228,158 types, a number that discouraged everyone from extending Moore's table to one more variable.

When a most economical circuit is not required, extra equipment can be used to protect against component failures. In 1956, Moore and Shannon showed how redundancy could be used effectively in the design of reliable relay circuits built from what they called "crummy" relays, that is, relays with a random tendency to stick open or closed.[214]

9.3 Automata

Boolean functions are only appropriate for describing circuits that perform an action determined entirely by the present state of certain relays or input leads. By allowing a relay-contact circuit to control the magnets of its own relays, or by using the output of an electronic logic circuit as an input to itself, one may build automata that perform more complicated tasks requiring memory. Even the simplest automaton, such as the flip-flop, can have an output depending on the entire past history of the input. A digital computer is an automaton having, like the relay (or electronic) circuits in a telephone switching exchange, a finite number of internal states. Its behavior, though determined wholly by its input data, can correspondingly be enormously complex.

Motivated in part by problems of an engineering nature in the design of switching systems, including the problem of minimizing the number of internal (memory) states, design theories for finite-state automata were developed by D. A. Huffman at MIT,[215] and by G. H. Mealy and Moore at Bell Labs.[216,217] All three workers devised orderly methods to determine, from the desired performance of the switching device, the irreducible minimum number of internal states required. Huffman and Mealy also addressed such practical questions as sensitivities to timing and the avoidance of ambiguous transient states. All three papers provide techniques applicable, at least in principle, to the design of efficient computer programs. Moore's paper studies automata by means of "gedanken (thought) experiments," input sequences by which one can learn about the external behavior of an automaton. For example one might want to decide, by a gedanken experiment, whether a given automaton always acts in the same way as another, simpler automaton.

One motivation for these inquiries, and an explicit motivation for many related studies by others, has been the analogy, both structural and behavioral, between the human nervous system and a finite state automaton.[218,219] Indeed, the logical capabilities of automata suggest so vividly the sapient behavior of man and animals that the term artificial intelligence arose almost spontaneously to refer to the properties of automata and to the study of such matters. Shannon built a few small, early artificial-intelligence machines, some from relays and parts from Erector* sets. One machine played a board game called Hex, using a fairly strong strategy based on ideas from electrostatic-potential theory.[220]

Shannon's most elaborate machine was Theseus, the maze solver.[221] [Fig. 1-28] It had a checkerboard array of square cells that could be made

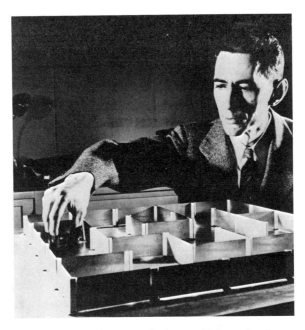

Fig. 1-28. C. E. Shannon, who invented information theory and pioneered in the field of artificial intelligence. He is shown here with his maze-solving mechanical mouse, Theseus, named for the legendary hero of antiquity who solved the labyrinth of King Minos of Crete. The maze shown had movable partitions so that a large number of different mazes could readily be built. When Shannon released him, Theseus wandered erratically about the maze, learning where the partitions were. Afterward, when released again in the maze, Theseus used this knowledge to reach the goal by a direct route.

---

* Trademark of Gabriel Industries.

into a maze by inserting metal partitions between pairs of adjacent cells. When a lifelike imitation mouse was placed in the maze, it wandered about erratically until it reached a goal. After that, the mouse always took a direct route to the goal when placed in the maze; it had solved the maze and remembered the solution. Actually, the relay logic circuits and magnetic equipment to propel the mouse were installed underneath the maze, being much too large to fit inside the mouse. Using modern microprocessor technology, maze solvers with logic and propulsion to fit inside an imitation mouse were invited to participate in a contest sponsored by the IEEE.[222]

D. W. Hagelbarger built a machine that could almost be described as a mind reader because it tended to beat human opponents in a guessing-game variant of penny matching.[223] Most humans have slightly systematic tendencies in their play, even when trying to play randomly. Hagelbarger's machine, Sequence Extrapolating Robot (SEER), remembered enough about past moves to discover these tendencies and win more than half the time. Shannon then built a stripped down version of the same machine with fewer internal states than SEER. Decreasing the number of states increased the vulnerability; the optimum strategy could beat SEER 60 to 40 compared with 75 to 25 for the smaller machine. When the two machines were pitted against each other in a long automated duel, speed of adaptation won over conservation; the smaller machine won by a slight margin.

The ability to reproduce has been simulated by machines that live in an environment of parts that they assemble into new machines like themselves. Moore pointed out a possible use for self-reproducing machines. He made a feasibility study of a large self-reproducing machine, an artificial living plant, that would extract minerals from the sea to build copies of

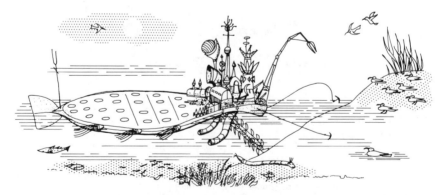

Fig. 1-29.   The artificial living plant as a possible future development in artificial intelligence. The plant, as suggested by E. F. Moore, is a self-reproducing machine that extracts minerals from the ocean to obtain material from which it builds copies of itself. Eventually the plant travels to port, where it is harvested for its minerals. [Moore, *Sci. Amer.* **195** (1956): 118, 119.]

itself.[224] The copies could then be harvested for their mineral content. [Fig. 1-29]

Shannon was the first person to take the idea of a chess-playing machine seriously enough to study carefully the strategies that a chess-playing machine might use. Although Shannon never actually wrote a chess-playing program, the computers of 1950 being too slow to play a good game, many of the machine chess players that appeared subsequently have been organized according to the general principles he gave. The Bell Labs chess-playing computer, Belle, built by J. H. Condon and K. Thompson in 1980, has won national and world computer-chess championships.[225]

9.4 Computational Complexity

From the time that T. C. Fry at Western Electric had a small staff to assist in computing (see section 1.1 earlier in this chapter), there has been a growing interest at Bell Laboratories in computers and computation. As digital computers became more powerful, and as those who used them addressed increasingly complicated problems, technical issues of a highly mathematical nature continually arose. During the late 1950s and the 1960s, researchers in mathematics and computer science began to encounter some unusually difficult computational problems, for which even the best methods of solution they could devise required astronomical amounts of computer time. Many came to suspect that this was due to more than just shortcomings in methodology or ingenuity; these problems might be inherently intractable, that is, impossible to solve exactly in a reasonable amount of time. This gave rise to fundamental questions about the powers and limitations of computers and computational processes: Do there exist inherently intractable problems? How can such problems be recognized when they arise? What can be done when confronted with such a problem in practice? Answers to these questions began to emerge in the early 1970s.

9.4.1 *Inherently Intractable Problems*

To investigate the existence of inherently intractable problems, researchers first had to settle on a meaning for this term that was more precise than just "too hard to solve in a practical amount of time." The definition that eventually gained acceptance was based on a classification of algorithms into two types, based on the rate of growth of their computation-time requirements as larger and larger problem instances are solved. An algorithm for which this rate of growth is at most n^k for some fixed number k, where n represents the size of an instance (e.g., the number of points to be interconnected in the minimal-tree problem of section 3.4 in this chapter), is called a polynomial time algorithm. An algorithm for which the rate of growth is larger than n^k for all k, such as a growth rate of 2^n, is called an exponential time algorithm. The distinction between these two types of algorithms was observed to correspond quite closely to the distinction that was sought, with polynomial time algorithms generally being usable in practice and exponential time algorithms normally requiring far too much computation time to be practical. Hence, a problem was deemed to be inherently intractable if there existed no way to solve it using a polynomial time algorithm.

In 1971, a key breakthrough in the study of inherently intractable problems was made by S. A. Cook at the University of Toronto.[226] He demonstrated the existence of a class of computational problems, now known as NP-complete problems (for nondeterministic polynomial time complete, a term derived from the formal definition of the class), with the surprising property that either all of them must be inherently intractable or else none of them is. The class was defined to consist of the hardest problems solvable using a certain computational model with a special ability to make good guesses. Moreover, since this guessing ability seemed to be impossible to achieve using an actual computing device, it was conjectured that all problems in the class were indeed intractable. Strong support for this conjecture was obtained in 1972, when R. M. Karp at the University of California showed that many of the problems for which earlier researchers had vainly sought efficient algorithms were also NP-complete.[227] Despite the fact that no one was able to provide a conclusive proof of the conjecture, its validity subsequently came to be widely accepted, and proving that a problem is NP-complete came to be regarded as tantamount to demonstrating its inherent intractability.

M. R. Garey and D. S. Johnson at Bell Labs were among the first to recognize the potential practical impact of this work, and they spent much of the remainder of the decade intensively investigating the class of NP-complete problems. In 1976, Garey, R. L. Graham, and Johnson proved that the minimal-length tree problem of section 3.4 in this chapter, when additional junction points are allowed, is NP-complete, finally bringing to an end the long quest for an efficient solution technique.[228] They also showed that the famous traveling salesman's problem is NP-complete; given a collection of cities and a map from which distances can be calculated, the salesman asks for the shortest route that visits all the given cities and then returns to its starting point.

The work of Garey and Johnson particularly emphasized the goal of precisely determining the boundary between intractability and efficient solvability by successively restricting and generalizing the constraints of various problems to find the most general versions that could be solved efficiently and the most restricted versions that remain NP-complete. In doing so, they illuminated what it was about particular problems that made them difficult and what special restrictions should be looked for in practice that might make an otherwise difficult problem tractable.

In 1979, Garey and Johnson published a book entitled *Computers and*

Intractability: A Guide to the Theory of NP-Completeness that provided the first comprehensive description of work on this topic.[229] It included an appendix listing over 300 NP-complete problems from mathematics, computer science, and operations research; their scope and number attested to the great impact and wide applicability of these concepts.

Although the book by Garey and Johnson frequently pointed to various problems for which efficient methods of solution were known, the theory of NP-completeness itself does not directly provide such methods. However, this theory can guide the search for practical algorithms by exhibiting model problems known to be difficult and by providing tools with which other problems can be shown to be as hard as one of the model problems. Use of these tools can help a computer scientist avoid vain searches for efficient algorithms that are unlikely to exist by revealing that such searches are simply disguised versions of unsuccessful searches previously conducted by others.

9.4.2 Coping with Intractable Problems

The discovery of the class of NP-complete problems provided added impetus to the study of approximate problem-solving methods, that is, methods which find good, but not necessarily exact, solutions for problems. Such methods had commonly been put forth as the only way to solve certain problems effectively, a claim that certainly gains credence when the problem is NP-complete. However, one of the shortcomings of such methods is that they can be very difficult to evaluate. In particular, it is hard to know how close the obtained solutions are to the exact, or optimum, solutions when the latter are effectively impossible to determine. This difficulty gave rise to the idea of mathematically providing performance bounds for algorithms; namely, bounds that state that a particular method always finds solutions that differ from optimum by no more than a specified error percentage.

The earliest results of this type preceded the theory of NP-completeness by several years. In two papers in 1966 and 1969, Graham reported on studies of scheduling problems that arose at Bell Laboratories during the design of a multiprocessor computer for a military project.[230,231] Tasks for the several identical processors of this computer were to be scheduled subject to given precedence constraints; the constraints specified that certain tasks had to be completed before certain others could be begun. The goal was to minimize the time needed to complete all the given tasks. It was found, surprisingly, that a certain intuitively natural scheduling algorithm would sometimes complete all tasks faster if the task length were increased or the number of processors available decreased. Graham sought to determine bounds on the largest change in the overall completion time that could occur due to such anomalies.

As part of his investigation of these anomalies, Graham determined bounds on how far the length of the constructed schedule could be from the length of the best possible schedule. In particular, for the model he considered, he showed that the natural algorithm could never construct a schedule more than twice as long as the best possible schedule and that the constructed schedules could in fact occasionally be that much longer.[232] In his second paper, Graham explicitly stated a fundamental goal: to establish, as a function of error percentage, bounds for the time required by any algorithm that always constructs schedules that differ from the optimum length by at most that error percentage.[233] This goal could apply as well to other optimization problems.

In 1972, Garey, Graham, and J. D. Ullman of Princeton University addressed a problem of allocating computer memory that arose in connection with computer operations at Bell Laboratories.[234] It was idealized as a problem of packing a given collection of objects, each of a given size, into bins of a given fixed capacity, with the aim of using as few bins as possible in total. Some simple algorithms were shown to use no more than 1.7 times the optimum number of bins; better ones came within about 1.2 of the optimum.

Johnson, while a student at MIT, strengthened some of the results on this bin-packing problem, and extended them to a large class of different packing algorithms.[235] After he joined Bell Laboratories, Johnson applied similar methods, with analogous results, to a number of other commonly occurring optimization problems.[236,237]

Garey, Graham, and Johnson contributed numerous further papers to a rapidly growing body of literature on performance bounds for approximation algorithms. Their results were a major stimulus to interest in this area. References to this literature can be found in the previously mentioned book by Garey and Johnson, which includes a detailed chapter on performance bounds and related complexity results.[238] For example, they show how it is sometimes possible to prove for a given problem that it is impossible even to come within a factor of two of the optimum solution unless all the NP-complete problems turn out to be tractable. Such a result indeed certifies a problem as being difficult.

This body of work made great strides toward the goal originally enunciated by Graham.[239] However, much remains to be done in formally studying approximation algorithms. For instance, a performance bound provides only one measure of the quality of an algorithm; often one is also interested in other measures such as its expected or average performance. Techniques for analyzing these other measures seem to be more difficult to derive, but they are an important object of study in the continuing investigation of methods for coping with inherently intractable problems.

X. QUEUEING THEORY AND TRAFFIC SYSTEMS

The modern theory of queues is a direct descendant of early work done on telephone switching. The central problem, from the telephone engineer's point of view, is to serve the randomly fluctuating demands of the using public without exceeding some specific criterion of overload or congestion and to do so with a minimum, or at least an economical, amount of equipment. Put in this way, the problem is not unique to telephone switching nor even to telephony.

If to each line and trunk entering, or internal to, a telephone switching machine one assigns a finite number of possible states—e.g., idle, busy, waiting for dial tone, or ringing—then the machine with its connecting lines and trunks is a finite-state automaton. Its set of possible states constitutes a space of a finite number of discrete points, the state-space. The history of its activities during, say, a busy hour can be described in terms of a kind of random walk on the state-space—the automaton jumps from point to point as the input and output lines change their states and the machine responds. One idealization of this situation is that in which there is no "memory" in the outside world, so that demands for service are not themselves affected by congestion within the machine. In this idealization, the automaton follows a true random walk or Markov process; i.e., the statistics of the next jump are wholly governed by the state from which that jump originates. Much of queueing theory deals with problems formulated in exactly this same way, with a Markov process or random walk on a discrete state-space. Most of the basic mathematical concepts and tools were available by 1940; queueing theory has since dealt with the peculiar properties of particular state spaces, or with exhibiting general properties of state spaces that lead to provable general results.

10.1 Interconnecting Networks

At the heart of every automatic switching system is the interconnecting network itself. Competition for resources within this network—for example, competition for connecting lines (links) and for switches (crosspoints)—is a source of congestion much more difficult to analyze than is, say, the competition for trunks in a finite trunk group. Many simplified analyses of congestion in switching networks focus wholly on the competitions for links and crosspoints, or upon only one of these. In his book on the subject, *Mathematical Theory of Connecting Networks and Telephone Traffic*, V. E. Beneš explicitly framed the model of traffic in the switching network as a whole (i.e., including not only crosspoints, links, and trunks, but also the supervisory and control equipment), as a random walk on the appropriate state-space, providing a uniform framework for much prior theory.[240] Within this framework, using probabilistic methods as well as combinatorial and algebraic methods that do not invoke probabilities, the book addressed in a very general setting the statistical problems of traffic congestion and the problems of comparing networks with respect to traffic capacity. Some specific results or later extensions are mentioned below.

In the earliest automatic telephone exchanges, the path of a call through the interconnecting network was established step by step as the caller dialed successive digits. By the time of the first No. 5 crossbar system, for which the engineering was done in the late 1930s, design methods had matured to the point that the interconnecting network was regarded as an entity totally distinct from the computer-like mechanisms that carried out such control functions as the selection of a route for a call being placed. Policies were built into the control systems that biased the selection of routes toward states in which as many routes as possible were left open for subsequent calls. Within the random-walk model, Beneš formulated the routing problem as one of optimal control in the presence of randomness (not the Gaussian noise of section 7.4 of this chapter). He showed the existence of optimal strategies, reduced some cases to the solution of linear programming problems, and compared known simple routing strategies to the optimal ones.[241] In all of this probabilistic traffic work, combinatorial facts about the interconnecting network, reflected as structural properties of its corresponding space of possible states, are central to the formulas and inequalities.

Probability began with combinatorial analyses—analyses of combinations of playing cards or of dice—and so it is that the design of, or comparison among, interconnecting networks often begins with combinatorial considerations. A network that allows more possible paths from a typical line to a typical trunk seems intuitively to be less likely at a particular level of load (number of calls in progress) to block (be unable to connect) the next call than is a network offering fewer options. Conditions of symmetry, suggested by the idealization in which all subscriber lines are identical in the statistics of their offered traffic, are further combinatorial considerations that are helpful in simplifying analyses. Beneš adapted concepts from group theory and from the algebra of partially ordered systems to describe methods for comparing networks on purely combinatorial criteria, relating, in some cases, the combinatorially derived criteria to probabilistic results.[242] He also showed, within the Markov model of traffic, how the group of symmetries of the network could be used to simplify the study of its behavior under load.[243]

In 1953, C. Clos[244] invented a form of network that was nonblocking in the sense that if the number of calls in progress was less than a number K fixed by the designer, any one additional call between previously idle lines could be placed. Beneš extended the concept of nonblocking to include networks that, perhaps by suitable rearrangement of established connections, always retained, up to the designed load K, the ability to connect any single further call between previously idle lines. Many of his sharper combinatorial results applied to networks nonblocking in either the strict or the more extended sense. A mathematical proof, based on classical results in the theory of groups, that networks of the form invented by Clos are nonblocking in the strict sense was circulated in an internal memorandum by D. Slepian. An extension of the proof was published by Beneš.[245]

The state spaces of many queueing problems have orderly structures; their analyses exploit the symmetries that are present and often emphasize combinatorial considerations. The combinatorial analyses of Graham, Johnson, and Garey cited in section 9.4.2 of this chapter are, for example, purely combinatorial attacks on queueing problems. An important tool in combinatorial analysis is the generating function—an analytic function of several complex variables, represented by a multiple-power series, in which the coefficients are the quantities, such as counting arrangements or configurations, that are of interest. Passage to a probabilistic analysis often simply substitutes a generating function of similar form, in which the coefficients are the probabilities of events of interest. The books of J. Riordan on combinatorial analysis and on queueing systems well illustrate the continuing close links between combinatorial theory and applications of probability.[246,247]

Mathematical tools used in the study of generating functions draw heavily upon the mathematical techniques that have evolved since the 18th century for the study of problems in mathematical physics, notably methods for solving boundary value problems and for finding the asymptotic behavior of functions defined by sums or integrals containing a parameter. The analytical methods of the 19th century and the early 20th century were, in the 1970s, supplemented by algorithms and computer programs that generated numerical answers to specifically stated problems. Indeed, as of 1980, queueing analyses had become important to the design of economical networks for interconnecting computers, and for assigning or apportioning resources within a network or even within a computer.

XI. TRADITIONAL APPLIED MATHEMATICS

Mathematicians tend naturally to describe applied mathematics in their own technical terms. In these terms, there was probably general agreement among mathematicians prior to, say, 1950 that applied mathematics consisted of (a) numerical methods, or mathematics related to computation: of the solution of differential equations, of tables of mathematical functions, of the inverses of matrices, of the zeros of analytic functions, and of approximations to complicated functions by simpler ones; and (b) the study of differential equations and their boundary value problems, as such matters arose in physics, astronomy, continuum mechanics, and electromagnetic theory. Whatever its exact content, however, a description framed in these terms tends to emphasize what an engineer would think of as method or technique (as may, of course, be appropriate for a mathematician who, in T. C. Fry's terms, conserves energy by solving several problems at once). This chapter has, in contrast, been largely framed around problems rather than around techniques of solution, reflecting more accurately the attitudes of those whose research it records.

Within the research described here, the traditional techniques of applied mathematics were important. Even a cursory review of what has been reported, however, shows that, as of 1980, a mathematician must include in any realistic definition of applied mathematics, not only the traditional material of (a) and (b) above, but also some of the deeper theorems of measure and probability theory, a significant element of mathematical logic, and much from combinatorics and graph theory. The brief paragraphs below touch on some of the relations between mathematical research at Bell Laboratories and the subject matter of the more traditional applied mathematics.

11.1 Numerical Methods

Computing, to help the engineer get his work done, has always been of importance in Bell Laboratories. Fry's original assignment in Western Electric was to head a computing group. Such a group remained a part of the mathematical research organization in Bell Laboratories until the high-speed digital computer revolutionized the usefulness and importance of computing as a tool, and revolutionized the organizational arrangements for accomplishing it. Chapter 9 tells much of this particular story. The story sketched here is about the application of or extension of some of the analytical tools that were originally developed as part of the science of numerical methods, a science that obtained an independent existence with or before Henry Briggs's calculation of a table of logarithms in the 16th century.

Approximation of functions by simpler functions has been a classical problem. During World War II the problem of storing ballistic data in a form suitable for the gunfire computers designed at Bell Laboratories became important. A ballistic table is a smooth function of two variables, say $f(r,e)$, where r and e are range and elevation and $f(\cdot,\cdot)$ may be, say, time of flight. The problem is mostly caused by the presence of two variables. A function of one variable, of almost arbitrary form, is relatively easy to store in the kind of computer at issue. Considerable ingenuity was expended developing representations in such forms as $f(r,e) = g(r) \cdot h(e)$, or $f(r,e) = \phi(g(r) \cdot h(e))$. In problems of broader scope, S. Darlington applied Tchebycheff's polynomial methods to the design of filters and equalizers,[248] and C. L. Dolph adapted the method to the design of phased-array antennas.[249] More recently, Tchebycheff methods have been studied and extended by B. Gopinath and R. P. Kurshan.[250] The control of round-off error has been of continuing concern in the mathematics of computation. I. W. Sandberg's result on the stability of recursive digital filters can be considered a recent example of such concern.[251] Sandberg has recently extended Newton's method for solving the equation $f(\chi) = a$ for χ when a is given, in which $f(\cdot)$ is a differentiable function.[252] He describes a convergent algorithm for solving this form of equation in a very general setting: the values of $f(\cdot)$ and of the variable χ may lie in a vector space or even in a function space.

11.2 Boundary Value Problems, Differential Equations

The boundary value problems of continuum mechanics appear in many guises in the work of Bell Laboratories. In the early 1950s, R. C. Prim and J. A. Lewis, working with R. D. Mindlin of Columbia University, purchased time on one of the first commercially available large-scale digital computers to analyze designs for a pressure seal for the repeater housing of the first transatlantic telephone cable.

Boundary value problems in which fluid flow, heat transfer, changes of state of the fluid itself, and possibly the diffusion of impurities must all be accounted for arise in the preparation of high-purity semiconductor materials and in the manufacture of optical fibers. The flow of charge and the behavior of the electromagnetic field inside a semiconductor are described by a somewhat different class of boundary value problems. Boundary value problems arising from queueing theory have already been mentioned (section X of this chapter). Work in this general domain, falling in or bordering on the classical domains of mathematical physics, has been and continues to be a significant component of the effort of mathematicians at Bell Laboratories. Increasingly, since the 1960s, work on such problems has combined an analytical attack with the development of algorithms for digital computation that have specifiable levels of accuracy and stability. For the most part, problems have been considered that have enough symmetry to be treated in two dimensions.

In 1974, L. A. Shepp and B. F. Logan found a new application for the digital-filtering ideas discussed earlier in the context of signal processing—computerized tomography. This technique, invented in England in 1972 by G. N. Hounsfield,[253] caused a revolution in medical diagnostic radiology. The Shepp and Logan paper gave the first published algorithm, based on digital filtering of the X-ray projection measurement data, that provided a general method for choosing appropriate filters and a simulation method for judging the performance. Their paper has been widely used in the computerized axial tomography (CAT) scanning industry, with resulting large improvements in resolution.[254] Applying similar methods, but using acoustic frequencies, which avoid ionizing radiation at some sacrifice of resolution, instead of X-rays, Shepp and J. B. Kruskal deduced the shape of the human vocal tract.[255] With the addition of stochastic elements they applied these techniques to the characterization of the irregularities and discontinuities in waveguides.

Pioneer work on the finite element method in elasticity theory (and heat flow) was done in the 1960s by F. T. Geyling,[256] and applications to the mechanical behavior of solid rocket motors and of motor cases during burning were made in connection with a military project.

Zabusky at Bell Labs with Kruskal while at Princeton University pioneered in the analytical and computational study of those special solutions of nonlinear partial differential equations that led to solitary waves or solitons—waves that persist in form and do not spread as they travel.[257]

Surface waves on deep water travel at a speed that varies as the square root of the wavelength. E. Y. Harper[258] showed that this dispersive property implies a curious resonance condition with a moving ship. Traveling in a homogeneously random wave field (the equivalent of spatially "white" noise, i.e., showing a uniform spectrum), a ship will always move as though immersed in an enhanced traveling wave, moving in the same direction as the ship and passing the ship with a velocity, relative to the ship, that is equal to the ship's velocity through the water.

The theory of ordinary differential equations began with Isaac Newton's determination of the form of a planetary orbit. Orbital calculations became important to Bell Laboratories when—building upon the feedback and control systems that, first, steered anti-aircraft guns and, later, steered anti-aircraft missiles—Bell Laboratories undertook to develop a guidance system for the launch of orbital vehicles. Geyling and A. J. Claus adapted smoothing and prediction techniques to the determination of orbital elements from noisy observations—a version of a problem important in astronomy since the 18th century. Work in this domain ultimately led to a book by Geyling and H. R. Westerman on mathematical methods in celestial mechanics.[259]

XII. STATISTICS

Originally statistics was "state science," the collection and presentation of numerical information about such things as births and deaths, agriculture, and trade. The subject became of scientific importance in the 19th century when it became necessary to deal with the large variability exhibited by biological populations. Many of the standard techniques of statistical estimation and experimental design were worked out in the context of agricultural experimentation. It was not until well into the 20th century that statistical methods were applied to engineering and manufacturing problems.

12.1 Statistical Foundations of Quality Assurance

The origin and development of the techniques of quality control and quality assurance in the Bell System have been described in Chapter 9 of the first volume of this series, subtitled *The Early Years (1875-1925)*. As discussed there, one of the first important contributions was the control chart invented by W. A. Shewhart [Fig. 1-30] in 1925. His 1931 text, *Economic Control of Quality of Manufactured Product*, also contains several chapters on the problem of presentation of data, in which such basic techniques as the use of sample means and variances, regression and correlation, scatter plots, tables, histograms, and cumulative frequency polygons are discussed in the context of quality control. Other chapters contain material on sampling, sampling distributions (both under normal

Fig. 1-30. W. A. Shewhart, who established
basic techniques for the presentation of statistical
data and quality control.

and some non-normal assumptions, the latter being quite novel at that
time), and estimation. Shewhart's book emphasized sound statistical methodology.

Another original innovation was the development by H. F. Dodge and
H. G. Romig in the early 1940s of double-sampling inspection plans and
later of continuous-sampling plans. Dodge and Romig were the first to
recognize and exploit the fact that such schemes require, on the average,
fewer observations than single sampling. During World War II, this idea
was developed into the method of sequential analysis by A. Wald and his
coworkers in the Statistical Research Group at Columbia University. The
books by Wald and by Dodge and Romig at Bell Labs were among the
first to appear in the prestigious Wiley Mathematical Statistics Series.[260]

12.2 Statistical Methods

An early worker in the application of statistical methods at Bell Labs
was P. S. Olmstead, a physicist who joined Bell Labs in 1925. One of his
interests was the development of simple statistical procedures, that were

later called "quick and dirty methods," in which computation is avoided as far as possible. He published papers on runs, in which only the signs of successive numerical observations are used, and on a simple test for association between two variables, in which the only computation involved is the counting of observations of various types.[261] Other early writers on statistical methods included E. C. Molina, R. P. Crowell, P. P. Coggins, and R. I. Wilkinson, who developed basic sampling theory (using Bayesian methods) and provided charts to aid in the determination of appropriate sample sizes.[262]

For several decades classical statistics has meant the theory of hypothesis testing that was developed by J. Neyman and E. S. Pearson at University College, London between 1928 and 1938.[263,264] In the simplest version of this theory, one assumes that there are only two possibilities for an observation that is about to be made: its probability distribution is either of a known form f_1 or of some other known form f_2. These possibilities are termed the null hypothesis and the alternative hypothesis. The Neyman-Pearson theory considers the choice of a rule for deciding, once the observation is made, whether f_1 and f_2 is truly the case. When such a rule is used, two kinds of error are possible; Neyman and Pearson called them errors of Type I and errors of Type II. A Type I error occurs when the null hypothesis f_1 is in fact true, but application of the rule results in f_2 being accepted; a Type II error occurs when the alternative hypothesis f_2 is in fact true, but the rule leads to accepting the null hypothesis f_1. The Neyman-Pearson theory shows how to find a rule that minimizes the probabilities of the two kinds of errors.

Many of the concepts in the Neyman-Pearson theory had forerunners in the work of Dodge and Shewhart at Bell Labs in the context of quality control. Dodge introduced the concepts of consumer's risk and average outgoing quality level (AOQL), in 1924 and 1927, respectively,[265] that are closely analogous to the two types of error considered by Neyman and Pearson. In fact the Neyman-Pearson theory has been criticized for being too much a theory of economic behavior than a theory of inference.

Shewhart had other reservations regarding the relevance of the formal Neyman-Pearson theory. In his 1939 book, he pointed out: "*We must continually keep in mind the fundamental difference* between the formal theory of testing a statistical hypothesis and the empirical testing of hypotheses employed in the operation of statistic control. In the latter, one must also test the hypothesis that the sample of data was obtained under conditions that may be considered random."[266]

This emphasis on the need for keeping statistical theory and practice in touch with reality has been a guiding principle in all subsequent work at Bell Labs.

Another of Shewhart's interests was what subsequently came to be known as the robustness of statistical techniques, the study of the effects of changes in the assumptions that underlie statistical techniques.[267] He investigated the joint distribution of the sample mean and sample standard deviation in samples drawn from two non-normal populations—namely, uniform (rectangular) and right triangular—and pointed out that the use of the statistic known as student's *t*, which is appropriate when the population is normal, would tend to give inaccurate (conservative) results in these cases. At about the same time in England, Pearson and his colleagues were beginning to study similar problems. In 1931, when Pearson studied the use of the analysis of variance in cases of non-normal variation, he used Shewhart's data to motivate and guide the discussion.

While the techniques developed by Shewhart, Dodge, and Romig were concerned with technical engineering in the telephone industry, the wider relevance of their statistical approach was noticed. An address by C. A. Heiss to the Bell System Educational Conference in June 1926 surveyed some of the statistical problems of the telephone industry, with emphasis on "the business side of the industry." There were three main classifications or problems:

1. Problems related to the analysis of current operations. These were problems connected with the statistical mechanism of current administrative control.

2. Problems of economic research. These were problems involved in the study and analysis of economic conditions outside the telephone industry.

3. Problems related to the anticipation of requirements. These were problems met in the broad work of planning in advance.

In succeeding years, work went forward in each of these areas. For example, one activity of the Operations Research Center was the development and dissemination of analytical forecasting methods. Work in the economics area is described in Chapter 12 of this volume.

The first person hired explicitly as a research statistician was M. E. Terry in 1952. One of Terry's early contributions was in the design and analysis of an experiment on the development of the card translator for the No. 4A toll crossbar system (see Chapter 8, section 2.2 of another volume of this series, subtitled *Switching Technology (1925-1975)*). The card translator was an electromechanical device that stored routing data for nationwide dialing.[268] The data were stored in the form of holes punched in metallic cards; as dialed digitals were received, appropriate cards were dropped into position and the corresponding information was read by means of a light beam falling on phototransistor detectors. Of great importance in the development of this system was an understanding of (a) the time intervals required to drop the cards into reading positions and (b) the maximum number of cards that a translator could operate reliably.

In the statistical study Terry considered variations in nine factors, including the number of cards in a bin, the position of a particular card within a bin, the overall load on the machine, and the choice between three-digit and six-digit codes.[269] Complex experimental designs were developed to study in detail the effect of varying these factors. Data on card-dropping times were obtained by means of shadowgrams of the light output from two of the translator's light channels. It was found that in normal operation only two of the factors studied, the load on the machine and the number of cards in the working bin, had significant effects on the card-dropping times. However, even these effects were not large enough to warrant special consideration in loading the translators. It was concluded that the machine could operate efficiently with as many as 100 cards per bin, an increase of 20 percent over design objectives.

12.3 Applications of Statistical Techniques

Several early issues of the *Bell System Technical Journal* contain applications of statistical techniques. The first volume, in 1922, contained a study of the relation between rents and incomes and the distribution of rental values, using cumulative empirical distributions and logarithmic probability plots; the second volume contained some graphical methods of smoothing data, using coded scatter plots.[270,271] E. Dietz and W. D. Goodale, Jr., gave a mathematical study of the composite noise resulting from several random sources, and displayed probability plots of noise peaks in a typing room and from food trays in a cafeteria.[272] R. I. Wilkinson analyzed data relating to holding-time (call-length) measurements.[273] He displayed average holding times by hours for 45 days, and he exhibited diurnal and day-of-week effects. In a later study, Wilkinson studied the dialing habits of telephone customers.[274]

As is evident from these examples, a common theme running through much of the work of Bell Labs statisticians has been an emphasis on graphical methods of display and analysis of data. Indeed much of the power of Shewhart's control-chart methodology derives from the fact that it is a graphical technique, readily understood by workers on the shop floor. This emphasis continued in the 1980s. Among Bell Labs contributions to the arsenal of graphical methods useful in the analysis of statistical data are stem-and-leaf displays, box plots, plots of residuals, and plots of high-dimensional data.[275]

12.4 Time-Series Analysis

In 1922, I. B. Crandall and D. MacKenzie used resonance tubes to measure the frequency distribution of the energy of speech.[276] The sound spectrograph was developed in 1946 by W. Koenig, H. K. Dunn, and

L. Y. Lacy;[277] a similar device, invented by W. R. Bennett, for displaying lag correlations appeared in 1953.[278]

Modern digital methods of spectrum estimation were developed by M. S. Bartlett in England in 1948 and by J. W. Tukey [Fig. 1-31] and his collaborators at Bell Labs in 1949. Tukey has described how his work got started.[279] H. T. Budenbom had obtained some radar tracking records and wished to show a slide of the power spectrum at a technical meeting. Tukey calculated some sample autocovariances and obtained a rough estimate of the spectrum. R. W. Hamming suggested smoothing this estimate with weights (1/4, 1/2, 1/4). The striking success of this smoothing stimulated the development of the sampling theory of spectral estimates; it also led to an understanding of the design relations essential for a proper application of the estimation techniques. Much of the jargon of this field derives from Tukey; in particular, he introduced the concepts and terms prewhitening, aliasing, tapering, bispectrum, and cepstrum.

More recent contributions to time-series methodology included a set of procedures for smoothing, seasonal adjustment, and calendar adjustment of time series.[280,281] These procedures give demonstrably more reliable

Fig. 1-31. J. W. Tukey, who pioneered in the formulation of mathematical methods for statistical data analysis.

results than the Census Bureau X-11 program. Methods for robust estimation of power spectra when the data is contaminated with bad values
have also been developed.[282]

Tukey joined Bell Labs in 1945. While his formal training had been in
chemistry and mathematics, his greatest impact at Bell Labs was on the
development of statistics research. He collaborated with J. W. Cooley of
IBM on a major breakthrough in 1965 with the publication of the Fast-
Fourier Transform (FFT), which is an ingenious and highly efficient method
for regrouping the computations of Fourier coefficients that are needed in
signal processing and in many other areas.[283] It revolutionized much of
engineering practice, making available many techniques that formerly
would have needed prohibitive amounts of computation; for example,
using FFT, speech spectrograms can be computed digitally in real time.
Two issues of the *IEEE Transactions on Audio and Electroacoustics* (**AU-15**,
June 1967, and **AU-17**, June 1969) were devoted entirely to the FFT.

12.5 Statistical Computing

When modern electronic computers became available in the mid-1950s,
statisticians at Bell Labs were quick to exploit this new power. Terry, in
particular, was influential in making the computer a useful tool in handling
statistical data. In 1967, J. D. Gabbe, M. B. Wilk, and W. L. Brown published
an analysis of an enormous mass of data on high-energy protons gathered
by the Telstar satellite.[284] This study involved fitting a nonliner model of
some 80,000 observations, and made extensive use of graphical methods
for analyzing the quality of the fit obtained. At about this time, libraries
of statistical computing subroutines were developed at Bell Laboratories;
the STATLIB computing library was accepted as the Bell System standard
in 1978.

In 1981, a flexible system for interactive statistical data analysis, called
S, was developed.[285] As of this writing (1983), one version of this system
runs under the UNIX* operating system and provides the user with an
extremely convenient environment for statistical work, including powerful
graphical output. Work aimed at providing an expert system in the domain
of regression analysis was reported in 1982.[286]

Research activity in statistics grew steadily over the years, and by the
early 1980s embraced consulting in data analysis in such areas as business
econometrics, management science, physical science and engineering, and
psychology; research in statistical theory and methodology; and statistical
computing, including a major emphasis on graphics.

---

* Trademark of AT&T Bell Laboratories.

XIII. TRENDS IN THE INDUSTRIAL USES OF MATHEMATICS

In 1964, T. C. Fry estimated the number of industrial mathematicians by counting the members of the American Mathematical Society employed by industry or the government.[287] By that standard, there was only one industrial mathematician, General Electric's Charles Steinmetz, in 1888, 15 in 1913, 150 in 1938, and 1800 in 1963. In these 75 years the numbers followed approximately an exponential growth law, increasing about 12-fold every 25 years.

Paralleling the growth in numbers of mathematicians in industry, there has been a proliferation of applications of mathematics to engineering. Probability, formerly a specialty of statisticians and switching engineers, has found widespread usage in telecommunications. Noise theory and information theory helped to establish the use of probability in transmission. The old blocking problems have reappeared in a new guise as part of queueing theory. A typical queue might now contain parts of a computation waiting to be served by an arithmetic unit in a computer. Probability has become an essential part of operations research and game theory, both of which have many military and economic applications. Complex function theory, which assumed importance in studies of filters, networks, and stability, has continued to be useful, although the applications have changed somewhat as signal processing methods have changed from analog to digital.

Partial differential equations form another analytical subject of increasing importance. Although Maxwell's equations once were the only partial differential equations of great telecommunications interest, many exist to-day. They may describe solid-state electronic phenomena or manufacturing processes like crystal growth or the drawing of optical fibers. The importance of partial differential equations is closely linked with the development of computers capable of solving equations that once were hopelessly complicated.

Other branches of mathematics that have continued to find frequent use in telecommunications research are geometry, modern algebra, number theory, combinatorial analysis, graph theory, and mathematical logic. Typical applications include code design, cryptography, routing layouts for telephone lines or for printed circuits, efficient computing algorithms, and new telephone switching systems.

REFERENCES

1. R. W. Clark, *Edison, the Man Who Made the Future* (New York: Putnam, 1977), p. 94.
2. "Mathematical Research," *Bell Lab. Rec.* **1** (September 1925), pp. 15-18.
3. See reference 1.
4. T. C. Fry, "Industrial Mathematics," *Bell Syst. Tech. J.* **20** (July 1941), pp. 255-292.
5. T. C. Fry, *Probability and Its Engineering Uses* (New York: D. Van Nostrand Co., 1928).

6. J. Riordan, *Stochastic Service Systems* (New York: John Wiley, 1962).
7. J. W. Strutt, Baron Rayleigh, *Theory of Sound*, Vol. 1 (London: Macmillan, 1877), pp. 145-148.
8. G. A. Campbell, "Cisoidal Oscillations," *Trans. Amer. Inst. Elec. Eng.* 30 (April 25, 1911), pp. 873-909.
9. O. Heaviside, *Electromagnetic Theory*, Vol. 2 (London: Ernest Benn, 1899); T. J. I'A. Bromwich, "Normal Coordinates in Dynamical Systems," *Proc. London Math. Soc.*, Series 2, 15 (February 1917), pp. 401-448; J. R. Carson, "Theory of the Transient Oscillations of Electrical Networks and Transmission Systems," *Trans. Amer. Inst. Elec. Eng.* 38 (February 21, 1919), pp. 345-427; J. R. Carson, *Electric Circuit Theory and the Operational Calculus* (New York: McGraw-Hill, 1926).
10. T. C. Fry, U.S. Patent No. 1,503,824; filed December 11, 1920; issued August 5, 1924.
11. For an early suggestion of multiplexed-carrier telephony, see G. O. Squier, "Multiplex Telephony and Telegraphy by Means of Electric Waves Guided by Wires," *Trans. Amer. Inst. Elec. Eng.* 30 (June 28, 1911), pp. 1617-1665.
12. "Historic Firsts: Single-Sideband Transmission," *Bell Lab. Rec.* 31 (April 1953), pp. 148-149.
13. A. A. Oswald, "Early History of Single-Sideband Transmission," *Proc. IRE* 44 (December 1956), pp. 1676-1679.
14. J. R. Carson, U.S. Patent No. 1,449,382; filed December 1, 1915; issued March 27, 1923.
15. R. V. L. Hartley, "Relations of Carrier and Side-Bands in Radio Transmission," *Bell Syst. Tech. J.* 2 (April 1923), pp. 90-112.
16. R. V. L. Hartley, U.S. Patent No. 1,666,206; filed January 15, 1925; issued April 17, 1928.
17. E. H. Colpitts and O. B. Blackwell, "Carrier Current Telephony and Telegraphy," *Trans. Amer. Inst. Elec. Eng.* 40 (February 17, 1921), pp. 205-300.
18. J. R. Carson, "Notes on the Theory of Modulation," *Proc. IRE* 10 (February 1922), pp. 57-64.
19. S. O. Rice, "Distortion Produced by Band Limitation of an FM Wave," *Bell Syst. Tech. J.* 52 (May/June 1973), pp. 605-626.
20. E. H. Armstrong, "A Method of Reducing Disturbances in Radio Signaling by a System of Frequency Modulation," *Proc. IRE* 24 (May 1936), pp. 689-740.
21. J. R. Carson, "Amplitude, Frequency and Phase-Angle Modulation," *Wireless Eng.* 17 (November 1940), p. 477, a letter to the editor in which Carson defended the negative statements he made about FM in his paper of 1922.
22. J. R. Carson and T. C. Fry, "Variable Frequency Electric Circuit Theory with Application to the Theory of Frequency-Modulation," *Bell Syst. Tech. J.* 16 (October 1937), pp. 513-540.
23. S. O. Rice, "Noise in FM Receivers," in *Time Series Analysis*, ed. M. Rosenblatt (New York: John Wiley, 1963), pp. 395-422.
24. D. Slepian, "The Threshold Effect in Modulation Systems that Expand Bandwidth," *Trans. IRE* IT-8 (September 1962), pp. 122-127.
25. H. Nyquist, "Certain Factors Affecting Telegraph Speed," *Bell Syst. Tech. J.* 3 (April 1924), pp. 324-346.
26. H. Nyquist, "Certain Topics in Telegraph Transmission Theory," *Trans. Amer. Inst. Elec. Eng.* 47 (April 1928), pp. 617-644.
27. A. C. Crehore and G. O. Squier, "A Practical Transmitter Using the Sine Wave for Cable Telegraphy; and Measurements with Alternating Currents upon an Atlantic Cable," *Trans. Amer. Inst. Elec. Eng.* 17 (May 1900), pp. 343-388; G. O. Squier, "On an Unbroken Alternating Current for Cable Telegraphy," *Proc. Phys. Soc. London* 27 (August 1915), pp. 540-564; G. O. Squier, "A Method of Transmitting the Telegraph Alphabet Applicable

for Radio, Land Lines, and Submarine Cables," *J. Franklin Inst.* **195** (May 1923), pp. 633-639.

28. D. Slepian, "On Bandwidth," *Proc. IEEE* **64** (March 1976), pp. 292-300.
29. L. A. MacColl, U.S. Patent No. 2,056,284; filed June 7, 1935; issued October 6, 1936.
30. H. S. Black, *Modulation Theory* (New York: D. Van Nostrand Co., 1953), pp. 101-115.
31. C. E. Shannon, "Communication in the Presence of Noise," *Proc. IRE* **37** (January 1949), pp. 10-21.
32. J. M. Whittaker, *Interpolatory Function Theory* (Cambridge: Cambridge University Press, 1935).
33. D. Slepian and H. O. Pollak, "Prolate Spheroidal Wave Functions, Fourier Analysis and Uncertainty-I," *Bell Syst. Tech. J.* **40** (January 1961), pp. 43-63; H. J. Landau and H. O. Pollak, "Prolate Spheroidal Wave Functions, Fourier Analysis and Uncertainty-II," *Bell Syst. Tech. J.* **40** (January 1961), pp. 65-84; H. J. Landau and H. O. Pollak, "Prolate Spheroidal Wave Functions, Fourier Analysis and Uncertainty-III: The Dimension of the Space of Essentially Time- and Band-Limited Signals," *Bell Syst. Tech. J.* **41** (July 1962), pp. 1295-1336; D. Slepian, "Prolate Spheroidal Wave Functions, Fourier Analysis and Uncertainty-IV: Extensions to Many Dimensions; Generalized Prolate Spheroidal Functions," *Bell Syst. Tech. J.* **43** (November 1964), pp. 3009-3057.
34. H. J. Landau, "Necessary Density Conditions for Sampling and Interpolation of Certain Entire Functions," *Acta Math.* **117** (February 1967), pp. 37-52.
35. H. J. Landau, "Sampling, Data Transmission, and the Nyquist Rate," *Proc. IEEE* **55** (October 1967), pp. 1701-1706.
36. For a short biography of Lockwood, see T. C. Martin and S. L. Coles, *The Story of Electricity* (New York: M. M. Marcy, 1919), pp. 281-282.
37. J. Burmeister, U.S. Patent No. 1,227,112; filed July 14, 1916; issued May 22, 1917.
38. G. A. Campbell, U.S. Patent No. 1,227,113; filed June 15, 1915; issued May 22, 1917.
39. W. Thomson, Baron Kelvin, "On a Mechanical Representation of Electric, Magnetic and Galvanic Forces," *Cambridge and Dublin Math. J.* **2** (March 1847), pp. 61-64; J. W. Strutt, Baron Rayleigh, *Theory of Sound,* 2nd ed. (London: Macmillan, 1894).
40. For a historical review, see W. P. Mason, "Electrical and Mechanical Analogies," *Bell Syst. Tech. J.* **20** (October 1941), pp. 405-414.
41. "Sound Recording and Reproducing," *Bell Lab. Rec.* **1** (November 1925), pp. 95-101; J. P. Maxfield and H. C. Harrison, "Methods of High Quality Recording and Reproducing of Music and Speech Based on Telephone Research," *Bell Syst. Tech. J.* **5** (July 1926), pp. 493-523; "Historic Firsts: The Orthophonic Phonograph," *Bell Lab. Rec.* **24** (August 1946), pp. 300-301.
42. R. L. Wegel and C. E. Lane, "The Auditory Masking of One Pure Tone by Another and Its Probable Relation to the Dynamics of the Inner Ear," *Phys. Rev.*, Series 2, **23** (February 1924), pp. 266-285; L. C. Peterson and B. P. Bogert, "The Dynamical Theory of the Cochlea," *J. Acoust. Soc. Am.* **22** (May 1950), pp. 369-381; B. P. Bogert, "A Network to Represent the Inner Ear," *Bell Lab. Rec.* **28** (November 1950), pp. 481-485.
43. L. Espenschied, U.S. Patent No. 1,795,204; filed January 3, 1927; issued March 3, 1931.
44. O. E. Buckley, "The Evolution of the Crystal Wave Filter," *Bell Tel. Quart.* **16** (January 1937), pp. 25-40.
45. W. P. Mason, *Electromechanical Transducers and Wave Filters* (Princeton: D. Van Nostrand Co., 1942).
46. W. P. Mason and R. A. Sykes, U.S. Patent No. 2,173,589; filed December 14, 1933; issued September 19, 1939; W. P. Mason, U.S. Patent No. 2,204,762; filed December 21, 1937; issued June 18, 1940; W. P. Mason, U.S. Patent No. 1,781,469; filed June 25, 1927; issued November 11, 1930; W. P. Mason, U.S. Patent No. 2,183,123; filed June 11, 1934; issued December 12, 1939; W. P. Mason, U.S. Patent No. 2,421,033; filed May 15, 1943; issued May 27, 1947.

47. R. M. Foster, "A Reactance Theorem," *Bell Syst. Tech. J.* **3** (April 1924), pp. 259-267.
48. G. A. Campbell, "Physical Theory of the Electric Wave-Filter," *Bell Syst. Tech. J.* **1** (November 1922), pp. 1-32.
49. O. J. Zobel, "Theory and Design of Uniform and Composite Electric Wave-Filters," *Bell Syst. Tech. J.* **2** (January 1923), pp. 1-46.
50. T. C. Fry, "The Use of Continued Fractions in the Design of Electrical Networks," *Bull. Am. Math. Soc.* **35** (July/August 1929), pp. 463-498.
51. O. Brune, "Synthesis of a Finite Two-Terminal Network Whose Driving-Point Impedance Is a Prescribed Function of Frequency," *J. Math. and Phys.* **10** (October 1931), pp. 191-236; W. Cauer, "Ein Reaktanztheorem," *Sitzungsberichte der Preussischen Akademie der Wissenschaften* **30** (November 26, 1931), pp. 673-681; C. M. Gerwertz, *Network Synthesis; Synthesis of a Finite Four-Terminal Network from Its Prescribed Driving-Point Functions and Transfer Function* (Baltimore: Williams and Wilkins, 1933); S. Darlington, "Synthesis of Reactance 4-Poles Which Produce Prescribed Insertion Loss Characteristics," *J. Math. and Phys.* **18** (September 1939), pp. 257-353; Y. Oono, "Synthesis of a Finite 2n-Terminal Network by a Group of Networks Each of Which Contains Only One Ohmic Resistance," *J. Math. and Phys.* **29** (April 1950), pp. 13-26; B. McMillan, "Introduction to Formal Realizability Theory-I," *Bell Syst. Tech. J.* **31** (March 1952), pp. 217-279; B. McMillan, "Introduction to Formal Realizability Theory-II," *Bell Syst. Tech. J.* **31** (May 1952), pp. 541-600.
52. R. Bott and R. J. Duffin, "Impedance Synthesis without Use of Transformers," *J. Appl. Phys.* **20** (August 1949), p. 816.
53. S. Darlington, "Network Synthesis Using Tchebycheff Polynomial Series," *Bell Syst. Tech. J.* **31** (July 1952), pp. 613-665.
54. H. W. Bode, U.S. Patent No. 2,342,638; filed October 9, 1942; issued February 29, 1944; W. Cauer, "Das Poissonsche Integral und seine Anwendungen auf die Theorie der linearer Wechselstromschaltungen (Netzwerke)," *Elektrische Nachrichtentechnik* **17** (January 1940), pp. 17-30.
55. S. Darlington, "The Potential Analogue Method of Network Synthesis," *Bell Syst. Tech. J.* **30** (April 1951), pp. 315-365.
56. N. Wiener and Y. W. Lee, U.S. Patent No. 2,024,900; filed September 2, 1931; issued December 17, 1935.
57. I. W. Sandberg, "The Zero-Input Response of Digital Filters Using Saturations Arithmetic," *IEEE Trans. Circuit Syst.* **CAS-26** (November 1979), pp. 911-915.
58. M. M. Sondhi and D. Mitra, "New Results on the Performance of a Well-Known Class of Adaptive Filters," *Proc. IEEE* **64** (November 1976), pp. 1583-1597.
59. M. M. Sondhi and D. Mitra, "Qualitative Behavior of Nonlinear Differential Equations Describing Adaptive Filters Using Non-Ideal Multipliers," *IEEE Trans. Automat. Contr.* **AC-24** (April 1979), pp. 276-283.
60. G. Kirchhoff, "Uber die Auflösung der Gleichungen, auf welche man bei Untersuchung der linearen Verteilung galvanischer Ströme geführt wird," *Ann. Phys. Chem.*, Series 2, **72** (1847), pp. 497-508.
61. G. A. Campbell, U.S. Patent No. 1,254,471 through 1,254,474; filed September 9, 1916; issued January 22, 1918; G. A. Campbell, U.S. Patent No. 1,254,475; filed March 15, 1917; issued January 22, 1918; G. A. Campbell, U.S. Patent No. 1,254,476; filed May 18, 1917; issued January 22, 1918; G. A. Campbell, U.S. Patent No. 1,254,116 through 1,254,118; filed August 18, 1917; issued January 22, 1918.
62. G. A. Campbell and R. M. Foster, "Maximum Output Networks for Telephone Substation and Repeater Circuits," *Trans. Amer. Inst. Elec. Eng.* **39** (February 19, 1920), pp. 231-280.
63. R. M. Foster, "Geometrical Circuits of Electrical Networks," *Trans. Amer. Inst. Elec. Eng.* **51** (June 1932), pp. 309-317.

64. J. Riordan and C. E. Shannon, "The Number of Two-Terminal Series-Parallel Networks," *J. Math. and Phys.* **21** (1942), pp. 83-93.

65. R. M. Foster, "The Number of Series-Parallel Networks," *Proc. 6th Int. Cong. Math.* **1,** Cambridge, Massachusetts (August 30-September 6, 1950), p. 646.

66. J. Riordan, *An Introduction to Combinatorial Analysis* (New York: John Wiley, 1958).

67. E. F. Moore, "The Shortest Path Through a Maze," *Proc. Int. Symp. Theory Switching, Part II, Comput. Lab. Harvard Univ. Ann.* **30** (April 1959), pp. 285-292.

68. R. C. Prim, "Shortest Connection Networks and Some Generalizations," *Bell Syst. Tech. J.* **36** (November 1957), pp. 1389-1401.

69. O. Borůvka, "On a Minimal Problem," *Prače Moravské Pridovedecké Spolecnosti* **3** (1926).

70. J. B. Kruskal, Jr., "On the Shortest Spanning Subtree of a Graph and the Traveling Salesman Problem," *Proc. Amer. Math. Soc.* **7** (February 1956), pp. 48-50.

71. Z. A. Melzak, "On the Problem of Steiner," *Can. Math. Bull.* **4** (May 1961), pp. 143-148; E. N. Gilbert, "Minimum Cost Communication Networks," *Bell Syst. Tech. J.* **46** (November 1967), pp. 2209-2227; E. N. Gilbert and H. O. Pollak, "Steiner Minimal Trees," *SIAM J. Appl. Math.* **16** (January 1968), pp. 1-29; F. K. Hwang, "On Steiner Minimal Trees with Rectilinear Distance," *SIAM J. Appl. Math.* **30** (January 1976), pp. 104-114.

72. D. E. Hughes, "On the Physical Action of the Microphone," *J. Soc. Telegr. Eng. Elec.* **12** (April 26, 1883), pp. 245-250.

73. H. Fletcher, "The Theory of the Operation of the Howling Telephone with Experimental Confirmation," *Bell Syst. Tech. J.* **5** (January 1926), pp. 27-49.

74. H. S. Black, U.S. Patent No. 2,003,282; filed August 23, 1928; issued June 4, 1935; H. S. Black, U.S. Patent No. 2,102,671; filed April 22, 1932; issued December 21, 1937; H. S. Black, "Stabilized Feedback Amplifiers," *Bell Syst. Tech. J.* **13** (January 1934), pp. 1-18.

75. H. Nyquist, "Regeneration Theory," *Bell Syst. Tech. J.* **11** (January 1932), pp. 126-147.

76. H. Nyquist, U.S. Patent No. 1,915,441; filed May 1, 1930; issued June 27, 1933.

77. H. J. Van der Bijl, *The Thermionic Vacuum Tube and Its Applications* (New York: McGraw-Hill, 1920), pp. 367-383.

78. E. J. Routh, *A Treatise on the Stability of a Given State of Motion* (London: Macmillan, 1877).

79. E. J. Routh, *The Advanced Part of a Treatise on the Dynamics of a System of Rigid Bodies,* Part 2 (London: Macmillan, 1905).

80. E. Peterson, J. G. Kreer, and L. A. Ware, "Regeneration Theory and Experiment," *Bell Syst. Tech. J.* **13** (October 1934), pp. 680-700.

81. R. L. Dietzold, "The Isograph-A Mechanical Root-Finder," *Bell Lab. Rec.* **16** (December 1937), pp. 130-134.

82. T. C. Fry, "Some Numerical Methods for Locating Roots of Polynomials," *Quart. Appl. Math.* **3** (July 1945), pp. 89-105.

83. L. A. MacColl, *Fundamental Theory of Servomechanisms* (New York: D. Van Nostrand Co., 1945).

84. H. W. Bode, U.S. Patent No. 2,123,178; filed June 22, 1937; issued July 12, 1938; H. W. Bode, "Relations Between Attenuation and Phase in Feedback Amplifier Design," *Bell Syst. Tech. J.* **19** (July 1940), pp. 421-454; H. W. Bode, *Network Analysis and Feedback Amplifier Design* (New York: D. Van Nostrand Co., 1945).

85. Y. W. Lee, "Synthesis of Electric Networks by Means of the Fourier Transforms of Laguerre's Functions," *J. Math. and Phys.* **11** (1931/1932), pp. 83-113.

86. I. W. Sandberg, "Some Results on the Theory of Physical Systems Governed by Nonlinear Functional Equations," *Bell Syst. Tech. J.* **44** (May 1965), pp. 871-898.

87. W. Thomson, Lord Kelvin, "On the Theory of the Electric Telegraph," *Proc. Roy. Soc. London* **7** (May 1855), pp. 382-410.

88. G. Kirchhoff, "Über die Bewegung der Electricitat in Drahten," *Ann. Phys. Chem.*, Series 2, **100** (February 9, 1857), pp. 193-217; O. Heaviside, "On the Extra Current," in *Electrical Papers*, Vol. I (New York: Chelsea Pub. Co., 1970), pp. 53-61; H. Poincaré, "Physique Mathématique-Sur la Propagation de l'Électricité," *Comptes Rendus* **117** (December 26, 1893), pp. 1027-1039.

89. M. I. Pupin, "Wave Transmission Over Non-Uniform Cables and Long-Distance Air-Lines," *Trans. Amer. Inst. Elec. Eng.* **17** (May 19, 1900), pp. 245-307.

90. G. A. Campbell, "On Loaded Lines in Telephonic Transmission," *Phil. Mag.*, Series 6, **5** (March 1903), pp. 313-330.

91. J. R. Carson and R. S. Hoyt, "Propagation of Periodic Currents over a System of Parallel Wires," *Bell Syst. Tech. J.* **6** (July 1927), pp. 495-545.

92. J. R. Carson and J. J. Gilbert, "Transmission Characteristics of the Submarine Cable," *J. Franklin Inst.* **192** (December 1921), pp. 705-735.

93. S. A. Schelkunoff, "The Electromagnetic Theory of Coaxial Transmission Lines and Cylindrical Shields," *Bell Syst. Tech. J.* **13** (October 1934), pp. 532-579.

94. S. A. Schelkunoff and T. M. Odarenko, "Crosstalk Between Coaxial Transmission Lines," *Bell Syst. Tech. J.* **16** (April 1937), pp. 144-164.

95. A. M. Clogston, "Reduction of Skin Effect Losses by the Use of Laminated Conductors," *Bell Syst. Tech. J.* **30** (July 1951), pp. 491-529.

96. S. P. Morgan, Jr., "Mathematical Theory of Laminated Transmission Lines—Part I," *Bell Syst. Tech. J.* **31** (September 1952), pp. 883-949.

97. S. P. Morgan, Jr., "Mathematical Theory of Laminated Transmission Lines—Part II," *Bell Syst. Tech. J.* **31** (November 1952), pp. 1121-1206.

98. J. R. Carson, "Wave Propagation Over Parallel Wires: The Proximity Effect," *Phil. Mag.*, Series 6, **41** (April 1921), pp. 607-633; J. R. Carson, "Wave Propagation in Overhead Wires with Ground Return," *Bell Syst. Tech. J.* **5** (October 1926), pp. 539-554; J. R. Carson, "Ground Return Impedance: Underground Wire with Earth Return," *Bell Syst. Tech. J.* **8** (January 1929), pp. 94-98.

99. J. J. Thomson, *Notes on Recent Researches in Electricity and Magnetism* (Oxford: Clarendon Press, 1893).

100. J. W. Strutt, Baron Rayleigh, "On the Passage of Electric Waves through Tubes, or the Vibrations of Dielectric Cylinders," *Phil. Mag.*, Series 5, **43** (February 1897), pp. 125-132.

101. G. C. Southworth, *Forty Years of Radio Research* (New York: Gordon and Breach, 1962).

102. J. R. Carson, S. P. Mead, and S. A. Schelkunoff, "Hyper-Frequency Wave Guides—Mathematical Theory," *Bell Syst. Tech. J.* **15** (April 1936), pp. 310-333; G. C. Southworth, "Hyper-Frequency Wave Guides—General Considerations and Experimental Results," *Bell Syst. Tech. J.* **15** (April 1936), pp. 284-309; G. C. Southworth, "Some Fundamental Experiments with Wave Guides," *Proc. IRE* **25** (July 1937), pp. 807-822; S. A. Schelkunoff, "Transmission Theory of Plane Electromagnetic Waves," *Proc. IRE* **25** (November 1937), pp. 1457-1492.

103. W. L. Barrow, "Transmission of Electromagnetic Waves in Hollow Tubes of Metal," *Proc. IRE* **24** (October 1936), pp. 1298-1328.

104. L. J. Chu and W. L. Barrow, "Electromagnetic Waves in Hollow Metal Tubes of Rectangular Cross-Section," *Proc. IRE* **26** (December 1938), pp. 1520-1555.

105. S. A. Schelkunoff, "The Impedance Concept and Its Application to Problems of Reflection, Refraction, Shielding and Power Absorption," *Bell Syst. Tech. J.* **17** (January 1938), pp. 17-48.

106. S. A. Schelkunoff, *Electromagnetic Waves* (New York: D. Van Nostrand Co., 1943).

107. P. H. Smith, "Transmission Line Calculator," *Electronics* **12** (January 1939), pp. 29-31.

108. P. H. Smith, "An Improved Transmission Line Calculator," *Electronics* **17** (January 1944), pp. 130-133.

109. See reference 101, p. 219.

110. L. Brillouin, "Propagation d'Ondes Électromagnétiques dans un Tuyau," *Revue Générale de l'Electricité* **40** (August 22, 1936), pp. 227-239.

111. S. A. Schelkunoff, "A Note on Certain Guided Waves in Slightly Noncircular Tubes," *J. Appl. Phys.* **9** (July 1938), pp. 484-488.

112. L. J. Chu, "Electromagnetic Waves in Elliptic Hollow Pipes of Metal," *J. Appl. Phys.* **9** (September 1938), pp. 583-591.

113. A. Sommerfeld, "Über die Ausbreitung der Wellen in der drahtlosen Telegraphie," *Annalen der Physik*, Series 4, **28** (March 16, 1909), pp. 665-736.

114. H. Weyl, "Ausbreitung elektromagnetischer Wellen über einem ebenen Leiter," *Annalen der Physik*, Series 4, **60** (November 20, 1919), pp. 481-500.

115. W. H. Wise, "The Physical Reality of Zenneck's Surface Wave," *Bell Syst. Tech. J.* **16** (January 1937), pp. 35-44; W. H. Wise, "The Grounded Condenser Antenna Radiation Formula," *Proc. IRE* **19** (September 1931), pp. 1684-1689; S. O. Rice, "Series for the Wave Function of a Radiating Dipole at the Earth's Surface," *Bell Syst. Tech. J.* **16** (January 1937), pp. 101-109; C. R. Burrows, "Radio Propagation Over Plane Earth—Field Strength Curves," *Bell Syst. Tech. J.* **16** (January 1937), pp. 45-75; C. R. Burrows, "The Surface Wave in Radio Transmission," *Bell Lab. Rec.* **15** (June 1937), pp. 321-324.

116. K. F. Niessen, "Zur Entscheidung Zwischen den beiden Sommerfeldschen Formeln für die Fortpflanzung von drahtlosen Wellen," *Annalen der Physik*, Series 5, **29** (July 3, 1937), pp. 585-596. Rice's discovery of Sommerfeld's error was independent but unpublished.

117. H. H. Beverage, C. W. Rice, and E. W. Kellogg, "The Wave Antenna," *J. Amer. Inst. Elec. Eng.* **42** (March 1923), pp. 258-269; ibid. (April 1923), pp. 372-381; ibid. (May 1923), pp. 510-519; ibid. (June 1923), pp. 636-644; ibid. (July 1923), pp. 728-738.

118. J. R. Carson, "Wave Propagation in Overhead Wires with Ground Return," *Bell Syst. Tech. J.* **5** (October 1926), pp. 539-554.

119. J. R. Carson and R. S. Hoyt, "Propagation of Periodic Currents Over a System of Parallel Wires," *Bell Syst. Tech. J.* **6** (July 1927), pp. 495-545.

120. J. R. Carson, "A Generalization of the Reciprocal Theorem," *Bell Syst. Tech. J.* **3** (July 1924), pp. 393-399.

121. J. W. Strutt, Baron Rayleigh, "On the Application of the Principle of Reciprocity to Acoustics," *Proc. Roy. Soc. London* **25** (June 15, 1876), pp. 118-122.

122. J. W. Strutt, Baron Rayleigh, *Scientific Papers*, Vol. 3 (Cambridge: Cambridge University Press, 1902), pp. 106-116.

123. S. G. Brown, British Patent No. 14,449 (1899); J. S. Stone, U.S. Patent No. 716,134; filed January 23, 1901; issued December 16, 1902; A. Blondel, Belgian Patent No. 163,516 (1902); British Patent No. 11,427 (1903).

124. G. A. Campbell, U.S. Patent No. 1,738,522; filed September 30, 1919; issued December 10, 1929.

125. R. M. Foster, "Directive Diagrams of Antenna Arrays," *Bell Syst. Tech. J.* **5** (April 1926), pp. 292-307.

126. G. C. Southworth, "Certain Factors Affecting the Gain of Directive Antennas," *Proc. IRE* **18** (September 1930), pp. 1502-1536.

127. S. A. Schelkunoff, "A Mathematical Theory of Linear Arrays," *Bell Syst. Tech. J.* **22** (January 1943), pp. 80-107.

128. S. A. Schelkunoff, U.S. Patent No. 2,286,839; filed December 20, 1939; issued June 16, 1942.

129. C. L. Dolph, "A Current Distribution for Broadside Arrays Which Optimizes the Relationship Between Beam Width and Side-Lobe Level," *Proc. IRE* **34** (June 1946), pp. 335-348.

130. E. N. Gilbert and S. P. Morgan, "Optimum Design of Directive Antenna Arrays Subject to Random Variations," *Bell Syst. Tech. J.* **34** (May 1955), pp. 637-663.

131. A. G. Bell, U.S. Patent No. 220,791; filed July 17, 1879; issued October 21, 1879.

132. A. G. Bell, U.S. Patent No. 244,426; filed June 4, 1881; issued July 19, 1881.
133. J. A. Barrett, U.S. Patent No. 392,775; filed May 9, 1888; issued November 13, 1888.
134. H. P. Lawther, Jr., "An Application of Number Theory to the Splicing of Telephone Cables," *Amer. Math. Mon.* **42** (February 1935), pp. 81-91.
135. J. Riordan, "Cable Splices and the Hostess Problem," *Bell Lab. Rec.* **21** (January 1943), pp. 114-116.
136. B. D. Holbrook and J. T. Dixon, "Load Rating Theory for Multi-Channel Amplifiers," *Bell Syst. Tech. J.* **18** (October 1939), pp. 624-644.
137. W. R. Bennett, "Cross-Modulation Requirements on Multi-Channel Amplifiers Below Overload," *Bell Syst. Tech. J.* **19** (October 1940), pp. 587-610.
138. W. R. Bennett, "The Biased Ideal Rectifier," *Bell Syst. Tech. J.* **26** (January 1947), pp. 139-169.
139. N. R. Campbell, "The Study of Discontinuous Phenomena," *Proc. Cambridge Phil. Soc.* **15** (February 1909), pp. 117-136.
140. J. R. Carson, "Selective Circuits and Static Interference," *Bell Syst. Tech. J.* **4** (April 1925), pp. 265-279.
141. J. R. Carson, "The Statistical Energy-Frequency Spectrum of Random Disturbances," *Bell Syst. Tech. J.* **10** (July 1931), pp. 374-381.
142. W. Shockley and J. R. Pierce, "A Theory of Noise for Electron Multipliers," *Proc. IRE* **26** (March 1938), pp. 321-332.
143. W. Schottky, "Über spontane Stromschwankungen in verschiedenen Elektrizitätsleitern," *Annalen der Physik*, Series 4, **57** (December 20, 1918), pp. 541-567.
144. J. B. Johnson, "Electronic Noise: The First Two Decades," *IEEE Spectrum* **8** (February 1971), pp. 42-46.
145. J. B. Johnson, "Thermal Agitation of Electricity in Conductors," *Phys. Rev.* **32** (July 1928), pp. 97-109.
146. H. Nyquist, "Thermal Agitation of Electric Charge in Conductors," *Phys. Rev.* **32** (July 1928), pp. 110-113.
147. A. Einstein, "Zur Theorie der Brownschen Bewegung," *Annalen der Physik*, Series 4, **19** (February 8, 1906), pp. 371-381.
148. J. W. Strutt, Baron Rayleigh, "On the Character of the Complete Radiation at a Given Temperature," *Phil. Mag.*, Series 5, **27** (June 1889), pp. 460-469.
149. S. O. Rice, "Mathematical Analysis of Random Noise," *Bell Syst. Tech. J.* **23** (July 1944), pp. 282-332.
150. S. O. Rice, "Mathematical Analysis of Random Noise," *Bell Syst. Tech. J.* **24** (January 1945), pp. 46-156.
151. S. O. Rice, "The Distribution of the Maxima of a Random Curve," *Amer. J. Math.* **61** (1939), pp. 409-416.
152. G. Crisson, "Irregularities in Loaded Telephone Circuits," *Bell Syst. Tech. J.* **4** (October 1925), pp. 561-585.
153. S. O. Rice, "Statistical Properties of a Sine Wave Plus Random Noise," *Bell Syst. Tech. J.* **27** (January 1948), pp. 109-157.
154. E. L. Kaplan, "Signal-Detection Studies, with Applications," *Bell Syst. Tech. J.* **34** (March 1955), pp. 403-437.
155. K. Ito and H. P. McKean, *Diffusion Processes and Their Sample Paths* (New York: Academic Press/Springer, 1965).
156. N. Wiener, *Extrapolation, Interpolation, and Smoothing of Stationary Time Series* (New York: John Wiley, 1949).
157. A. Kolmogoroff, "Interpolation und Extrapolation von stationären zufälligen Folgen," *Bulletin de l'académie des Sciences de l'Union des Républiques Soviétiques Socialistes* **5** (1941), pp. 11-14.

158. R. B. Blackman, H. W. Bode, and C. E. Shannon, "Data Smoothing and Prediction in Fire Control Systems," *Summary Tech. Rep. Div. 7, Nat. Defense Res. Committee Rep.* **1** (1948), pp. 71-160.

159. H. W. Bode and C. E. Shannon, "A Simplified Derivation of Linear Least Square Smoothing and Prediction Theory," *Proc. IRE* **38** (April 1950), pp. 417-425.

160. D. Slepian and T. T. Kadota, "Four Integral Equations of Detection Theory," *SIAM J. Appl. Math.* **17** (November 1969), pp. 1102-1117.

161. J. L. Doob, *Stochastic Processes* (New York: John Wiley, 1953), pp. 560-598, gives a status report as of circa 1950.

162. L. A. Shepp, "Radon-Nikodym Derivatives of Gaussian Measures," *Ann. Math. Statist.* **37** (April 1966), pp. 321-354.

163. T. T. Kadota, "Optimal, Causal, Simultaneous Detection and Estimation of Random Signal Fields in Gaussian Noise Field," *IEEE Trans. Inform. Theory* **24** (May 1978), pp. 297-308.

164. V. E. Beneš, "Existence of Optimal Stochastic Control Laws," *SIAM J. Contr.* **9** (August 1971), pp. 446-472.

165. V. E. Beneš, "Full 'Bang' to Reduce Predicted Miss is Optimal," *SIAM J. Contr. Optim.* **14** (January 1976), pp. 62-84.

166. V. E. Beneš, "Composition and Invariance Methods for Solving Some Stochastic Control Problems," *Adv. Appl. Prob.* **7** (June 1975), pp. 299-329.

167. V. E. Beneš, L. A. Shepp, and H. S. Witsenhausen, "Some Solvable Stochastic Control Problems," *Stochastics* **4** (1980), pp. 39-83.

168. H. S. Witsenhausen, "On Information Structures, Feedback and Causality," *SIAM J. Contr.* **9** (May 1971), pp. 149-160.

169. "The Intrinsic Model for Discrete Stochastic Control: Some Open Problems," *Lecture Notes in Economics and Mathematical Systems No. 107: Int. Conf. Contr. Theory, Numerical Methods and Comput. Syst. Modeling*, Rocquencourt, France (June 17-21, 1974), pp. 322-335.

170. C. E. Shannon, "A Mathematical Theory of Communication," *Bell Syst. Tech. J.* **27** (July 1948), pp. 379-423, and (October 1948), pp. 623-656.

171. R. J. McEliece, *The Theory of Information and Coding* (Reading, Massachusetts: Addison-Wesley, 1977).

172. A. D. Wyner, "Another Look at the Coding Theorem of Information Theory," *Proc. IEEE* **58** (June 1970), pp. 894-913.

173. J. R. Pierce, *Symbols, Signals and Noise: The Nature and Process of Communication* (New York: Harper, 1961), pp. 45-63 and pp. 255-263.

174. C. E. Shannon, "Prediction and Entropy of Printed English," *Bell Syst. Tech. J.* **30** (January 1951), pp. 50-64.

175. S. O. Rice, "Communication in the Presence of Noise—Probability of Error for Two Encoding Schemes," *Bell Syst. Tech. J.* **29** (January 1950), pp. 60-93.

176. C. E. Shannon, "The Zero Error Capacity of a Noisy Channel," *IRE Trans. Inform. Theory* **IT-2** (September 1956), pp. 8-19.

177. A. D. Wyner, "On the Probability of Error Using a Repeat-Request Strategy on the Additive White Gaussian Noise Channel," *Bell Syst. Tech. J.* **48** (January 1969), pp. 71-86.

178. T. T. Kadota and A. D. Wyner, "Coding Theorem for Stationary, Asymptotically Memoryless Continuous-Time Channels," *Ann. Math. Statist.* **43** (October 1972), pp. 1603-1611; L. H. Brandenburg and A. D. Wyner, "Capacity of the Gaussian Channel with Memory: The Multivariate Case," *Bell Syst. Tech. J.* **53** (May/June 1974), pp. 745-778; A. D. Wyner, "Capacity of the Band-Limited Gaussian Channel," *Bell Syst. Tech. J.* **45** (March 1966), pp. 359-395.

179. C. E. Shannon, "Two-Way Communication Channels," *Proc. 4th Berkeley Symp. Math.*

Statist. Prob. **1,** University of California at Berkeley (June 20-July 30, 1960), pp. 611-644.

180. T. M. Cover, "Broadcast Channels," *IEEE Trans. Inform. Theory* **IT-18** (January 1972), pp. 2-14.

181. D. Slepian and J. K. Wolf, "Noiseless Coding of Correlated Information Sources," *IEEE Trans. Inform. Theory* **IT-19** (July 1973), pp. 471-480.

182. A. D. Wyner and J. Ziv, "A Theorem on the Entropy of Certain Binary Sequences and Applications—Part I," *IEEE Trans. Inform. Theory* **IT-19** (November 1973), pp. 769-772.

183. A. D. Wyner, "A Theorem on the Entropy of Certain Binary Sequences and Applications—Part II," *IEEE Trans. Inform. Theory* **IT-19** (November 1973), pp. 772-777.

184. A. D. Wyner, "The Common Information of Two Dependent Random Variables," *IEEE Trans. Inform. Theory* **IT-21** (March 1975), pp. 163-179; H. S. Witsenhausen and A. D. Wyner, "A Conditional Entropy Bound for a Pair of Discrete Random Variables," *IEEE Trans. Inform. Theory* **IT-21** (September 1975), pp. 493-501; A. D. Wyner and J. Ziv, "The Rate-Distortion Function for Source Coding with Side Information at the Decoder," *IEEE Trans. Inform. Theory* **IT-22** (January 1976), pp. 1-10; L. Ozarow, "On a Source-Coding Problem with Two Channels and Three Receivers," *Bell Syst. Tech. J.* **59** (December 1980), pp. 1909-1921.

185. J. W. Dehn, "Code Patterns in Telephone Switching and Accounting Systems," *Bell Lab. Rec.* **30** (January 1952), pp. 9-11. The code itself was not patented, but U.S. Patent No. 2,317,191, filed by B. D. Holbrook on January 24, 1941, and issued on April 20, 1943, gives circuits to implement the code for multifrequency tone signaling systems.

186. W. F. Friedman, "Report on the History of the Use of Codes and Code Language," in *International Radio Telephone Conference of Washington: 1927* (Washington, D.C.: U.S. Government Printing Office, 1928).

187. W. F. Friedman and C. J. Mendelsohn, "Notes on Code Words," *Amer. Math. Mon.* **39** (August/September 1932), pp. 394-409.

188. R. W. Hamming and B. D. Holbrook, U.S. Patent No. 2,522,629; filed January 11, 1950; issued May 15, 1951.

189. D. Slepian, "A Class of Binary Signaling Alphabets," *Bell Syst. Tech. J.* **35** (January 1956), pp. 203-234; "A Note on Two Binary Signaling Alphabets," *IRE Trans. Inform. Theory* **IT-2** (June 1956), pp. 84-87.

190. D. Slepian, "Some Further Theory of Group Codes," *Bell Syst. Tech. J.* **39** (September 1960), pp. 1219-1252.

191. E. R. Berlekamp, "On Decoding Binary Bose-Chaudhuri-Hocquenghem Codes," *IEEE Trans. Inform. Theory* **IT-11** (October 1965), pp. 577-579.

192. E. R. Berlekamp, *Algebraic Coding Theory* (New York: McGraw-Hill, 1968).

193. J. L. Massey, "Shift-Register Synthesis and BCH Decoding," *IEEE Trans. Inform. Theory* **IT-15** (January 1969), pp. 122-127.

194. E. R. Berlekamp, "Factoring Polynomials Over Finite Fields," *Bell Syst. Tech. J.* **46** (October 1967), pp. 1853-1859; E. R. Berlekamp, "Factoring Polynomials Over Large Finite Fields," *Math. Comp.* **24** (July 1970), pp. 713-735.

195. See reference 192.

196. F. J. MacWilliams, "Combinatorial Problems of Elementary Abelian Groups," Ph.D. Thesis, Department of Math., Radcliffe College/Harvard University (May 1962).

197. F. J. MacWilliams, "A Theorem on the Distribution of Weights in a Systematic Code," *Bell Syst. Tech. J.* **42** (January 1963), pp. 79-94.

198. F. J. MacWilliams, "Permutation Decoding of Systematic Codes," *Bell Syst. Tech. J.* **43** (January 1964), pp. 485-505.

199. S. Y. Tong, "Synchronization Recovery Techniques for Binary Cyclic Codes," *Bell Syst. Tech. J.* **45** (April 1966), pp. 561-596; S. Y. Tong, "Correction of Synchronization Errors with Burst-Error-Correcting Cyclic Codes," *IEEE Trans. Inform. Theory* **15** (January 1969), pp. 106-109; S. Y. Tong, "Burst-Trapping Techniques for a Compound Channel," *IEEE*

Trans. Inform. Theory **IT-15** (November 1969), pp. 710-715; S. Y. Tong, "Performance of Burst-Trapping Codes," *Bell Syst. Tech. J.* **49** (April 1970), pp. 477-491.

200. F. J. MacWilliams and N. J. A. Sloane, *The Theory of Error-Correcting Codes* (Amsterdam: North Holland, 1977).
201. D. W. Hagelbarger, "Recurrent Codes: Easily Mechanized, Burst-Correcting, Binary Codes," *Bell Syst. Tech. J.* **38** (July 1959), pp. 969-984.
202. E. N. Gilbert, "A Comparison of Signalling Alphabets," *Bell Syst. Tech. J.* **31** (May 1962), pp. 504-522; D. Slepian, "Bounds on Communication," *Bell Syst. Tech. J.* **42** (May 1963), pp. 681-707; D. Slepian, "Permutation Modulation," *Proc. IEEE* **53** (March 1965), pp. 228-236; D. Slepian, "Group Codes for the Gaussian Channel," *Bell Syst. Tech. J.* **47** (April 1968), pp. 575-602; J. Leech and N. J. A. Sloane, "Sphere Packing and Error-Correcting Codes," *Can. J. Math.* **23** (July 1971), pp. 718-745.
203. C. E. Shannon, "A Symbolic Analysis of Relay and Switching Circuits," *Trans. Amer. Inst. Elec. Eng.* **57** (December 1938), pp. 713-723.
204. C. E. Shannon, "The Synthesis of Two-Terminal Switching Circuits," *Bell Syst. Tech. J.* **28** (January 1949), pp. 59-98.
205. G. Boole, *The Mathematical Analysis of Logic* (Cambridge: Macmillan, 1847).
206. G. Boole, *An Investigation of the Laws of Thought* (London: Dover, 1854).
207. M. Karnaugh, "Map Method for Synthesis of Combinational Logic Circuits," *Trans. Amer. Inst. Elec. Eng.—Pt. 1, Commun. Electron.* **72** (November 1953), pp. 593-598.
208. A. Marquand, "On Logical Diagrams for *n* Terms," *Phil. Mag.*, Series 5, **12** (October 1881), pp. 266-270.
209. M. Gardner, *Logic Machines and Diagrams* (New York: McGraw-Hill, 1958).
210. W. V. Quine, "The Problem of Simplifying Truth Functions," *Amer. Math. Mon.* **59** (October 1952), pp. 521-531.
211. E. J. McCluskey, Jr., "Minimization of Boolean Functions," *Bell Syst. Tech. J.* **35** (November 1956), pp. 1417-1444.
212. Moore's table appears in R. A. Higonnet and R. A. Grea, *Logical Design of Electrical Circuits* (New York: McGraw-Hill, 1958), pp. 195-216.
213. D. Slepian, "On the Number of Symmetry Types of Boolean Functions of *n* Variables," *Can. J. Math.* **5** (1954), pp. 185-193.
214. E. F. Moore and C. E. Shannon, "Reliable Circuits Using Less Reliable Relays," *J. Franklin Inst.* **262** (September 1956), pp. 191-208, and (October 1956), pp. 281-297.
215. D. A. Huffman, "The Synthesis of Sequential Switching Circuits," *J. Franklin Inst.* **257** (March 1954), pp. 161-190 and pp. 275-303.
216. G. H. Mealy, "A Method for Synthesizing Sequential Circuits," *Bell Syst. Tech. J.* **34** (September 1955), pp. 1045-1079.
217. E. F. Moore, "Gedanken-Experiments on Sequential Machines," in *Automata Studies*, ed. C. E. Shannon and J. McCarthy (Princeton: Princeton University Press, 1956), pp. 129-153.
218. C. E. Shannon and J. McCarthy, ed., Preface to *Automata Studies* (Princeton: Princeton University Press, 1956), pp. v-viii; S. C. Kleene, "Representation of Events in Nerve Nets and Finite Automata," in *Automata Studies*, ed. C. E. Shannon and J. McCarthy (Princeton: Princeton University Press, 1956), pp. 3-42; J. von Neumann, "Probabilistic Logics and the Synthesis of Reliable Organisms from Unreliable Components," in *Automata Studies*, ed. C. E. Shannon and J. McCarthy (Princeton: Princeton University Press, 1956), pp. 43-98; W. R. Ashby, "Design for an Intelligence-Amplifier," in *Automata Studies*, ed. C. E. Shannon and J. McCarthy (Princeton: Princeton University Press, 1956), pp. 215-234; A. M. Uttley, "Conditional Probability Machines and Conditioned Reflexes," in *Automata Studies*, ed. C. E. Shannon and J. McCarthy (Princeton: Princeton University Press, 1956), pp. 253-276; A. M. Uttley, "Temporal and Spatial Patterns in a Conditional Probability Machine," in *Automata Studies*, ed. C. E. Shannon and J. McCarthy (Princeton: Princeton University Press, 1956), pp. 277-285.

219. S. Eilenberg, *Automata, Languages, and Machines*, Vol. A (New York: Academic Press, 1974), pp. xiii-xvi.
220. C. E. Shannon, "Computers and Automata," *Proc. IRE* **41** (October 1953), pp. 1234-1241.
221. C. E. Shannon, "Presentation of a Maze-Solving Machine," *Trans. 8th Cybernetics Conf.* (New York: Josiah Macy, Jr. Foundation, 1952), pp. 173-180.
222. "Amazing Micro Mouse Maze Contest," *IEEE Spectrum* **15** (February 1978), pp. 12-13.
223. D. W. Hagelbarger, "SEER, A SEquence Extrapolating Robot," *IRE Trans. Electron. Comput.* **EC-5** (March 1956), pp. 1-7.
224. E. F. Moore, "Artificial Living Plants," *Sci. Amer.* **195** (October 1956), pp. 118-126.
225. C. E. Shannon, "Programming a Computer for Playing Chess," *Phil. Mag.*, Series 7, **41** (March 1950), pp. 256-275; J. H. Condon and K. Thompson, "Belle Chess Hardware," in *Advances in Computer Chess 3*, ed. M. R. B. Clarke (Oxford, England: Pergamon Press, 1982), pp. 45–54.
226. S. A. Cook, "The Complexity of Theorem-Proving Procedures," *Proc. 3rd Ann. ACM Symp. Theory Comput.* (New York: Association for Computing Machinery, 1971), pp. 151-158.
227. R. M. Karp, "Reducibility Among Combinatorial Problems," in *Complexity of Computer Computations*, ed. R. E. Miller and J. W. Thatcher (New York: Plenum Press, 1972), pp. 85-103.
228. M. R. Garey, R. L. Graham, and D. S. Johnson, "Some NP-Complete Geometric Problems," *Proc. 8th Ann. ACM Symp. Theory Comput.* (New York: Association for Computing Machinery, 1976), pp. 10-22.
229. M. R. Garey and D. S. Johnson, *Computers and Intractability: A Guide to the Theory of NP-Completeness* (San Francisco: W. H. Freeman, 1979).
230. R. L. Graham, "Bounds for Certain Multiprocessing Anomalies," *Bell Syst. Tech. J.* **45** (November 1966), pp. 1563-1581.
231. R. L. Graham, "Bounds on Multiprocessing Timing Anomalies," *SIAM J. Appl. Math.* **17** (March 1969), pp. 416-429.
232. See reference 230.
233. See reference 231.
234. M. R. Garey, R. L. Graham, and J. D. Ullman, "Worst Case Analysis of Memory Allocation Algorithms," *Proc. 4th Ann. ACM Symp. Theory Comput.* (New York: Association for Computing Machinery, 1972), pp. 143-150.
235. D. S. Johnson, "Near-Optimal Allocation Algorithms," Doctoral Thesis, MIT (1973).
236. D. S. Johnson, "Fast Algorithms for Bin Packing," *J. Comput. Syst. Sci.* **8** (June 1974), pp. 272-314.
237. D. S. Johnson, "Approximation Algorithms for Combinatorial Problems," *J. Comput. Syst. Sci.* **9** (December 1974), pp. 256-278.
238. See reference 229.
239. See reference 231.
240. V. E. Beneš, "Some Inequalities in the Theory of Telephone Traffic," *Bell Syst. Tech. J.* **44** (November 1965), pp. 1941-1975.
241. V. E. Beneš, "Optimal Routing in Connecting Networks Over Finite Time Intervals," *Bell Syst. Tech. J.* **46** (December 1967), pp. 2341-2352.
242. V. E. Beneš, "Applications of Group Theory to Connecting Networks," *Bell Syst. Tech. J.* **54** (February 1975), pp. 407-420.
243. V. E. Beneš, "Reduction of Network States Under Symmetries," *Bell Syst. Tech. J.* **57** (January 1978), pp. 111-149.
244. C. Clos, "A Study of Non-Blocking Switching Networks," *Bell Syst. Tech. J.* **32** (March 1953), pp. 406-424.
245. V. E. Beneš, "Toward a Group-Theoretic Proof of the Rearrangeability Theorem for Clos' Network," *Bell Syst. Tech. J.* **54** (April 1975), pp. 797-805.
246. See reference 66.

247. J. Riordan, *Stochastic Service Systems* (New York: John Wiley, 1962).
248. See reference 53.
249. See reference 129.
250. B. Gopinath and R. P. Kurshan, "Embedding an Arbitrary Function into a Tchebycheff Space," *J. Approximation Theory* **21** (October 1977), pp. 126-142; B. Gopinath and R. P. Kurshan, "The Fundamental Theorem for Tchebycheff Spaces," *J. Approximation Theory* **21** (October 1977), pp. 143-150; B. Gopinath and R. P. Kurshan, "The Oscillation Theorem for Tchebycheff Spaces," *J. Approximation Theory* **21** (October 1977), pp. 151-173.
251. See reference 57.
252. I. W. Sandberg, "Diffeomorphisms and Newton-Direction Algorithms," *Bell Syst. Tech. J.* **59** (November 1980), pp. 1721-1733.
253. G. N. Hounsfield, "Computerized Transverse Axial Scanning (Tomography): Part I—Description of System," *Brit. J. Radiology* **46** (December 1973), pp. 1016-1022.
254. L. A. Shepp and B. F. Logan, "The Fourier Reconstruction of a Head Section," *IEEE Trans. Nucl. Sci.* **NS-21** (June 1974), pp. 21-43.
255. L. A. Shepp and J. B. Kruskal, "Computerized Tomography: The New Medical X-ray Technology," *Amer. Math. Mon.* **85** (June/July 1978), pp. 420-439.
256. N. J. Zabusky and M. D. Kruskal, "Interaction of 'Solitons' in a Collisionless Plasma and the Recurrence of Initial States," *Phys. Rev. Lett.* **15** (August 9, 1965), pp. 240-243.
257. N. J. Zabusky, "Solitons and Bound States of the Time-Independent Schrödinger Equation," *Phys. Rev.*, Series 2, **168** (April 5, 1968), pp. 124-128.
258. E. Y. Harper, "Motion-Induced Singularities in Power Spectra Associated with Ocean Gravity-Wave Fluctuations," *SIAM J. Appl. Math.* **39** (December 1980), pp. 492-511.
259. F. T. Geyling and H. R. Westerman, *Introduction to Orbital Mechanics* (Reading, Massachusetts: Addison-Wesley, 1971).
260. A. Wald, "Sequential Analysis of Statistical Data: Theory," report submitted by the Statistical Research Group, Columbia University, to the Applied Mathematics Panel, National Defense Research Committee (September 1943); A. Wald, *Sequential Analysis* (New York: John Wiley, 1947); H. F. Dodge and H. G. Romig, *Sampling Inspections Tables* (New York: John Wiley), 1944.
261. P. S. Olmstead, "Distribution of Sample Arrangements for Runs Up and Down," *Ann. Math. Stat.* **17** (March 1946), pp. 24-33; P. S. Olmstead and J. W. Tukey, "A Corner Test for Association," *Ann. Math. Stat.* **18** (December 1947), pp. 495-513; P. S. Olmstead, "Runs Determined in a Sample by an Arbitrary Cut," *Bell Syst. Tech. J.* **37** (January 1958), pp. 55-82.
262. E. C. Molina and R. P. Crowell, "Deviation of Random Samples from Average Conditions and Significance to Traffic Men," *Bell Syst. Tech. J.* **3** (January 1924), pp. 88-99; P. P. Coggins, "Some General Results of Elementary Sampling Theory for Engineering Use," *Bell Syst. Tech. J.* **7** (January 1928), pp. 26-29; E. C. Molina and R. I. Wilkinson, "The Frequency Distribution of the Unknown Mean of a Sampled Universe," *Bell Syst. Tech. J.* **8** (October 1929), pp. 632-645.
263. J. Neyman and E. S. Pearson, "The Use and Interpretation of Certain Test Criteria for Purposes of Statistical Inference," *Biometrika*, Series A, **20** (1928), pp. 175-240 and pp. 263-294.
264. J. Neyman and E. S. Pearson, "On the Problem of the most Efficient Tests of Statistical Hypotheses," *Phil. Trans. Roy. Soc. London*, Series A, **231** (March 1933), pp. 289-337.
265. H. F. Dodge and H. G. Romig, "Single Sampling and Doubling Sampling Inspection Tables," *Bell Syst. Tech. J.* **20** (January 1941), pp. 1-61.
266. W. A. Shewhart, *Statistical Method from the Viewpoint of Quality Control* (Washington, D.C.: The Graduate School, Dept. of Agriculture, 1939), p. 40.
267. See reference 266.
268. L. N. Hampton and J. B. Newsom, "The Card Translator for Nationwide Dialing," *Bell Syst. Tech. J.* **32** (September 1953), pp. 1037-1098.

269. C. B. Brown and M. E. Terry, "The Application of Designed Experiments to the Card Translator," *Bell Syst. Tech. J.* **33** (March 1954), pp. 369-398.

270. W. C. Helmle, "The Relation Between Rents and Incomes, and the Distribution of Rental Values," *Bell Syst. Tech. J.* **1** (November 1922), pp. 82-109.

271. H. C. Bateman, "A Method of Graphical Analyses," *Bell Syst. Tech. J.* **2** (July 1923), pp. 77-100.

272. E. Dietze and W. D. Goodale, Jr., "The Computation of the Composite Noise Resulting from Random Variable Sources," *Bell Syst. Tech. J.* **18** (October 1939), pp. 605-623.

273. R. I. Wilkinson, "The Reliability of Holding Time Measurements," *Bell Syst. Tech. J.* **20** (October 1941), pp. 365-404.

274. C. Clos and R. I. Wilkinson, "Dialing Habits of Telephone Customers," *Bell Syst. Tech. J.* **31** (January 1952), pp. 32-67.

275. M. B. Wilk and R. Gnanadesikan, "Graphical Analysis of Multi-Response Experimental Data Using Ordered Distances," *Proc. Nat. Acad. Sci.* **47** (August 1961), pp. 1209-1212; F. J. Anscombe and J. W. Tukey, "The Examination and Analysis of Residuals," *Technometrics* **5** (May 1963), pp. 141-160; M. B. Wilk and R. Gnanadesikan, "Graphical Methods for Internal Comparisons in Multiresponse Experiments," *Ann. Math. Statist.* **35** (June 1964), pp. 613-631; D. F. Andrews, "Plots of High-Dimensional Data," *Biometrics* **28** (March 1972), pp. 125-136; W. A. Larsen and S. J. McCleary, "The Use of Partial Residual Plots in Regression Analysis," *Technometrics* **14** (August 1972), pp. 781-790; C. L. Mallows, "Some Comments on Cp," *Technometrics* **15** (November 1973), pp. 661-675; J. W. Tukey, *Exploratory Data Analysis* (Reading, Massachusetts: Addison-Wesley, 1977).

276. I. B. Crandall and D. MacKenzie, "Analysis of the Energy Distribution in Speech," *Bell Syst. Tech. J.* **1** (July 1922), pp. 116-128.

277. W. Koenig, H. K. Dunn, and L. Y. Lacy, "The Sound Spectrograph," *J. Acoust. Soc. Am.* **18** (July 1946), pp. 19-49.

278. W. R. Bennett, "The Correlatograph: A Machine for Continuous Display of Short-Term Correlation," *Bell Syst. Tech. J.* **32** (September 1953), pp. 1173-1185.

279. M. S. Bartlett, "Periodogram Analysis and Continuous Spectrum," *Biometrika* **37** (June 1950), pp. 1-16; J. W. Tukey, "The Sampling Theory of Power Spectral Estimates," *Symp. Appl. Autocorrelation Analysis Phys. Problems, Office Naval Research* NAVEXOS-P-735, Woods Hole (June 13, 1949); R. B. Blackman and J. W. Tukey, "The Measurement of Power Spectra from the Point of View of Communications Engineering—Part I," *Bell Syst. Tech. J.* **37** (January 1958), pp. 185-282; R. B. Blackman and J. W. Tukey, "The Measurement of Power Spectra from the Point of View of Communications Engineering—Part II," *Bell Syst. Tech. J.* **37** (March 1958), pp. 485-569; B. P. Bogert, M. J. Healey, and J. W. Tukey, "The Frequency Analysis of Time Series for Echoes: Cepstrum, Pseudo-Autocovariance, Cross-Cepstrum and Saphe-Cracking," in *Time Series Analysis,* ed. M. Rosenblatt (New York: John Wiley, 1963), pp. 201-243.

280. W. S. Cleveland, D. M. Dunn, and I. J. Terpenning, "SABL: A Resistant Seasonal Adjustment Procedure with Graphical Methods for Interpretation and Diagnosis," *Proc. Conf. Seasonal Analysis Econ. Time Series,* Washington, D.C. (September 9-10, 1976), pp. 201-231.

281. W. S. Cleveland and S. J. Devlin, "Calendar Effects in Monthly Time Series: Detection by Spectrum Analysis and Graphical Methods," *J. Amer. Statist. Assoc.* **75** (September 1980), pp. 487-496.

282. B. Kleiner, R. D. Martin, and D. J. Thomson, "Robust Estimation of Power Spectra," *J. Roy. Statist. Soc.,* Series B, **41** (1979), pp. 313-351.

283. J. W. Cooley and J. W. Tukey, "An Algorithm for the Machine Calculation of Complex Fourier Series," *Math. Comput.* **19** (April 1965), pp. 297-301; W. M. Gentleman and G. Sande, "Fast Fourier Transforms—for Fun and Profit," *Proc. Amer. Federation Inform.*

Process. Soc. Fall Joint Comput. Conf., San Francisco **29** (November 7-10, 1966), pp. 563-578; See also special issues of *IEEE Trans. Audio Electroacoust.* **AU-15** (June 1967), and **AU-17** (June 1969).

284. J. D. Gabbe, M. B. Wilk, and W. L. Brown, "Statistical Analysis and Modeling of the High-Energy Proton Data from the *Telstar*® I Satellite," *Bell Syst. Tech. J.* **46** (September 1967), pp. 1301-1450.

285. R. A. Becker and J. M. Chambers, *S: A Language and System for Data Analysis* (Bell Laboratories, 1981).

286. W. A. Gale and D. Pregibon, "An Expert System for Regression Analysis," *Proc. 14th Ann. Symp. Comput. Sci. Statist. Interface,* Troy, New York (July 8, 1982), pp. 110-117.

287. T. C. Fry, "Mathematicians In Industry—The First 75 Years," *Science* **143** (February 28, 1964), pp. 934-938.

Chapter 2

Communication Acoustics

Sound is an effective means by which humans convey and assimilate information. Speech is a particularly useful form of sound, and the human vocal apparatus and auditory system are especially refined information processors. But sound in air is not suitable for communication at a distance. It must be converted into a more transportable form, such as an electrical signal. Communication acoustics deals with the generation, transduction, transmission, processing, and perception of sound information, primarily for human communication. It not only concerns fundamental phenomena in speech and hearing but embraces issues as varied as microphone and earphone design, conference telephone systems, human reaction to alerting signals (such as tone ringers), digital encoding and encryption of speech signals, echo cancellation in satellite circuits, computer synthesis of voice announcements, and machines actuated by human voices.

I. RESEARCH FROM 1925 THROUGH 1950

The period from 1925 through 1950 was an era in which advances in electronics opened new horizons for research and applications in acoustics. Electronic amplification and electrical filtering provided new tools for research in speech and hearing. Talking pictures and electrical recording came into being, supported by new electroacoustic advances in microphones, loudspeakers, and sound amplifiers. Overseas radiotelephone service began early in this period. Later on, flourishing research—built upon the new electronic capabilities—was, for a period, deflected into new directions by World War II, but afterward was quick to resume mainstream directions in telecommunications.

For acoustics research at Bell Laboratories, the period between 1925 and 1950 can best be identified with Harvey Fletcher. [Fig. 2-1] For more than two decades, until his retirement in 1949, Fletcher led and influenced major portions of the Bell Labs acoustics effort.

Principal author: J. L. Flanagan.

Fig. 2-1.   H. Fletcher, who pioneered in research
in hearing and psychoacoustics.

1.1 Fundamental Research in Speech and Hearing

From its beginning, research in speech and hearing emphasized the
need to quantify speech and acoustic signals, and human listeners' responses
to them, in ways that relate directly to the engineering design of voice
communications systems. The research approach was to determine the
physical dimensions of acoustic signals to which listeners are sensitive, to
analyze and characterize these dimensions in speech, and to develop design
criteria for transmission systems so that the perceptually important signal
dimensions would be transmitted faithfully.

The early work stressed hearing and psychoacoustics somewhat more
than it did speech. In Fletcher's book, *Speech and Hearing,* first published
in 1929, approximately one-third is devoted to the physical characteristics
and analysis of speech, music, and noise, and the remaining two-thirds
to hearing and perception.[1] Early hearing research concentrated on such
concerns as the ear's sensitivity to sound intensity, periodicity, spectral
distribution, subjective loudness, and the effects of the presence of competing noise sources. Speech research focused largely on measurements
of the acoustic power of speech signals, sound pressure distributions around
a talker's head, and the spectral characteristics of speech sounds.

1.1.1 Sensitivity of the Ear to Sound Intensity, Frequency, and Spectral Distribution

One of the earlier perceptual studies was by R. R. Riesz who, in the mid-1920s, determined the sensitivity of the ear to changes in the intensity of sounds, specifically sinusoidal tones.[2] Riesz's results showed that, at normal listening levels and in close comparisons, the ear can detect intensity changes of the order of 0.5 decibel (dB). Closely related to this differential-intensity sensitivity is the human ear's absolute threshold of detectability. In 1933, L. J. Sivian and S. D. White, making use of carefully calibrated transducers, measured the monaural minimum audible sound pressure as a function of tone frequency and the minimum audible free-field sound pressure for binaural listening.[3] Their results established norms for many audiometric studies. [Fig. 2-2]

The frequency discrimination of the ear was also an early concern. Research by E. G. Shower and R. Biddulph in 1931 quantified the ear's remarkable ability to detect changes in tone frequency, changes that under favorable conditions can be as acute as about 1 hertz (Hz) in 1000 Hz or 0.1 percent.[4] Many subsequent psychoacoustic studies on the perception of pitch and timbre were stimulated by Shower's and Biddulph's results, and their data later provided design criteria for frequency stability in carrier telephony and sound recording.

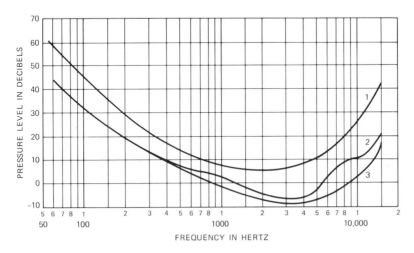

Fig. 2-2. Minimum audible sound levels in decibels: (1) monaural minimum audible pressure; (2) binaural minimum audible field, 0-degree azimuth; (3) binaural minimum audible field, random horizontal incidence. [Sivian and White, *J. Acoust. Soc. Am.* **4** (1933): 313.]

1.1.2 *Subjective Loudness—The Fletcher-Munson Curves*

It was noted very early that two tones of the same sound pressure but of different frequencies did not necessarily have the same perceived loudness. Fletcher and W. A. Munson [Fig. 2-3] measured this effect with human listeners and determined contours of equal subjective loudness for various magnitudes of loudness level.[5] Their data, known as the Fletcher-Munson curves, formed the basis for frequency equalization and tone control in modern high-fidelity sound systems.

Fletcher and Munson continued their research to derive a link between subjective and objective loudness levels. They derived the relation between the objective loudness level (measured in phons) and the subjective loudness (given in sones).[6] This loudness relation has provided the foundation for predicting the total loudness of complex sounds by determining the loudness of individual components. [Fig. 2-4]

Fig. 2-3. W. A. Munson, who, along with H. Fletcher, measured subjective loudness of tones over the range of human hearing and later developed relationships that, from objective measurements of sound levels, allow the determination of subjective loudness.

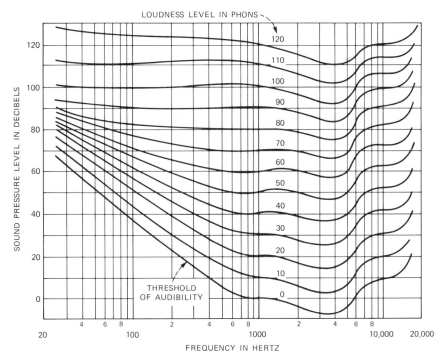

Fig. 2-4. Contours of equal subjective loudness as a function of loudness level in phons. At 1000 Hz, 0 dB corresponds to a pressure of 0.0002 dyne/cm². [Fletcher and Munson, *J. Acoust. Soc. Am.* **5** (1933): 91.]

1.1.3 *Application to Hearing Aids*

An integral part of research in hearing was the assessment and quantification of hearing loss. This research suggested telephone designs that could aid people with hearing problems and eventually led to the manufacture by Western Electric of an electronic, body-worn hearing aid. Fletcher wrote in his book, *Speech and Hearing,* about the design and widespread use of the Western Electric Model 2A pure-tone audiometer, an acoustic measuring device for determining hearing impairment. This and subsequent instruments enabled demographic data on hearing loss to be accumulated in the United States. Seizing upon an exceptional opportunity for gaining information, J. C. Steinberg, H. C. Montgomery, and M. B. Gardner designed apparatus and procedures to administer voluntary hearing tests to visitors to the Bell System exhibits at the New York and San Francisco World's Fairs in 1939.[7] Their results established base-line data for hearing assessment. [Fig. 2-5]

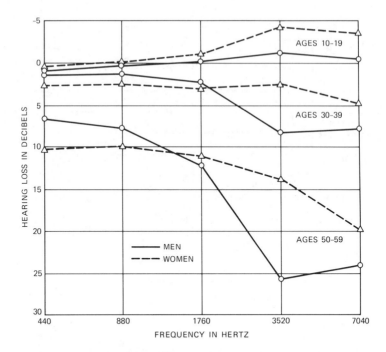

Fig. 2-5.   Hearing loss for various age groups, from data obtained at the New York and San Francisco World's Fairs, 1939.

1.1.4 *Spectral Characteristics of Speech Sounds*

One of the earliest speech studies concerned the amplitude spectrum of periodic vowel sounds. Using oscillographic displays of speech waveforms, W. Koenig in the late 1920s measured amplitude values and manually calculated the Fourier-series coefficients for the English vowel sounds. These and related studies revealed the importance of vocal-tract resonances, or formants, as information-bearing elements in speech. An exhaustive study of the formant structure of speech, however, awaited the development of the sound spectrograph some 20 years later and the intensive phonetics research of G. E. Peterson and H. L. Barney.[8]

In another early study, H. K. Dunn and D. W. Farnsworth measured the sound pressure distribution around a talker's head to determine the directivity characteristics that would influence telephone transmitter designs.[9] [Fig. 2-6] Subsequently, Dunn and White quantified the spectral characteristics of conversational speech and established, in probabilistic terms, the dynamic intensity range that any voice-transmission system must accommodate.[10] These data formed the basis for the characteristics of the volume unit (VU) meter, used for control of signal level in recording and broadcasting.

Fig. 2-6. H. K. Dunn conducting acoustic measurement of the sound field around a talker's head. [Dunn and Farnsworth, *J. Acoust. Soc. Am.* **10** (1939): 186.]

1.2 Speech Analysis and Synthesis

In the mid-1930s, work on speech and hearing was expanded to include analysis/synthesis techniques for speech transmission. Initial efforts, guided by H. Dudley [Fig. 2-7] and E. Peterson, culminated in the development of a speech analyzer, called "vocoder," and an electrical speech synthesizer, named "voder," and led to the concepts of formant coding for speech transmission over reduced bandwidths.

1.2.1 The Vocoder

In conceiving the vocoder, Dudley recognized the "carrier nature of speech."[11] He observed that the speech signal is formed by modulating (with the slowly changing vocal resonances) the spectral shape of the

Fig. 2-7.   H. Dudley, in research aimed at analyzing speech to reduce transmission bandwidth, conceived the vocoder, which took advantage of the fact that vocal resonances modulate human voice sounds. The reduced-bandwidth signal was then reconstituted in a type of talking machine called the voder.

sound produced by vocal sources. The vocal sound sources may be periodic, as produced by vocal-cord vibration, or aperiodic, as produced by turbulent airflow at a constriction.

The modulations in shape of the speech spectrum could, therefore, be measured in terms of the relative energy in contiguous filter bands, and the periodic (voiced) or aperiodic (unvoiced) sources could be characterized by a "pitch" detector (a frequency meter). The signal could be reconstituted (synthesized) from these data by allowing the spectral energy signals to amplitude modulate the respective outputs of an identical filter bank, which was excited by either a periodic pulse source or a noise source. Because the spectrum and excitation signals vary relatively slowly with time (and hence occupy little bandwidth), the vocoder could be used as a bandwidth reduction device for speech transmission. In fact, it could achieve speech transmission over about 300-Hz total bandwidth, a 10-fold reduction in the conventional voice-channel bandwidth. [Fig. 2-8]

While one of the original reasons for vocoder research was the hope

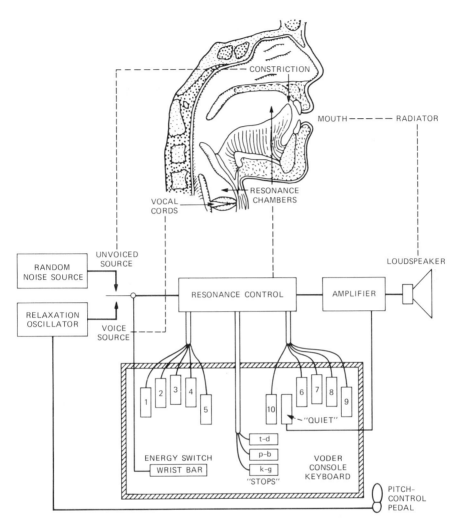

Fig. 2-8.   The vocoder speech synthesizer. [Dudley, Riesz, and Watkins, *J. Franklin Inst.* **227** (1939): 748.]

of transmitting speech over early transatlantic telegraph cables, which were severely limited in bandwidth, the actual applications came in voice encryption for transmission privacy. It served defense communications in this capacity during World War II, and later it was used in more refined digital forms.

1.2.2 The Voder

The synthesizer component of the vocoder was essentially a talking machine driven by the narrow bandwidth spectrum and excitation signals.

These signals need not be derived directly from analysis of human speech, as Dudley, Riesz, and S. A. A. Watkins showed.[12] They produced the voder, an electrical synthesizer of speech that was operated by a human from a keyboard. A trained operator could make it speak reasonably intelligible utterances. The device's ability to amaze and amuse, while demonstrating new scientific principles and understanding, made it a natural choice for inclusion in the Bell System exhibits at the New York and San Francisco World's Fairs of 1939. [Fig. 2-9]

1.2.3 The Formant Vocoder

The remarkable achievements of the voder and vocoder sparked related interest in bandwidth-conserving methods of speech transmission. Munson

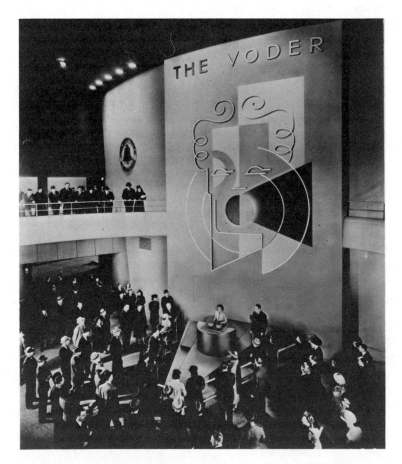

Fig. 2-9. Exhibit of the voder at the New York World's Fair, 1939.

and Montgomery were among the first to recognize in 1950 that the spectrum-defining signals of the channel vocoder are not linearly independent.[13] They proposed and implemented the first formant vocoder, a device to estimate the frequency and amplitude of the major spectral resonances, or formants, of the speech signal. From the formant data, all other values of the amplitude spectrum could be deduced. Their work was soon combined with first efforts, carried on by E. Peterson, to devise an automatic means for solving the difficult problem of formant extraction from connected speech.[14]

1.3 Acoustics in Military and Defense Problems

With the beginning of World War II and the subsequent involvement of the United States, many of the scientists who were doing speech, hearing, and transmission research were called upon to contribute their acoustics expertise to military and defense problems. Only parts of this story will be covered here; for a more complete account see Chapters 4 and 8 of an earlier volume in this series subtitled *National Service in War and Peace (1925-1975)*.

People under Fletcher were given several acoustics projects. The largest and perhaps the most urgent was the development of an acoustic homing torpedo for defense against submerged submarines. The torpedo, designated Mine Mark 24, was to be dropped by aircraft and to have vertical and horizontal control.[15] The prototype model was completed in less than 11 months and was successfully demonstrated in Long Island Sound off New London, Connecticut. Guidance for depth and azimuth was achieved through an array of four hydrophones set 90 degrees apart around the body of the torpedo. Sound shadowing at high frequencies provided the differential signals needed by the servo motors to operate the directional fins and home on the source of sound.

Another project was the design and fabrication of an air-raid siren of sufficient power and range to alert metropolitan areas. The work resulted in a 40-kilowatt acoustic siren, which was driven by an air compressor.[16] The siren produced sound pressure levels in the range of 90 dB over most of lower Manhattan. Subsequently the design was further improved, and the siren was manufactured by the Chrysler Corporation.

Other acoustics research during the war years produced a sound-locating set, designated GR-6, that was designed and implemented by Munson, F. K. Harvey, and S. Balashek (reported in an internal memorandum). The equipment utilized two arrays of three microphones each and a magnetic recorder for recording the arriving sound from a distant gunshot. When the equipment was properly sited, the measured differences in arrival times of the sound were used with a specially designed slide rule to compute the position of the firing gun. Sound Locating Set GR-6 was put into service and was reported to have been effective in locating active gun emplacements, especially mortars, at ranges up to several thousand yards.

Concomitantly, others considered speech transmission problems. The earlier work on the vocoder formed the basis for a speech-secrecy system, Project X (also known as the "Sigsaly" system), for encrypting the vocoder channel signals for transmission. The system depended upon a scrambling key that was recorded as 12 separate functions on a phonograph disc. A similar disc, run in synchronism at the receiver, allowed the encrypted channel signals to be recovered.

Researchers with expertise in radio transmission development were drawn to acoustic techniques to analyze intercepted radio information. Initial work on the sound spectrograph, later to be a valuable tool for speech analysis, was stimulated by the need for machine aids in identifying a given radio operator's "fist," or personal characteristics in manually transmitting Morse code with a key. Tracking the whereabouts of identified operators gave valuable information on the movements of field units.

With cessation of hostilities in 1945, all these researchers made the transition to peacetime activities and again took up their normal responsibilities in telecommunications research.

1.4 Phonetics Research

Substantial postwar interest centered on turning defense-catalyzed developments to purposes of civil telephony. Several of these interests related to phonetic analysis, speech perception, and speech production.

1.4.1 Articulation Index

Formal articulation testing was born in part by the need to characterize degradations in speech transmission from aircraft and tanks. Expanding and quantifying these techniques, N. French and Steinberg originated the concept of the Articulation Index.[17] This index, widely used in derived forms, predicted the intelligibility of a speech transmission system from its measured frequency response, dynamic range, and masking noise spectrum.

1.4.2 The Sound Spectrograph

The extensive wartime interest in sound spectrography resulted in a valuable peacetime tool—the sound spectrograph. This instrument, put into refined form by Koenig, Dunn, and L. Y. Lacy, became a staple in phonetics laboratories throughout the world.[18] It permitted detailed, graphic representation of short-time speech spectra in a form that revealed important temporal and spectral properties, such as stop articulation and formant frequency. [Fig. 2-10] G. E. Peterson and Barney, using the sound

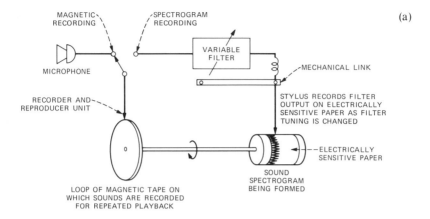

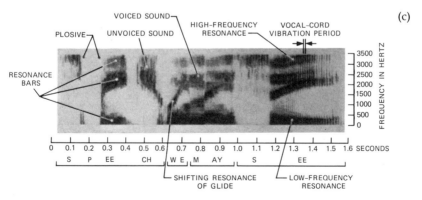

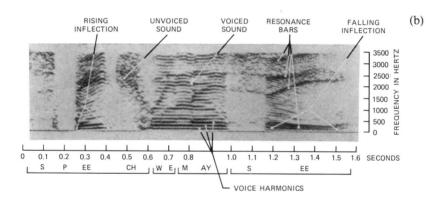

Fig. 2-10. First laboratory implementation of the sound spectrograph. (a) Its schematic diagram. [Dudley, *J. Audio Eng. Soc.* **3** (1955): 179.] (b) and (c) Examples of the output spectrograms for the words "speech we may see."

spectrograph, made comprehensive studies of the formant structure of vowel sounds.[19] Their analysis was so complete that the results became the definitive specification of formants for English vowel sounds. Their experimental design was later duplicated for several other languages.

1.4.3 Visible Speech

The real-time sound spectrograph—called the direct translator—was devised by Riesz and L. Schott.[20] This device provided visual displays of running speech and could be used as a speech perception aid by deaf persons. This instrument, together with its graphic cousins, allowed R. K. Potter, G. A. Kopp, and H. C. Green to conduct extensive studies on visually characterizing speech sounds. Their landmark book, *Visible Speech*,[21] became a classic reference on speech spectrography. In tests with an experimental class, Potter, Kopp, and Green found that visual assimilation of speech in real time was exceptionally difficult, but that humans could acquire word vocabularies with about the same facility as in learning a foreign language.

1.4.4 Vocal-Cord Behavior

Characterization of vocal-cord function was recognized to be fundamental to understanding speech production and synthesis. Farnsworth pioneered in direct observation of vocal-cord motion using high-speed motion pictures of cord displacement during phonation.[22] His films became classic references in phonetics courses.

R. L. Miller devised a unique method for studying the acoustic properties of the vocal-cord sound wave.[23] He designed an electronic system with variable filters that provided a frequency response inverse to the vocal-tract resonances, thereby removing the vocal-tract effects from the speech wave and placing the excitation source in evidence. These acoustic results could then be related to Farnsworth's data on vocal-cord motion.

1.5 Electrical Analog Models in Speech and Hearing

The concept of modeling one-dimensional acoustic wave motion by analog electrical transmission lines was conceived and used in two remarkable ways—one for simulation of acoustic properties of the vocal tract, and one for simulation of inner-ear behavior.

1.5.1 Transmission-Line Model of the Vocal Tract

In 1950, Dunn analyzed the acoustic properties of the vocal tract in terms of a one-dimensional, nonuniform transmission line.[24] He substantiated his theory by constructing an electrical transmission-line synthesizer, the control elements for which were direct analogs of articulatory parameters, such as mouth opening and tongue constriction. His theory and experiment established the quantitative basis for speech formants, and his work had notable impact on speech synthesis research over the next two decades, both domestically and internationally.

1.5.2 Transmission-Line Model of the Inner Ear

The immense value of transmission-line theory (as developed over many years in electrical engineering) in characterizing analogous behavior of acoustic systems was also utilized in 1950 by L. C. Peterson and B. P. Bogert.[25] They performed a one-dimensional wave analysis of the acoustic and mechanical behavior of the basilar membrane in the inner ear—the sensory mechanism that gives the ear its ability to function as a frequency analyzer. They developed a theory and confirmed it by constructing an artificial basilar membrane (an electrical transmission line) that gave quantitative understanding to physiological experiments conducted earlier by G. von Bekesy of Harvard University.

1.6 Studies of Sound Propagation: Diffraction, Absorption, and Acoustic Lenses

While the main thrust of communications acoustics in early Bell Labs research was voice communications, related issues of sound propagation frequently entered.

In 1946, F. M. Wiener developed new theory and performed confirming experiments on sound diffraction around the human head and on sound-pressure distribution in the ear canal.[26,27] In 1947, Sivian published fundamental measurements on sound absorption in gases.[28] Capitalizing on previous experience in microwave antennas for telephone communication, W. E. Kock and Harvey undertook, in 1948, studies on sound refraction by periodic structures and on the design of acoustic lenses.[29] In 1951, Kock and Harvey also devised a novel technique for visualizing the directivity patterns of acoustic horns and lenses.[30] They used a field-scanning microphone, the output of which modulated the illumination of a gas-discharge lamp co-located with the microphone. The lamp, in turn, exposed a photographic film. The spatial-intensity pattern of sound focused by a lens could therefore be recorded. Further, by electrically adding the source driving signal to the microphone output, phase cancellation and reinforcement could be obtained as the microphone moved in distance from the lens. The "stroboscopically" stopped wave fronts (of a freely propagating wave) could then be recorded on the film. [Fig. 2-11]

1.6.1 Quartz Crystal Oscillators and Filters

One of the most fundamental tasks of the Bell System as a common communications carrier was the combining and simultaneous transmission of a great many messages over a single long-distance channel, such as coaxial cable or microwave radio. Precise electrical filtration is required to combine the many individual speech signals into a single, wideband signal and to separate them after transmission.

The wave filters required for this task must have high stability and frequency selectivity. In the 1940s, W. P. Mason and his collaborators pioneered in the application of especially cut quartz crystals for this purpose.[31] Their designs contributed to the economical development of wideband carriers for high-capacity telephone systems.

These systems also required extremely stable, yet economical, oscillators. Mason introduced appropriately cut quartz crystals to achieve frequency stabilities of 1 part in 10^9 over long periods of time. This early work of Bell Laboratories led ultimately to the widespread use of quartz crystals in modern clocks and wristwatches and to the emergence of the quartz crystal industry.

1.6.2 Wave Filters with Distributed Elements

As early as 1927, Mason filed a patent for a wave filter using distributed rather than "lumped" elements.[32] In one such filter, sections of coaxial transmission lines were employed for the first time. Distributed-element filters have since been widely used in radio, television, and microwave transmission. Discrete versions of distributed-element filters have also played an increasing role in digital filtering for speech synthesis and acoustic signal processing.

1.7 Stereophonic Sound

Even the first research in binaural (two-ear) hearing showed the human's ability to locate the direction of sound sources. This ability and the more complex spatial percepts, such as apprehending the distributed nature of an orchestral source or appreciating the volumetric mixing (by reverberation) of complex sounds in an auditorium, depend critically upon the signals received at the two ears. Reproduction of some of these natural effects was the goal of stereophonic transmission.

In 1933, Fletcher and his colleagues joined with conductor Leopold Stokowski and the Philadelphia Orchestra to demonstrate live transmission

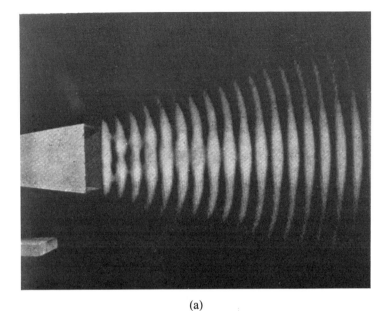

(a)

(b)

Fig. 2-11.   Wave crests in sound beams. (a) Sound beam from a 6-inch aperture horn loudspeaker, showing fairly flat wavefronts. (b) Introducing a diverging acoustic lens in front of the horn's aperture converts the straight wavefronts into spherical wavefronts.

of stereo sound from Philadelphia to Washington.[33] Also in the 1930s, this interest resulted in the design of recording techniques by A. C. Keller, who produced the precursors of high-fidelity stereo disc records that were later to become a thriving industry.[34]

II. RESEARCH SINCE 1950

The period after 1950 brought digital techniques to the fore. The evolution was influenced in part by the extensive new understanding of pulse circuitry developed for radar systems during the war years. (Bistable and free-running multivibrators, as designed for pulse-shaping and timing duties in a microwave radar, made good counters, shift registers, and clocks for digital processors.) Also, the reliability and low power consumption of transistors permitted circuit complexity and sophistication previously impossible, so that the logical operations of binary computation could be realized successfully. Joining with these emerging capabilities was new work in sampled-data theory, or ways to represent continuous signals by time-discrete, amplitude-quantized samples. This period, therefore, witnessed the rapid emergence of solid-state digital computers and the techniques for simulating and testing continuous physical systems by numerical methods.

Acoustics research was quick to capitalize on these new tools. A new idea could be rapidly tested by numerical simulation in a high-speed digital computer rather than through laborious design and construction of special laboratory hardware.* Hardware capability could be largely reserved for special computer facilities, for prototype constructions, and for electroacoustic systems. This mode of operation also meant that a wider variety of research issues could be attacked in a shorter span of time. Under the leadership of J. R. Pierce and E. E. David, Jr., who strongly fostered the use of computer tools, the acoustics research of this period ranged broadly over fundamental speech analysis and synthesis problems, low-bit-rate transmission of speech, information coding in the auditory system, perceptual evaluation of sound, electroacoustic transducer design, digital-filter design, adaptive echo-canceller implementation, and, to a lesser extent, room-acoustics studies.

---

* Actually it might be claimed that acoustics research pioneered in techniques for digital simulation. The development of digital filters stemmed largely from speech processing research and from digital techniques for speech synthesis. Refinements in spectral analysis (such as the Fast Fourier Transform) and fast convolution were prompted by digital simulation of speech communications systems.

Large-scale integration of solid-state circuits also became feasible, and speech technology eventually moved toward a stance where digital simulation and final electronic implementation are nearly the same, namely, a microprocessor chip.

2.1 Computers in Acoustics

One of the first issues in processing real-world signals by computer-simulated systems involved conversion of the signals from analog to digital representation and, afterward, back to analog (A/D and D/A conversion). An initial system for digital conversion and recording was designed and built by David, M. V. Mathews, and H. S. McDonald.[35,36] Almost at once the application of the computer to acoustic simulation and to speech analysis produced useful results. Mathews experimented with coding of speech waveforms by passing prescribed curves through selected sample points, such as the maxima and minima in the waveforms.[37] J. L. Flanagan calculated Fourier transforms for the acoustic volume velocity at the vocal cords to establish the spectral characteristics of the voiced sound source.[38] The computer similarly aided visual research on bandwidth reduction for picture transmission.

2.1.1 Block Diagram Compiler

The evolving computer technology required easy-to-use programming methods, and one of the first tools created was a software compiler system called BLODI (for Block Diagram Compiler), designed in 1961 by J. L. Kelly, Jr., C. Lochbaum, and V. A. Vyssotsky.[39] This program package allowed computer simulation of simple transmission systems using programming statements directly related to terms familiar to the engineer, namely a functional block diagram of the system.

Using this compiler, M. R. Schroeder and B. F. Logan demonstrated "colorless" artificial reverberation and stereophonic sound.[40,41] They also produced by simulation a 2:1 bandwidth-reduction system called the "harmonic compressor."[42] The system utilized 160 sharply tuned filters programmed in the simulation. Design details for the harmonic compressor, which could also accelerate speech signals by a factor of two, were made available to the American Foundation for the Blind, and a hardware system was implemented for the foundation's recorded-books program.

2.1.2 Digital Filtering

Sophisticated wave filtering was a basic need in establishing the techniques of digital simulation. The whole field of digital filtering emerged from this need. The first efforts in digital filtering were to devise digital equivalents for most of the well-known classical wave filters, such as the Butterworth, Bessel, and elliptic forms. These designs typically were specified in terms of poles or singularities of the sampled-data equivalent (z-transform) of the classical filter transmission function. Then the filter could be realized numerically by recursive calculations that produced the correct singularities. In 1964, J. F. Kaiser and R. M. Golden were leaders in establishing these techniques for classical designs.[43,44] In 1974, L. R. Rabiner developed a completely new area of digital filter design based upon transversal (finite impulse response) filters.[45]

With these and related advances, digital computers became the laboratory wherein speech research was conducted, at least up to the point where human auditory assessment was required. It rapidly became commonplace to simulate complete transmission processes or signal-analysis functions for research studies as varied as bandwidth conservation, pitch extraction, inner-ear mechanics, and sound transmission in rooms.

2.1.3 *Interactive Computation*

As the cost and size of computers declined with advances in their design, small computers could be dedicated to laboratory experiments for on-line interactive computation. In 1960, P. B. Denes[46] initiated this use of interactive laboratory computation with studies of inverse filtering to obtain the vocal-cord waveform, producing a digital implementation of Miller's 1959 study.[47] Applications of laboratory computation expanded rapidly as computer costs continued to decline and arithmetic capability increased. Dedicated computers became common fixtures in speech research laboratories in the late 1960s.

2.2 Systems for Speech Transmission

The earlier advances of the vocoder and the voder stimulated broad interest in efficient representation of speech signals. The earlier work suggested that sizable transmission economies (as much as a factor of ten) might be achieved by appropriate analysis and coding of the signal. The versatility of the digital computer and the possibility of using sampled-data theory to represent continuous systems made computer simulation an attractive means for rapidly implementing and testing new ideas for speech transmission.

2.2.1 *Computer Simulation in Vocoder Design*

A particularly difficult problem in vocoder implementation was obtaining accurate detection of voice pitch. This parameter was susceptible to interference by noise in the input speech and was often talker-dependent, being obtained more accurately for some talkers than for others. Around 1960, David, Schroeder, and Logan proposed the voice-excited vocoder as a solution to the problem of pitch extraction.[48]

In this system a low-pass band of the original speech was transmitted intact, along with the spectrum-defining signals of the conventional vocoder. This system was implemented for computer simulation, using the digital filter designs of Golden.[49,50] Its transmission performance was measured in listening tests and was shown to produce voice quality comparable to a conventional telephone channel while achieving a three-to-one saving in transmission bandwidth. The system was constructed in analog hardware by A. J. Prestigicomo and was tested on transatlantic cable circuits. This same voice-excited vocoder technique was later used by Schroeder and David to transmit a 10-KHz bandwidth, high-quality signal over a 3.5-KHz channel.[51]

Another effort to solve the pitch tracking problem utilized J. W. Tukey's concept of the "cepstrum" (the Fourier transform of the log-amplitude spectrum) to obtain accurate pitch measurement. The fundamental periodicity of voiced speech is manifested as a pronounced peak in the cepstrum. In 1964, A. M. Noll made computer simulations of a complete vocoder system to demonstrate the superior properties of pitch detection by cepstrum computation.[52]

Also around 1960, the concept of the formant vocoder, pioneered by Munson and Montgomery, was pursued by computer simulation. C. H. Coker, using a dedicated laboratory computer, implemented an automatic formant tracker and a hardware synthesizer that operated as a real-time transmission system.[53,54] Because formant data are more concise than channel vocoder signals, the system achieved a bandwidth reduction on the order of twenty to one. While maintaining intelligibility, this degree of reduction also reduced voice naturalness and speaker recognition, a typical occurrence in all systems of very low transmission rate.

In 1965, Flanagan invented and demonstrated the phase vocoder as a means for achieving moderate bandwidth conservation with good quality transmission. This device, like the voice-excited vocoder, obviated the pitch extraction problem. But, because it represented the signal in terms of both the short-time amplitude and phase-derivative spectra, it could also be used to change the time scale of the speech signal (make it either faster or slower) by arbitrary factors. This system was implemented by computer simulation using Golden's filter designs, and was demonstrated to provide analog band saving of the order of three to one.[55,56] Later, full digital implementations were made, and transmission was demonstrated for digital bit rates in the range of 7.2 to 16 kilobits per second (kb/sec).

The quality achieved was comparable to delta modulation, which required approximately twice these transmission rates. Also later, the theory of the phase vocoder was expanded into a general form for parametric description of speech signals.

In 1967, B. S. Atal, Schroeder, and S. L. Hanauer conceived the method of linear prediction as an improvement for characterizing the amplitude spectrum of speech.[57,58] The strength of the linear prediction coefficient (LPC) method stemmed from its approximating, in a least-squares sense, the short-time speech spectrum envelope by an all-pole model of the signal. Coefficients for the model were updated periodically, typically at intervals of about 15 milliseconds (ms), and vocoders utilizing this spectral description gave improved performance over other pitch-tracking vocoders for transmission rates down to the 2.4-kb/sec range. For higher transmission rates, typically 9.6 kb/sec, linear prediction was used along with its residual prediction error signal to achieve voice transmission of exceptionally good quality. This method was termed adaptive predictive coding (APC). Both the LPC vocoder and the APC system were later adapted by the military for special communications applications.

Applications of the LPC characterization expanded into numerous uses related to low-bit-rate transmission of voice. The all-pole description proved valuable in later work on speech recognition and speaker identification. Also subsequently, the linear prediction method was applied by Atal to a vocoder method in which multiple pulses in successive time intervals were used to optimally describe the residual prediction error signal.[59] The method, termed multipulse LPC, was especially attractive for voice storage and announcement applications. Again, throughout these studies, simulation by computer was the tool by which designs were initially implemented and tested.

2.2.2 Echo Cancellation

In a telephone circuit, the final four-wire to two-wire junction (usually the subscriber loop) is difficult to balance in impedance level because the final link may have a variety of characteristics. A bridge transformer, a hybrid, typically is used for this junction, and because of the impedance imbalance some received signal leaks around the junction and is returned to the sender. If the circuit has significant delay, such as a synchronous satellite path, the returned signal is heard by the sender as a distinct echo. The echo, if not attenuated or eliminated, significantly interferes with two-way conversation.

Around 1965, Kelly and Logan conceived the idea of an adaptive transversal filter that, by correlation measurements on the received and returned signals, could cancel the signal that leaked around the offending hybrid.[60] They, and subsequently M. M. Sondhi, established by computer simulation the design and theoretical stability of such an "echo canceller."[61] Sondhi and A. J. Presti constructed a working hardware model of the canceller, which was passed on to the development organization.[62] [Fig. 2-12] Some time later, with the advance of microelectronics, this adaptive echo canceller was widely deployed in the telephone plant in the form of a single integrated circuit chip, designed by D. L. Duttweiler.[63]

2.2.3 Digital Waveform Coding of Speech

As digital transmission evolved in the telephone plant, pulse-code modulation (PCM) was the initial format used, transmitted typically at 56 to 64 kb/sec. But these rates were known to be higher than needed for voice information. Therefore, research studies were conducted to design simple, economical encoders that could improve transmission efficiency by factors of two to three.

In 1970, N. S. Jayant analyzed the properties of a delta modulator (DM) that could adaptively change its quantizing step-size to accommodate time-varying properties of the voice signal.[64] He demonstrated adaptive delta modulation (ADM) between 20 and 60 kb/sec, and his results directly influenced the design of experimental codecs (coder/decoder) used with the first digital subscriber loop systems. [Fig. 2-13]

In 1973, Flanagan suggested the concept of adaptively quantized differential PCM, or ADPCM. With P. Cummiskey and Jayant, he carried out computer simulations to demonstrate good performance at coding rates in the range of 24 to 32 kb/sec.[65] Jayant analytically derived stability criteria for the adaptive quantization, and Cummiskey constructed real-time hardware to demonstrate the codec in the laboratory. Subsequently, refined designs of ADPCM found application in voice storage and voice answer-back systems, as well as in digital voice terminals. [Fig. 2-14] The

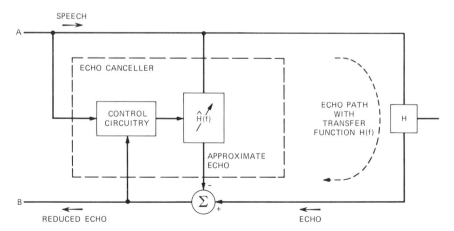

Fig. 2-12. Block diagram for the adaptive echo canceller.

Fig. 2-13. J. L. Flanagan conducted and led research in digital speech processing. He initiated work that resulted in adaptive differential pulse code modulation (ADPCM) and in systems for automatic speech and speaker recognition. He originated computer techniques for modeling the acoustics of human speech generation, providing a comprehensive basis for digital speech synthesis.

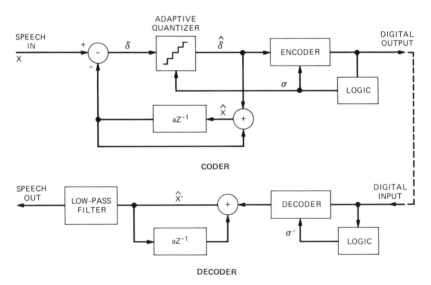

Fig. 2-14. Encoder and decoder for digital voice transmission by ADPCM. At the encoder, the step-size of the quantizer is automatically adjusted to reduce quantization error. The same step-size adjustment, determined from the transmitted digital signal, is also made at the decoder.

fundamental ADPCM concept, further refined by development to accommodate voice-band data signals, was later incorporated into specifications of the Comité Consultatif International Télégraphique et Téléphonique (CCITT) for a worldwide standard on 32-kb/sec transmission.

As a consequence of differing code formats that might be used in digital systems, attention was directed towards finding a means for converting directly (with digital logic) among differing code formats. D. J. Goodman and Flanagan conceived and demonstrated direct conversion among PCM, DM, and ADM.[66] Flanagan invented a technique for direct conversion between ADPCM and PCM, and this technique was applied to efficient voice storage in computer memories for voice-response purposes.

Another technique was conceived in 1976 by R. E. Crochiere, S. A. Webber, and Flanagan for achieving good transmission quality with moderate savings in digital rate. Called subband coding (SBC), this technique divided the signal spectrum into contiguous bands and adaptively quantized each independently.[67] Quantizing noise was therefore confined to a small spectral width instead of spreading over the whole spectrum. The SBC technique was applied to the transmission of telephone bandwidth voice at 24 kb/sec, and to the transmission of amplitude-modulated (AM) radio commentary grade signals (0- to 7-kilohertz bandwidth) at 56 kb/sec.

2.3 Speech Synthesis by Computer

The expanding capabilities of the digital computer also made it an attractive tool for studies in speech synthesis. One of the earliest efforts built upon the use of formant resonances as the synthesis medium. In 1960, Kelly and L. J. Gerstman implemented a complete formant synthesis system on the large central computer of the Bell Labs computer center.[68] Phonetic input sequences that could be specified on punched cards were transformed into smoothed control functions for three formant resonators and for pitch and voiced/unvoiced control (all implemented in the program). The transformation was based upon data measured from natural human speech. While the machine spoke with all the attributes of an automaton, it was able to cope with most input sentences that had been appropriately converted into a phonetic transcription. In 1967, an issue of the *Bell Laboratories Record* magazine included a demonstration disc recording on the system.[69]

Subsequently Kelly, with Lochbaum, modified the synthesizer component to a distributed transmission-line model, described in terms of reflection coefficients along the vocal-tract length, and demonstrated one of the first computer-synthesis systems using a vocal-tract model.[70] Kelly's reflection-coefficient characterization of the nonuniform vocal tract widely influenced other work of the time, and later contributed to the representation of LPC parameters as vocal-tract area ratios.

2.3.1 Synthesis from Printed Text

An ultimate ambition in speech synthesis is a machine that converts unrestricted printed English text into the spoken equivalent. Using a dedicated laboratory computer, Coker designed the initial form of such a system in 1968.[71,72] Coker's system included several components: a pronouncing dictionary (*Webster's Seventh Collegiate*) stored on disk file, programmed rules for English syntax, a dynamic model of articulation (to produce time-varying, vocal-tract area functions), and a hardware formant synthesizer external to the computer. The computer sent to the synthesizer the computed resonances, pitch, and voiced/unvoiced information to synthesize continuous speech. Albeit with automaton-like quality, the machine could speak virtually any English text composed from words contained in the dictionary. [Fig. 2-15] Follow-up improvements utilized linguistic rules for voice pitch and sound duration, established by N. Umeda, and a hardware digital-filter synthesizer to supplant the original analog model. This system was notable in that it was among the first to speak unrestricted printed text by calculating the synthetic signal from first principles, using no vestige of stored human speech.[73]

A subsequent alternative effort in text-to-voice conversion eliminated the need for a stored pronouncing dictionary and converted English graphemes into phonetic symbols by programmed rules. J. P. Olive produced a text-synthesis system that used a formant synthesizer whose control signals were obtained from a library of stored "dyad" elements—partial syllables that were analyzed from natural speech—and whose grapheme-to-phoneme conversion was performed by rules designed by M. D. McIlroy.[74,75] Pitch and excitation information were calculated using linguistic data produced by Olive and M. Y. Liberman.[76] The system was constructed compactly from a dedicated minicomputer and a digital synthesizer.

2.3.2 Vocal-Cord/Vocal-Tract Models for Speech Synthesis

The original vocoder model of the speech signal, promulgated by Dudley, did not permit acoustic interaction between sound source and resonator system. Limitations in voice quality were imposed by this characterization. Stimulated by the possibilities for representing more of the detailed physics of speech sound generation in a signal model, Flanagan, in 1968, formulated a computer model for the self-oscillating vocal cords and for the acoustically coupled vocal tract. He and L. Landgraf synthesized steady-state speech sounds using this physiologically detailed computer model.[77] They demonstrated natural, sustained vibration of the cord model, driven by Bernoulli pressures in the glottal orifice, and they produced physiologically realistic excitation of the programmed vocal tract.

K. Ishizaka and Flanagan expanded the effort in 1972 to a two-mass formulation for the cords and incorporated further physiological detail

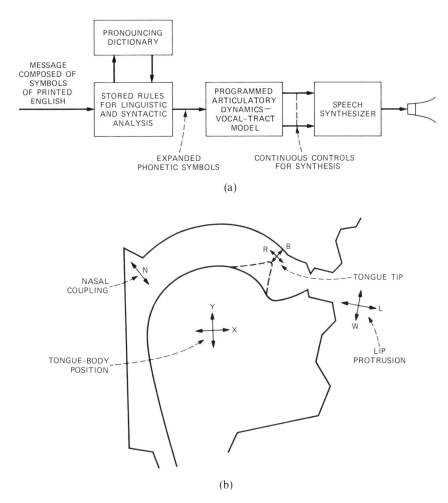

Fig. 2-15. Computer speech synthesis. (a) Computer system for speech synthesis directly from printed English text. (b) Representation of vocal-tract shape by articulatory parameters. [Flanagan, *J. Acoust. Soc. Am.* **51** (1972): 1385.]

into the tract model. Finally, with K. L. Shipley, they demonstrated in 1975 a complete speech-synthesis system based upon the interacting cord and tract models.[78] [Fig. 2-16] The system represented a first departure from the original source-system model of the vocoder, and pointed a new direction for achieving higher quality voice coding at very low bit rates.

2.4 Studies in Sound Generation, Propagation, and Reverberation

Digital simulation and computation also opened new vistas for acoustic studies related to communications. These included the areas of underwater sound, room acoustics, and musical acoustics.

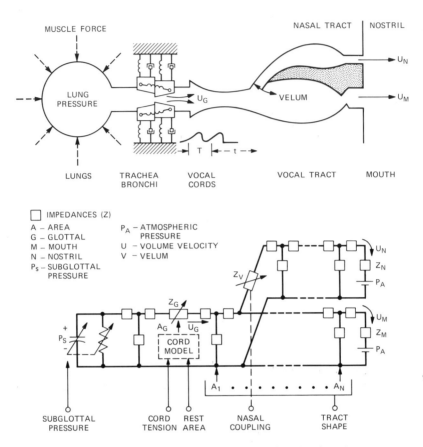

Fig. 2-16.   Speech synthesis based on a model of the vocal-cord and vocal-tract systems.

2.4.1 *Sound Propagation in the Ocean*

During a brief period in the mid-1960s, acoustics researchers were drawn back into work on underwater sound, primarily because of their expertise in digital processing and in the use of the computer for acoustic signal analysis. In one of these studies, Sondhi used geometric acoustics and computer graphics to produce motion pictures of soundwave propagation in the ocean. Ray propagation was determined by applying Snell's law of refraction to the undersea velocity profile, which typically exhibits a wave-guiding velocity minimum at a depth of about one mile. Schroeder characterized the "volume focusing" properties of matched filters to show that a volume selectivity of dimensions comparable to a wavelength could be obtained from multiple receivers. Using these results, Flanagan, Landgraf, and D. J. MacLean, Jr. programmed a large-scale digital computer to produce matched-filter processing of the output of underwater hydrophone arrays.

This technique gave the array a steerable volume selectivity and a sensitivity that surpassed the detection capabilities of conventional beam-forming arrays.[79] The computer techniques of these studies pointed the way to increased sophistication in digital processing of undersea signals.

2.4.2 Room Acoustics

The computer was also used in the study of room acoustics to model the reverberation characteristics of a given room or concert hall. The classic scale-modeling methods using light rays and ultrasonic waves were therefore supplanted. To a certain extent, the computer could model room reverberation using a program based upon geometric acoustics, calculate a room impulse response, and process real signals by controlling them digitally with this impulse response. This allowed the room or auditorium to be "listened in" before it was constructed. Similarly, the computer aided the acoustic measurement and analysis of existing rooms and halls.

One such analysis in 1966 confirmed the deficient low-frequency response in the original New York Philharmonic Hall—later rebuilt and renamed Avery Fisher Hall. Schroeder, G. M. Sessler, Atal, and J. E. West used computer-generated tone bursts to measure the acoustic behavior of the hall.[80] The recorded responses, also computer analyzed, revealed the locations where deficiencies were especially pronounced.

In related work Schroeder devised the integrated-impulse method for measuring reverberation time, a method that became a widely used standard for such measurement.[81] [Fig. 2-17] E. N. Gilbert devised a new method for solving integral equations and used it to calculate reverberation times that properly reveal the dependence upon room shape and absorber location.[82] J. B. Allen and D. A. Berkley, using the computer as the laboratory, made models of sound images in rooms and derived relations between frequency response and the so-called "critical distance"—the distance from a sound source where direct- and reverberant-sound energies become equal.[83] Their results established criteria for field installation of audio communications equipment, notably speakerphones and teleconferencing systems.

2.4.3 Acoustic Imaging

In other research around 1969, Sondhi devised inverse techniques for reconstructing the shapes of objects from the amplitude and phase values of the sound field that they scatter when illuminated by single-frequency or impulsive sound.[84] Schroeder and P. M. Mermelstein, and Sondhi and B. Gopinath derived methods for determining the shape of the human vocal tract from acoustic measurements at the mouth.[85] Such measurements were valuable for an understanding of the human articulatory process that

Fig. 2-17. M. R. Schroeder, who made fundamental contributions to communication acoustics, including the acoustics of concert halls and the analysis and synthesis of speech.

underlies speech-synthesis techniques. Because they used acoustic signals, these methods avoided the hazardous exposure that X-rays incur to gain the same data.

2.4.4 Synthesis of Musical Sounds

The production of musical sounds was studied through digital computation of sound waveforms. Mathews [Fig. 2-18], Pierce, and N. Guttman used a large-scale computer to synthesize new types of musical sounds and to produce recordings of complete pieces.[86,87] In 1970, Mathews and F. R. Moore produced a software system called GROOVE to compose, store, and edit synthesized music.[88] They, with J. C. Risset and J. Kohut, used the computer to simulate the sounds of conventional instruments, such as the violin and trumpet.[89] Mathews later designed a music synthesizer in which a dedicated minicomputer could control a variety of independent electronic tone generators; it was capable of great flexibility in generating complex musical sounds.

Fig. 2-18. M. V. Mathews, who pioneered in the use of computers to produce graphics output and subsequently to generate original musical sounds and compositions, with an electronic violin.

2.5 Signal Processing in the Auditory System

Digital signal processing was also applied as a laboratory tool in the analysis of inner-ear function. Using the physiological data of G. von Bekesy of Harvard University, Flanagan produced a computer model for calculating and displaying the motion of the basilar membrane in response to complex sound inputs.[90] Motion of the basilar membrane actuates electrical activity in the auditory nerve. The model, which characterized the transfer function to any place on the frequency-selective membrane, provided a physical correlate to perceptual observations about sound pitch. For example, the auditory cues for temporal envelope periodicity, as contrasted with those for fundamental frequency, could be identified in the computed displacements.

Using the graphic capability of the computer to produce successive photographic frames, R. C. Lummis generated 16-mm moving pictures of the mechanical traveling wave on the basilar membrane, as described by the computer model.[91] In related work, Flanagan, David, and B. J. Watson used the calculated basilar-membrane displacements to explain binaural perception and lateralization of pulsive sounds.[92]

Digital computation also supported new work on the transmission-line properties of the basilar membrane (see section 1.5 of this chapter). Berkley and M. B. Lesser formulated detailed hydrodynamic principles to reveal the interactions between acoustic waves in the inner-ear fluid and the mechanical motion of the membrane.[93] J. L. Hall and Schroeder created models for mechanical-to-neural transduction, and showed that their programmed nerve models exhibited excitatory and inhibitory behavior representative of mammalian physiology.[94]

Research was also conducted in three principal areas of auditory electrophysiology and neurophysiology: hair-cell function, evolution of the acoustico-lateralis system, and behavioral correlates of the neural code. W. A. van Bergeijk studied the evolution of vertebrate hearing.[95] Several fundamental findings were made on the many facets of hair-cell function. G. G. Harris, L. S. Frishkopf, and A. Flock measured the receptor potential in lateral-line hair cells for the first time.[96] Using cochlear microphonic measurements, Harris and van Bergeijk demonstrated that the lateral line is a displacement sensor, and Harris modeled the Brownian motion of stereocilia, thereby estimating the noise limit of this detector.[97,98] Additionally, Frishkopf, R. R. Capronica, and their colleagues demonstrated behavioral effects of differences in the neural code from one subspecies to another.[99,100] Later on, Allen, working in collaboration with the medical center of Columbia University, used a dedicated minicomputer and sophisticated signal-processing techniques to measure, on-line, neural tuning curves and phase responses for mammalian ears.[101]

2.6 Linguistic Studies

Continuing the earlier tradition of Potter, Kopp, Green, Peterson, and others, new studies in linguistics aimed to improve the understanding of speech articulation and perception. In particular, analysis of natural human speech led to descriptive rules for speech synthesis. In 1974, Umeda established programmed rules for the way voice pitch and phoneme duration vary in continuous speech for prescribed contexts.[102] These results were applied directly in Coker's articulatory text-to-speech system.

Olive studied the pitch structure for declarative sentences and produced rules for speech synthesis from fractional syllable elements called dyads.[103] In 1976, L. H. Nakatani carried out subjective listening experiments to demonstrate the perceptual adequacy of dyad synthesis.[104,105] Following the earlier basic notions of French and Steinberg, Nakatani also devised articulation tests that were improved in sensitivity by using carefully controlled masking signals.

The computer was used to analyze X-ray data for human articulation obtained from a microbeam X-ray system implemented earlier in Japan by O. Fujimura.[106] Somewhat later, Liberman, working with Olive, generated programmable rules for speech prosody, pitch, intensity, and duration that were utilized in the dyad text-to-speech system constructed by Olive and McIlroy.[107]

2.7 Research in Psychoacoustics and Perception

One area of work where the computer could not be the central arena was auditory perception. Here the human was the ultimate decision element. As in Fletcher's era, the thrust was to characterize human response and auditory acuity. These behavioral efforts profited from insights gained by computer modeling of auditory information processes.

Around 1960, David, Guttman, van Bergeijk, and Harris conducted a series of experiments on binaural perception, elucidating the trading relations between temporal and intensity parameters for binaural interaction.[108] They showed that, in a binaural presentation, the more intense signal is perceived as though it had occurred earlier. These cues were correlated with lateralization of the sound image toward the more intense side. They also related their behavioral measurements to electrophysiological measurements on laboratory preparations. Guttman studied the perceived pitch of complex stimuli, and explained this behavior with observations on inner-ear models.[109] L. D. Harmon, J. Levinson, and van Bergeijk programmed artificial neurons on the computer, and they showed that neural processes limit the temporal resolution of pulsive sounds.[110]

Somewhat later, Gardner and R. L. Hanson quantified the human's ability to externalize and localize sound sources in free space (as opposed to lateralization of sound images perceived inside the head for earphone listening). They demonstrated the human's limited ability to estimate range from sound intensity alone and the difficulty of localizing sound sources in the vertical plane.[111]

Many of the binaural studies related to stereophonic recording. Harvey, Schroeder, and E. H. Uecke measured the subjective effects of physical parameters in stereophonic broadcasting in collaboration with the National Stereophonic Radio Communications Commission to establish standards for frequency-modulated (FM) multiplex stereobroadcasting in the United States.[112,113] These standards were later adopted in other countries.

Around 1960, L. G. Kersta applied a visual perception technique to speech information.[114] He measured the ability of humans to identify talkers by visual interpretation of their sound spectrograms. High accuracies were reported for limited populations of talkers identified in closed sets. The work eventually moved into forensic applications and was subsequently conducted as a private enterprise.

Around 1970, Hall took up the study of auditory distortion products.[115,116] His perceptual measurements on human listeners supported the conjecture that for a two-tone complex of frequencies f_1 and f_2, the cubic distortion component $2f_1 - f_2$ is generated at the spatial location on the basilar membrane having greatest displacement response to the primary frequencies. The distortion component then propagates to, and is physically present in, the displacement at the place on the membrane maximally responsive to the $f_1 - f_2$ frequency. Hall incorporated nonlinearities into his computer model of the basilar membrane to account for this measured behavior. He later utilized these and other masking data to design perceptually favored noise shaping characteristics for digital voice encoders, especially the APC and LPC coders.[117]

Another valuable tool for designing and assessing the quality of digital transmission was a product of psychological research, namely, multidimensional scaling (see Chapter 11, section III in this volume). Pioneered by R. N. Shepard, and refined by J. D. Carroll and B. J. McDermott, the strength of the method was that it could reveal perceptual dimensions used by a human listener in assessing transmission quality. The physical parameters of a signal could therefore be related to the subjective percept. McDermott used this link to optimize the design of voice encoders to provide the best quality for a given transmission rate.[118,119]

2.8 Electroacoustic Systems and Transducers

2.8.1 Electret Microphone

About 1960, new work on acoustic transducers was initiated by Sessler and West.[120,121] Building upon the older notion that some dielectrics can retain electrostatic polarization, they pioneered in the design of electret transducers. The electret, inexpensively composed of a pre-charged metalized dielectric film (such as Teflon*), could be used as a condenser microphone. It provided the high-quality, linear performance of a conventional air-capacitor microphone, but it required no high-voltage supply for bias.[122] Further, its seismic properties were exceedingly favorable for speakerphone use. The electret, over the course of years, found enormously broad use—not only in telephone equipment but in recording and acoustic measuring equipment throughout the world. [Fig. 2-19] Manufacture was initiated by Western Electric and by others, and production rapidly escalated into the hundreds of thousands per year.

---

* Trademark of E. I. duPont de Nemours & Co., Inc.

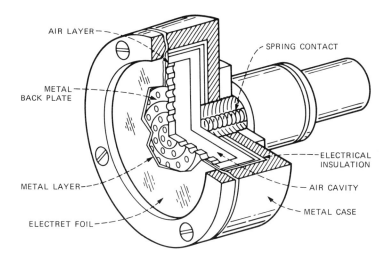

AIR LAYER

SPRING CONTACT

METAL BACK PLATE

ELECTRICAL INSULATION

METAL LAYER

AIR CAVITY

METAL CASE

ELECTRET FOIL

Fig. 2-19.   Construction of an electret microphone.

2.8.2 Frequency Shifter

Around the same time, Schroeder analyzed the mechanism of acoustic feedback in rooms and devised a method of frequency shifting to combat the electroacoustic "howling" frequently encountered in public address systems.[123] He successfully demonstrated the system at a public convention having an audience of 23,000 people.

2.8.3 Electronic Artificial Larynx

The advances with solid-state circuitry made possible a unique transducer application—the electronic artificial larynx. Barney, F. E. Haworth, and Dunn modified the U-type telephone receiver to produce high-intensity pulsive output.[124] They designed a transistor oscillator to produce periodic pulses such as those generated by the human vocal cords during voiced speech. When pressed against the throat and actuated by a pitch-controlling thumb switch, the artificial larynx could supply a source of sound similar to that of the normal vocal cords. The device was manufactured by Western Electric and put on the market as the Model 5 Electronic Artificial Larynx for use by individuals who have lost normal vocal-cord function. [Fig. 2-20]

2.8.4 Teleconferencing Systems

Electroacoustic systems for teleconferencing increased in importance as businesses sought more efficient ways to communicate among their sub-

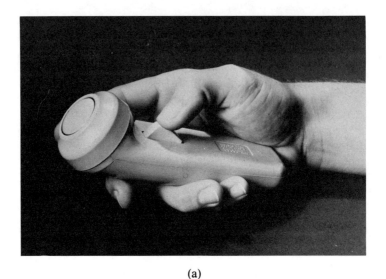

(a)

NASAL
CAVITY

TONGUE

—EPIGLOTTIS AND
LARYNX REMOVED
BY OPERATION

VIBRATING—
DIAPHRAGM

BATTERY—
SWITCH

BATTERIES—

—TRACHEA

ON-OFF AND
PITCH CONTROL KNOB

(b)

Fig. 2-20.   Electronic artificial larynx. (a) Western Electric Model 5 electronic
artificial larynx. (b) Use of the electronic artificial larynx. [For (b) only: Flanagan,
J. Acoust. Soc. Am. **51** (1972): 1380.]

sidiaries and customers. In early studies R. L. Wallace devised conference-room systems for stereo reproduction, having small loudspeakers placed in chair backs. Wallace also demonstrated that externalization of sound images could be obtained from stereo earphones that were carefully compensated for ear-canal response. Wallace went on to design a monophonic conference microphone, composed of a vertical line array of electret transducers and giving a doughnut-shaped directivity pattern suitable for conference participants seated around large tables. The system, put into manufacture by Western Electric, became part of the offering called QUORUM* teleconferencing equipment.

2.9 Human-Machine Communication

The period beginning around 1970 saw some new emphases emerge in voice communications. Research had accumulated substantial fundamental understanding in speech analysis and synthesis, mostly directed towards bandwidth conservation for transmission. Significant advances were made in digital techniques and microelectronics. Computers became faster, the cost of memory and processing power declined rapidly, and the algorithm complexity that could be supported in integrated circuits increased markedly. As computers and information management techniques evolved, it became apparent that ease of use for humans was a key factor in expanding the applications in communications. The ability to interact with machines by voice was one route to making computers friendlier for humans.

In 1970, Flanagan and colleagues in acoustics research began to focus overtly on human-machine communication.[125,126] Over the subsequent five years they concentrated especially on computer voice response, talker verification, and automatic speech recognition. They constructed and demonstrated computer systems that operated over conventional telephone connections for these three modes of interactive communication.

2.9.1 Computer Voice Response

Results from speech synthesis and digital coding work were employed to give the computer a voice. In 1972, Flanagan, Rabiner, and R. W. Schafer designed a computer system that could speak messages composed from a stored vocabulary of formant-coded words and phrases, digitized at less than 1000 bits per second.[127] In one application, the computer could accept and read printed wire lists, and then speak the instructions for wiring telephone equipment. [Fig. 2-21] For applications requiring higher voice quality, 24 kb/sec ADPCM (a product of parallel efforts in digital voice

---

* Registered service mark of AT&T.

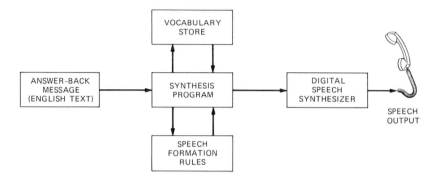

Fig. 2-21.   Computer voice-response system for synthesizing spoken instructions for the assembly of telephone equipment. [Flanagan, *Proc. IEEE* **64** (1976): 406.]

coding) was used to store the vocabulary and synthesize the messages. The system was applied experimentally for the manufacture of telephone switching equipment in two Western Electric plants (Oklahoma City, Oklahoma and Kearny, New Jersey) and for 1ESS* electronic switch mainframe wiring in the New Jersey Bell Company (Williamstown, New Jersey).

Later, the same system was adapted by L. H. Rosenthal and others to serve as an experimental directory-assistance system, using an algorithm devised by M. Lesk, who described it in an internal memorandum.[128,129] The system was employed for two years within Bell Laboratories to supplement the traditional information-operator service. It was based on a dedicated minicomputer, and it could serve multiple calling lines, simultaneously producing different output messages from a common vocabulary of several hundred words and phrases. Separate ADPCM hardware codecs served each access line. The system accepted names spelled by a caller on the Touch-Tone telephone dial, looked up (in its disk-stored telephone directory of 20,000 names of Bell Laboratories employees) the number and location of the desired party, and then spoke the information to the caller. A valued feature of the system was that its directory was updated each week, while the conventional printed directory was issued only twice a year. The design of this system later provided the model for the Western Electric Automatic Data Test Set (ADTS), used to speak instructions to installers in the field. It also served for several years as the voice-response component in research systems for talker verification and automatic speech recognition.

At the same time, it was recognized that the ultimate in computer voice response was a machine that could speak unrestricted contextual information, using its own calculated voice, independent of vocabularies pro-

---

* Trademark of AT&T Technologies, Inc.

duced by a human. The work on text-to-voice conversion (see section 2.3.1 of this chapter) was in part initiated to achieve such versatility.

2.9.2 Talker Verification

The expanding sophistication of computers suggested that by "listening" to a caller's voice and by making spectral measurement that characterized the individual the machine might be able to verify the claimed identity of the caller. The motivations for research on voice verification were several, not the least being the promise of electronic banking and the "checkless society." Credit purchases by telephone and credit charging of long-distance toll calls were also applications of interest, as was the automatic authentication of an individual who requested a read-out of privileged information from a voice-response system.

An initial experimental system that utilized measurements of voice pitch and intensity and an early form of dynamic programming for pattern registration were demonstrated in 1973 by G. R. Doddington, Lummis, and A. E. Rosenberg.[130] The system accomplished verification over conventional, dialed-up telephone connections with an accuracy greater than 90 percent, even under worst case conditions when all talkers used the same verification sentence. Sequential tests on different sentences could elevate the accuracy even further. In additional tests the system was shown to be relatively resistant to deception by skilled, professional voice mimics and to perform substantially better than human listeners in detecting imposters.

Later refinements to the talker verification philosophy, made by Rosenberg and M. R. Sambur, and by S. Furui (an exchange scientist from Nippon Telephone and Telegraph (NTT), Japan) were based upon linear prediction coefficient (LPC) and short-time cepstral characterization of the speech spectrum. Verification accuracies of 95 percent were demonstrated for conventional telephone connections and large populations of talkers.[131]

2.9.3 Automatic Speech Recognition

Early in the 1950s, the possibilities for automatic recognition of spoken commands were the focus of serious interest and work. Initial motivations included the prospect of automatically dialing telephone numbers simply by speaking them, and the prospect of very low-rate speech transmission using a vocoder that recognized specified patterns of speech spectra (a technique that later came to be identified with vector quantization).

In 1952, K. H. Davis, Biddulph, and Balashek constructed a system that accomplished automatic recognition of digits spoken singly.[132] When carefully set for a given individual's voice, it achieved high accuracy but could not function well for arbitrary talkers. It was implemented in analog vacuum-tube circuitry and occupied most of a 6-foot relay rack. About 1958, and in much the same manner, Dudley and Balashek produced and demonstrated a "pattern-matching" vocoder that could deal with a relatively small number of spectral patterns.[133] Both of these forward-looking ideas were ahead of the technology. The processor sophistication and storage of digital computers were needed to support the complexities necessary to achieve speaker independence and to store large numbers of spectral templates. Therefore, a hiatus of about a decade occurred in this work, mainly to let the technology catch up.

Around 1972, Flanagan and others initiated new work that brought Bell Labs back into this area of work. F. Itakura, coming as an exchange scientist from NTT in Japan, commenced work on a computer system to recognize a speaker-dependent vocabulary of 200 words. In the course of this work, Itakura devised a template distance metric based upon the log-likelihood ratio for linear-prediction residuals—a metric that became widely used in the field and subsequently carried his name.[134] [Fig. 2-22]

Sambur and Rabiner [Fig. 2-23] produced a system for speaker-independent recognition of spoken digits.[135] This system was based upon phonetic feature labeling of the input speech. Because vocabulary expansion proved difficult, it was discarded in favor of the more robust template matching approach. To achieve a high-performance, speaker-independent system, Rabiner and colleagues devised a spectral "clustering" procedure

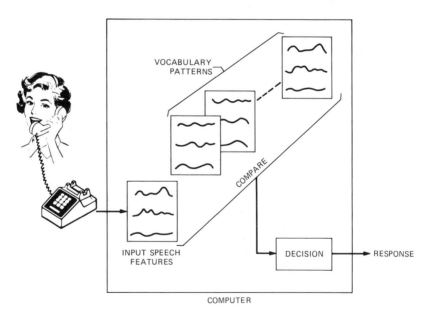

Fig. 2-22.   Components of the computer system for automatic recognition of spoken words and sentences. [Flanagan, *IEEE Trans. Bio-Med. Eng.* **BME-29** (1982): 228.]

Fig. 2-23.   L. R. Rabiner, who made fundamental contributions
to automatic speech recognition.

to produce multiple templates that spanned the articulatory space for a
wide range of talkers.[136] This system achieved speaker-independent digit
recognition with accuracy greater than 98 percent for dialed-up telephone
circuits.

Rosenberg, building upon the Itakura work, designed and implemented
a computer system to provide, in response to voice commands, flight information for domestic airlines.[137,138] This system had the official airlines
guide stored on disk file. After recognizing a caller's request, the system
would look up the information and speak it, using the ADPCM voice
response system described earlier (section 2.9.1 of this chapter).

Making further advances in the use of dynamic programming (dynamic
time warping) for comparison of recognition templates, Rabiner produced
a speaker-trained recognizer to perform automatic repertory dialing of
telephone numbers.[139] The user spoke the names of up to 20 frequently
called individuals into the memory of the dialer. A call could then be
placed automatically to any individual simply by speaking the person's
name. Rabiner also produced a speaker-independent digit recognizer capable of accepting telephone numbers uttered in a natural, connected
manner.[140] He demonstrated performance accuracies greater than 90 percent
for this connected speech system, again over conventional telephone
circuits.

Subsequent work on practicable recognition systems advanced further from the limitations of individual word vocabularies to a computer system that could accept whole sentences. S. E. Levinson programmed syntax and semantic analysis into a "conversational-mode" system that could, within the constraints of its topic area and information task, recognize input spoken sentences and generate voice-synthesized intelligent replies.[141] The system utilized a finite-state grammar on which to base its recognition of whole sentences and to synthesize its spoken replies. This application opened a new area of work in automatic speech recognition; namely, the theory and design of tractable recognition languages—languages that were sufficiently large subsets of natural English that humans could use to carry on meaningful conversational exchanges with a computer.

Computers and digital machines, from their inception, were designed to communicate in the cryptic symbols of program assemblers and compilers. This medium of exchange was never easy or convenient for humans, who prefer natural spoken language. The advent of automatic speech recognition (to give computers "ears" to listen to human-spoken instructions) and speech synthesis (to give computers a voice to generate spoken responses) represented a major step in making complex machines "user friendly."

REFERENCES

1. H. Fletcher, *Speech and Hearing* (New York: D. Van Nostrand Co., 1929).
2. R. R. Riesz, "Differential Intensity Sensitivity of the Ear for Pure Tones," *Phys. Rev.* **31** (May 1928), pp. 867-875.
3. L. J. Sivian and S. D. White, "On Minimum Audible Sound Fields," *J. Acoust. Soc. Am.* **4** (April 1933), pp. 288-321.
4. E. G. Shower and R. Biddulph, "Differential Pitch Sensitivity of the Ear," *J. Acoust. Soc. Am.* **3** (October 1931), pp. 275-287.
5. H. Fletcher and W. A. Munson, "Loudness, Its Definition, Measurement and Calculation," *J. Acoust. Soc. Am.* **5** (October 1933), pp. 82-108.
6. H. Fletcher and W. A. Munson, "Relation Between Loudness and Masking," *J. Acoust. Soc. Am.* **9** (July 1937), pp. 1-10.
7. J. C. Steinberg, H. C. Montgomery, and M. B. Gardner, "Results of the World's Fair Hearing Tests," *Bell Syst. Tech. J.* **19** (October 1940), pp. 533-562.
8. G. E. Peterson and H. L. Barney, "Control Methods Used in a Study of the Vowels," *J. Acoust. Soc. Am.* **24** (March 1952), pp. 175-184.
9. H. K. Dunn and D. W. Farnsworth, "Exploration of Pressure Field Around the Human Head During Speech," *J. Acoust. Soc. Am.* **10** (January 1939), pp. 184-199.
10. H. K. Dunn and S. D. White, "Statistical Measurements on Conversational Speech," *J. Acoust. Soc. Am.* **11** (January 1940), pp. 278-288.
11. H. Dudley, "Remaking Speech," *J. Acoust. Soc. Am.* **11** (October 1939), pp. 169-177; H. Dudley, "The Vocoder," *Bell Lab. Rec.* **18** (December 1939), pp. 122-126; H. Dudley, "The Vocoder—Electrical Re-Creation of Speech," *J. Soc. Motion Pict. Eng.* **34** (March 1940), pp. 272-278; H. Dudley, "The Carrier Nature of Speech," *Bell Syst. Tech. J.* **19** (October 1940), pp. 495-515.
12. H. Dudley, R. R. Riesz, and S. S. A. Watkins, "A Synthetic Speaker," *J. Franklin Inst.* **227** (June 1939), pp. 739-764.

13. W. A. Munson and H. C. Montgomery, "A Speech Analyzer and Synthesizer," *J. Acoust. Soc. Am.* **22**, Abstract (1950), p. 678.
14. E. Peterson, "Frequency Detection and Speech Formants," *J. Acoust. Soc. Am.* **23** (November 1951), pp. 668-674.
15. M. B. Gardner, "Mine Mark 24: World War II Acoustic Torpedo," *J. Audio Eng. Soc.* **22** (October 1974), pp. 614-626.
16. R. C. Jones, "A Fifty Horsepower Siren," *J. Acoust. Soc. Am.* **18** (October 1946), pp. 371-387.
17. N. R. French and J. C. Steinberg, "Factors Governing the Intelligibility of Speech Sounds," *J. Acoust. Soc. Am.* **19** (January 1947), pp. 90-119.
18. W. Koenig, H. K. Dunn, and L. Y. Lacy, "The Sound Spectrograph," *J. Acoust. Soc. Am.* **18** (July 1946), pp. 19-49.
19. See reference 8.
20. R. R. Riesz and L. Schott, "Visible Speech Cathode-Ray Translator," *J. Acoust. Soc. Am.* **18** (July 1946), pp. 50-61.
21. R. K. Potter, G. A. Kopp, and H. C. Green, *Visible Speech* (New York: D. Van Nostrand Co., 1947).
22. D. W. Farnsworth, "High-Speed Motion Pictures of the Human Vocal Cords," *Bell Lab. Rec.* **18** (March 1940), pp. 203-208.
23. R. L. Miller, "Nature of the Vocal Cord Wave," *J. Acoust. Soc. Am.* **31** (June 1959), pp. 667-679.
24. H. K. Dunn, "The Calculation of Vowel Resonances, and an Electrical Vocal Tract," *J. Acoust. Soc. Am.* **22** (November 1950), pp. 740-753.
25. L. C. Peterson and B. P. A. Bogert, "Dynamical Theory of the Cochlea," *J. Acoust. Soc. Am.* **22** (May 1950), pp. 369-381.
26. F. M. Wiener, "On the Diffraction of a Progressive Sound Wave by the Human Head," *J. Acoust. Soc. Am.* **19** (January 1947), pp. 143-146.
27. F. M. Wiener and D. A. Ross, "The Pressure Distribution in the Auditory Canal in a Progessive Sound Field," *J. Acoust. Soc. Am.* **18** (October 1946), pp. 401-408.
28. L. J. Sivian, "High Frequency Absorption in Air and Other Gases," *J. Acoust. Soc. Am.* **19** (September 1947), pp. 914-916.
29. W. E. Kock, "Metallic Delay Lenses," *Bell Syst. Tech. J.* **27** (January 1948), pp. 58-82.
30. W. E. Kock and F. K. Harvey, "A Photographic Method for Displaying Sound Wave and Microwave Space Patterns," *Bell Syst. Tech. J.* **30** (July 1951), pp. 564-587.
31. W. P. Mason, *Piezoelectric Crystals and their Application to Ultrasonics* (New York: D. Van Nostrand Co., 1950).
32. W. P. Mason, *Electromechanical Transducers and Wave Filters*, 2nd ed. (New York: D. Van Nostrand Co., 1948).
33. P. C. Mabon, *Mission Communications* (Murray Hill, New Jersey: Bell Telephone Laboratories, 1975).
34. A. C. Keller, "Direct Recording and Reproducing Materials for Disk Recording," *J. Soc. Motion Pict. Eng.* **28** (April 1937), pp. 411-426.
35. E. E. David, Jr., M. V. Mathews, and H. S. McDonald, "Description and Results of Experiments with Speech Using Digital Computer Simulation," *Proc. Natl. Elect. Conf.* (1958), pp. 766-775.
36. E. E. David, Jr., M. V. Mathews, and H. S. McDonald, "A High-Speed Data Translator for Computer Simulation of Speech and Television Devices," *IRE Western Joint Comp. Conf.* (1959), pp. 354-357.
37. M. V. Mathews, "Extremal Coding for Speech Transmission," *IRE Trans. Inform. Theory* **IT-5** (September 1959), pp. 129-136.
38. J. L. Flanagan, "Some Properties of the Glottal Sound Source," *J. Speech Hear. Res.* **1** (June 1958), pp. 99-116.
39. J. L. Kelly, Jr., C. Lochbaum, and V. A. Vyssotsky, "A Block Diagram Compiler," *Bell Syst. Tech. J.* **40** (May 1961), pp. 669-676.

40. M. R. Schroeder and B. F. Logan, " 'Colorless' Artificial Reverberation," *J. Audio Eng. Soc.* 9 (July 1961), pp. 192-197.

41. M. R. Schroeder and B. F. Logan, "Improved Quasi-Stereophony and 'Colorless' Artificial Reverberation," *J. Acoust. Soc. Amer.* 33 (August 1961), pp. 1061-1064.

42. M. R. Schroeder, "Vocoders: Analysis and Synthesis of Speech—A Review of 30 Years of Applied Speech Research," *Proc. IEEE* 54 (May 1966), pp. 720-734.

43. R. M. Golden and J. F. Kaiser, "Design of Wideband Sampled-Data Filters," *Bell Syst. Tech. J.* 43 (July 1964), pp. 1533-1546.

44. L. R. Rabiner, "The Design of Finite Impulse Response Digital Filters Using Linear Programming Techniques," *Bell Syst. Tech. J.* 51 (July/August 1972), pp. 1177-1198.

45. L. R. Rabiner and R. W. Shafer, "On the Behavior of Minimax FIR Digital Hilbert Transformers," *Bell Syst. Tech. J.* 53 (February 1974), pp. 363-390; L. R. Rabiner and R. W. Shafer, "On the Behavior of Minimax Relative Error FIR Digital Differentiators," *Bell Syst. Tech. J.* 53 (February 1974), pp. 333-361; L. R. Rabiner and R. W. Schafer, *Digital Processing of Speech Signals* (Englewood Cliffs, New Jersey: Prentice-Hall, 1978).

46. P. B. Denes, "The Use of Computers for Research in Phonetics," *Proc. 4th Int. Congr. Phonetic Sci.*, Helsinki (September 4-9, 1961), pp. 149-154; P. B. Denes, "On-Line Computing in Speech Research," paper presented at the *5th Int. Congr. Acoust.*, Liege, Belgium (September 14, 1965).

47. See reference 23.

48. E. E. David, M. R. Schroeder, B. F. Logan, and A. J. Prestigiacomo, "Voice-Excited Vocoders for Practical Speech Bandwidth Reduction," *IRE Trans. Inform. Theory* IT-8 (September 1962), pp. 101-105.

49. R. M. Golden, "Digital Computer Simulation of a Sampled-Data Voice-Excited Vocoder," *J. Acoust. Soc. Am.* 35 (September 1963), pp. 1358-1366.

50. R. M. Golden, "Digital Computer Simulation of Sampled-Data Communication Systems Using the Block Diagram Compiler: BLODIB," *Bell Syst. Tech. J.* 45 (March 1966), pp. 345-358.

51. M. R. Schroeder and E. E. David, Jr., "A Vocoder for Transmitting 10 kc/s Speech over a 3.5 kc/s Channel," *Acoustica* 10 (1960), pp. 35-43.

52. A. M. Noll, "Short-Time Spectrum and 'Cepstrum' Techniques for Vocal-Pitch Detection," *J. Acoust. Soc. Am.* 36 (February 1964), pp. 296-302.

53. C. H. Coker, "Computer-Simulated Analyzer for a Formant Vocoder," *J. Acoust. Soc. Am.* 35, Abstract (July 1963), p. 1911.

54. C. H. Coker, "Real-Time Formant Vocoder, Using a Filter Bank, a General-Purpose Digital Computer, and an Analog Synthesizer," *J. Acoust. Soc. Am.* 38, Abstract (November 1965), p. 940.

55. J. L. Flanagan, *Speech Analysis, Synthesis and Perception*, 2nd ed. (New York: Springer-Verlag, 1972).

56. J. L. Flanagan and R. M. Golden, "Phase Vocoder," *Bell Syst. Tech. J.* 45 (November 1966), pp. 1493-1509.

57. B. S. Atal and M. R. Schroeder, "Adaptive Predictive Coding of Speech Signals," *Bell Syst. Tech. J.* 49 (October 1970), pp. 1973-1986.

58. B. S. Atal and S. L. Hanauer, "Speech Analysis and Synthesis by Linear Prediction of the Speech Wave," *J. Acoust. Soc. Am.* 50 (August 1971), pp. 637-655.

59. B. S. Atal and J. R. Remde, "A New Model of LPC Excitation for Producing Natural-Sounding Speech at Low Bit Rates," *Proc. ICASSP*, Paris, France (May 3-5, 1982), pp. 614-617.

60. J. L. Kelly and B. F. Logan, U.S. Patent No. 3,500,000; filed October 31, 1966; issued March 10, 1970.

61. M. M. Sondhi, "An Adaptive Echo Canceller," *Bell Syst. Tech. J.* 46 (March 1967), pp. 497-511.

62. M. M. Sondhi and A. J. Presti, "A Self-Adaptive Echo Canceller," *Bell Syst. Tech. J.* 45 (December 1966), pp. 1851-1854.

63. D. L. Duttweiler and Y. S. Chen, "A Single Chip VLSI Echo Canceler," *Bell Syst. Tech. J.* **59** (February 1980), pp. 149-160.

64. N. S. Jayant, "Adaptive Delta Modulation with a One-Bit Memory," *Bell Syst. Tech. J.* **49** (March 1970), pp. 321-342; N. S. Jayant, "Characteristics of a Delta Modulator," *Proc. IEEE* **59** (March 1971), pp. 428-429; N. S. Jayant, "Adaptive Quantization with a One-Word Memory," *Bell Syst. Tech. J.* **52** (September 1973), pp. 1119-1144.

65. P. Cummiskey, N. S. Jayant, and J. L. Flanagan, "Adaptive Quantization in Differential PCM Coding of Speech," *Bell Syst. Tech. J.* **52** (September 1973), pp. 1105-1118.

66. D. J. Goodman, "The Application of Delta Modulation to Analog-to-PCM Encoding," *Bell Syst. Tech. J.* **48** (February 1969), pp. 321-343; D. J. Goodman and J. L. Flanagan, "Direct Digital Conversion Between Linear and Adaptive Delta Modulation Formats," *Proc. IEEE Int. Commun. Conf.*, Montreal, Canada (June 14, 1971); D. J. Goodman and L. J. Greenstein, "Quantizing Noise of $\Delta M/PCM$ Encoders," *Bell Syst. Tech. J.* **52** (February 1973), pp. 183-204.

67. R. E. Crochiere, S. A. Webber, and J. L. Flanagan, "Digital Coding of Speech in Sub-Bands," *Bell Syst. Tech. J.* **55** (October 1976), pp. 1069-1085.

68. J. L. Kelly, Jr. and L. J. Gerstman, "An Artificial Talker Driven from a Phonetic Input," *J. Acoust. Soc. Am.* **33**, Abstract (June 1961), p. 835.

69. "Digital Computer Synthesizes Human Speech," *Bell Lab. Rec.* **40** (June 1962), p. 216.

70. J. L. Kelly, Jr. and C. Lochbaum, "Speech Synthesis," *Proc. Stockholm Speech Commun. Seminar* **2**, Stockholm, Sweden (August 29-September 1, 1962), Item F7.

71. C. H. Coker, "Speech Synthesis with a Parametric Articulatory Model," in *Speech Synthesis*, ed. J. L. Flanagan and L. R. Rabiner (Stroudsburg, Pennsylvania: Dowden, Hutchinson, and Ross, 1973), pp. 135-139.

72. C. H. Coker and N. Umeda, "Text-to-Speech Conversion," *IEEE Int. Conv. Digest*, New York (March 23-26, 1970), pp. 216-217.

73. C. H. Coker, N. Umeda, and C. P. Browman, "Automatic Synthesis from Ordinary English Text," *IEEE Trans. Audio Electroacoust.* **AU-21** (June 1973), pp. 293-298.

74. J. P. Olive and N. Spickenagel, "Speech Resynthesis from Phoneme-Related Parameters," *J. Acoust. Soc. Am.* **59** (April 1976), pp. 993-996.

75. M. D. McIlroy, "Synthetic English Speech by Rule," *Comput. Sci. Tech. Rep.* **14** (March 1974).

76. J. P. Olive, "Fundamental Frequency Rules for the Synthesis of Simple Declarative English Sentences," *J. Acoust. Soc. Am.* **57** (February 1975), pp. 476-482.

77. J. L. Flanagan and L. Landgraf, "Self-Oscillating Source for Vocal-Tract Synthesizers," *IEEE Trans. Audio Electroacoust.* **AU-16** (March 1968), pp. 57-64.

78. J. L. Flanagan, K. Ishizaka, and K. Shipley, "Synthesis of Speech from a Dynamic Model of the Vocal Cords and Vocal Tract," *Bell Syst. Tech. J.* **54** (March 1975), pp. 485-506.

79. J. L. Flanagan, L. Landgraf, and D. J. MacLean, "Matched-Filter Processing of Hydrophone Arrays," *J. Acoust. Soc. Am.* **42**, Abstract (November 1967), p. 1165.

80. M. R. Schroeder, B. S. Atal, G. M. Sessler, and J. E. West, "Acoustical Measurements in Philharmonic Hall (New York)," *J. Acoust. Soc. Am.* **40** (August 1966), pp. 434-440.

81. M. R. Schroeder, "Integrated-Impulse Method of Measuring Sound Decay Without Using Impulses," *J. Acoust. Soc. Am.* **66** (August 1979), pp. 497-500.

82. E. N. Gilbert, "An Iterative Calculation of Auditorium Reverberation," *J. Acoust. Soc. Am.* **69** (January 1981), pp. 178-184.

83. J. B. Allen and D. A. Berkley, "Image Method for Efficiently Simulating Small-Room Acoustics," *J. Acoust. Soc. Am.* **65** (April 1979), pp. 943-950.

84. M. M. Sondhi, "Reconstruction of Objects from their Sound-Diffraction Patterns," *J. Acoust. Soc. Am.* **46** (November 1969), pp. 1158-1164.

85. B. Gopinath and M. M. Sondhi, "Determination of the Shape of the Human Vocal Tract from Acoustical Measurements," *Bell Syst. Tech. J.* **49** (July/August 1970), pp. 1195-1214; M. M. Sondhi and B. Gopinath, "Determination of Vocal-Tract Shape from Impulse Response at the Lips," *J. Acoust. Soc. Am.* **49** (June 1971), pp. 1867-1873; M.

R. Schroeder, "Determination of the Geometry of the Human Vocal Tract by Acoustic Measurements," *J. Acoust. Soc. Am.* **41** (April 1967), pp. 1002-1010.

86. M. V. Mathews, J. R. Pierce, and N. Guttman, "Musical Sounds from Digital Computers," *Gravesaner Blatter* **VI**, No. 23/24 (1962), pp. 119-125.

87. M. V. Mathews, "The Digital Computer as a Musical Instrument," *Science* **142** (November 1, 1963), pp. 553-557.

88. M. V. Mathews and F. R. Moore, "GROOVE—A Program to Compose, Store, and Edit Functions of Time," *Commun. ACM* **13** (December 1970), pp. 715-721.

89. J. R. Pierce, M. V. Mathews, and J. C. Risset, "Further Experiments on the Use of the Computer in Connection with Music," *Gravesaner Blatter*, No. 27/28 (November 1965), pp. 92-97; M. V. Mathews and J. Kohut, "Electronic Simulation of Violin Resonances," *J. Acoust. Soc. Am.* **53** (June 1973), pp. 1620-1626; M. V. Mathews, F. R. Moore, and J. C. Risset, "Computers and Future Music," *Science* **183** (January 1974), pp. 263-268.

90. J. L. Flanagan, "Models for Approximating Basilar Membrane Displacement—Part II," *Bell Syst. Tech. J.* **41** (May 1962), pp. 959-1009.

91. R. C. Lummis, "The Secret Code of Hearing," *Bell Lab. Rec.* **46** (September 1968), pp. 261-266.

92. J. L. Flanagan, E. E. David, and B. J. Watson, "Binaural Lateralization of Cophasic and Antiphasic Clicks," *J. Acoust. Soc. Am.* **36** (November 1964), pp. 2184-2193.

93. M. B. Lesser and D. A. Berkley, "Fluid Mechanics of the Cochlea, Part 1," *J. Fluid Mech.* **51** (February 1972), pp. 497-512.

94. M. R. Schroeder and J. L. Hall, "A Model for Mechanical to Neural Transduction in the Auditory Receptor," *J. Acoust. Soc. Am.* **55** (May 1974), pp. 1055-1060.

95. W. A. van Bergeijk, "The Evolution of Vertebrate Hearing," in *Contributions to Sensory Physiology*, Vol. 2, ed. W. D. Neff (New York: Academic Press, 1966), pp. 1-49.

96. G. G. Harris, L. S. Frishkopf, and A. Flock, "Receptor Potentials from Hair Cells of the Lateral Line," *Science* **167** (January 2, 1970), pp. 76-79.

97. G. G. Harris and W. A. van Bergeijk, "Evidence that the Lateral-Line Organ Responds to Near-Field Displacements of Sound Sources in Water," *J. Acoust. Soc. Am.* **34** (December 1962), pp. 1831-1841.

98. G. G. Harris, "Brownian Motion in the Cochlear Partition," *J. Acoust. Soc. Am.* **44** (July 1968), pp. 176-186.

99. L. S. Frishkopf, R. R. Capranica, and M. H. Goldstein, Jr., "Neural Coding in the Bullfrog's Auditory System: A Teleological Approach," *Proc. IEEE* **56** (June 1968), pp. 969-980.

100. R. R. Capranica, L. S. Frishkopf, and E. Nevo, "Encoding of Geographic Dialects in the Auditory System of the Cricket Frog," *Science* **182** (December 21, 1973), pp. 1272-1275.

101. J. B. Allen, "Magnitude and Phase-Frequency Response to Single Tones in the Auditory Nerve," *J. Acoust. Soc. Am.* **73** (June 1983), pp. 2071-2092.

102. N. Umeda and C. H. Coker, "Allophonic Variation in American English," *J. Phonetics* **2** (January 1974), pp. 1-5.

103. See reference 76.

104. L. H. Nakatani, "On the Evaluation of Models for the Word-Frequency Effect," *Psychol. Rev.* **80** (May 1973), pp. 195-202.

105. L. H. Nakatani and J. A. Schaffer, "Hearing 'Words' Without Words: Speech Prosody and Word Perception," *J. Acoust. Soc. Am.* **60**, Supplement 1 (Fall 1976), p. S28.

106. O. Fujimura and S. Kiritani, "Computer Controlled X-ray Microbeam Method for Articulatory Observations," paper presented at the *8th Int. Congr. Phonetic Sci.*, Leeds, England (August 17-23, 1975); O. Fujimura, J. E. Miller, and S. Kiritani, "X-ray Observation of Movements of the Velum and the Tongue," *J. Acoust. Soc. Am.* **58**, Supplement 1 (Fall 1975), p. S40; O. Fujimura, S. Kiritani, K. Itoh, H. Fujisak, and M. Sawashima, "Observing Tongue Movement by Computer-Controlled X-ray Microbeam," in *Biomedical Computing*, ed. W. J. Perkins (Baltimore: University Park Press, 1977), pp. 156-160.

107. M. D. McIlroy, "Synthetic English Speech by Rule," *Comput. Sci. Tech. Rep.* 14 (March 1974); J. P. Olive, "Rule Synthesis of Speech from Dyadic Units," *Proc. ICASSP* (May 1977), pp. 568-571; J. P. Olive, "A Real-Time Phonetic Synthesizer," *J. Acoust. Soc. Am.* 69, Supplement 1 (Spring 1981), p. S83.

108. E. E. David, Jr., N. Guttman, and W. A. van Bergeijk, "On the Mechanism of Binaural Fusion," *J. Acoust. Soc. Am.* 30 (August 1958), pp. 801-802.

109. N. Guttman and J. L. Flanagan, "Pitch of High-Pass Filtered Pulse Trains," *J. Acoust. Soc. Am.* 36 (April 1964), pp. 757-765.

110. L. D. Harmon, J. Levinson, and W. A. van Bergeijk, "Studies with Artificial Neurons, Part IV: Binaural Temporal Resolution of Auditory Clicks," *J. Acoust. Soc. Am.* 35 (December 1963), pp. 1924-1931.

111. M. B. Gardner, "A Study of Talking Distance and Related Parameters in Hands-Free Telephony," *Bell Syst. Tech. J.* 39 (November 1960), pp. 1529-1551; M. B. Gardner, "Effect of Noise, System Gain, and Assigned Task on Talking Levels in Loudspeaker Communication," *J. Acoust. Soc. Am.* 40 (November 1966), pp. 955-965; M. B. Gardner, "Lateral Localization of 0° or Near 0°-Oriented Speech Signals in Anechoic Space," *J. Acoust. Soc. Am.* 44 (September 1968), pp. 797-802; M. B. Gardner, "Distance Estimation of 0° or Apparent 0°-Oriented Speech Signals in Anechoic Space," *J. Acoust. Soc. Am.* 45 (January 1969), pp. 47-53.

112. F. K. Harvey and M. R. Schroeder, "Subjective Evaluation of Factors Affecting 2-Channel Stereophony," *J. Audio Eng. Soc.* 9 (January 1962), pp. 8-12.

113. F. K. Harvey and E. H. Uecke, "Compatibility Problems in Two-Channel Stereophonic Recordings," *J. Audio Eng. Soc.* 10 (January 1961), pp. 19-28.

114. L. G. Kersta, "Voiceprint Identification," *Nature* 196 (December 29, 1962), pp. 1253-1257.

115. J. L. Hall, "Auditory Distortion Products $f_2 - f_1$ and $2f_1 - f_2$," *J. Acoust. Soc. Am.* 51 (June 1972), pp. 1863-1871.

116. J. L. Hall, "Monaural Phase Effect: Cancellation and Reinforcement of Distortion Products $f_2 - f_1$ and $2f_1 - f_2$," *J. Acoust. Soc. Am.* 51 (June 1972), pp. 1872-1881.

117. M. R. Schroeder, B. S. Atal, and J. L. Hall, "Optimizing Digital Speech Coders by Exploiting Masking Properties of the Human Ear," *J. Acoust. Soc. Am.* 66 (December 1979), pp. 1647-1652.

118. B. J. McDermott, "Multidimensional Analyses of Circuit Quality Judgments," *J. Acoust. Soc. Am.* 45 (March 1969), pp. 774-781.

119. B. J. McDermott, "Perceptual Mapping of Telephone Circuit Parameters," *Intelligibilite de la Parole*, Liege, Belgium (November 15, 1973).

120. G. M. Sessler and J. E. West, "Condenser Earphones with Solid Dielectric," *J. Audio Eng. Soc.* 10 (July 1962), pp. 212-215.

121. G. M. Sessler and J. E. West, "Condenser Earphones with Multiple Layers of Solid Dielectric," *J. Acoust. Soc. Am.* 34 (November 1962), pp. 1774-1779.

122. G. M. Sessler and J. E. West, "Self-Biased Condenser Microphone with High Capacitance," *J. Acoust. Soc. Am.* 34 (November 1962), pp. 1787-1788; G. M. Sessler, "Electrostatic Microphones with Electret Foil," *J. Acoust. Soc. Am.* 35 (September 1963), pp. 1354-1357; G. M. Sessler and J. E. West, "The Foil-Electret Microphone," *Bell Lab. Rec.* 47 (August 1969), pp. 244-248.

123. M. R. Schroeder, "Improvement of Feedback Stability of Public Address Systems by Frequency Shifting," *J. Audio Eng. Soc.* 10 (April 1962), pp. 108-109.

124. H. L. Barney, F. E. Haworth, and H. K. Dunn, "An Experimental Transitorized Artificial Larynx," *Bell Syst. Tech. J.* 38 (November 1959), pp. 1337-1356.

125. J. L. Flanagan, C. H. Coker, L. R. Rabiner, R. W. Schafer, and N. Umeda, "Synthetic Voices for Computers," *IEEE Spectrum* 7 (October 1970), pp. 22-45.

126. J. L. Flanagan, "Computers that Talk and Listen: Man-Machine Communication by Voice," *Proc. IEEE* 64 (April 1976), pp. 405-415.

127. J. L. Flanagan, L. R. Rabiner, R. W. Schafer, and J. Denman, "Wiring Telephone Apparatus from Computer-Generated Speech," *Bell Syst. Tech. J.* **51** (February 1972), pp. 391-397.

128. L. H. Rosenthal, L. R. Rabiner, R. W. Schafer, P. Cummiskey, and J. L. Flanagan, "A Multiline Computer Voice Response System Utilizing ADPCM Coded Speech," *IEEE Trans. Acoust., Speech, Sig. Process.* **ASSP-22** (October 1974), pp. 339-352.

129. L. H. Rosenthal, L. R. Rabiner, R. W. Schafer, P. Cummiskey, and J. L. Flanagan, "Automatic Voice Response: Interfacing Man with Machine," *IEEE Spectrum* **11** (July 1974), pp. 61-68.

130. A. E. Rosenberg, "Listener Performance in Speaker Verification Tasks," *IEEE Trans. Audio Electroacoust.* **AU-21** (June 1973), pp. 221-225; R. C. Lummis, "Speaker Verification: A Step Toward the 'Checkless' Society," *Bell Lab. Rec.* **50** (September 1972), pp. 254-259; G. R. Doddington, "A Method of Speaker Verification," *J. Acoust. Soc. Am.* **49,** Abstract (January 1971), p. 139; G. R. Doddington, J. L. Flanagan, and R. C. Lummis, U.S. Patent 3,700,815; filed April 20, 1971; issued October 24, 1972.

131. A. E. Rosenberg, "Evaluation of an Automatic Speaker-Verification System over Telephone Lines," *Bell Syst. Tech. J.* **55** (July/August 1976), pp. 723-744; A. E. Rosenberg and M. R. Sambur, "New Techniques for Automatic Speaker Verification," *IEEE Trans. Acoust., Speech, Sig. Process.* **ASSP-23** (April 1975), pp. 169-176; A. E. Rosenberg, "Automatic Speaker Verification: A Review," *Proc. IEEE* **64** (April 1976), pp. 475-487.

132. K. H. Davis, R. Biddulph, and S. Balashek, "Automatic Recognition of Spoken Digits," *J. Acoust. Soc. Am.* **24** (November 1952), pp. 637-642.

133. H. Dudley and S. Balashek, "Automatic Recognition of Phonetic Patterns in Speech," *J. Acoust. Soc. Am.* **30** (August 1958), pp. 721-732.

134. F. Itakura, "Minimum Prediction Residual Principle Applied to Speech Recognition," *IEEE Trans. Acoust., Speech, Sig. Process.* **ASSP-23** (February 1975), pp. 67-72.

135. M. R. Sambur and L. R. Rabiner, "A Speaker-Independent Digit-Recognition System," *Bell Syst. Tech. J.* **54** (January 1975), pp. 81-102.

136. L. R. Rabiner, S. E. Levinson, A. E. Rosenberg, and J. G. Wilpon, "Speaker-Independent Recognition of Isolated Words Using Clustering Techniques," *IEEE Trans. Acoust., Speech, Sig. Process.* **ASSP-27** (August 1979), pp. 336-349.

137. A. E. Rosenberg and F. Itakura, "Evaluation of an Automatic Word Recognition System Over Dialed-Up Telephones Lines," *J. Acoust. Soc. Am.* **60,** Supplement 1 (Fall 1976), p. S12.

138. J. L. Flanagan, S. E. Levinson, L. R. Rabiner, and A. E. Rosenberg, "Techniques for Expanding the Capabilities of Practical Speech Recognizers," in *Trends in Speech Recognition,* ed. W. A. Lea (Englewood Cliffs, New Jersey: Prentice-Hall, 1980), pp. 425-444.

139. L. R. Rabiner, J. G. Wilpon, and A. E. Rosenberg, "A Voice-Controlled Repertory-Dialer System," *Bell Syst. Tech. J.* **59** (September 1980), pp. 1153-1163.

140. C. S. Myers and L. R. Rabiner, "Connected Digit Recognition Using a Level Building DTW Algorithm," *IEEE Trans. Acoust., Speech, Sig. Process.* **ASSP-29** (June 1981), pp. 351-363.

141. S. E. Levinson, "The Effects of Syntactic Analysis on Word Recognition Accuracy," *Bell Syst. Tech. J.* **57** (May/June 1978), pp. 1627-1644; S. E. Levinson, A. E. Rosenberg, and J. L. Flanagan, "Evaluation of a Word Recognition System Using Syntax Analysis," *Bell Syst. Tech. J.* **57** (May/June 1978), pp. 1619-1626; S. E. Levinson and K. L. Shipley, "A Conversational-Mode Airline Information and Reservation System Using Speech Input and Output," *Bell Syst. Tech. J.* **59** (January 1980), pp. 119-137.

Chapter 3

Picture Communication Research

After early demonstrations of television beginning in 1927, Bell Laboratories researchers went on to make important contributions leading to television systems. These included the development of a theory of scanning, the principle of frequency interleaving to obtain color transmission, and the fundamentals of visual perception as it relates to picture communication. In subsequent years, much research attention was focused on reducing the redundancy of television signals as a way of conserving bandwidth and thus lowering transmission and storage costs. Highly sophisticated signal-processing and frame-replenishment schemes are determining the boundaries within which digital television, video teleconferencing, and graphics adjuncts to telephony will be developed.

I. EARLY EXPLORATIONS—PICTURE SCANNING, COLOR TELEVISION, PICTUREPHONE* VISUAL TELEPHONE SERVICE

Bell Laboratories interest in picture transmission dates back to the early 1920s. Work on still picture transmission and the early television demonstrations by H. E. Ives in 1927 and 1930 are discussed in sections 9.7 and 9.8 of Chapter 7 of the first volume of this series, subtitled *The Early Years (1875-1925)*. Ives's demonstrations were of landmark significance, proving beyond doubt that electronic television was a real possibility and stimulating research throughout the industry. Although Bell Labs was not as deeply involved in developing television in the 1930s and 1940s as some other laboratories, Bell Labs research scientists contributed substantially to the theory of scanning, to the understanding of color as related to television, and to the solution of many problems of signal modulation and transmission.

Principal authors: C. C. Cutler and A. N. Netravali.

* Registered service mark of AT&T.

1.1 Picture Scanning

During the 1927 demonstrations, television was considered an adjunct to the telephone.[1] Even so, there was a large-screen display consisting of a 2500-element neon discharge tube driven by pulse-amplitude-modulated (PAM) signals obtained by sampling the television signal with a 2500-element commutator.[2] The scene was scanned with a spot of light (flying-spot camera) and the reflected light collected by a bank of photocells.[3] [Fig. 3-1] Somewhat later, the camera system was reversed and an optical image of a scene, illuminated by sunlight, was scanned by holes making a spiral pattern in a disc in front of a photocell. Spot scanning and image scanning were alternative methods to be considered by other workers in the field for at least another 20 years, eventually to give way to electronically scanned camera tubes. In 1929, Ives[4] demonstrated color television, and in 1930, he conducted a two-way demonstration between Bell Laboratories at 463 West Street and AT&T at 195 Broadway, both in New York City—the first experiment using PICTUREPHONE visual telephone service.[5]

One of the most important contributions to understanding the basic properties of picture communication was the development of a theory of scanning. The concept of scanning pictures is as old as the idea of picture transmission itself (dating back to 1846), but what scanning meant in terms of signal characteristics was explained by P. Mertz and F. Gray in 1934.[6,7] They derived the basic spectral line characteristic familiar to all modern television transmission engineers.[8] [Fig. 3-2] Gray conceived the fundamental idea of color transmission, putting color information in the interline gaps of the video spectrum.[9] His idea was to duplex two independent television signals by modulating one on an elevated carrier so that its lower (inverted) sideband overlapped the spectrum of the other signal,

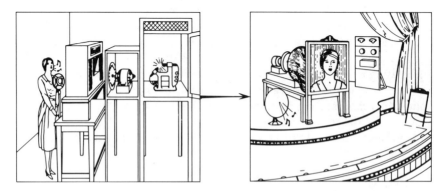

Fig. 3-1.   Configurations used in the 1927 demonstrations of television transmission by wire from Washington, D.C., to New York City. Flying-spot scanning, with an arc lamp as a source of light, was used at the camera end (left).

Fig. 3-2.   F. B. Jewett, first president of Bell Laboratories (left), with F. Gray in the booth of the experimental television-telephone that permitted each person in a telephone conversation to see as well as hear the other.

the spectrum components falling squarely between the components of the first signal. [Fig. 3-3] The discrimination provided by this operation was not adequate to eliminate crosstalk completely, but it was used in this form for the transmission of pilot tones. Only after the National Television Systems Committee (NTSC) color television signal format had been devised 20 years later was it realized that Gray had invented the frequency interleaving principle.

1.1.1 Standards for Television

Work on devices and broadband circuits and transmission systems continued in the 1930s. In 1937, coaxial cable transmission, having a bandwidth of 1 megahertz (MHz), was demonstrated between New York and Philadelphia. By this time the Radio Manufacturers Association had agreed

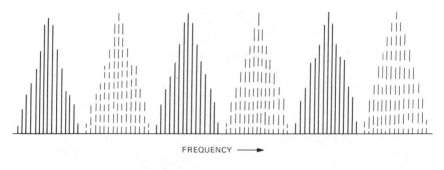

FREQUENCY ⟶

———— MONOCHROME SIGNAL COMPONENTS
— — — CHROMINANCE SIGNAL COMPONENTS

Fig. 3-3.   Distribution of monochrome signal components and chrominance signal components in the frequency spectrum when a chrominance signal is added to the usual video signal. The chrominance signal is obtained by modulating a subcarrier—which is a half integer multiple of the line frequency—by camera signals. The television scanning of a picture results in a spectrum having concentrations of energy at multiples of the horizontal scan rate. F. Gray proposed using the gaps between spectral components to send a second television signal. Many years later this idea was used to multiplex color information onto an otherwise monochrome television signal. [Adapted from Zworykin and Morton, in *Television* (1954): 865.]

on a standard of 441 lines. At Bell Labs M. E. Strieby and C. L. Weis carried out successful experiments on television transmission over coaxial cables and other lines.[10,11] A. G. Jensen designed a film scanner, making use of an image dissection tube, a kinescope display, and specially printed motion picture film.[12] The quality of pictures was comparable to today's (monochrome) pictures, lacking mostly in brightness and size; but the means for building the system were pushing the technology. Vacuum tube repeater amplifiers for coaxial cable systems, with a bandwidth of 1 MHz, were developed for this system. Bandwidth of 2 MHz and negative feedback were soon to follow.

The early research work had an important impact on setting the standards for broadcast television. Many different picture formats were used as television was developed, and the question of line rates was a subject for debate. Proposals ranged from 441 to 800 lines, using arguments based mostly on intuition. Much of the heat was removed from the question when M. W. Baldwin, Jr., [Fig. 3-4] at Bell Labs (who, with R. Bown, was a member of the NTSC formed by industry at the request of the Federal Communications Commission (FCC)) measured the perceived sharpness of images as a function of several factors, including the ratio of the horizontal and vertical resolutions.[13] He showed that, within a factor of two, the number of scanning lines had an imperceptible effect on picture sharpness if the total bandwidth was constant. [Fig. 3-5] In the process he coined a unit for the minimum perceptible change in picture quality, the liminal

Fig. 3-4. M. W. Baldwin, Jr., who did important early research on the relationships among scanning lines, perceived image sharpness, and bandwidth in TV transmission.

unit. This is a difference such that 25 percent of forced human judgments of the relative sharpness of two images would be incorrect. (Seventy-five percent would agree with the measured difference.)

Work on television was interrupted by the exigencies of World War II. Bell Labs scientists doing television research turned to radar work and used their skills and expertise in designing radar displays, plan position indicators (PPI), range gating, and fire control systems. (See Chapters 2 and 9 of the second volume of this series, subtitled *National Service in War and Peace (1925-1975)*.) Some of their electronic skills were immediately applicable to radar problems, but the direct application of the radar work to television was small. Nevertheless, by 1946 a 525-line, 30 frame/second (sec) 2:1 interlaced picture, the present U.S. television standard, was successfully sent from New York to Washington, D.C. by coaxial cable.[14]

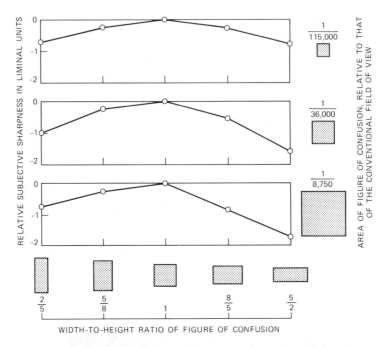

Fig. 3-5.   Graphs showing perceived sharpness in liminal units (left scales) as a function of the relative values of horizontal and vertical resolutions. Since anything less than a liminal unit represents an imperceptible change in picture quality, M. W. Baldwin's data showed a wide latitude in numbers of scanning lines, provided total bandwidth remains constant. Each point on the graphs represents 150 observations.

When commercial broadcast television started seriously in 1947, the Bell System was ready with well-equalized broadband circuits at microwave frequencies. (Broadcast television started on July 1, 1941, but expansion was delayed by the war.) In 1951, television was transmitted coast-to-coast via microwave radio. There was no other medium for long distance television transmission until the Telstar satellite was launched in 1962.

1.2 Color Television

Early work on color television at Bell Labs was modest; but, besides the original demonstrations by Ives, very significant contributions were made. Baldwin[15] and his associates studied the subjective sharpness of color images and determined that high detail in the blue and red primary colors is not required; they found that high detail is needed only in the green or alternatively in the luminance signal.[16] These contributions, along with Gray's interleaving (frequency multiplexing) invention, paved the way for the NTSC color television standard for compatible color transmission.

1.3 Early Research into PICTUREPHONE Visual Telephone Service

In the late 1940s, work on speech recording had resulted in an instrument using magnetic recording on a drum that could write a signal rapidly and play it back repetitively for signal analysis and spectrum display.[17] This instrument had been developed as an audio spectrum analyzer and had been used in speech therapy. The researchers realized that such an instrument could be useful with pictures and built a television system based on it. A picture was scanned from a television camera tube, transmitted slowly over telephone facilities, and stored at the receiving end, where it was rescanned for presentation. During presentation, another frame would be transmitted and stored. This work, by W. E. Kock and associates, resulted in an experimental videotelephone—50-line pictures displayed for 2-second intervals. It was the first of a series of videotelephone station set designs before the Mod 1 PICTUREPHONE visual telephone set evolved. There was impressive coverage in the press,[18] and several papers on the system were presented at the IRE WESCON meeting in 1956.[19] It would appear that the public was ready for a videotelephone, but subsequent events indicated that the technology was not yet ready. (In 1970, it appeared that technology was ready, but the public was not.) Development of PICTUREPHONE telephone service was organized as a project in systems and apparatus departments in Bell Labs in 1956. Further research work on PICTUREPHONE visual telephone service is described in sections 2.2.2 through 2.2.5 below.

II. BANDWIDTH COMPRESSION—BIT-RATE REDUCTION

The large bandwidth required by television was a major concern to picture communication researchers from the very beginning. The situation was helped immensely by the use of 2:1 line interlace and NTSC frequency interleaved color. However, it was widely recognized that considerable redundancy still existed in the video signal. For example, most scenes contained sizable areas of nearly uniform brightness. Also, many scenes contained regions that did not change significantly from frame to frame.

2.1 Redundancy in Television Transmission

The idea of removing redundancy in television transmission to save bandwidth goes back at least to Ives in the 1920s and was widely discussed in the 1940s. However, it was not until the advent of pulse-code modulation (PCM) that implementation of these ideas was seriously undertaken. PCM was developed in the 1940s as a means of achieving very low noise transmission and easy multiplexing (see Chapter 10, section 1.4 in this volume). By itself PCM does not reduce bandwidth. On the contrary, binary PCM often expands bandwidth by almost an order of magnitude. The great advantage of PCM, at least for video, was that it made possible signal processing with realizable circuitry and little distortion. As we shall see later, such processing capability is indispensable to video redundancy reduction.

Spurred by the early PCM work of B. M. Oliver, J. R. Pierce, C. E. Shannon, and others at Bell Labs,[20] W. M. Goodall proceeded in 1944 to apply PCM to television. By 1947, he succeeded and showed that 7- to 8-bit quantization was necessary for a high-quality picture.[21] In 1962, L. G. Roberts at the Massachusetts Institute of Technology found that something more than one bit could be saved by adding a small amount of noise to the signal to break up the contouring caused by the quantization process.[22] He added pseudorandom noise to the transmitter before quantization and subtracted the same noise at the receiver. In 1969, J. O. Limb at Bell Labs found that deterministic repetitive patterns, called ordered dither, worked better than noise.[23] Much work has been done since then to use ordered dither patterns for displaying halftone pictures.[24,25]

2.1.1 Differential Pulse-Code Modulation (DPCM)

Much of the redundancy in video stems from the fact that adjacent picture elements (or pels as they later became known) are highly correlated. Thus, a pel to be transmitted can be predicted with fair accuracy from previously transmitted pels, and, in principle, only the difference between the actual value and the prediction need be transmitted. Work by C. C. Cutler [Fig. 3-6], C. W. Harrison, and Oliver[26] in the early 1950s realized some of the possibilities of prediction in the coding of pictures; their work resulted in the invention of DPCM and error feedback coding, ideas that took a decade or more to come to fruition. In their simplest form these ideas, and the related one of delta modulation, allowed the transmission of high-quality television with as few as 4 bits per picture element, and it was some time before more sophisticated coding did much better. [Fig. 3-7] Delta modulation, invented by F. DeJager at the N. V. Philips Research Laboratory[27] in Holland at about the same time that DPCM was invented at Bell Labs, may be thought of as a 1-bit DPCM system that operates at a sampling rate well above the Nyquist rate (see Chapter 1, section 2.3 in this volume) for the signal.

DPCM is a feedback scheme that, in addition to reducing the redundancy, alters the distribution of quantization errors so that they are less visible.

Fig. 3-6. C. C. Cutler, who invented DPCM and error feedback coding. He made fundamental contributions to their application in picture communication.

A quantitative statistical basis for such systems was developed in 1952 by
E. R. Kretzmer,[28,29] and a subjectively oriented basis was contributed subsequently by R. E. Graham[30] and later extended by Limb, A. N. Netravali,
and B. Prasada.[31,32] The initial DPCM concept included an adaptation
feature and multiple steps of integration, anticipating later developments.

Another proposal involved partitioning the video frequency band, sending samples of the low-frequency information with many bits (finely quantized) and samples of the high-frequency part with fewer bits, but at a
higher sampling rate. However, techniques based on DPCM proved more
practical. After many years of research, and with refined technology, two
DPCM coders were eventually developed for PICTUREPHONE visual
telephone transmission in the late 1960s.

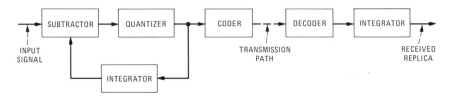

Fig. 3-7. Block diagram of DPCM system. Refinements to this circuit show up in many of the more sophisticated redundancy reduction systems. [Adapted from C. C. Cutler, U.S. Patent No. 2,605,361.]

These inventions formed a foundation of knowledge upon which intraframe coders for future video transmission systems were designed. They were also instrumental to the success of the more sophisticated frame-to-frame or interframe coders to be described later.

2.2 Application of Digital Processing to Picture Communication

The electronic digital computer became a large and useful enough device just in time to figure in this development. A data translator nicknamed Tapex, built by E. E. David, Jr., M. V. Mathews, and H. S. McDonald in 1950, became the vehicle for the simulation and testing of a number of speech and picture coding algorithms.[33] The machine could digitize an analog input, such as the signal from a picture scanner, and store the result on a computer tape. The tape was then fed to an IBM 704 computer where various picture processing algorithms were carried out, and the resulting output was again written on magnetic tape. Finally, the data translator produced a glossy print from which such problems as coding defects or noise could be assessed visually. It was another ten years before R. C. Brainard and J. D. Beyer constructed an improved computer system having a cathode ray tube (CRT) display and provision for including noise and motion in system simulations.[34] Meanwhile, a multitude of experiments in picture processing were performed, setting a base for even more sophisticated studies.

For example, with a technique called transform coding, subblocks of a picture are represented as linear combinations of a predefined set of basis blocks. The weighting values in the linear combination are called the transform coefficients, and these are transmitted to the receiver for use in reconstruction. In 1970, some fundamental work was done by H. J. Landau and D. Slepian using computer simulation,[35] and the technique has been studied at length at other laboratories. Block-to-block DPCM coding of the transform coefficients, later known as hybrid transform coding, was invented by D. O. Reudink and also studied by computer simulation.[36] Later work by Netravali, Prasada, and F. W. Mounts, using three-dimensional blocks, optimized the quantization of the transform coefficients to take advantage of the properties of human vision.[37]

Computer simulation also enabled study of the effects of digital transmission errors on coded pictures. In 1972, D. J. Connor showed that certain error effects in DPCM systems, while practically invisible when viewed on a single frame, become highly objectionable in a real-time television system.[38]

Early frame-repeating experiments copied an idea from the motion picture industry, avoiding flicker at the display by presenting each transmitted frame a number of times before replacing it with a new one. This technique saved bandwidth in proportion to the number of repetitions, but it gave a picture with jerky motion reminiscent of silent movies or, in the extreme, gave a series of snapshots, as did the aforementioned system of Kock. Frame repeating was studied at some length in 1958 using cinema techniques. However, electronic systems of frame repeating, with reasonably good quality signals, were not to be demonstrated until 1966. Mounts then found that with the brighter pictures of a television display, motion defects were much more objectionable than had been believed previously.

2.2.1 Selective Frame Replenishment

With the newer acoustic delay line memory, developed for computer systems, and a sampled digitized signal, it was possible to replenish elements of the picture on a sample-by-sample basis instead of by whole frames. This was an attempt to avoid the large-area motion defects of frame repeating. In 1966, Mounts did just this,[39] replenishing a fraction of the picture elements distributed over the screen in a prescribed fashion in each 1/60 second field time. The variety of algorithms for selective replenishment of the picture elements seemed endless, but a simple 4:1 interlace replenishment system in a fixed sequence called the lazy 8 was found to be best. Many people proposed a randomly distributed replenishment, but this was worst of all; an ordered replenishment is finer grained in time and space. This method of replenishment is an extension of dot interlace, made more practical by using a frame memory.

With 4:1 selective replenishment, flicker and jerkiness were eliminated. However, when an object in the scene moved quickly, a checkerboard pattern would appear to follow it; thus the picture was less than perfect. Replenishment at slower rates with reasonably bright display was not satisfactory in any sense,[40] and it was learned that people are very sensitive to fluctuation rates near the psychological moment, a natural biological period of about 0.1 second. Mertz had shown this 30 years earlier when he demonstrated that more than 10 frames/sec were needed for lip reading.

Frequently, a gross form of dot interlace is suggested as a bandwidth saver, and some extravagant claims have been made for it in the literature.

As in the foregoing, $1/n$ elements are transmitted and displayed in each $1/60$ second in a pseudorandom pattern on the screen, where n may be as much as 16, and a slow phosphor and eye retentivity are called upon to reduce small area flicker. The success of such schemes always depends on very dim displays viewed by viewers whose eyes have adjusted to the dark. Too often, researchers have been deceived by the subjective tolerance of the eye adjusted to the dark. The lesson has had to be relearned periodically. The temptation to consider dot interlace for the PICTUREPHONE visual telephone system was laid to rest in experiments performed and demonstrated by E. F. Brown at high brightness using the system described above.

Improved versions of dot and line interlace were studied in the late 1960s by Limb and R. F. W. Pease.[41,42] In these systems, spatial resolution and temporal resolution were traded off one against the other, depending on the amount of movement in the scene. Thus, at the receiver display, pels that were not transmitted were replaced by previous frame values if movement was low but by an average of their neighbors if movement was significant. These algorithms considerably improved picture quality in these systems compared with their predecessors.

2.2.2 *Conditional Frame Replenishment*

Conditional replenishment systems (the transmission of only the changed pels in a frame) had been discussed from the time of Ives (1927), but they lacked a plan for locating and addressing the changed elements. In 1967, Mounts [Fig. 3-8] implemented a digital conditional replenishment system,[43,44] which could code scenes containing low-to-moderate movement at a transmission rate of 1 bit/pel (i.e., one-fourth of that required by DPCM, or one-eighth of that required by PCM). The digital coding and memory lent itself to the selection and brightening (flagging) of changed points only. [Fig. 3-9] These are very useful in system studies, giving an easily assessed measure of coding algorithms.

Conditional replenishment uses a digital memory sufficiently large to store the PCM-coded signal of a complete television frame. The coded value of any pel on the picture can then be compared to the value of the corresponding point in the previous frame. A similar picture store is maintained at the receiver and is updated by the transmission signal. No transmission is needed if the difference between corresponding pels in adjacent frames is small, i.e., below a predetermined threshold. Thus, for a slowly changing scene, little transmission is necessary. The coded brightness value is combined with a coded number that defines the horizontal position in the picture (at least one point is sent for each line so that lines can be counted). Since the signal so generated is intermittent, a buffer store is used to smooth the transmission. Feedback from the buffer controls the threshold value in order to prevent filling.

Fig. 3-8. F. W. Mounts with experimental apparatus used for selective frame replenishment.

Realizing a conditional replenishment system was a giant step and presaged a number of further improvements. For example, frame-to-frame differences were sent by J. C. Candy, B. G. Haskell, and their coworkers, instead of brightness values for the changed pels; clusters of changes were addressed, instead of each individual change; and during rapid movement the sampling rate was reduced.[45,46] A new term, FRODEC, was coined as a generic name for adaptive frame replenishment coders. A FRODEC was demonstrated in 1970. It operated at 1 bit/pel (2 megabits/second (Mb/sec)), a rate that could handle scenes with very active movement. In 1970, when the PICTUREPHONE visual telephone service was demonstrated as a feature program at the annual convention of the IEEE in New York City, the simulated 1 bit/pel FRODEC system was also included. In 1974, Limb [Fig. 3-10] and his coworkers demonstrated two FRODECs that could accept and deliver a PICTUREPHONE visual telephone signal, which was

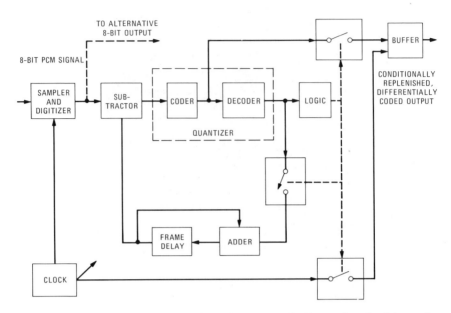

Fig. 3-9.   Basic functions of a conditional replenishment television coder. The delay in the frame memory loop must equal the frame period. When there is no interframe change, the stored signal simply recirculates, and nothing is given to the buffer for transmission. When a significant difference is detected, the new signal is stored and transmitted along with a code that indicates position in a scan line. The decision threshold is adjusted to prevent buffer overflow or underflow.

DPCM-coded at 6 Mb/sec, while transmitting between intermediate points in the toll plant at only 1.5 Mb/sec.[47] These three-level hierarchical systems for transmission would use analog transmission in the local plant, DPCM for short haul, and FRODECs for long haul. This can be accomplished with complete compatibility and no loss in quality from recoding at the system interfaces. Also during this time Haskell studied interframe predictive coder statistics and showed that considerable saving is possible if several FRODECs share the same transmission channel.[48] This was to be expected, since separate FRODECs rarely produce a high data rate simultaneously.

Following the success with the 1.5 Mb/sec transmission rate, a new goal was set, namely, to achieve the lowest possible rate at which pictures could be sent that were subjectively acceptable even though there was visible motion degradation. It was felt that a considerable amount of motion distortion could be accommodated provided the image cleared up quickly when movement stopped and provided enough was saved on transmission costs. In 1973, using a wide variety of sophisticated controls, a PIC-

Fig. 3-10. J. O. Limb, seated in front of the control panel of the video processing equipment used in many of the intraframe and frame-to-frame coding studies. The video processing system was built by J. D. Beyer and R. C. Brainard.

TUREPHONE visual telephone service FRODEC requiring only 0.2 Mb/sec[49] transmission was demonstrated by Haskell and R. L. Schmidt. However, it was no better than marginal for face-to-face conversation.

2.2.3 Minicomputers and the PICTUREPHONE Visual Telephone Service

By 1975, management realized that for the PICTUREPHONE visual telephone service to be better accepted by the public it should use the standard 4-MHz, 525-line format of broadcast television, and many of the earlier conclusions on coding would have to be reassessed. A new 525-line experimental system, built by Haskell and his coworkers, used a minicomputer and semiconductor shift registers for the frame memory. Using many of the features of the 0.2-Mb system, it operated successfully at a 1.5-Mb/sec transmission rate for 525-line conference television.[50]

2.2.4 Delay in the Picture Channel

Some of the frame-to-frame picture coding operations delay the video signal significantly, and this delay was a factor that required study. Typically, frame repeating delayed the picture by 1/30 second, and some of the conditional replenishment schemes called for large buffer stores that could delay transmission even more. One is not bothered by up to 120 milliseconds (ms) of sound delay with respect to pictures, but one is very sensitive to sound preceding picture motion by as little as 20 to 30 ms. Therefore, interframe coding systems require introduction of sound delay to match that of the picture.

A more serious question is the effect on two-way communication of coding delay plus the 600-ms round-trip delay in a synchronous satellite circuit. It became evident in the 1960s that domestic satellite (DOMSAT) systems were in the offing and that PICTUREPHONE telephone service would be requiring large channel capacity at about the same time that satellites would be supplying them. Thus, a series of subjective tests was undertaken to determine the effects of this delay. Tests by P. T. Brady, reported in an internally published technical memorandum, comparing a PICTUREPHONE visual telephone service circuit having 600-ms round-trip delay with a (simulated) 3000-mile terrestrial circuit (both circuits had standard echo suppressors), showed that the percentage of subjects having conversational difficulty increased markedly when the larger delay was used. The conclusion was that the degradation in performance due to satellite delay was not negligible, and that attention should be given to improving audio echo cancellation or suppression.

2.2.5 PICTUREPHONE Visual Telephone Service Standards

Setting standards for television was a long and difficult process. The same proved to be true for the PICTUREPHONE visual telephone service where the factors of picture size and proportion, brightness, contrast, bandwidth, frequency emphasis, scanning structure, scanning linewidth, frame rate, linearity, noise requirements, and crispening (the emphasis of edge detail by filtering) all came up for study and sometimes led to controversy. The question of picture size and proportion, in particular, was a difficult one. Early unpublished research tests (1958) indicated that a nearly square or slightly wider than high proportion was preferable for the portrait mode of the PICTUREPHONE visual telephone display, but later tests in the systems area came to the opposite conclusion. The 4-3/4 inch wide by 5-3/4 inch high Mod 1 PICTUREPHONE telephone service display resulted, later to revert to 5-1/2 inches by 5 inches in the Mod II set.[51]

A wide variety of opinions on brightness and contrast was laid to rest by a series of subjective tests (1963 to 1967) that indicated that people like very bright pictures if those pictures are clean, but the preference is not strong. In the presence of a moderate amount of interlace flicker or other visible defects, a lower luminance is preferred. High brightness makes picture defects more visible, but low brightness sacrifices contrast in a well-lighted environment. The compromise, roughly 80 foot-lamberts, was bright by television set performance at that time, but was about half the luminance preferred for really clean pictures.

The question of interlace and scanning rate was resolved at the same time as the brightness question. Early experiments indicated that under some conditions interlace had little advantage in picture quality because the small-scale interline flicker was objectionable. Indeed, much of the early research into PICTUREPHONE visual telephone service was done using a sequential rather than an interlaced scan. Brown conducted a long series of subjective tests using a very versatile system that allowed investigation of a wide range of scanning line structure, brightness, contrast, and many other factors.[52] His results indicated that the subjective advantage of interlace, related to equipment bandwidth, was worth approximately 20 percent when line width, line spacing, brightness, and contrast were optimized and less than 20 percent when other factors were not optimum. Sequential scanning had a potential advantage in the design of coders for bandwidth saving because of the greater proximity of picture elements in a field. However, a cost study by T. V. Crater showed that the extra 20 percent bandwidth required in the local loop for sequentially scanned pictures of equivalent quality required closer repeater spacing and increased system cost.[53] It was very unlikely that any potential bandwidth saving peculiar to sequential scanning could overcome the increase in cost of the transmission equipment. Because of this, interlaced scanning was specified for the PICTUREPHONE visual telephone service, even though a very significant fraction of people preferred sequentially scanned pictures because they had less flicker.

2.2.6 Color Pictures

At a presentation to management in 1966 on the progress of PICTUREPHONE telephone service, the question of color pictures was raised. In the optimism of the day, with color television in its period of greatest growth, it seemed inconceivable that telephone customers would long be satisfied with a monochrome video telephone. Unfortunately, color television technology was far from ready for development as a two-way transmission system without full-time maintenance. Moreover, color TV cameras at that time were expensive, had dozens of adjustments, and were erratic in operation. In addition, color receivers were dim, requiring subdued lighting, and cameras, being insensitive, required a bright environment. Furthermore, these problems seemed basic.

The first serious research directed at color PICTUREPHONE visual telephone service arose as a result of a discussion at a game of golf between the president of Bell Labs, J. B. Fisk, and the president of the Polaroid Corporation, E. H. Land. Land was experimenting with color, and he contended that a two-primary-color system could work for PICTURE-PHONE visual telephone service, with obvious advantages in simplicity and economy. Land demonstrated his system to a group of executives from Bell Labs, greatly impressing the viewers. Indeed, with just two projectors, using white and red illuminants, beautiful full color scenes were seen.

After several attempts by D. E. Pearson and C. B. Rubinstein to reproduce Land's demonstration, the researchers were able to produce good color effects only by working at night in a darkened room with subdued projections.[54] They concluded that customers were not likely to be willing to restrict their PICTUREPHONE visual telephone usage to such a darkened environment. However, this was the beginning of some very effective research on color displays.

The conditions for the appearance of a full gamut of colors were quantified, as was the range of colors that could be perceived. This work quite naturally led to work on predicting perceived color in three-primary-color displays.

Another branch of research came from an earlier invention of R. L. Eilenberger. Eilenberger had devised a prism arrangement that separated and transposed three-color images and let them be focused with one lens on a single camera tube screen using a special tube having a fiber-optic face plate.[55] Thus, the color separations could be scanned by a single electron beam scanner and the color signal components separated by sampling the response. Eilenberger solved many problems and in due course demonstrated a single-tube camera with very few mechanical adjustments. It would require special signal processing and involved some rather critical parts.

A third direction of research toward a color PICTUREPHONE telephone service eventually came from a new look at an old invention of R. D. Kell of RCA.[56] This was a single-tube camera system that gave three color channels by using color gratings in the optical path, close to the camera screen. The gratings caused the scanning beam of the camera tube to be modulated. The amplitude was proportional to the intensity of light of the grating color. Thus, the color information appeared as sidebands on a carrier. This idea had been impractical for color television in earlier years, but with the lower resolution of the PICTUREPHONE visual telephone service, better technology, and some new ideas, it looked promising.

The Kell approach eliminated the problem of misregistration of the separate color images that plagued the conventional cameras, but its own inherent problem of color shading (variation in hue with position) had to be painstakingly reduced to an acceptable level by a succession of improvements in both grating design and signal processing techniques. The final design of A. B. Larsen[57] used three superposed gratings with orientation and spacing optimized to minimize the differential effect of the spatially varying resolution of the camera tube scanning beam on the three-primary-color signal outputs.

The first color pictures using this new technique were obtained early the following year (1972), but other developments took the edge off this achievement. The rapid advance of charge-coupled device (CCD) technology not only made possible much simpler index-type color cameras but, even more fundamentally, eliminated the registration problems that led to their use in the first place.[58] [Fig. 3-11]

Fig. 3-11. The first solid-state color television camera. Light from a scene being viewed was split into three colors (red, green, and blue) and focused onto three separate silicon CCD image sensors. The light was converted by the sensors into electrical charge, stored and sequentially read out of each device as video signals corresponding to each color image. The signals were applied to a color television monitor to recreate the image of the scene.

The coding of color video signals presented other challenges. Rather than working with the composite frequency multiplexed signal, Limb and Rubinstein encoded the individual luminance and chrominance components.[59,60] Being able to code each component in a manner best suited to the human observer's response to the individual component was an advantage. More important, it allowed exploration of subjective and statistical redundancies across the components.[61]

III. FURTHER ADVANCES IN PICTURE COMMUNICATIONS

In the late 1950s, it appeared that the public was ready for and wanted some kind of picture transmission as an adjunct to the telephone but that the technology was not ready to supply such services reliably. Ten years later it appeared, through a series of user experiments (networks at Bell Labs, and public demonstrations in 1964 at the World's Fair and Disneyland, the Union Carbide trials (1969), and the Westinghouse trials (1969)), that both the technology and the public were ready. However, later events indicated that too few were ready to pay the cost of a public system. Subsequently, research continued, taking advantage of new circuits and devices to further refine the coding system for a more efficient transmission and devising a system for coding color signals.[62]

Research on subjective factors has added insight into the limitations of the human viewer and has improved subjective measurement techniques materially. For example, it has been observed that more coding noise can be tolerated at rapid transitions in the image. This has led to new ways of designing quantitizers for DPCM systems. In particular, Limb showed that images can be segmented based on local detail of the image and quantitizers can be adapted to hide the quantization noise.[63] [Fig. 3-12]

3.1 Scanned Graphics

It is believed that a simple graphical adjunct with interactive capabilities may be useful for conferencing. An experimental telephone system with graphic displays was devised by T. P. Sosnowski.[64] It permitted a camera or keyboard input and light pen annotation of a display from either end of a communication circuit. A microprocessor supplied logic to aid graphical input, and a built-in memory was used to store pictures for further reference. [Fig. 3-13] Since the transmission of such graphical material on telephone lines (low bandwidth) takes a long time, the ability to interact is reduced. Therefore, some significant research to reduce the transmission times has taken place. A pattern-recognition-based coder in which documents are

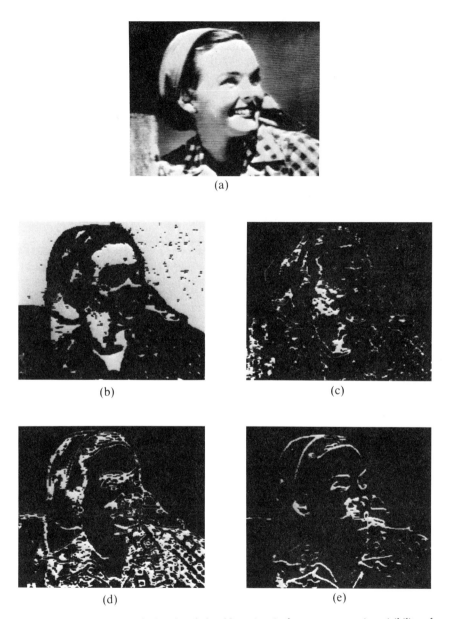

(a)

(b)   (c)

(d)   (e)

Fig. 3-12. Segmentation of a head and shoulders view in four segments using visibility of the quantization noise based on local measures of detail. The original picture is (a). Pictures (b), (c), (d), and (e) are arranged in order of increasing amount of detail and therefore increasing tolerance to noise. [Adapted from Netravali and Limb, *Proc. IEEE* **68** (1980): 388.]

Fig. 3-13. Experimental graphic display system. A plasma panel was used for viewing a picture common to both terminals of a communication system. Pictures can be entered and annotated from either terminal with the aid of a microprocessor or from a digital memory. [Sosnowski and Brainard, *Proc. SID* **20/3** (1979): 132.]

scanned from top to bottom was designed by O. Johnsen.[65] Patterns (not necessarily characters) are isolated and are matched to already transmitted patterns. If a correct match is detected, only the position of the pattern and the identification of the matching pattern are transmitted. Such techniques can transmit documents in 10 to 20 seconds on a 9600-bit/sec line. Even this much transmission time is considered too large for many applications. Therefore, progressive or hierarchical transmission schemes, which exploit the growing use of soft display media, such as the CRT, and the decreasing costs of electronic memory, have been devised. In these schemes, a crude version of the document is transmitted first, requiring much less transmission time, and a gradual update is made to get the final good quality image. Such systems may find use in interactive graphics conferencing as well as picture data bases and in retrieving the pictures in the data bases.

3.2 Video Conferencing

New techniques have also been introduced to reduce the transmission cost of conference quality television. In television scenes that contain moving objects, a more efficient coding can be performed by estimating the motion of the objects and then using the motion to compare intensities in successive frames that are spatially displaced by an amount equal to the motion of the object. [Fig. 3-14] Netravali and J. D. Robbins showed in 1974 that such schemes, called motion compensation,[66] achieve transmission rates below 1.5 Mb/sec, while maintaining a picture quality adequate for conferences.

In addition to bandwidth compression, different modes of operation of the conferencing systems are also being studied. One mode uses frame storage techniques to provide a continuous presence (in contrast to voice-switched operation) by multiplexing several pictures in a band normally filled by one picture.[67] [Fig. 3-15]

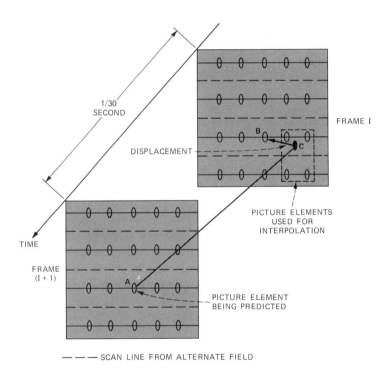

Fig. 3-14. Diagram showing part of the operation of a motion-compensated coding scheme. Picture element *A* in the current frame is predicted by an element *C* in the previous frame that is spatially displaced by an amount equal to the motion of an object in the scene. Vector *CB* is computed recursively such that it minimizes the difference in intensity between pels *A* and *C* using a steepest-descent method.

(a)

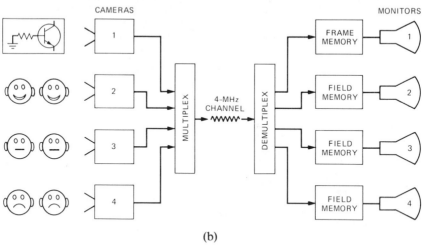

(b)

Fig. 3-15.   Conferencing television system. (a) Continuous presence conference television. (b) By using frame storage techniques and conditional replenishment, three pictures plus a graphics signal can be transmitted in the same bandwidth occupied by a conventional television signal. A reduction in spatial and temporal resolution is more than compensated for (subjectively) by having all participants in a conference continuously visible. Subjective studies indicated that continuous presence conference television resulted in much better conferences compared to those using traditional voice-switched systems, which switch the camera to the person in the conference who talks the loudest.

Fig. 3-16. A. N. Netravali, who has made research contributions to cost-effective transmission and improved picture quality in conference and network television.

3.3 Network Quality Television

The use of computer graphics, special effects, and digital processing within the television studio led to research in 1981 by Brainard, Netravali [Fig. 3-16], and Pearson in digital coding and transmission of network quality television.[68] Network television signals contain many more frame-to-frame changes than conference television, and coding degradations should not be visible. Experiments have been made to encode such signals at 45 Mb/sec for transmission over terrestrial and satellite links.

The research activities of the 1970s provided a strong technological base for the development of greatly improved picture transmission systems and led to the optimism that picture communications has a bright future in telecommunications.

REFERENCES

1. See special issue on Television, *Bell Lab. Rec.* **4** (May 1927), pp. 297-328.
2. F. Gray, J. W. Horton, and R. C. Mathes, "The Production and Utilization of Television Signals," *Bell Syst. Tech. J.* **6** (October 1927), pp. 560-603.
3. F. Gray, "Direct Scanning in Television," *Bell Lab. Rec.* **7** (March 1929), pp. 276-278.
4. H. E. Ives, "Television in Colors," *Bell Lab. Rec.* **7** (July 1929), pp. 439-444.
5. H. E. Ives, "Two-Way Television," *Bell Lab. Rec.* **8** (May 1930), pp. 399-404.
6. P. Mertz and F. Gray, "Theory of Scanning and Its Relation to the Characteristics of the Transmitted Signal in Telephotography and Television," *Bell Syst. Tech. J.* **13** (July 1934), pp. 464-515.
7. P. Mertz, "Television—The Scanning Process," *Proc. IRE* **29** (October 1941), pp. 529-537.
8. E. W. Engstrom, "A Study of Television Image Characteristics," *Proc. IRE* **21** (December 1933), pp. 1631-1651.
9. F. Gray, U. S. Patent No. 1,769,920; filed April 30, 1929; issued July 8, 1930.
10. M. E. Strieby, "Coaxial Cable System for Television Transmission," *Bell Syst. Tech. J.* **17** (July 1938), pp. 438-457.
11. M. E. Strieby and C. L. Weis, "Television Transmission," *Proc. IRE* **29** (July 1941), pp. 371-381.
12. A. G. Jensen, "Film Scanner for Use in Television Transmission Tests," *Proc. IRE* **29** (May 1941), pp. 243-249.
13. M. W. Baldwin, Jr., "The Subjective Sharpness of Simulated Television Images," *Bell Syst. Tech. J.* **19** (October 1940), pp. 563-586.
14. "Coaxial Cable in Regular Use by Television Broadcasters," News Note, *Bell Lab. Rec.* **24** (October 1946), p. 371.
15. M. W. Baldwin, Jr., "Subjective Sharpness of Additive Color Pictures," *Proc. IRE* **39** (October 1951), pp. 1173-1176.
16. W. T. Wintringham, "Color Television and Colorimetry," *Proc. IRE* **39** (October 1951), pp. 1135-1172.
17. R. K. Potter, G. A. Kopp, and H. C. Green, *Visible Speech* (New York: D. Van Nostrand Co., 1947).
18. For example, *Newark* [New Jersey] *Sunday News* (February 26, 1956), p. 14.
19. Unpublished papers presented at *IRE WESCON Convention,* Los Angeles, California (August 21-22, 1956).
20. B. M. Oliver, J. R. Pierce, and C. E. Shannon, "The Philosophy of PCM," *Proc. IRE* **36** (November 1948), pp. 1324-1331.
21. "Pulse Code Modulation Demonstrated to IRE," *Bell Lab. Rec.* **25** (November 1947), pp. 422-424; W. M. Goodall, "Television by Pulse Code Modulation," *Bell Syst. Tech. J.* **30** (January 1951), pp. 33-49; R. W. Sears, "Electron Beam Deflection Tube for Pulse Code Modulation," *Bell Syst. Tech. J.* **27** (January 1948), pp. 44-57.
22. L. G. Roberts, "Picture Coding Using Pseudo-Random Noise," *IRE Trans. Inform. Theory* **IT-8** (February 1962), pp. 145-154.
23. J. O. Limb, "Design of Dither Waveforms for Quantized Visual Signals," *Bell Syst. Tech. J.* **48** (September 1969), pp. 2555-2582.
24. J. F. Jarvis, C. N. Judice, and W. H. Ninke, "A Survey of Techniques for the Display of Continuous Tone Pictures on Bilevel Displays," *Comput. Graph. Image Process.* **5** (March 1976), pp. 13-40.
25. A. N. Netravali and E. G. Bowen, "Display of Dithered Images," *Proc. SID* **22/3** (1981), pp. 185-190.
26. C. C. Cutler, U.S. Patent 2,605,361; filed June 29, 1950; issued July 29, 1952; B. M. Oliver, "Efficient Coding," *Bell Syst. Tech. J.* **31** (July 1952), pp. 724-750; C. W. Harrison, "Experiments with Linear Prediction in Television," *Bell Syst. Tech. J.* **31** (July 1952), pp. 764-783.

27. F. DeJager, "Delta Modulation: A Method of PCM Transmission Using a One Unit Code," *Philips Res. Rep.* **7** (1952), pp. 442-466.
28. E. R. Kretzmer, "Statistics of Television Signals," *Bell Syst. Tech. J.* **31** (July 1952), pp. 751-763.
29. E. R. Kretzmer, "Reduced-Alphabet Representation of Television Signals," *IRE Conv. Rec.* **4**, Part 4 (1956), pp. 140-147.
30. R. E. Graham, "Subjective Experiments in Visual Communication," *IRE Nat. Conv. Rec.* **6**, Part 4 (1958), pp. 100-106.
31. J. O. Limb, "Adaptive Encoding of Picture Signals," in *Picture Bandwidth Compression*, ed. T. S. Huang and O. J. Tretiak (New York: Gordon and Breach, 1972), pp. 343-382.
32. A. N. Netravali and B. Prasada, "Adaptive Quantization of Picture Signals Using Spatial Masking," *Proc. IEEE* **65** (April 1977), pp. 536-548.
33. E. E. David, Jr., M. V. Mathews, and H. S. McDonald, "A High-Speed Data Translator for Computer Simulation of Speech and Television Devices," *Proc. IRE Western Joint Comput. Conf.*, San Francisco (March 1959), pp. 354-357.
34. D. J. Connor, R. C. Brainard, and J. O. Limb, "Intraframe Coding Techniques," *Proc. IEEE* **60** (July 1972), pp. 779-791.
35. H. J. Landau and D. Slepian, "Some Computer Experiments in Picture Processing for Bandwidth Reduction," *Bell Syst. Tech. J.* **50** (May/June 1971), pp. 1525-1540.
36. D. O. Reudink, "Intraframe Coding Using Transform Techniques," paper presented at *1971 Picture Coding Symp.*, Purdue University, Lafayette, Indiana (October 28-29, 1971).
37. A. N. Netravali, B. Prasada, and F. W. Mounts, "Some Experiments in Adaptive and Predictive Hadamard Transform Coding of Pictures," *Bell Syst. Tech. J.* **56** (October 1977), pp. 1531-1547.
38. D. J. Connor, "Techniques for Reducing the Visibility of Transmission Errors in Digitally Encoded Video Signals," *IEEE Trans. Commun.* **COM-21** (June 1973), pp. 695-706.
39. F. W. Mounts, "Low-Resolution TV: An Experimental Digital System for Evaluating Bandwidth-Reduction Techniques," *Bell Syst. Tech. J.* **46** (January 1967), pp. 167-198.
40. R. C. Brainard, F. W. Mounts, and B. Prasada, "Low Resolution TV: Subjective Effects of Frame Repetition and Picture Replenishment," *Bell Syst. Tech. J.* **46** (January 1967), pp. 261-271.
41. J. O. Limb and R. F. W. Pease, "Exchange of Spatial and Temporal Resolution in Television Coding," paper presented at *SMPTE Meeting*, Los Angeles (October 1969).
42. J. O. Limb and R. F. W. Pease, "A Simple Interframe Coder for Video Telephony," *Bell Syst. Tech. J.* **50** (July/August 1971), pp. 1877-1888.
43. F. W. Mounts, "A Video Encoding System with Conditional Picture-Element Replenishment," *Bell Syst. Tech. J.* **48** (September 1969), pp. 2545-2554.
44. F. W. Mounts and D. E. Pearson, "Apparent Increase in Noise Level When Television Pictures are Frame-Repeated," *Bell Syst. Tech. J.* **48** (March 1969), pp. 527-539.
45. J. C. Candy, M. A. Franke, B. G. Haskell, and F. W. Mounts, "Transmitting Television as Clusters of Frame-to-Frame Differences," *Bell Syst. Tech. J.* **50** (July/August 1971), pp. 1889-1917.
46. D. J. Connor, B. G. Haskell, and F. W. Mounts, "A Frame-to-Frame *Picturephone®* Coder for Signals Containing Differential Quantizing Noise," *Bell Syst. Tech. J.* **52** (January 1973), pp. 35-51.
47. J. O. Limb, R. F. W. Pease, and K. A. Walsh, "Combining Intraframe and Frame-to-Frame Coding for Television," *Bell Syst. Tech. J.* **53** (July/August 1974), pp. 1137-1173.
48. B. G. Haskell, "Buffer and Channel Sharing by Several Interframe *Picturephone®* Coders," *Bell Syst. Tech. J.* **51** (January 1972), pp. 261-289.
49. B. G. Haskell and R. L. Schmidt, "A Low-Bit-Rate Interframe Coder for Videotelephone," *Bell Syst. Tech. J.* **54** (October 1975), pp. 1475-1495.
50. B. G. Haskell, P. L. Gordon, R. L. Schmidt, and J. V. Scattaglia, "Interframe Coding of 525-Line Monochrome Television at 1.5 Mbits/s," *IEEE Trans. Commun.* **COM-25** (November 1977), pp. 1339-1348.

51. T. V. Crater, "The *Picturephone*® System: Service Standards," *Bell Syst. Tech. J.* **50** (February 1971), pp. 235-269.

52. E. F. Brown, "Low-Resolution TV: Subjective Comparison of Interlaced and Noninterlaced Pictures," *Bell Syst. Tech. J.* **46** (January 1967), pp. 199-232.

53. See reference 51.

54. D. E. Pearson, C. B. Rubinstein, and G. J. Spivack, "Comparison of Perceived Color in Two-Primary Computer-Generated Artificial Images with Predictions Based on the Helson-Judd Formulation," *J. Opt. Soc. Am.* **59** (May 1969), pp. 644-658.

55. R. L. Eilenberger, F. W. Kammerer, and J. F. Muller, "Compact Optical System for Field/Line Sequential Color Videotelephone Camera," *J. SMPTE* **79** (December 1970), pp. 1063-1070.

56. R. D. Kell, British Patent No. 341,811; April 25, 1929.

57. A. B. Larsen, U.S. Patent No. 3,730,977; filed February 29, 1972; issued May 1, 1973.

58. M. F. Tompsett, W. J. Bertram, D. A. Sealer, and C. H. Séquin, "Charge-Coupling Improves Its Image, Challenging Video Camera Tubes," *Electronics* **46** (January 18, 1973), pp. 162-169.

59. J. O. Limb, C. B. Rubinstein, and K. A. Walsh, "Digital Coding of Color Picturephone Signals by Element-Differential Quantization," *IEEE Trans. Commun. Technol.* **COM-19** (December 1971), pp. 992-1006.

60. J. O. Limb and C. B. Rubinstein, "Plateau Coding of the Chrominance Component of Color Picture Signals," *IEEE Trans. Commun.* **COM-22** (June 1974), pp. 812-820.

61. A. N. Netravali and C. B. Rubinstein, "Quantization of Color Signals," *Proc. IEEE* **65** (August 1977), pp. 1177-1187.

62. A. N. Netravali and J. O. Limb, "Picture Coding: A Review," *Proc. IEEE* **68** (March 1980), pp. 366-406.

63. See reference 31.

64. W. H. Ninke, R. C. Brainard, P. D. T. Ngo, and T. P. Sosnowski, "An Experimental Display Telephone," *Proc. Int. Seminar Dig. Commun.*, Zurich (March 9-11, 1976), pp. B6.1-B6.6.

65. O. Johnsen and J. Segen, "A Pattern Matching Technique for Facsimile Coding," *Proc. IEEE Int. Conf. Commun.*, Philadelphia (June 13-17, 1982), pp. 2G.2.1-2G.2.7.

66. A. N. Netravali and J. D. Robbins, "Motion-Compensated Television Coding: Part I," *Bell Syst. Tech. J.* **58** (March 1979), pp. 631-670.

67. E. F. Brown, V. J. Geller, J. E. Goodnow II, D. G. Hoecker, and M. Wish, "Some Objective and Subjective Differences Between Communication Over Two Videoconferencing Systems," *IEEE Trans. Commun.* **COM-28** (May 1980), pp. 759-771.

68. R. C. Brainard, A. N. Netravali, and D. E. Pearson, "Predictive Coding of Composite NTSC Color TV Signals," *SMPTE J.* **91** (March 1982), pp. 245-252.

Chapter 4

Vacuum Tube Electronics Research

The potential importance of the triode vacuum tube as an amplifier in communications systems was recognized by H. D. Arnold in 1912 when L. de Forest demonstrated his audion. As discussed in the first volume of this series, subtitled "The Early Years (1875-1925)," Arnold and his colleagues made many contributions to the early science and technology of vacuum tubes. Much of the subsequent work on electron tubes is described in another volume in this series, subtitled "Electronics Technology (1925-1975)." This chapter records fundamental investigations of the interaction of electron streams with electromagnetic waves, including space charge and transit time effects. It deals with reflex klystrons, electron guns, multicavity magnetrons, and traveling wave tubes, including spatial harmonic amplifiers and oscillators.

I. ELECTRON BEAMS

Fundamental theoretical and experimental studies in electronics research, with emphasis on the behavior of electron beams in vacuum tubes, began in the 1930s. In his paper on "Vacuum Tube Electronics at Ultra High Frequencies,"[1] published in 1934, F. B. Llewellyn took into account the time of flight of the electron in a vacuum tube. In a subsequent paper, published in 1935,[2] Llewellyn extended his analysis to calculate the rectifying properties of diodes at very high frequencies and the amplifying properties of negative grid triodes. In 1938, C. E. Fay, A. L. Samuel, and W. Shockley published a paper, "On the Theory of Space Charge Between Parallel Plane Electrodes."[3] This work resulted in a very useful equivalent network for grid control tubes that included the effects of electron transit times and interelectrode capacitances. In the same year, Shockley and J. R. Pierce carried out a theoretical investigation of noise in electron multipliers, distinguishing between noise due to the input and noise gen-

---

Principal authors: C. C. Cutler and S. Millman.

169

erated in the secondary emission process of the several stages of amplification.[4] In 1944, Llewellyn and L. C. Peterson wrote down the frequency-dependent equations that accurately describe the electron stream in a diode.[5]

1.1 The Pierce Electron Gun

An important Bell Labs contribution in the early 1940s was Pierce's electron gun.[6] [Fig. 4-1] Previously, electron beams were formed by focusing the electrons diverging from a cathode with electrostatic or magnetic lenses, and the lens system was designed by trial and error. Pierce studied the boundary conditions that must be met to confine electrons emerging from a flat cathode under space charge limited conditions to flow in rectilinear

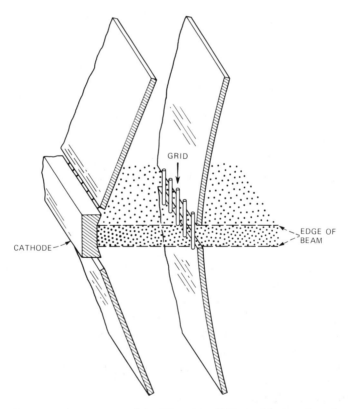

GRID

CATHODE

EDGE OF BEAM

Fig. 4-1. The geometry of the "Pierce gun." Electrodes were shaped to produce an electric field outside the beam to be parallel to the beam edge for high-density conditions. The metallic cathode is shaped so as to produce an angle of precisely 67-1/2 degrees with the beam edge. At greater distances, the electrodes were shaped empirically. [Pierce, *Theory and Design of Electron Beams* (1954): 178.]

fashion, and showed that the electric field may be obtained by the simple expedient of supplying a nonemitting conical conductor adjacent to the cathode and inclined at an angle of 67.5 degrees to the beam edge. By using a concave cathode surface and appropriately shaped electrodes, higher-current densities of electron beams were easily obtained. Electrode shapes were determined empirically in an electrolytic water tank where the potentials in the electrolyte satisfied Laplace's equations, and the beam was represented by an insulator, displacing the electrolyte. A tilted tank simulated a circular cross section. The electrode shapes were adjusted until the potential distribution along the edge of the insulator, simulating the electron beam, matched that calculated to satisfy Laplace's equation outside and Poisson's equation inside the beam.

1.2 The Reflex Klystron

The invention of the klystron in 1935 by the Varian brothers at Stanford University was a real breakthrough in the technology of vacuum tube amplifiers at microwave frequencies. Their research was not published until 1939,[7] and soon thereafter Bell Labs engineers began to apply their skills with very high frequency (VHF), waveguides, and electron dynamics to the design of devices useful at microwave frequencies. A microwave oscillator that played a particularly important role in World War II radar work was the reflex klystron invented by Pierce and W. G. Shepherd in the early 1940s.[8]

In the klystron the electron transit time is used constructively. Electrons from a cathode first pass a gap in the capacitive part of a microwave cavity. The change in phase of the radio frequency (RF) electric field during a period of oscillation causes electrons passing earlier and at the proper phase to be retarded relative to those passing the gap later. The resulting "bunched" beam passes a second similar microwave cavity gap to interact with its RF field. The RF power is extracted from the cavity through a suitable coupling loop and a metal-to-glass seal. In the reflex klystron, which has only one microwave cavity, the bunched electron beam is reflected back to the cavity gap by the application of suitable negative voltage to interact with the RF field of the cavity from which the power is extracted. [Fig. 4-2]

The Pierce-Shepherd reflex klystron, together with its derivatives, were the workhorses for heterodyning oscillator receivers throughout World War II. A multicavity Varian-type klystron having a very wide tuning range, 2 to 13 gigahertz (GHz), was developed by J. W. Clark and Samuel.[9] It was used as an amplifier in the Bell Laboratories TDX microwave radio-relay transmission system introduced in 1948 (see Chapter 5, section 2.2 in this volume).

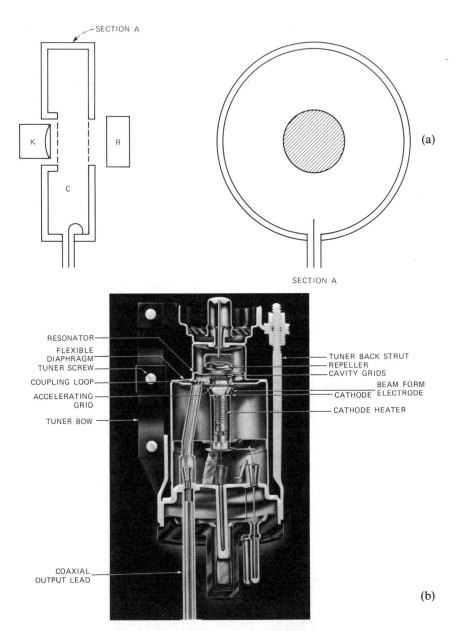

Fig. 4-2. The reflex klystron. (a) Schematic cross section of a reflex oscillator. Above left: *C* is the cavity, *K* is the hot cathode, and *R* is the repeller. Above right: a cross section of the cavity. (b) The reflex klystron (bottom). Many versions of this tube were built for use as beating oscillators for wartime radar. Output was about 100 milliwatts. The tube was tuned over a small range by bending the envelope structure so that the cavity dimensions were changed. The electron focusing was such that the electrons transversed the cavity just twice, avoiding hysteresis effects that took place in early tubes where reflected electrons reentered the cathode region.

II. MULTICAVITY MAGNETRON RESEARCH

2.1 Magnetron Research During World War II

The main contribution by Bell Labs scientists to vacuum tube electronics research during World War II was through the work on the multicavity magnetron oscillator under the leadership of J. B. Fisk, who was to become vice president of research and later president of Bell Laboratories. This work was described in some detail in Chapter 2, section IV of the second volume of this series, subtitled *National Service in War and Peace (1925-1975)*.

In a magnetron oscillator, electrons emitted from a cylindrical cathode are drawn by a radial electric field toward the multicavity anode structure surrounding the cathode and suitably spaced from it. An axial magnetic field is provided. In the crossed electric-magnetic field, the motions of individual electrons are cycloidal. Electrons gaining energy from interacting with the anode RF field return to the cathode and contribute energy to keep it hot. Electrons losing energy are drawn closer to the anode, and, under the proper synchronous conditions, these electrons continue to lose energy until they impinge on the anode, leading to fairly efficient transfer of their kinetic energy to RF energy. The RF power is drawn from the resonating structure to the outside by suitable coupling to one of the cavities, either by a coaxial loop or by a slot leading directly to the waveguide, with the appropriate glass-to-metal vacuum seal.

Since a microwave magnetron has a multicavity anode structure, it can, in principle, oscillate in more than one of the resonant frequencies characteristic of the assembly of coupled resonators. It becomes highly important in the design of a microwave magnetron oscillator to insure that with the application of the proper dc magnetic and electric field it will oscillate in only one of these resonant frequencies. The most efficient and most stable mode of operation is one for which alternate anode segments are 180 degrees out of phase in the RF oscillating cycle (the singlet π-mode). In 1941, J. T. Randall and J. Sayers of the University of Birmingham found that tying the alternate anode segments together with short pieces of wire straps at each end of the anode block helped to insure such single-mode operation. The studies of Fisk, H. D. Hagstrum, and P. L. Hartman[10] increased the understanding of the role that the various possible modes of oscillation played in magnetron operation and the effect of the wire straps—which later evolved into two pairs of concentric copper rings—on the frequency separation between the desirable π-mode and the other resonant modes associated with the multicavity structure. The research of the Bell Labs group, in collaboration with Professor J. C. Slater of the Massachusetts Institute of Technology, also produced an experimental verification of the scaling principle, making it technically feasible to design with confidence a multicavity magnetron at a shorter wavelength from a magnetron known to be operating successfully at a given longer wavelength by appropriately scaling the physical dimensions and operating voltages, currents, and magnetic fields.

2.2 Postwar Magnetron Research

Magnetron research declined rapidly after 1945. While Fisk continued his leadership of the Electron Dynamics Research Department, the activities shifted toward traveling wave tube research, particularly after Fisk temporarily left Bell Laboratories early in 1947, at which point the leadership was assigned to Pierce and S. Millman. In 1949, the group moved from the "Biscuit Building" at the old Bell Labs headquarters (463 West Street, New York City), where major vacuum tube problems had frequently been soot and sweat, to the antiseptically clean quarters of a new building at Murray Hill, New Jersey. The air-filtered and air-conditioned tube assembly area—patterned in part after a laboratory set up at West Street by J. A. Morton for the fabrication of his close-spaced triode—was a showplace for some time.

2.2.1 Solution of a Magnetron Moding Problem

In 1950, the Vacuum Tube Electronics Research Department became aware of some problems encountered in the operation of the high-power, tunable magnetron transmitters used in the M33 Fire Control System.[11] Two principal problems were encountered: (1) very short life (averaging about a few dozen hours compared with an expected several hundred hours), caused mainly by the suck-in of the glass window in the waveguide output, and (2) a tendency to oscillate in an unwanted mode rather than the π-mode. The magnetron operating efficiency was also not up to expectation, but that was not unrelated to the moding problem.

It was soon established that the overheating of the glass window in the output seal of the tube was occasioned by the initiation of arcs in the waveguide section leading from the magnetron to the rotating joint associated with the radar antenna. Although the rotating joint was designed to produce a good impedance match to free space for the entire wavelength band over which the tunable magnetron was supposed to operate (12 percent), the match was quite poor when the magnetron fired in a non-π-mode, with a wavelength about 10 percent lower than that of the π-mode. The high standing-wave ratio set up in the waveguide when the magnetron started in the wrong mode caused the breakdown in the guide. The resulting arc quickly moved to the window and, after about 2 minutes, the glass window became soft enough to melt and suck in.

It was believed that the problem arose from a possible variation in the loading for the competing non-π-mode frequency (which is a frequency doublet as compared with the singlet π-mode), arising from small uncontrolled asymmetries in the anode construction (e.g., in the concentric close-spaced copper ring straps). If this non-π-mode oscillating frequency is too lightly loaded, the magnetron can start in this undesirable mode. The solution arrived at (as described in an unpublished internal memorandum) was to introduce a deliberate asymmetry in the anode block, large enough to mask the uncontrolled asymmetries but not so large as to distort in any significant manner the operation of the magnetron in the normal operating π-mode. This asymmetry, which consisted of a slight enlargement of two of the holes of the 16 hole-and-slot cavities of the anode block, was so placed with respect to the output waveguide as to insure an appreciable loading for the competing non-π-mode.

It was very gratifying to the researchers and to those responsible for the development of the magnetrons that this very simple solution of a serious magnetron problem resulted in the manufacture of highly efficient magnetrons, free from moding problems and having long life.

2.2.2 The Circular Electric Mode Magnetron

A novel approach for obtaining stable π-mode magnetron operation was the coaxial cavity magnetron invented in 1954 by J. Feinstein and R. J. Collier at Bell Labs.[12] In this magnetron anode design, the backs of alternate resonators are coupled through slots to a microwave cavity, oscillating in the TE_{011} mode, which surrounds the anode. Since the RF currents in alternate resonators are all in phase, under π-mode operation, they couple easily to circumferential currents of the cavity. The cavity also improves the frequency stabilization and provides easy tuning of the magnetron frequency. [Fig. 4-3]

III. TRAVELING WAVE TUBES

Although R. Kompfner [Fig. 4-4] was the inventor of the traveling wave tube,[13,14] it was Pierce [Fig. 4-5] who exploited its great potential as a broadband ultrahigh frequency (UHF) and microwave amplifier. Pierce heard of Kompfner's early work on the traveling wave amplifier through the British Committee on Vacuum Tube Development in 1944. He visited Kompfner at Oxford University, and from this visit there developed a long and fruitful collaboration between the two men. Kompfner was relatively

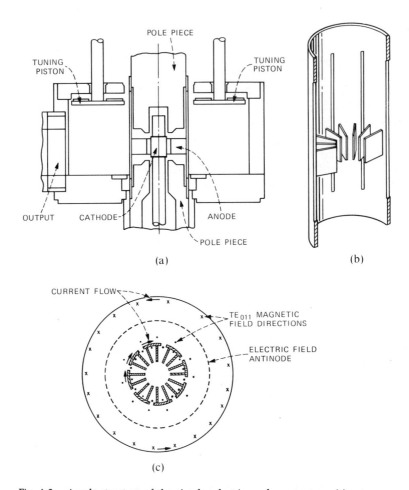

Fig. 4-3. Anode structure of the circular electric mode magnetron: (a) cutaway of the magnetron, (b) cutaway of the anode—a longitudinal view, and (c) cross section of anode coupled to the cavity—looking down. [Feinstein and Collier, *Crossed-Field Microwave Devices*, Vol. 2 (1961): 125.]

new in electronics. He was educated in Vienna as an architect and started a career in this profession in London. He was caught up in electronics activities during World War II. In 1943, he initiated an experimental investigation of the interaction of an electron beam with an electromagnetic wave propagating in a slow-wave circuit. He envisioned it as a means of obtaining very low noise microwave amplification, and was building tubes

Fig. 4-4. R. Kompfner, who invented the traveling wave tube and the backward-wave, voltage-tunable oscillator.

and analyzing the results to test the idea. Pierce, on the other hand, had a wealth of experience in electronics, including work on multicavity klystrons, which bore a strong resemblance to traveling wave tubes. He quickly saw the possibilities of obtaining larger gain and almost unlimited bandwidth operation with a traveling wave tube amplifier compared with the Morton close-spaced triode tubes. He was less impressed with the low noise possibilities that had appealed to Kompfner.

Immediately after he returned from his visit to Oxford, Pierce set about developing his own analysis, and designed a traveling wave tube with an intentionally lossy helix. The addition and optimal distribution of loss, together with the appropriate proportioning of the beam and circuit, turned out to be vital ingredients to the success of the tube. Pierce's initial successes with the new amplifier and his theoretical analysis of the operation of the traveling wave principle[15,16] provided a stimulus for colleagues at Bell Labs and workers elsewhere to enter this field of research. Kompfner joined Bell Laboratories in December 1951.

Fig. 4-5.   J. R. Pierce, who pioneered in fundamental theoretical studies
of traveling wave amplification with electron beams and made a major
contribution to the development of the traveling wave tube as an extremely
wide-band microwave amplifier.

3.1 The Helix Traveling Wave Tube Amplifier

Pierce and his collaborator, L. M. Field, designed a helix traveling wave
tube amplifier[17] in which the helix was made of molybdenum wire, with
a few turns in the center coated with a carbon particle colloid (Aquadag*)
to provide appropriate RF loss. [Fig. 4-6] The early tests were successful
enough that further development of the helix traveling wave tube could
be turned over to a development group of which Morton was supervisor.
In the meantime a group concerned with radio research, under the supervision of C. C. Cutler at the Murray Hill, New Jersey laboratory in
close proximity to Pierce and his colleagues working on traveling wave
tubes, started in 1949 to work on the high-frequency circuitry that would

---

* Trademark of Acheson Colloids Co.

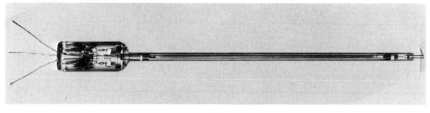

(a)

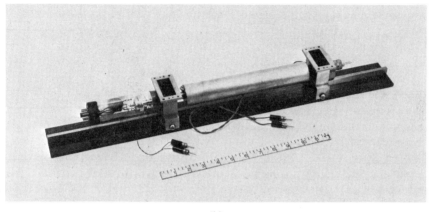

(b)

Fig. 4-6.   The helix traveling wave tube. (a) An early traveling wave tube. (b) A traveling wave tube coupled to the input and output waveguides for amplification of 4-GHz RF signals.

be associated with the tube for microwave radio applications. The group began a very fruitful study of the traveling wave tube using demountable, continuously pumped vacuum techniques. They determined the optimized loss distribution on the helix of the traveling wave tube, designed appropriate permanent magnet focusing of the electron beam, and contributed to the understanding of spurious modulation. One of the spurious modulation effects was found to be caused by ion oscillations and was eliminated by learning how to bake out and evacuate electron tubes more effectively.

3.1.1 Focusing of Electron Beams

The brute force method of focusing electron beams was to immerse everything in a uniform magnetic field. In 1945, L. Brillouin[18] of the IBM Watson Laboratories, and Pierce[19] at Bell Labs derived analytically the conditions for obtaining a smooth electron beam with a minimal magnetic field by exactly balancing the space charge repulsion with the magnetic force on electrons traveling helically through the field, and by initiating the electron current from a cathode outside the magnetic field. Later, Pierce and L. R. Walker extended the theory to include the thermal velocity distribution of the electrons.[20] Nevertheless, focusing an electron beam with permanent magnets was not very attractive, since the magnets were very bulky, expensive, and often inconvenient.

In 1952, a new method for focusing beams of high-energy ions was announced by E. D. Courant, M. S. Livingston, and H. S. Snyder at Brookhaven National Laboratory.[21] They called it strong focusing; it is also known by the more descriptive term, quadrupolar focusing. In this method, transverse magnetic fields between sets of four pole pieces intersect the ion beam; these fields cause small undulations in the flow, and eventually a drift of the ion toward the axis. The method was not particularly good for traveling wave tube beams, but it generated a lot of research activity and resulted in the application of periodic focusing to traveling wave tubes, which was first proposed by Pierce.[22,23] The focusing field in a traveling wave tube could be reversed periodically along the direction of electron flow to great advantage in reducing magnet size. Fortunately, magnets of ferrite material (see Chapter 12 of the fourth volume in this series, subtitled *Physical Sciences (1925-1980)*) became available at this time, and it was possible to make very strong fields in short gaps with ferrite material in the form of many small tori, oppositely and axially poled; the assembly weighed a total of only 2 pounds. By contrast, an alnico magnet to focus a 10-inch-long electron beam of 10 milliamperes weighed hundreds of pounds.

Electric field reversals also have a focusing action on electron beams, and many configurations of slow-wave structures and dc electric field configurations were devised in hopes of eliminating magnets altogether; one of these was Kompfner's slalom focusing tube. Perhaps it is apocryphal that the idea came to him on a ski slope, but it is a fact that he came to work one morning with the notion that a beam weaving its way through a positively charged ladder structure would be focused by the electric field. Two of his colleagues, J. S. Cook and W. H. Yocom, built an experimental tube that embodied the ladder structure and demonstrated the focusing action,[24] although it was never incorporated in one of the traveling wave tubes. An analysis of focusing an electron beam with periodic permanent magnets was given in 1954 by J. T. Mendel, C. F. Quate, and Yocom[25] and another for focusing with both magnetic and periodic electric fields was given by A. M. Clogston and H. Heffner.[26]

3.1.2 Instabilities in Electron Beam Tubes

As noted in section 3.1 above, instabilities were a problem in electron beam tubes from the beginning. Characterizing, eliminating, and sometimes capitalizing on instabilities accounted for a considerable effort, and resulted in a few important discoveries in the field. Electron and ion beam instabilities are discussed in section 2.3.1 of Chapter 6 of *Physical Sciences (1925-1980)*. Hollow and strip beams were also found to be inherently unstable configurations, a fact first observed in 1955 by H. F. Webster at General Electric Research Laboratory[27] and later by Cutler.[28]

A source of instability in traveling wave tubes is the phenomenon of phase defects caused by reflected electrons. Electrons reaching the collector in the tube give rise to secondary electrons that are generally of somewhat lower energy than the beam energy, are not difficult to contain, and are relatively harmless because they are not synchronous in velocity under any circumstances. However, a small fraction of the electrons are elastically reflected at the collector, and may traverse the helix at a velocity synchronous with the backward traveling wave, bypassing the loss region. These were first discovered by Cutler during a study of nonlinear behavior of the tube as a source of very low-level oscillations. Even when subdued, the feedback signal slightly modulates the forward wave in phase and amplitude, and for most telephone applications must be eliminated completely. This was done by meticulous collector design, with magnetic focusing asymmetry in the collector to steer the reflected electrons out of the circuit.[29]

3.1.3 Large-Signal Computer Calculations

The digital computer was developing into a useful tool at the same time that the proliferation of activity in electron beam tubes was taking place. Probably the first attempt to use computers for studying tube behavior was made in 1953 by A. T. Nordsieck.[30] He reformulated the traveling wave tube equations in parametric form suitable for the computer, approximated the electron stream by equations describing a one-dimensional charge distribution of point charges in a field, and iterated the interaction until the distribution of charges was severely distorted. The result was an approximation of nonlinear, overloading behavior of the tube. Somewhat later, P. K. Tien, Walker, and V. M. Wolontis[31] refined the process, including space charge and using a disc approximation to account for beam diameter. Their results agreed with experimental observations made at Bell Labs on a 10-times scale-model tube and with experiments conducted in other laboratories. These calculations provided a basis for designing medium-power traveling wave tubes. Computer modeling of electron interaction was also used widely in studying focusing and noise, and has supplanted empirical methods.

3.1.4 Short Pulses and the Traveling Wave Oscilloscope

The large gain and enormous bandwidth of the helix traveling wave tube gave rise to a number of effects, particularly oscillations in the form of short recirculating pulses when the nature of the oscillations was a means of generating very short pulses. Thus, by feeding the output of a traveling wave tube back to the input through a nonlinear element (called an expandor), Cutler was able to obtain repetitive pulses of 3-nanosecond duration.[32] The generation of such short pulses by feedback in a traveling wave tube stimulated the development of very fast pulsed circuitry at Bell Labs and was generic to the use of mode locking in lasers in the next decade (see Chapter 5, section 2.2 of *Physical Sciences (1925-1980)*). The traveling wave principles were also applied by Pierce to make a broadband micro-oscilloscope,[33] which he used to resolve the short pulses. His micro-oscilloscope was copied and replicated in new generations of very high-speed oscilloscopes by commercial test instrument manufacturers.

3.2 The Spatial Harmonic Amplifier

While the research on the helix traveling wave tube was influenced by the need for wideband amplifiers for the microwave relay systems in the frequency range of 4 to 6 GHz, other traveling wave tube activities, stimulated by research in the 50-GHz region, aimed at exploiting the highly desirable properties of the TE_{01} mode of the circular waveguide (see Chapter 6 in this volume). Not being optimistic about the feasibility of scaling down the helix structure by a factor of ten, Millman [Fig. 4-7] looked for

Fig. 4-7.   S. Millman, who made fundamental contributions to magnetron and traveling wave tube research.

other slow-wave circuit structures that would be more rugged than the helix for a millimeter-wave amplifier but at the same time would not require higher voltage for operation.

In 1950, Millman designed a microwave circuit consisting of a large number of quarter-wave slot resonators, with RF input and output coupled to the respective end resonators by means of tapered waveguides. However, instead of operating this traveling wave tube in the typical traveling wave fashion with the beam velocity about equal to the phase velocity of the wave traveling in a direction perpendicular to the slots, he proposed to operate the amplifier in a mode that required the electrons to fall back a full RF period as the wave moved from one slot to the next adjacent slot, with a consequent reduction of about a factor 5 in speed and a factor of 25 in voltage.

Millman first experimented with this novel amplifier at the 25-GHz microwave region (K-band), where good test equipment was readily available and the fabrication of tubes was relatively easy. After achieving encouraging results at this frequency, he constructed a 50-GHz amplifier, having 100 resonator slots, and achieved a gain of about 20 dB at a bandwidth of about 2 percent.[34,35] [Fig. 4-8]

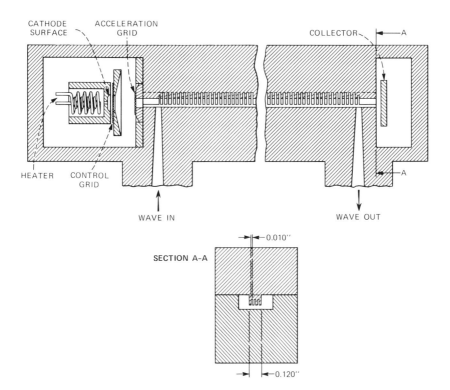

Fig. 4-8.   Millman's spatial-harmonic traveling wave tube, which amplified 6-mm waves.

While experimenting with his spatial harmonic amplifier and trying to drive the amplifier to higher and higher power, Millman found that oscillations set in at frequencies different from the input frequency. A careful measurement of the wavelengths at the corresponding beam voltage at which oscillations took place served to establish that these oscillations were produced in waves propagating in the direction *opposite* to the beam velocity. This backward-wave, spatial-harmonic operation is highly voltage sensitive, in contrast with the operation of the tube as an amplifier for which a constant voltage, independent of frequency, is desired. With his interest focused on the amplifier, Millman improved the operation of his traveling wave tube by making the waveguide output somewhat more broadband to minimize the competition from oscillations that required voltage close to the operating voltage of the amplifier.

3.3 Backward-Wave Voltage-Tunable Oscillator

Many structures besides the helix support a slow wave, and many researchers hoped to find the one that would make the helix obsolete. The periodicities in slow-wave structures, such as the one described in section 3.2, result in spatial variations in the field that are best described as the sum of space harmonics of the fundamental propagating field; the electron beam can interact with these fields if the synchronous velocity condition is satisfied. Some of these phase harmonics have effective phase velocities in a direction that is the reverse of the respective group velocities, and for these space harmonics the phase velocities are inherently dispersive. Synchronism obtains at only one frequency for a given beam voltage, but changes with voltage. Kompfner realized this possibility while still in England. When he arrived at Bell Labs in December 1951, he found that the traveling wave amplifier that Millman built for millimeter wavelengths was ideally suited for a voltage-tunable oscillator and that the structure was a natural for space harmonics. Thus, Kompfner's first successful backward-wave oscillator[36] was built sooner than he expected. It appears that B. Epsztein, at Companie Generale Télégraphique sans Fil in France, was first to file for a patent on an application of the backward-wave structure for a voltage-tunable oscillator in April 1951. A U.S. patent was issued to Epsztein in 1960.[37]

It is amusing that when Kompfner's patent application on the voltage-tunable backward-wave oscillator reached the Patent Office, the military usefulness was evident and the subject matter was classified secret, and Kompfner, being a noncitizen, was not allowed to know about the tube he himself invented.

The backward-wave oscillator became very important for certain military applications, but particularly as a signal generator that is voltage tunable over a wide bandwidth for laboratory purposes. It also found application as a signal source for millimeter- and submillimeter-wavelength radiation.

3.4 The Karp Space-Harmonic Oscillator at Millimeter Waves

Another slow-wave circuit structure for traveling wave tubes for use at millimeter wavelengths was proposed in 1955 by A. Karp.[38,39] The circuit consisted of a ridged, rectangular waveguide overwound with a fine wire, spaced to form a slotted surface opposite the ridge. The electron beam traveling perpendicular and very close to the slots was coupled to space harmonics of waves traveling in such a circuit. [Fig. 4-9] Karp obtained forward-wave interaction and backward-wave oscillations in a wavelength band centered at 5.6 GHz. He later extended the application of this circuit structure to obtain electronically tuned oscillations at frequencies between 100 and 200 GHz. Several dozen of these tubes were built and used in physics millimeter-waveguide research.

3.5 The Easitron Amplifier

In 1950, Pierce proposed a microwave amplifier that, because of its conceptual simplicity, became known as the "easitron." An electron beam is arranged to travel parallel to a closely spaced grid of wires between two plates that are separated by less than half a wavelength. Walker and Pierce analyzed the performance of such an amplifier, which was described in an unpublished internal technical memorandum.

A thin sheet of electrons moving uniformly in the plane of the sheet through empty space sees a capacitive admittance. An applied RF field along the beam then produces two unattenuated waves, one faster and

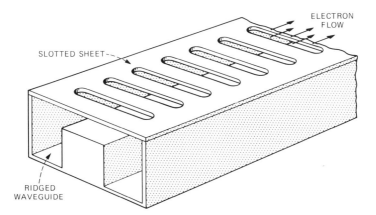

Fig. 4-9. Karp's space-harmonic circuit for traveling wave amplifiers and backward-wave oscillators of millimeter waves. [Karp, *Proc. IRE* **45** (1957): 496.]

one slower than the beam. On the other hand, when a nonpropagating circuit is introduced and the admittance seen by the beam is constant and inductive, the phase of the resultant RF field causes the beam-density modulation to increase. As a result, a growing and a decaying wave are produced traveling at the beam velocity. The system thus amplifies at any beam velocity and at any frequency for which the circuit is inductive. Such a device was built by Walker and gave a net gain of 70 dB at 7.9 GHz. Because of the success of other amplifiers, the problems of frequency sensitivity and coupling to input-output circuits were not further explored.

3.6 Double-Stream Amplification

In the late 1940s, the efforts of a number of scientists and engineers at many electronics research institutions were directed toward inventing microwave oscillators and amplifiers that, it was hoped, would be applicable to millimeter waves. We noted earlier in this chapter that a specific motivation for Millman's 50-GHz spatial harmonic amplifier was the research activity at the Holmdel, New Jersey laboratory, aimed at exploiting the desirable propagation properties of the TE_{01} mode in the circular cross-section waveguide. Several researchers in different laboratories independently came up with the idea of achieving RF amplification in two electron beams of slightly different average velocities and traveling close to each other (i.e., at a distance small compared with the free space wavelength of the RF oscillation to be amplified). The published papers of L. E. Neergard[40] of RCA, A. V. Haeff[41] of the Naval Research Laboratory, and the two papers from Bell Labs by Pierce and W. B. Hebenstreit[42] and by A. V. Hollenberg[43] appeared within two months in late 1948 and early 1949. An extensive analysis of the operation of the double-stream amplifier was published by Pierce.[44]

In the double-stream amplifier the two electron streams support a space charge wave that travels with a phase velocity, which is intermediate between the two electron velocities, and that increases in amplitude with distance as it travels. Circuits, such as helixes or resonators, are required at the two ends to couple with the electron streams, one at the input end to set up a space charge wave and one at the output end to extract the power from the amplified wave. Hollenberg used a helix circuit for input and output and obtained a gain of about 33 dB at about 250 megahertz (MHz) with a bandwidth of 110 MHz. The need for helixes or other RF circuits of very close tolerances for coupling to the electron beams at the input and at the output remained as a fundamental limitation of the double-stream amplifier at millimeter waves.

IV. NOISE IN MICROWAVE AMPLIFIERS AND DETECTORS

Even before the problem of electronic noise in microwave tubes was recognized, Shockley and Pierce developed a theory of noise for electron multipliers.[45] We have noted in section II above that a motivation for work leading to the invention of the traveling wave tube by Kompfner was to find ways of avoiding the noise inherent in other microwave detectors. The early tubes had a noise figure (a measure of the increase in the noise-to-signal ratio in the output compared with that at the input) of about 30 dB at a time when silicon or germanium diode mixers were giving a 12- to 15-dB noise figure. In traveling wave tubes and klystrons, the electron beam used to amplify the signal carried shot noise that was amplified along with the signal, resulting in a significant degradation of the signal-to-noise ratio of the output.

4.1 Noise Studies in Traveling Wave Tubes

Space charge smoothing of noise in thermionic diodes was studied in the late 1930s, and reached a milestone with publication of the Llewellyn-Peterson equations (referred to in section I above).[46] Pierce used these in electron beams and predicted that standing waves of noise would exist in the beam, with noise energy alternating between a modulation of charge density and velocity in the same way as a signal in a klystron drift space. Experimental verification soon followed, and in due course it was accepted that, in a narrow band, noise is just another signal but with a natural origin.

Realizing and quantifying the electron beam noise led to a number of spectacular advances in the traveling wave tube. First, it was clear that starting the helix at an optimum phase in the noise wave would lower the amplification of the noise, since, in the helix, traveling wave tube noise is coupled through space charge. Then, L. M. Field (by this time at Stanford University) and his student, P. K. Tien, realized that by suddenly accelerating an electron beam at the right distance from the cathode, the noise could be amplified or subdued.[47] Work at Stanford University and at Bell Labs that was done by Tien and others after he joined Bell Labs produced a series of experimental tubes[48] that inhibited noise and enhanced gain by appropriately placed velocity jumps. With these advances, noise figures of less than 3 dB were realized, thus reducing the noise output power by a factor of several hundred. The noise figures in traveling wave tubes became comparable to those in other microwave amplifiers, such as the parametric amplifier. [Fig. 4-10]

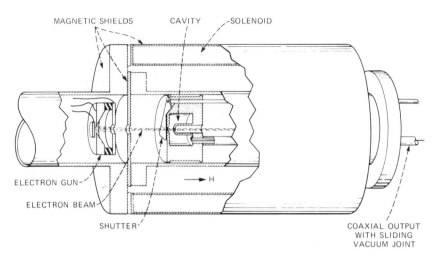

Fig. 4-10. The apparatus used by Cutler and Quate in measuring the noise current along an electron beam. The gun is at the left. The beam passes through a resonant cavity that can be slid along so that the noise current can be picked up and measured as a function of distance along the beam. [Cutler and Quate, *Phys. Rev.* **80** (1950): 875.]

4.2 Noise and Parametric Amplification

In 1957, H. Suhl[49,50] proposed a gyromagnetic parametric amplifier that consisted of two resonant circuits coupled by a variable reactance (see also Chapter 1, section 2.2.3 of *Physical Sciences (1925-1980)*). The amplifier involved a frequency condition f(pump) = f_1 (signal) + f_2 (idler), in accord with the analysis of parametric amplifiers given by J. M. Manley and H. E. Rowe.[51] Shortly thereafter, Tien[52,53] invented a traveling wave parametric amplifier. In addition to the frequency condition mentioned earlier, he proposed a phase-matching condition for the phase velocity of the above oscillatory frequencies, β(pump) = β_1(signal) + β_2(idler), which is also known as the Tien-Beta relation, a phase-matching condition widely used in nonlinear optics applications of quantum electronics.

The wave-type parametric amplifiers, including the forward-wave-type and the backward-wave-type amplifiers as proposed by Tien, were quickly demonstrated in the form of semiconductor diode amplifiers by M. Uenohara and W. M. Sharpless,[54] and in the form of cyclotron-wave electron-beam amplifiers by R. Adler of Zenith Radio Corporation[55] and by T. J. Bridges and A. Ashkin.[56,57] The Uenohara-Sharpless amplifier, operating at a frequency of 5 GHz, had a noise figure as low as 0.3 dB, which is to be compared with a noise figure of 3 to 6 dB in typical traveling wave tubes. What makes the parametric amplifiers important is that signals are amplified by an electron beam or by semiconductor diodes in the form of a variable reactance that does not contribute noise.[58]

V. CONCLUDING COMMENT ON VACUUM TUBE ELECTRONICS RESEARCH

The achievement in the noise reduction of the helix traveling wave tube notwithstanding, vacuum tube electronics research at Bell Laboratories declined rapidly beginning with the mid-1950s. The noise figures obtained with the microwave maser used in the Telstar communication system and with the semiconductor diode parametric amplifiers, as noted in section 4.2 above, were even lower than with the best traveling wave tubes. However, traveling wave tubes have continued to play a very important role in high-power microwave applications, such as transmitters in satellites. Moreover, the solid-state amplifiers were small, rigid, and relatively inexpensive, requiring negligible power and no magnetic fields to operate. With the proliferation of solid-state microwave devices and the expectation of more to come, particularly after the invention of the laser with its virtually unlimited bandwidth potential, interest in vacuum tube electronics research at Bell Laboratories ceased.

REFERENCES

1. F. B. Llewellyn, "Vacuum Tube Electronics at Ultra-High Frequencies," *Bell Syst. Tech. J.* **13** (January 1934), pp. 59-101.
2. F. B. Llewellyn, "Operation of Ultra-High-Frequency Vacuum Tubes," *Bell Syst. Tech. J.* **14** (October 1935), pp. 632-665.
3. C. E. Fay, A. L. Samuel, and W. Shockley, "On the Theory of Space Charge Between Parallel Plane Electrodes," *Bell Syst. Tech. J.* **17** (January 1938), pp. 49-79.
4. W. Shockley and J. R. Pierce, "A Theory of Noise for Electron Multipliers," *Proc. IRE* **26** (March 1938), pp. 321-332.
5. F. B. Llewellyn and L. C. Peterson, "Vacuum Tube Networks," *Proc. IRE* **32** (March 1944), pp. 144-166.
6. J. R. Pierce, "Rectilinear Electron Plane in Beams," *J. Appl. Phys.* **11** (August 1940), pp. 548-554; J. R. Pierce, "A Gun for Starting Electrons Straight in a Magnetic Field," *Bell Syst. Tech. J.* **30** (October 1951), pp. 825-829; J. R. Pierce, *Theory and Design of Electron Beams*, 2nd ed. (New York: D. Van Nostrand Co., 1954), p. 178.
7. R. H. Varian and S. F. Varian, "High Frequency Oscillator and Amplifier," *J. Appl. Phys.* **10** (May 1939), pp. 321-327.
8. J. R. Pierce and W. G. Shepherd, "Reflex Oscillators," *Bell Syst. Tech. J.* **26** (July 1947), pp. 460-681.
9. J. W. Clark and A. L. Samuel, "A Wide-Tuning Range Microwave Oscillator Tube," *Proc. IRE* **35** (January 1947), pp. 81-83.
10. J. B. Fisk, H. D. Hagstrum, and P. L. Hartman, "The Magnetron as a Generator of Centimeter Waves," *Bell Syst. Tech. J.* **25** (April 1946), pp. 167-348.
11. See pp. 368-372 of an earlier volume in this series, subtitled *National Service in War and Peace (1925-1975)*.
12. J. Feinstein and R. J. Collier, "The Circular Electric Mode Magnetron," in *Crossed-Field Microwave Devices*, Vol. 2, ed. E. Okress (New York: Academic Press, 1961), pp. 123-134.
13. R. Kompfner, "Travelling Wave Valve—New Amplifier for Centimeter Wavelengths," *Wireless World* **52** (November 1946), pp. 369-372.

14. R. Kompfner, "Traveling-Wave Tube as Amplifier at Microwaves," *Proc. IRE* **35** (February 1947), pp. 124-127.

15. J. R. Pierce, "Theory of the Beam-Type Traveling-Wave Tube," *Proc. IRE* **35** (February 1947), pp. 111-123.

16. J. R. Pierce, *Traveling Wave Tubes* (New York: D. Van Nostrand Co., 1950).

17. J. R. Pierce and L. M. Field, "Traveling Wave Tubes," *Proc. IRE* **35** (February 1947), pp. 108-111.

18. L. Brillouin, "A Theorem on Larmor and its Importance for Electrons in Magnetic Fields," *Phys. Rev.* **67** (April 1 and 15, 1945), pp. 260-266.

19. J. R. Pierce, "Electron Beams in Strong Magnetic Fields," *Phys. Rev.* **68** (November 1 and 15, 1945), pp. 229-230.

20. J. R. Pierce and L. R. Walker, " 'Brillouin Flow' with Thermal Velocities," *J. Appl. Phys.* **24** (October 1953), pp. 1328-1330.

21. E. D. Courant, M. S. Livingston, and H. S. Snyder, "The Strong-Focusing Synchroton—A New High Energy Accelerator," *Phys. Rev.* **88** (December 1, 1952), pp. 1190-1196.

22. J. R. Pierce, "Spatially Alternating Magnetic Fields for Focusing Low-Voltage Electron Beams," *J. Appl. Phys.* **24** (September 1953), p. 1247.

23. C. C. Cutler, U. S. Patent No. 2,942,141; filed June 6, 1957; issued June 21, 1960.

24. J. S. Cook, R. Kompfner, and W. H. Yocom, "Slalom Focusing," *Proc. IRE* **45** (November 1957), pp. 1517-1522.

25. J. T. Mendel, C. F. Quate, and W. H. Yocom, "Electron Beam Focusing with Periodic Permanent Magnet Fields," *Proc. IRE* **42** (May 1954), pp. 800-810.

26. A. M. Clogston and H. Heffner, "Focusing of an Electron Beam by Periodic Fields," *J. Appl. Phys.* **25** (April 1954), pp. 436-447.

27. H. F. Webster, "Breakup of Hollow Electron Beams," *J. Appl. Phys.* **26** (November 1955), pp. 1386-1387.

28. C. C. Cutler, "Instability in Hollow and Strip Electron Beams," *J. Appl. Phys.* **27** (September 1956), pp. 1028-1029.

29. C. C. Cutler, "Spurious Modulation of Electron Beams," *Proc. IRE* **44** (January 1956), pp. 61-64.

30. A. T. Nordsieck, "Theory of the Large Signal Behavior of Traveling-Wave Amplifiers," *Proc. IRE* **41** (May 1953), pp. 630-637.

31. P. K. Tien, L. R. Walker, and V. M. Wolontis, "A Large Signal Theory of Traveling-Wave Amplifiers," *Proc. IRE* **43** (March 1955), pp. 269-276.

32. C. C. Cutler, "Regenerative Pulse Generator," *Proc. IRE* **43** (February 1955), pp. 140-148; C. C. Cutler, U. S. Patent No. 2,617,930; filed September 30, 1949; issued November 11, 1952; C. C. Cutler, U. S. Patent No. 2,652,541; filed September 30, 1949; issued September 15, 1953.

33. J. R. Pierce, "Traveling Wave Oscilloscope," *Electronics* **22** (November 1949), pp. 97-99.

34. S. Millman, "A Spatial Harmonic Traveling-Wave Amplifier for Six Millimeters Wavelength," *Proc. IRE* **39** (September 1951), pp. 1035-1043.

35. S. Millman, "Spatial Harmonic Traveling-Wave Amplifier," *Bell Lab. Rec.* **30** (November 1952), pp. 413-416.

36. R. Kompfner and N. T. Williams, "Backward-Wave Tubes," *Proc. IRE* **41** (November 1953), pp. 1602-1611.

37. B. Epsztein, U.S. Patent No. 2,932,760; filed April 9, 1952; issued April 12, 1960.

38. A. Karp, "Traveling-Wave Tube Experiments at Millimeter Wavelengths with a New, Easily Built, Space Harmonic Circuit," *Proc. IRE* **43** (January 1955), pp. 41-46.

39. A. Karp, "Backward-Wave Oscillator Experiments at 100 to 200 Kilomegacycles," *Proc. IRE* **45** (April 1957), pp. 496-503.

40. L. E. Neergard, "Analysis of a Simple Model of a Two-Beam Growing Wave Tube," *RCA Rev.* **9** (December 1948), pp. 585-601.

41. A. V. Haeff, "The Electron-Wave Tube—A Novel Method of Generation and Amplification of Microwave Energy," *Proc. IRE* **37** (January 1949), pp. 4-10.
42. J. R. Pierce and W. B. Hebenstreit, "A New Type of High-Frequency Amplifier," *Bell Syst. Tech. J.* **28** (January 1949), pp. 33-51.
43. A. V. Hollenberg, "Experimental Observation of Amplification by Interaction Between Two Electron Streams," *Bell Syst. Tech. J.* **28** (January 1949), pp. 52-58.
44. J. R. Pierce, "Double-Stream Amplifiers," *Proc. IRE* **37** (September 1949), pp. 980-985.
45. See reference 4.
46. See reference 5.
47. L. M. Field, P. K. Tien, and D. A. Watkins, "Amplification by Acceleration and Deceleration of a Single-Velocity Stream," *Proc. IRE* **39** (February 1951), p. 194.
48. C. C. Cutler and C. F. Quate, "Experimental Verification of Space Charge and Transit Time Reduction of Noise in Electron Beams," *Phys. Rev.* **80** (December 1, 1950), pp. 875-878.
49. H. Suhl, "Proposal for a Ferromagnetic Amplifier in the Microwave Range," *Phys. Rev.* **106** (April 15, 1957), pp. 384-385.
50. H. Suhl, U. S. Patent No. 3,066,263; filed February 15, 1957; issued November 27, 1962.
51. J. M. Manley and H. E. Rowe, "Some General Properties of Nonlinear Elements—Part I. General Energy Relations," *Proc. IRE* **44** (July 1956), pp. 904-913.
52. P. K. Tien, U. S. Patent No. 3,012,203; filed March 7, 1960; issued December 5, 1961.
53. P. K. Tien, "Parametric Amplification and Frequency Mixing in Propagating Circuits," *J. Appl. Phys.* **29** (September 1958), pp. 1347-1357.
54. M. Uenohara and W. M. Sharpless, "An Extremely Low-Noise 6-kmc Parametric Amplifier Using GaAs Point-Contact Diodes," *Proc. IRE* **47** (December 1959), pp. 2114-2115.
55. R. Adler, G. Hrbek, and G. Wade, "A Low-Noise Electron-Beam Parametric Amplifier," *Proc. IRE* **46** (October 1958), pp. 1756-1757.
56. T. J. Bridges and A. Ashkin, "A Microwave Adler Tube," *Proc. IRE* **48** (March 1960), pp. 361-363.
57. A. Ashkin, "Low Noise Microwave Quadrupole Amplifier," *Proc. IRE* **49** (1961), pp. 1016-1020.
58. P. K. Tien, "Noise in Parametric Amplifiers," *Acta Electron.* **4** (July 1960), pp. 424-446.

Chapter 5

Radio Systems Research

The extensive contributions by Bell Labs scientists and engineers to radio communications began first in the shortwave radio region, with research on propagation, antenna design, and the fundamentals of noise encountered in receiving systems. Motivated by the need for ever-increasing bandwidths in radio transmission and by the recognition of the advantages of using shorter wavelengths in radar applications, research in the 1940s focused on microwaves. This research led to the microwave relay TDX system in 1947 and the subsequent, widely used TD radio relay systems in the 4- and 6-gigahertz (GHz) regions of the electromagnetic spectrum, with extension of the frequency range to 11 GHz for short-haul systems. Satellite communications research started in the mid-1950s, first using reflection of microwaves from a balloon placed in orbit around the earth. This was followed in the early 1960s with research on communication via a repeater system placed in the Telstar orbiting satellite, thus demonstrating the feasibility of commercial satellite communications. The more recent accomplishments in mobile radio communications laid the ground-work for cellular radio, which involved the division of a given metropolitan area into a number of adjoining hexagonal cells. Techniques were devised for dynamic channel assignment and efficient use of allotted frequency bands for handling short-term statistical fluctuations in communications demands.

I. RESEARCH AT SHORT AND ULTRASHORT WAVELENGTHS

Radio research before about 1940 was primarily directed toward establishing shortwave transoceanic circuits as well as setting a base for understanding the generation, propagation, and detection of radio frequencies up to about 300 megahertz (MHz). The accomplishments of Bell System scientists and engineers before 1925 are discussed in some detail in another volume of this series, subtitled *The Early Years (1875-1925)*.

The radio research activities at Bell Laboratories were centered at two laboratories in New Jersey.[1] The "receiving" laboratory (so-called because it was used for reception of transatlantic radio signals) was first set up at

---

Principal authors: C. C. Cutler and D. O. Reudink.

Fig. 5-1.   The Holmdel Radio Research Laboratory in 1931.

Cliffwood and later moved to a 400-acre tract in Holmdel. It became
known thereafter as the Holmdel laboratory. [Fig. 5-1] It was the location
of much work on antennas, shortwave and ultra-shortwave receivers, and
measurement technology. The other laboratory at Deal Beach, 15 miles
(mi.) south of Holmdel, housed the high-power shortwave transmitter
work and also was the source of many advances in measurement techniques.
The geographical separation was a primitive but effective method of isolation, or radio frequency (RF) shielding, between the two related but
differing endeavors. The Deal laboratory shared space with overseas radio
operators in a combined dormitory-laboratory structure, in addition to
occupying two small frame structures called the longwave and the shortwave buildings. Both the Holmdel and Deal laboratories sprouted temporary
structures to house measuring apparatus and field equipment. Another
part of the radio organization was at the Bell Labs headquarters building
at West Street in New York City, New York. In 1962, radio research was
consolidated in one building called the Crawford Hill Laboratory in Holmdel, New Jersey.

There was considerable collaboration with the development and research
engineers of the AT&T Long Lines Department and with the engineers at
the Bell Labs Whippany, New Jersey location engaged in radio research
related to broadcast and other commercial interests in the period from
1925 to 1955.

1.1 Shortwave Propagation and Detection

Much of the early work in radio at Bell Laboratories, and indeed worldwide, was concerned with the challenge of shortwave propagation. In the

early 1920s, G. Marconi as well as radio amateurs discovered that short-wavelength radio waves, after skipping large areas, reappeared at ground level at very great distances—even completely circumnavigating the globe. In 1925, R. A. Heising, J. C. Schelleng, and G. C. Southworth, using a sensitive and cleverly designed measuring set, made the first quantitative shortwave measurements over substantial distances.[2] They measured the variations in the sky wave from Deal to cities such as Cleveland, Ohio; Chicago, Illinois; and Minneapolis, Minnesota. [Fig. 5-2] In 1926, the measurements were extended to California and England. Transmission was tracked by ship from New York to Bermuda and, later, to England.

Establishing predictable and reliable shortwave radio transmission was a high-priority activity. In 1925, H. W. Nichols and Schelleng calculated the natural frequency of the electrons in the earth's magnetic field to be about 140 MHz.[3] Their calculations were based on mostly hypothetical properties of the ionosphere, or the Kennelly-Heaviside layer,[4] and on the interactions of atmospheric ions with radio frequency waves and the earth's magnetic field. These interactions had earlier been postulated as a cause of anomalous propagation at lower frequencies. Soon the vagaries of shortwave transmission and "skip" were better understood, and, by shifting frequencies several times during a 24-hour period, reasonably consistent communication could be maintained.[5] This was very fortunate, since the newly established longwave transmissions ran into serious noise problems during the summer months, and the experimental shortwave circuits became available for trial operations.

The design of measuring sets was also a high-priority activity, as more sensitive tubes and circuits became available and interests moved progressively to higher and higher frequencies.[6] In 1926, H. T. Friis [Fig. 5-3], using a battery-powered, double-detection (later called superheterodyne) receiver with a number of plug-in loop antennas, made a measuring set that was copied for many years.[7] These sets were calibrated by using the first and second detectors as vacuum tube voltmeters with a calibrated attenuator in the intermediate frequency (IF) amplifier, thus establishing the set gain. The field strength was then determined from calculated properties of the loop antenna. This superheterodyne receiver was widely replicated and used extensively over the next decade, both in the United States and in other countries.

As shortwave propagation became better understood, it became clear that not one but many propagation paths were involved. The ionosphere was investigated by studying the time and direction of arrival of pulsed signals as a function of frequency. Large arrays and steerable antennas were built at Holmdel, and vertical soundings were made at Deal.[8] The soundings consisted of transmitting radio frequency pulses vertically and analyzing the waves returning to the point of origin. Plotting pulse delay as a function of frequency revealed interesting layering in the ionosphere.

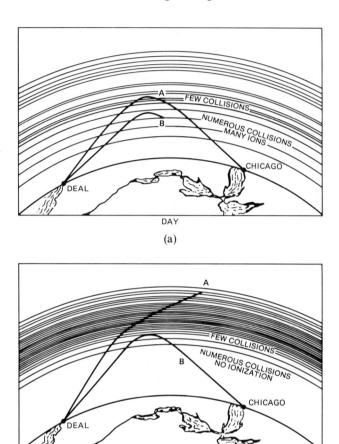

Fig. 5-2.   Anomalous atmospheric propagation of shortwave radio.
A is a higher-frequency radio wave (about 12 MHz). *B* is a lower-
frequency radio wave (about 3 MHz). (a) With many ions in the
atmosphere during the day, *A* is refracted to reach Chicago; *B* is just
attenuated and does not reach its goal. (b) At night, however, the
ions have disappeared. *A* is not refracted much, and *B* is much less
attenuated.

It was found that there was not just one, but up to six reflecting layers.[9,10]
Studies of solar eclipses and meteorite showers revealed the dynamics of
ionospheric fluctuations and added a great deal to the knowledge of the
ionosphere. These measurements were continued until 1939, when it became clear that a similar program at the United States National Bureau
of Standards adequately covered Bell System needs.

Fig. 5-3. H. T. Friis, who made fundamental contributions to the understanding of the role of noise in radio receivers and in the direction of research in microwave and millimeter-wave systems.

1.2 Beyond-the-Horizon Tropospheric Propagation

In 1950, K. Bullington pointed out that very-short-wavelength radio power propagating beyond the horizon greatly exceeds the power calculated for diffraction around the earth.[11] This provided a surge of interest in these potentially useful properties and led to early studies at Bell Labs[12] and elsewhere. Several theories were proposed to explain this propagation. Scattering by atmospheric turbulence was investigated by H. G. Booker and W. E. Gordon in 1950.[13] Mode propagation was studied by T. J. Carroll and R. M. Ring.[14] A theory of reflection from atmospheric layers was later advanced by Friis, A. B. Crawford, and D. C. Hogg.[15] Crawford, Hogg, and W. H. Kummer conducted an extensive set of experiments on a 171-mi. path, between Pharsalia, New York and Crawford Hill, New Jersey, from May 1955 to September 1958. Using two different sizes of receiving antennas, 60 and 8 feet (ft.), and frequencies at 4000 and 460 MHz, they accumulated much propagation data and were able to shed light on the beyond-the-horizon propagation mechanism.[16]

Crawford and associates found agreement with the predictions of the theory of reflection from a large number of randomly disposed atmospheric layers, due to the steep gradients in the dielectric constant of air in the volume of the atmosphere common to the beams of the transmitting and receiving antennas. At 4000 MHz, the ratio of the mean signal levels received by the 60-ft. antenna to that received by the 8-ft. antenna was not as large as expected from the ratio of antenna sizes (6 decibels (dB) compared with an expected 17 dB). This was found to be related to the observed variation in the angular distribution of the received signal due to local bending effects, which affect the large antenna with its higher resolving power more than the smaller antenna. With a given antenna, the received power was proportional to wavelength, as expected. Signal fading rates were shown to be related to the size of the antennas and to the velocity of the horizontal drift wind normal to the propagation direction. While some commercial use of tropospheric scatter for communication was realized, the Bell System generally chose higher-capacity, more reliable alternatives such as satellites, undersea cable, or microwave radio-relay systems.

1.3 Early Antenna Research—The Rhombic Antenna

Interest in antenna directivity, beyond that obtained with simple loops and dipoles, reawakened when the possibilities of shortwaves began to be understood in the first half of the 1920s. R. M. Foster of the AT&T Development and Research Department contributed to the understanding of antenna arrays when, in 1926, he published the directive diagrams of arrays of various numbers of elements and element spacings.[17] Southworth extended this work in 1930.[18]

An important result of the antenna research activities was the invention of the rhombic antenna by Friis and E. Bruce.[19] [Fig. 5-4] A straight wire radiates radio waves symmetrically from each end. To make a unidirectional receiving antenna, Bruce slanted a wire upward from the receiver so that the lower part of the cone of radiation pointed horizontally. He then bent the wire downward from the top of a pole so that the upper part of the cone of radiation from this segment coincided with the same desired horizontal direction. This made an inverted V. He terminated the end with a resistor to ground having a resistance equal to the radiation resistance of the wire. In accordance with known theory, the ground below an antenna acts like a mirror to produce the equivalent of an image of the antenna at the same distance below the ground plane. [Fig. 5-5] Thus, it was soon realized that the properly terminated, inverted V antenna was nearly equivalent to a vertical diamond-shaped antenna in free space. From this it was only one further step to a realization that the antenna could be turned on its side and, with some modification of dimensions and replacement of the image with real wire, become a horizontal double-V antenna. The resistor dissipated any signals coming from behind while

Fig. 5-4.   E. Bruce, who made fundamental contributions to shortwave radio communications with his invention of the rhombic antenna and his arrangement of antenna arrays for magnifying the effective signal in radio transmission.

the signal from the desired forward direction was delivered to the receiver. From horizontal double-V, the name gradually changed to diamond and finally (about 1935) to rhombic.

The rapid acceptance of this type of antenna throughout the world led to continuing demands for detailed design and construction information. This resulted in the writing of the book *Rhombic Antenna Design* by A. E. Harper, which was the definitive work on the subject for nearly two decades.[20]

The impact of the rhombic antenna is evident from the foreword to Harper's book, written by R. Bown, director of the Radio Research Department and later to become vice president of research at Bell Laboratories.

When there was built in 1929 at Lawrenceville, New Jersey, a radio telephone station for initiating overseas short-wave service, the most pictured feature of the new establishment was a gigantic wire fence or net, a mile long, stretched across the landscape on a row of 185 foot towers. This comprised the transmitting antenna complement for the three telephone circuits to Europe.

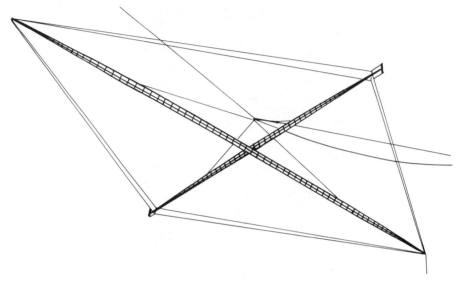

Fig. 5-5. A schematic of the Bruce antenna.

A year ago the nets were taken down, the towers dismantled and sold for junk. Near them has arisen a number of telephone poles carrying at odd looking angles a few almost invisible wires.[21]

While this was then the most spectacular conquest of the rhombic antenna, it is not the only measure of its impact on shortwave radio telephony. Subsequent stations constructed in Florida and California made use of this simple, efficient radiator from the start, and its modest cost was a factor in justifying the establishment of the new shortwave radio routes to South America, Hawaii, and the Orient.

1.4 Angle of Arrival of Radio Waves

For the transmission of electromagnetic waves, antenna gain can be as effective as an increase in power so long as the gain is in the right direction. For receiving such waves, gain is effective insofar as it increases the ratio of the signal to the various sources of noise and interference. Measurements of antenna gain were more conveniently and generally done with receiving antennas because existing signals from remote transmitters could be used. Such measurements showed that, as predicted by theory, the vertical angle of arrival of the signals varied widely, depending on the heights of the layers of the ionosphere from which the signal was reflected and on the number of signal bounces between the earth and ionosphere. General problems relating to antenna gain and system design were discussed by Schelleng [Fig. 5-6] in 1930.[22]

The earliest receiving antennas had a very small vertical dimension and consequently did not discriminate vertical angles of arrival. When inverted-V and rhombic antennas came into use, it was soon found that, as the gain of the antenna was increased, a point was reached where, although the size of the antenna was still economically feasible, an increase in the vertical directivity did not necessarily give rise to an increase in output. High gain was obtained only when the angle of arrival coincided with the vertical angle of reception. To design suitable antennas required, therefore, more knowledge about angles of arrival. From a series of measurements made by Friis, comparing the amplitudes of the outputs of two antennas having markedly different vertical directivities, the angles of arrival could be calculated.[23] Varying the vertical angle of reception made it possible to obtain information on the angle of arrival of pulses received from England.

In 1933, while investigating ground constants and their effect on directivity, C. B. Feldman found that with horizontal polarization, ground constants were not very important, but with vertical polarization, lower

Fig. 5-6. J. C. Schelleng, who made fundamental contributions to shortwave radio propagation.

angles of transmission could be obtained if the ground conductivity was high.[24] Often, ground conductivity is augmented by wires just above ground or buried in shallow trenches. In 1937, C. R. Burrows published a set of graphs that greatly expedited the calculation of the effects of ground constants, which previously had to be calculated laboriously by hand.[25] These graphs were extensively reproduced in various handbooks and manuals.

1.5 Overcoming the Effects of Fading

At short wavelengths, there are interferences in reception due to waves arriving over more than one path via the highly variable ionosphere. With multiple paths, out-of-phase addition of signals can result in very deep nulls in signal reception that change as the layers move. Investigations carried out in the late 1920s and early 1930s showed that when the same signal is received on two separate antennas, the instantaneous fading is not the same on the two receivers. Spacings of as little as six wavelengths gave sufficiently low correlation to encourage combining the output from two or more receivers with separate, spaced antennas to get a resultant "post detection" combined signal that was more satisfactory than that obtained from either receiver alone. Since each receiver was sensitive to signals arriving from different angles in the vertical plane, this system did little to combat selective fading in the audio band caused by interference between signal components with large delay differences.

A different approach to the problem resulted in a receiving system called the Multiple Unit Steerable Antenna (MUSA), which was set up at Holmdel in 1936 by Friis and his collaborators.[26,27] [Fig. 5-7] This system employed sharp vertical-plane directivity, which could be electronically steered to receive signals arriving at a particular angle and exclude signals arriving at other angles. Six rhombic antennas, each about 315 ft. long, were arranged in a line to form a phased array extending about three-quarters of a mile toward England. The antenna outputs were conducted over coaxial cable to double-detection receivers, one for each antenna, located at the receiving building. Here the phasing for the array was accomplished by means of rotatable phase shifters operating at the intermediate frequency of the receivers. The phase shifters, one for each antenna, were geared together, and the favored direction in the vertical plane could be steered by rotating the phase-shifter assembly. Three sets of phase shifters were placed in parallel to provide three separately steerable receiving branches. One branch served as an exploring or monitoring circuit to determine the angles at which waves were arriving. The other two branches were then set to receive at these angles, thus providing diversity in angle of reception. To obtain full benefit of the angular resolution afforded by the sharp directivity of the array, the different delays corresponding to the different angles were equalized by audio delay net-

Fig. 5-7. The six-element Multiple Unit Steerable Antenna (MUSA). This first electronically steerable antenna had good vertical-plane directivity and could be electronically steered with phase shifters for angular directivity, resulting in improved reception, signal-to-noise ratio, and audio quality.

works before combining in the final output. The benefits of the MUSA system were a signal-to-noise improvement of 7 to 8 dB referred to one antenna alone, and a substantial improvement in audio quality, due jointly to the diversity action and a reduction of selective fading. Subsequently, a 16-element antenna was built at Manahawkin, New Jersey, for operational use.

MUSA was the first electronically steerable antenna. The application of this pioneering work has continued into the 1980s, albeit in a much more sophisticated manner, to radar, satellites, and mobile radio.

1.6 Receiving System Noise

It was known that noise in the form of static interfered with radio reception. Less well understood, however, was the way in which noise internal to the radio receiver affected its sensitivity. A significant advance was made in 1928 when J. B. Johnson[28] and H. Nyquist[29] determined the cause of noise in amplifier circuits. Johnson showed that the thermal motion of electrons results in potentials across a resistance that are superimposed on the other expected voltage sources. The noise became known as "Johnson noise." The power due to the Johnson noise is simply kTB, where k is Boltzman's constant, T is the absolute temperature, and B is the bandwidth. This was an important contribution of physics to communication. (See Chapter 1, section 7.3 in this volume and Chapter 10, section I in *Physical Sciences (1925-1980)*, another volume of this series.) It was the basis of work by Friis reported in an internal memorandum in 1928 and published as a part of a paper in 1944,[30] where he related resistance noise to the design of radio receiving systems, contributing the concept of noise figure— a convenient and, thereafter, universally used way of determining a figure of merit for the sensitivity of radio receivers. When the use of much higher frequencies became common at the time of World War II, the importance of internal receiver noise became even more evident.[31] For a discussion of K. G. Jansky's research on galactic radio noise, see *Physical Sciences (1925-1980)*, Chapter 7, section 1.1.

1.7 Shortwave Radio Multiplex

It was natural to want to put more than one telephone channel on a radio circuit (multiplex), but nonlinearities in high-power amplifiers and the spot allocation of channels were inhibiting such extensions. Two channels were used at first, modulating a carrier in a way that intermodulation products fell out of band. In 1937, a project was initiated to study the possibility of multiplexing 12 channels, achieving the necessary linearity by using RF feedback around a chain of amplifiers from an input at a few milliwatts to peak output levels of 200 kilowatts (kw). New tubes and novel circuits, including a grounded grid final amplifier and a self-neutralized stage provided unusual stability with very low parasitic capacitance. (See Tube, electron in the index of *The Early Years (1875-1925)*.) Linear operation adequate to transmit 12 telephone channels with acceptable crosstalk was obtained. The transfer to war work brought the project to a halt before the actual transmission of telephone signals. After the war, emphasis was focused on submarine cables, which offered more capacity and reliability than shortwave circuits.

1.8 Ultra-Shortwave Studies

The problems encountered with the shorter waves were similar to those at the longer wavelength region, but in some ways were more difficult. They highlighted the need for improved measurement techniques and circuits, and for a deeper understanding of transmission at the higher frequencies.

Since frequencies above about 30 MHz are not reflected by the ionosphere, it was realized that ultrashort waves could be used for small-distance (line-of-sight) communications links. The selective fading and severe static characteristic of shortwave transmission would not be problems. However, since commercial equipment was not available, considerable effort at Deal and Holmdel was required to develop transmitters, receivers, and measurement gear in this wavelength range. In the late 1920s, C. R. Englund found that the shortwave limit of existing vacuum tubes was about 1.5 meters (m) (200 MHz),[32] due to the length of the leads inside the tube envelope. Later, RCA produced a tube (the acorn tube) that reduced greatly the lead length.

Beginning about 1930, extensive studies of ultra-shortwave propagation were carried out by Englund, Crawford, and W. W. Mumford.[33,34] These showed that ultra-shortwave propagation was influenced by the phenomena familiar in optics, namely, reflection, diffraction, and refraction by the atmosphere. In one set of experiments, a receiver carried in a Ford Tri-Motor airplane received 4-m signals from a transmitter located at Beir's Hill, New Jersey, near the Holmdel laboratory. These flights at altitudes between 1000 and 8000 ft. revealed the unexpected result that, at near grazing angles of incidence, the rolling and wooded countryside of New Jersey could produce almost perfect reflection of the incident wave, causing a deep fade in the received signal when the direct and ground-reflected signals were in phase opposition. (Schelleng liked to demonstrate this effect by holding a piece of paper horizontally at a window and observing the optical image of the horizon at grazing incidence, in spite of the roughness of the paper at optical wavelengths.) These results indicated that careful siting of terminals was necessary for ultra-shortwave communications links.

Another series of flights, over water, conducted from late summer to late fall, showed that reception at and beyond the optical horizon was largely influenced by variable atmospheric refraction caused by the temperature and, particularly, the water vapor gradients in the lower atmosphere. A difference in signal level of some 5 dB was observed at distances somewhat beyond the optical horizon between flights made in late September and late November when the amount of moisture in the air was small. Schelleng suggested that the average refraction of the atmosphere could be taken into account by increasing the radius of the earth by one-third.[35] This stratagem was widely used for plotting profile maps of projected ultra-shortwave links.

1.8.1 *Propagation Over Line-of-Sight Paths*

Extended measurements were made on two paths, a 70-mi. over-water path and a 39-mi. over-land one. Propagation on the long path was characterized by highly variable day-to-day signal levels and omnipresent fading. A frequency-sweep experiment demonstrated the presence of long-delayed signals arising from reflections from dielectric constant disconti-nuities in the atmosphere at the boundaries of different air masses. The average signal level was some 50 dB below the free-space value for that distance. On the other hand, a two-year study of reception on the 39-mi. path on wavelengths of 4 and 2 m showed only small variations in signal level from day to day and season to season. The average daytime signal level was at free-space level, and only rarely was fading caused by observed atmospheric discontinuities. Static, except for local storms, was absent. These results indicated that ultrashort waves were useful for communi-cations links on properly engineered optical paths.

1.8.2 Ultra-Shortwave Systems

By 1934, it was established through propagation measurements by Heis-ing that radio transmission with frequencies above 30 MHz could be usefully employed as an adjunct to wire and cable circuits, which sometimes required lengthy routing to avoid obstructions.[36] In Massachusetts, a communications link connecting Boston with Cape Cod was built, which provided wire circuits from Boston to Green Harbor and radio transmission from Green Harbor to Provincetown, a distance of 25 mi. The transmitting frequency was 63 MHz at Green Harbor and 65 MHz at Provincetown. The system, using 15 watts (w) of power, featured automatic, unattended, remote start-stop operation, piezoelectric frequency control, and automatic gain control. During the 1938 hurricane, this link provided the only communications circuits to Cape Cod.

It soon became apparent that even higher frequencies would be required for communications circuits. The new broadcast services, television and frequency modulation (FM), required large frequency bandwidths, and two-way mobile communications services were starting to crowd the line-of-sight frequency spectrum. Higher frequencies increase the communi-cations capacity, since the amount of information that can be transmitted depends on the bandwidth of the signal. Thus higher frequencies held the promise for increasing telecommunications potential. In addition, higher frequencies allow radio waves to propagate in a narrow beam with smaller antennas, since the directivity of the beam depends on the ratio of antenna aperture to wavelength.

By 1939, the success of the single-channel radio system from Green Harbor to Provincetown had established the usefulness of ultrashort waves. The properties of FM and FM with feedback had been investigated, and broadband feedback amplifiers promised low-distortion transmitter circuits suitable for multiplex telephony. The question of which modulation method,

FM or amplitude modulation (AM), should be used was to be answered by operating trial systems.

An experimental AM system in the frequency range of 156 to 161 MHz was designed by C. C. Taylor and A. C. Peterson to serve the Virginia Capes.[37,38] In 1941, a communication system from Norfolk to Cape Charles was installed. The standard K carrier, 12 to 60 kilohertz (kHz), multiplex was used to provide 12 channels. The system consisted of a 12-mi. wire link and a 26-mi. radio link to replace a 450-mi. wire route. Separate, directive, horizontally polarized antennas placed one above the other were used for the transmitters and receivers at each end. Each antenna consisted of 48 half-wave elements. This experimental system, operating with a radiated power of 50 w, showed that the transmission quality would meet communications objectives. For security reasons, the published description of the system was deferred until 1945.

II. MICROWAVE RADIO-RELAY SYSTEMS

By the end of World War II, there was a pent-up demand for new long-distance voice circuits, and the emergence of broadcast television had established the need for network distribution of large bandwidth channels.[39] Commercial network television required channels having a bandwidth of 4 MHz. The transmission media capable of providing these communication services were the coaxial cable and radio-relay systems. For the radio media, a new modulation method, pulse-code modulation (PCM), was ready to contend with AM and FM for providing the needed information capacity.[40] (See Chapter 10, section I.) The relative merits of the various contending systems required experimental evaluation in terms of the technology that was available or could be developed.

Accordingly, the radio system work proceeded along three directions: continuation of the radio-relay systems research work aimed at providing new knowledge; the field trials in the New York-to-Boston TDX radio-relay system; and experimentation with PCM systems, using time-division multiplex techniques. Based upon the available knowledge at that time, pulse transmission appeared to require more bandwidth to transmit information than the more familiar AM and FM techniques. Although microwave radio could provide the bandwidth, the required PCM components were not available, and it was decided that it was too early to incorporate the promising PCM technique in the new transmission system.

Friis's philosophy on designing large complex systems by partitioning the research into a number of smaller and more easily understood portions is exemplified in his paper "Microwave Repeater Research" published in 1948.[41] Portions of this carefully organized study were written by the originators of terrestrial radio-relay science and technology and summarized many of their previously published results. Problem areas were identified for future studies that would extend over the subsequent five years.

2.1 Microwave Propagation Studies

Based on experience with ultrashort waves, it was expected that free-space transmission should obtain between line-of-sight terminals in the centimeter-wave range. However, the effects of ground and atmospheric refraction were not known. Consequently, propagation tests, in which signal levels were recorded continuously, were conducted over a number of "optical" paths in New Jersey. It was found that the signals were usually stable, with intensities close to the free-space level during the daytime hours and during periods of inclement weather. However, on clear, calm nights, particularly in the summertime, severe fading was often present, with the signal occasionally dropping to levels as much as 40 dB below free space for short time intervals.[42]

Beginning in 1944 and continuing intermittently through 1950, Crawford [Fig. 5-8] and collaborators conducted an extensive series of propagation experiments designed primarily to study the mechanisms involved in the anomalous propagation.[43,44] The most relevant information was obtained

Fig. 5-8.   A. B. Crawford, who made fundamental contributions to radio propagation and antenna design at microwave frequencies.

using a narrow-beam (0.1 degree) scanning antenna (see section 1.3) and by observing the transmission characteristics of the paths by means of a frequency-sweep technique and very short pulses. These observations showed that the severe fading was caused by wave interference among two, three, or more signal components arriving at the receiver at various angles up to three-quarters of a degree above the normal daytime line of sight and with path differences varying from less than 30 to about 300 centimeters (cm). The long delay and large-angle components were usually of low intensity. These experiments and others, using a vertically separated receiving antenna, suggested that either space or frequency diversity would be effective in reducing the effects of fading.

A very important type of fading was observed on a path with minimum (first Fresnel zone) clearance. Normally the dielectric constant of the atmosphere decreases with height above ground so that the ray path usually is refracted downward. However, under certain meteorological conditions, the dielectric constant of the atmosphere may increase with height above ground; in this case the ray path curvature is opposite that of the earth and the limiting or tangent ray does not reach the receiver, and only a very weak signal is received by virtue of diffraction. Neither space nor frequency diversity is effective in this situation.

Other experiments showed that vertically and horizontally polarized waves behaved alike. Variable antenna-height tests showed that, even at grazing incidence, the reflection coefficient for centimeter waves of terrain typical of the eastern seaboard was very small (0.2) as compared with near unity in the ultra-shortwave range. Thus ground reflections need not be a consideration in the choice of location of the repeater stations except for paths over water or flat terrain, such as the Salt Lake flats.

2.2 New York-Boston TDX and the TD-2 Radio Systems

The forerunner of the way most long-distance telephone messages would be carried in the next half century was the research-inspired TDX radio system. This research effort, based on many radio techniques developed at ultrahigh frequencies (UHF), took a frequency leap to 4 GHz in the design of a repeater system linking New York City and Boston.

In April 1944, an announcement was made in the *Bell Laboratories Record* of plans to build an intercity system "as rapidly as the war situation permits." The announcement said, in part:

Plans for the trial of a new type of intercity communications facility were announced on March 16 by the American Telephone and Telegraph Company. The work will take at least two years to complete and will cost more than $2,000,000. It will supplement present commercial long distance telephone facilities and provide network facilities for the transmission of television programs between New York, Boston and intermediate points.

Application is being made to the Federal Communications Commission for approval to begin the project, which is expected to proceed as rapidly as the war situation permits.

At present engineers of these Laboratories essential to technical phases of the undertaking are engaged in war work.

The new system will be operated by radio relays of a type which was under development by the Laboratories prior to the war. This system applies to communication by radio many of the techniques which have played an important part in the development of long distance wire telephone circuits. Directed radio beams at ultra-high frequencies will operate simultaneously in both directions and these will be relayed at stations spaced at an average of about thirty miles throughout the route. It is hoped that, ultimately, each radio beam will carry a large number of communications channels.[45]

The TDX system provided two 2-way broadband channels, each 10-MHz wide, within the frequency band of 3930 to 4170 MHz.[46,47] The 4-GHz band had been chosen on the basis of fading, rain attenuation, and directivity considerations. Route selection proceeded even before all the components had been assembled. Repeater hops varied between 11 and 35 mi. with an average spacing of 27.5 mi.

The horn lens antenna combination using horizontal polarization was chosen for this initial installation. Each broadband channel was designed to handle several hundred telephone circuits or one television picture over a large number of hops. This system established what came to be the standard approach to microwave system design for decades to come: channel separation filters, a down-converter, an IF amplifier, an up-converter, an RF amplifier, and the transmitting antenna.

This field trial was under the direction of G. N. Thayer [Fig. 5-9], whose original group later formed a nucleus for engineering of the final production system. Tests were started on breadboard models of the TDX system in May 1946. The New York-Boston installation was completed on November 13, 1947, and the first television signals were sent over the system on that day. An excerpt of Thayer's report on the first tests follows:

> This relay system was formally opened for experimental service on November 13, 1947, and at that time its capabilities for television and multichannel telephone transmission were demonstrated. As a part of the television demonstration, the two two-way channels were connected in tandem to form a double loop, and provision was made for viewing a test pattern at New York before and after making two round trips to Boston. It was difficult to detect any impairment in the test pattern after transmission through this 880-mile system.[48]

An experimental link using the coaxial system from New York to Washington, DC was added to the New York-Boston radio link. Based on the success achieved with the TDX microwave radio system, it was decided that a system linking New York with Chicago would be the next step for further development and exploration of the technical feasibility of a nationwide relay network.

The microwave radio-relay system rapidly evolved into a nationwide radio network system, TD-2. Radio systems at 6 GHz were also developed to satisfy the nation's increasing need for long-distance circuit capacity.

Fig. 5-9. G. N. Thayer, who directed research
efforts leading to the experimental TDX microwave radio-relay transmission system, which was
later adopted for the widely used TD-2 radio
systems at 4 and 6 GHz.

Technical innovations and improvements over the years increased the
capacity of a microwave system from 2400 to 21,600 telephone channels.

2.3 Detectors, Modulators, Converters, and Other Components

Amplification at the microwave carrier frequencies in the experimental
TDX system and the subsequent TD-2 radio transmission systems was
provided first by an externally tuned cavity klystron, designed by J. W.
Clark and A. L. Samuel[49] and later by the close-space Morton triode vacuum
tube.[50,51] The biggest problem was providing low-distortion transmitters
that could meet the power and large bandwidth required for television
networks and multichannel telephone carrier distribution. By amplifying
and shaping the signal with IF components and then "up-converting" the
signal energy to the microwave region using heterodyne mixing, many of
the problems associated with the power amplifier could be mitigated.[52]

A major cause of distortion in communications systems is introduced by echoes.[53] Echoes result from imperfections described as impedance variations that reflect energy. Loss tends to minimize the effect of echoes, since some of the unwanted energy is absorbed, but this results in a loss of signal energy also. The invention of the gyrator by C. L. Hogan, based on ferromagnetic resonance and Faraday rotation (see *Physical Sciences (1925-1980)*, Chapter 1, section 2.3.1) of the electromagnetic wave, was used to design isolators to eliminate the echo problem. Microwave components to utilize these effects were designed by A. G. Fox, S. E. Miller, and M. T. Weiss.[54] IF amplifiers, limiters, FM modulators, and solid-state microwave system components were significantly improved. Each played a role in increasing the capacity of the TD-2 radio and in providing the means of moving radio systems to even higher frequencies. Continuing technical innovations and improvements have, over the years, increased the total system capacity from 2400 to 21,600 channels.

2.4 Experimental 11-GHz Short-Hop Radio System

Early radio systems at 11 GHz had demonstrated that there were enough advantages to using radio repeaters for lighter traffic routes over moderate distances to consider new simplified systems of this type.[55] Research on radio systems prior to 1960 was directed toward designing simplified short-hop systems that would reduce engineering, installation, and maintenance costs and still meet the reliability and transmission performance required for Bell System service.

An experimental system, designed and placed into operation in 1957, satisfied many of these requirements.[56] This hybrid system, operating at 11 GHz, incorporated new technology for this period, such as ferrite isolators and circulators[57] and improved limiters and discriminators,[58] and was designed for repeater spacings of 5 to 10 mi. instead of the 30 mi. used at the lower frequencies. With shorter repeater spacings, antennas could be mounted on short poles or towers. Power requirements were small, which simplified the standby power system. Only ten vacuum tubes were used in this repeater, and eight of these tubes were replaced in 1958 by solid-state devices when these became available.

After 28 months of continuous field operation, this experimental system showed little deterioration in performance, required little maintenance, and demonstrated the feasibility of the short-haul concept.

2.5 Microwave Short-Haul Radio Systems

The need for short-haul radio systems was explored by L. C. Tillotson and C. L. Ruthroff in the mid-1960s and "Use of Frequencies Above 10 GHz for Common Carrier Applications" was published in the *Bell System*

Technical Journal in 1969.[59] The 4- and 6-GHz bands were well suited for long- or short-haul terrestrial radio applications. As the long-haul network continued to expand, it became more feasible to devote these bands exclusively to long-haul applications and to use frequencies above 10 GHz for short-haul purposes. This was reinforced by the fact that the Federal Communications Commission (FCC) had allocated a number of bands over 1000-MHz wide in the 10- to 40-GHz range for fixed and mobile radio system use.[60] Higher frequencies were also more suitable for short-haul use because closer spacing was needed to overcome rain attenuation.

To investigate the characteristics of rainstorms, about 100 rain gauges spaced 1.34 kilometers (km) apart and covering a rectangular area of 13 km by 14 km were installed around Holmdel, New Jersey.

To investigate the interference problems in a dense radio network, research effort was directed toward designing a solid-state repeater operating at 11 GHz that would transmit a digital signal of at least 100 megabits per second (Mb/sec). The repeater had to be physically small and light so that it could be mounted on top of a pole as opposed to a tower, and operate with little or no maintenance and very little electrical power.[61] Theoretical work was pursued to determine the advisability of using coherent phase-shift keyed signals on such a system which would operate in the presence of cochannel interference.[62,63]

An experimental radio system was placed into operation in 1968, and the results of this work were reported in a series of articles in the July 1969 issue of the *Bell System Technical Journal*. In addition to the overview article mentioned earlier,[64] the papers described the design features of an antenna suitable for mounting on a slender mast,[65] an efficient broadband (0.3 to 11.9 GHz) varactor up-converter,[66] a low noise receiving down-converter,[67] and a broadband 300-MHz IF amplifier and variolossers.[68,69]

Propagation measurements at 18.5 GHz in Holmdel also provided information on desirable repeater spacing at these high frequencies.[70] Although the short-hop repeater was designed at 11 GHz because of the availability of microwave measuring equipment at this frequency, it became evident that at frequencies of about 30 GHz a considerably lighter pole line system could be designed. Research was therefore pursued at 30 GHz in an attempt to build millimeter-wave integrated circuits, including hybrid integrated frequency multipliers, circulators, and filters for use in experimental radio systems.[71] Theoretical work investigating broadband digital phase modulation with noise and interference provided a basic understanding of how well these systems would operate in broadband, high-bit-rate digital systems.[72]

Later a pole line radio was designed at 60 GHz to demonstrate the basic concepts originally tried at 11 GHz. Beginning in 1975, a 60-GHz digital radio system for short-hop, urban data transmission was tested, and a digital bipolar signal was transmitted at 50 Mb/sec. The usable frequency range of the system was selected to be oxygen-absorption limited to allow frequency reuse every few miles. An error rate of one in a million at a path length of 1.1 mi. was achieved.

III. PROPAGATION STUDIES AT MILLIMETER WAVES

The wide bandwidths available at millimeter wavelengths motivated Hogg and Crawford to initiate propagation studies in this spectral region. Atmospheric propagation measurements of oxygen and water-vapor absorptions showed clear-air transmission windows around 30 and 90 GHz.[73,74] However, early measurement of rain attenuation indicated that further study was needed to determine whether this source of attenuation may be a severe limiting factor on radio transmission through the atmosphere.[75]

3.1 Effect of Rain

Measured attenuations by R. A. Semplak and coworkers at frequencies above 10 GHz were combined with path-rainfall statistics obtained from a rain-gauge network to produce plots of attenuation versus path length for a given probability of fading and to evaluate dual parallel-path-diversity.[76] Interference caused by forward scattering due to raindrops was measured and compared with theory.

The advent of the laser gave impetus to the test of coherent optical wave transmission through the atmosphere. Data were obtained at 0.63, 3.5, and 10.6 micrometers (μm) for attenuation by liquid water drops, which are the dominant obstacles in open-air laser communication.[77] It was found that attenuation by rain is of the same order of magnitude at optical wavelengths as at millimeter wavelengths. However, fog attenuation is much greater at optical wavelengths than at millimeter wavelengths. The attenuation produced by a typical dense fog ($\sim$0.1 milligrams of water per cubic meter of air) in the visible region of the electromagnetic spectrum is about 100 times that produced by a rain shower of 25 millimeters per hour.

The effects of oxygen and water vapor in the atmosphere as well as the cosmic background noise were determined in 1967 to be small for microwave satellite communication.[78] Looking forward to the use of frequencies above 10 GHz, the fundamental obstacle became attenuation by rain.[79] Over the microwave band, the attenuation is considerably greater for rain than for fog.

3.2 Earth-Space Propagation

The sun is a source of relatively strong microwave energy. By constructing an antenna that tracks the sun from sunrise to sunset, it is possible to determine impairments in propagation caused by rain or fog.[80] A radiometer that measures the temperature of the sky can also be used to determine signal attenuation due to rain, but over a limited dynamic range. Early propagation studies used both techniques and continued with receiving systems that monitor beacon signals from synchronous satellites.

The sun temperature is of the order of 10^4 Kelvin (K) at centimeter wavelengths, and the apparent absorber temperature of a very heavy rainstorm is about 280 K. The ratio between these two noise powers gives a measuring range of only 15 dB. However, the dynamic measuring range can be extended by a technique of switching a narrow antenna beam on and off the sun. If the switching is rapid enough, the noise attributable to the rain and the antenna can be canceled electronically in the receiver, greatly increasing the measuring range of the attenuated radiation from the sun.

P. S. Henry carried out simultaneous measurements of rain attenuation at 16 and 30 GHz for more than a year. The measured results indicated that for about 7 hours per year the attenuation exceeds the typically available clear-day fading margin of 10 dB in the 18-GHz down-link of a broadband satellite system for the 18- and 30-GHz bands.[81] Simultaneous multifrequency measurements provided a measure of confidence in frequency extrapolation often employed by system designers. The measured ratio between attenuations at two frequencies can be compared with the theoretical ratio versus rain rate to determine the apparent rain rate and the extent of rain cells along the earth-space path.[82]

3.2.1 Passive Radiometers

Some early studies with radiometers for military applications were made by D. H. Ring for 8.5 millimeter (mm) microwave radiometer systems, one installed on an 85-ft. tower and the other mounted on a truck, to obtain data on radiation, reflection, absorption, and attenuation from objects in various parts of the country. Since there is no active source in the measurements, this method is referred to as passive radiometry. Relationships were established between the thermal radiation from a typical target and the radio power reflected from the target. Targets included mowed grass, plowed ground, sand, concrete, water, and sheets of copper. Mowed grass proved to be an almost perfect absorber, yielding an effective temperature difference of about 235 K between it and copper sheets. Zenith sky temperatures ranged from 5 to 20 K. Fog and cumulus clouds had a very small effect on radiometer response at 8.5 mm. In the case of water, the reflection coefficient checked closely with theoretical values.

More extensive studies on rain attenuation were initiated in the late 1960s by R. W. Wilson using radiometers in the range of 10- to 60-GHz wavelengths. The rain medium emits noise in the fashion of a blackbody at some apparent absorber temperature. This noise, which increases with the rain attenuation until saturation at about 10 dB, can be utilized to measure attenuation up to this level. To remove the background noise at the lower limit to the sensitivity of the radiometer, the receiver can switch between the antenna and a reference waveguide load.[83,84] In this way, synchronous detection can be used, and receivers of relatively high noise figure can resolve small changes in antenna temperature. The limited 10-dB measuring range of a radiometer fortunately coincides with or approaches the fading margin of many satellite communication down-links. The radiometer measurements can be conducted on a fixed earth-space path, day and night, whereas the sun tracker is limited to an ever-changing path toward the sun in the daytime only. The simplicity of radiometry also facilitated long-term, continuous field measurements to collect statistical data on space-diversity schemes.[85,86]

Since raindrops not only absorb but also scatter radiation, the apparent absorber temperature of the effective blackbody radiation from the rain medium is expected to be lower than the physical temperature. This effect has been demonstrated in the calibration of radiometer readings by attenuation measurements using the sun tracker and the satellite beacon developed later.[87]

3.3 Space Diversity

To take advantage of the space inhomogeneity of heavy rain, which degrades radio transmission at frequencies above 10 GHz, Hogg proposed the use of path diversity in radio transmission.[88] Using the rainfall data on a highly resolving area rain gauge network in Bedfordshire, England, he carried out calculations that demonstrated the degree of correlation of attenuation on both orthogonal and parallel paths.

Semplak and H. E. Keller designed the dense rain gauge network (see section 3.1) for the New Jersey studies. Data were collected from the rapid-response rain gauges every 10 seconds during 27 rainfalls in a 6-month period during 1967. Analysis of these data led to statistics concerning the behavior of rain rates at a point in space, the relationship of rain rates separated in space or time, and the relationship of average rain rates on pairs of paths in various configurations.[89]

Cumulative distributions of measured attenuations using 16-GHz radiometers, which were pointed at the same elevation angle and spaced several kilometers apart, indeed confirmed the path diversity advantage. Data from the radiometers pointing at the same 30-degree elevation angle and spaced 11, 19, and 30 km apart were collected[90] for the full year of 1970. It was found that the percentage of time with attenuation exceeding 10 dB decreased by a factor of 20 by using path diversity. It was also found that the path diversity advantage is generally maximized for a given separation between two earth stations when the base line is normal to the path and to the direction of convective weather fronts.

3.4 Cross Polarization

Using two orthogonal polarizations at the same frequency can double the capacity of a communication system. The interest in dual-polarization radio communication gave rise to the need for understanding depolarization by the transmission medium and methods for overcoming it. Early recognition by T. S. Chu of cross-polarization interference as a removable, nonfundamental obstacle[91,92] facilitated the decision to implement dual-polarization frequency reuse on 4- and 6-GHz Common Carrier Satellites (COMSTARs).

Measurements of cross polarization and differential attenuation between vertical and horizontal polarizations were made over terrestrial paths at 18, 30, and 60 GHz.[93] Theoretical calculations of the effect due to oblate raindrops on microwave propagation agreed with these measurements and provide extensive numerical predictions for the scattering of electromagnetic waves by oblate spheroidal drops over a wide range of conditions.[94]

Combining theoretical and experimental studies led to the following conclusions on the effect of rain-induced cross polarization.[95] Cross polarization of vertical and horizontal polarizations are at least an order of magnitude (i.e., 10 dB) less than those of circular and 45-degree linear polarizations. Very little rain-induced cross-polarization interference is expected in a terrestrial microwave network where two orthogonal polarizations can always be arranged as vertical and horizontal. However, these preferred linear polarizations are often not available in satellite communications systems. Depolarization generally increases with rain rate and frequency. The cross-polarization amplitude is found to be approximately proportional to frequency for a given earth-space path throughout the centimeter wavelengths.

3.5 Satellite Beacon Measurements

Participation by Bell Labs scientists in measurements of a 15.3-GHz beacon signal from the synchronous satellite ATS-5 served the useful function of calibration of radiometers. Measurements of the 20-GHz beacon on ATS-6 provided data on initial cross polarization versus attenuation on an earth-space path. These beacons were not continuous, but operated in an on-demand mode. They were useful calibration sources, but did not supply cumulative attenuation and depolarization distribution information. Direct measurements of these distributions from satellites were not available until the COMSTAR and CTS beacon experiments conducted by D. C. Cox and A. J. Rustako, Jr.[96,97]

The importance of gaining fundamental knowledge of earth-space propagation was well recognized. Thus, when the COMSTAR communication satellites designed for 4- and 6-GHz operation were procured, a provision was made to carry an experimental package for studying millimeter-wave propagation. The beacons were designed to operate continuously, transmitting at both 19 and 28 GHz. An extensive receiving facility was established at Crawford Hill for measuring attenuation, depolarization, coherence bandwidth, and scatter of the beacon signal by atmospheric processes. The facility included a precision 7-m antenna designed by Chu and his collaborators[98] and multichannel receiving electronics[99] designed by H. W. Arnold and collaborators to obtain optimum benefit from the COMSTAR beacons. Other Bell Laboratories receiving facilities in Georgia and Illinois accumulated statistics on signal attenuation and diversity improvements for other climatic conditions.

Rain attenuation data[100,101] collected for over two years at Holmdel, together with COMSTAR measurements at other locations, confirmed the previous results that path diversity is necessary for high-reliability performance of 18- and 30-GHz satellite communications. At 12 and 14 GHz, path diversity might not be required if the longitude of the satellite is nearly the same as the earth station.

When the COMSTAR series of satellites was planned, researchers anticipated the need to operate at higher frequencies to meet increasing capacity requirements. Thus beacons at 18 and 28 GHz were placed on the COMSTAR satellites to gain the knowledge necessary for designing future satellites. For the first time, this permitted the opportunity to determine the much-needed, long-term statistics of signal attenuation and cross polarization on earth-space paths.

Rain attenuation of the 28-GHz COMSTAR signal was measured simultaneously with the 19-GHz beacon using the 7-m antenna and an auxiliary 0.6-m antenna. For attenuations up to 30 dB, no significant difference was found between the two antennas. This result implies very little phase front distortion over a 7-m aperture and very little angle of arrival fluctuation even in dense rain.

The statistical relation between depolarization and attenuation for various linear polarization angles was measured.[102] As expected from theoretical predictions, maximum depolarization occurs for the 45-degree polarization (and circular polarization). Measured depolarization versus attenuation data were found to agree with theoretical predictions on frequency scaling and elevation-angle dependence.

Depolarization with little attenuation was often observed under clouds without rain. This phenomenon, due to differential phase shift of ice particles, is basically similar to rain-induced cross polarization at lower microwave frequencies with little attenuation.[103]

Measurements showed nearly perfect amplitude correlation and very little phase dispersion at 28 GHz, and between 28- and 19-GHz carriers.[104] Therefore rain and other atmospheric processes are not expected to affect the coherence bandwidth of satellite communication. Significant amplitude scintillations up to several decibels with weak frequency dependence were often observed under clouds.

The wide scanning capability and low side lobe level of the 7-m antenna facilitated testing the theoretical prediction[105] of negligible rain-scatter coupling between two closely spaced earth-satellite paths with high-gain antenna beams.

IV. ANTENNA RESEARCH AT MICROWAVE FREQUENCIES

The advent of UHF and waveguides opened up many new antenna possibilities. The horn, or flared waveguide, is a natural method of radiating energy. An optimum and calculable configuration was derived in 1939 by G. C. Southworth and A. P. King, which created a primary standard for antenna gain of immense value.[106] A horn can be designed for any amount of gain, but good performance dictates that the flare angle be modest. In general, it was found that the aperture area or the gain increases only in proportion to the square root of the length, so horns with apertures more than 10 wavelengths in diameter, i.e., gain greater than 25 dB, became inconveniently long.

Early antenna research involved studies of arrays, paraboloidal structures, horns, horn-lens combinations, and horn reflectors.[107] These studies included components connecting an antenna with receiver and transmitter networks.[108] In addition to designing specific antennas for the microwave TDX system (see section 2.2 in this chapter), researchers were motivated to find compact structures and antennas with higher gain.

4.1 The Horn Reflector Antenna

One of the most widely used antennas, and almost the simplest, was the horn reflector antenna invented by A. C. Beck and Friis.[109] [Fig. 5-10] This antenna consisted of a vertical waveguide horn topped by an off-axis parabolic section tilted at nearly 45 degrees. The structure had the shielding advantage of the horn with the shorter dimension of a paraboloid.

The horn antenna is free of aperture blockage, has an excellent input match, is very efficient, and is extremely broadband. Furthermore, the radiating far side lobes and back lobes are very small. Because of its excellent performance, thousands of antennas of this type have been placed in use throughout the world in microwave radio-relay systems. Large versions of this antenna were also used for the Bell Labs and National Aeronautics and Space Administration (NASA) Echo experiment and the Bell System Telstar experiment. For these experiments, a horn reflector with an aperture of 400 square feet was built at the Crawford Hill, New Jersey laboratory.[110] Such an antenna was needed because of its very low

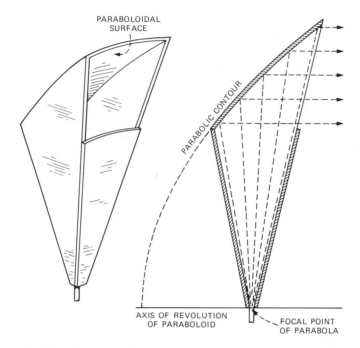

Fig. 5-10.   The horn reflector antenna. It is a compact antenna used in microwave relay systems and in astrophysics research. [Schelkunoff and Friis, *Antennas: Theory and Practice* (1952): 569.]

noise temperature. Its use, together with a maser of very low noise figure, was essential in reducing the noise contributions due to the environment to negligible values. The Crawford Hill horn reflector antenna was also used for investigations of noise from the sky and played an important role in the measurement that led to the discovery of the microwave background radiation temperature of the universe by A. A. Penzias and Wilson.[111] (See *Physical Sciences (1925-1980)*, Chapter 7, section 1.2.)

Another early microwave antenna was the polyrod (shortened from polystyrene rod) antenna, which consisted of a tapered dielectric rod projecting from the end of a waveguide[112] and gave a gain of about 20 dB. It was used in radar antennas during World War II. (See Chapter 2, section 2.3 in *National Service in War and Peace (1925-1975)*, another volume in this series.) Again, since the gain increased only in proportion to the square root of length, a single polyrod was not useful for larger gains. By paralleling several units in a broadside array, the antenna could be scanned and was used in radar applications.

Much of the early waveguide and antenna work was given a security classification because of its possible application to wartime radar and withheld from publication for five years or longer. An example is the guiding

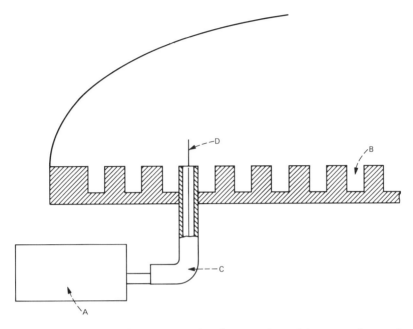

Fig. 5-11. Antenna with quarter wavelength corrugations. *A* is a transceiver used for coupling transmitted pulse radio frequency power to the antenna and receiving detected radar signals. *B* is one of the large number of quarter wavelength slots. *C* is a coaxial connector with a protruding short rod, *D*.

of waves by corrugated surfaces and a family of antennas which were derived as a result.[113,114] Corrugations slightly less than one-quarter wavelength deep give an effective inductive impedance to a metallic surface and cause waves polarized perpendicular to the surface to travel very slowly, close to the surface. When the corrugations are a quarter wave deep, or slightly deeper, the guided wave is cut off, and the waves of neither polarization can propagate near the surface. Antennas built with quarter-wavelength-deep corrugations have identical characteristics regardless of polarization, and are useful in dual polarization systems. [Fig. 5-11]

4.2 Multireflector Antennas

Most reflector antennas use the same kind of reflecting surfaces that were used more than 50 years ago; namely, paraboloids, hyperboloids, and ellipsoids. When the aperture is large, the main reflector is usually combined with a subreflector, and the arrangement is often similar to the 17th century optical telescope devised by A. Cassegrain. In most commercial satellite earth stations, the main reflector is derived from a paraboloid and its aperture is centered around the axis of this paraboloid. The feed is usually a horn, with its metal walls corrugated to minimize longitudinal currents. The horn is located between the vertex and a focus of the paraboloid, and a subreflector is needed to transform the wave radiated by the horn into a spherical wave originating from the paraboloid focus.

The first Cassegrainian antenna at Bell Labs was a centered arrangement of two paraboloids.[115] Its side-lobe performance was limited because of aperture blockage. Blockage in a Cassegrainian arrangement with circular symmetry occurs because the subreflector and its supporting structure block the plane wave emanating from the main reflector while the feed blocks the spherical wave coming from the subreflector. This blockage is undesirable. It causes lower efficiency, higher side lobes, higher noise temperature, and a mismatch at the input of the feed. Thus, shortly after that experiment, Hogg proposed a new design in which the aperture of the Cassegrainian arrangement was displaced from the axis of the paraboloid to eliminate aperture blockage entirely, improving the performance considerably.

4.3 Antennas for Satellite Communications

Satellite communications created a need for new and better antennas. The first satellites required the use of ground stations with antennas of large aperture. Thus, these antennas were expensive and were designed to minimize cost and maximize efficiency. As satellites became more prolific and transmission power increased, other factors became important.

For ground stations, it would be desirable to operate an antenna with several feeds communicating simultaneously with several satellites. Furthermore, it should be possible to operate these antennas in a noisy environment. This requires the use of antennas with very low side lobes. Also, these antennas should be broadband, with good cross-polarization discrimination.

Many of these requirements were understood and anticipated very early.[116] In 1978, construction of a Cassegrainian antenna without aperture blockage having an aperture of 7 m was completed at Crawford Hill.[117] This antenna was used for the COMSTAR propagation experiments discussed previously, and has been used for radio astronomy (see *Physical Sciences (1925-1980)*, Chapter 7, section 1.3) and other experiments related to satellite communications. In addition to excellent performance, this antenna can be used to communicate simultaneously with many satellites.[118,119] The only modification needed to permit efficient operation with many feeds is an increase of the subreflector size to reflect all the rays emanating from the various feeds. By properly orienting the axis of each feed, it is possible to efficiently illuminate the entire antenna aperture with each feed. In a conventional Cassegrainian arrangement, on the other hand, use of many feeds is limited by the subreflector, whose size cannot be increased appreciably without causing a significant increase in aperture blockage.

4.3.1 Multibeam Antennas

In 1968, Tillotson[120] pointed out that very high capacity and reduced cost per telephone channel can be obtained in a domestic satellite communications system by the use of multibeam antennas. (See section 5.3.1.) Each satellite can communicate simultaneously with many ground stations by using a multibeam antenna with many feeds. Similarly, each ground station can use a multibeam antenna communicating with many satellites. In the satellite antenna, the equivalent focal length has to be reduced to decrease the size of the feeds and their separation. To minimize the resulting aberrations, the subreflector parameters must be properly chosen. When several properly designed feeds are placed in the focal plane of such a satellite antenna, each beam produces an image of the corresponding feed aperture on the earth.

An imaging arrangement of two cylindrical reflectors, suitable for a satellite antenna, was designed in 1974 by C. Dragone to produce a magnified image of the aperture field distribution of a corrugated feed over the continental United States.[121] In 1975, R. H. Turrin designed a multibeam antenna using a periscopic arrangement of a spherical reflector and a flat plate.[122] A similar antenna was designed in 1977 by Semplak,[123] and, in 1979, Dragone and M. J. Gans produced an imaging arrangement of reflectors, combined with a relatively small array, for use in a satellite to form a scanning beam.[124]

Through theoretical studies, it was shown that by applying imaging techniques in combination with spatial filtering in the focal plane to decrease side lobes, aperture blockage can be eliminated without increasing aberrations or causing cross-polarized components.[125]

The design of a satellite communications system can be greatly simplified by the use of a phased array. (See section 5.3.3.) Then, the direction of the beam transmitted by the array can be varied continuously by changing the phases of the array elements. Thus, a single beam used in the time-division mode can provide high-capacity service to the entire continental United States.

A. S. Acampora, Dragone, and D. O Reudink proposed a technique to subdivide the continental United States into several regions, for the purpose of satellite communication and use several linear arrays combined with suitable reflectors to produce several scanning beams, one for each region. A model satellite antenna using a linear array was built and performed as expected.[126]

V. SATELLITE RESEARCH

The primary motivation for carrying on research on satellite systems at Bell Laboratories has been the transfer of information among geographically remote terrestrial users. In such systems, information and communication theories play a major role. In particular, both modulation and detection techniques are crucial elements in the design of a system. Antennas and propagation also play major roles, since the satellite link is created by the radiation and reception of electromagnetic waves at microwave frequencies by open structures (the antennas). These waves must propagate, at least partially, through an atmospheric medium where they are subject to phenomena different from those encountered in free space. Microwave devices are important hardware elements for amplification of the radio waves prior to radiation and subsequent to reception, and both analog and digital electronic circuitry are important for signal processing and system control.

5.1 Analysis of Performance of Proposed Communications Satellites

Satellite systems research at Bell Laboratories began in 1955 when J. R. Pierce [Fig. 5-12] published a paper in which he explored the possibility of using a satellite repeater for transoceanic communication.[127] Since the transmitted power from a satellite is likely to be very low, a primary limitation in the information rate to be transmitted was likely to be the noise introduced by the medium and the receiving apparatus.[128] He therefore proposed the use of PCM to exploit the large communication bandwidth that might be provided by microwave satellite transmission.[129]

When electromagnetic power is radiated from an antenna, the power flux density at a given point varies inversely with the square of the distance, L, from the radiator. The well-known Friis formula[130] relates the power received to the power transmitted simply as $P_R/P_T = (A_1 A_2)/(\lambda^2 L^2)$, where A_1 and A_2 are the areas of the respective apertures and λ is the wavelength. To overcome the path loss due to the large distances involved in satellite communications, Pierce found that an antenna diameter of about 75 m, a transmit power of about 100 kw at a 10-cm wavelength, and a receiver with 6-dB noise figure at the ground would be adequate to permit the use of a string of 30-m diameter spherical reflector satellites at an altitude of 2200 mi.

An alternative is satellites in the geostationary orbit. This is a circular orbit in the plane of the earth's equator about 22,000 mi. above the surface of the earth. The period of revolution of the satellite around the earth in this orbit is exactly one day, so that from any point on earth, the satellite appears stationary in the sky. Pierce found that a 30-m plane-reflecting mirror in such an orbit would compensate for the increased path loss and would permit a reduction of transmit power to about 50 kw. Pierce also

Fig. 5-12. J. R. Pierce with the traveling wave tube of 1946. In addition to his pioneering contributions to traveling wave research, Pierce made fundamental contributions to satellite and digital communications research.

considered a satellite having an active repeater and a 3-m antenna in geosynchronous orbit. For this case, 100 w would be needed by the ground transmitter and only 30 milliwatts (mw) by the satellite transmitter. The possibility of transoceanic communication by satellite was explored further by Pierce and R. Kompfner.[131]

5.2 Project Echo—Balloon Reflector

Early in 1956 a proposal was made by W. J. O'Sullivan of the National Advisory Committee for Aeronautics (predecessor of NASA) to orbit balloon satellites to measure air density at high altitudes. His work led to the construction of a balloon that was 33 m in diameter. It was made of 0.013-cm thick aluminized plastic, light enough to be launched to a 1000-mi. altitude by existing rockets.

When Pierce and Kompfner learned of the balloon, they proposed using it as a passive reflector for a satellite communication experiment, and in early 1959, Project Echo was born with W. C. Jakes, Jr. [Fig. 5-13], appointed as the project leader. A special issue of the *Bell System Technical Journal* of July 1961 documents in some detail the planning, operation, and results of this experiment. On August 12, 1960, the balloon was placed in orbit around the earth by NASA. A two-way coast-to-coast voice circuit was established between the Jet Propulsion Laboratories (JPL) facility at Goldstone, California and a station provided for this purpose by Bell Laboratories at Holmdel.[132] Similar tests were also planned with the Naval Research Laboratory (NRL) in Maryland and other stations.

An east-west channel was provided by transmission from an 18-m paraboloid antenna at Bell Laboratories to a 26-m paraboloid at JPL via reflection from the balloon, using a frequency of 960 MHz and transmitter power of 10 kw.[133] The west-east channel utilized transmission from another paraboloid dish at JPL to a specially constructed receiver[134] and horn reflector antenna at Bell Labs having a 6-m by 6-m aperture.[135] The radiation in each channel was circularly polarized, and the Bell Labs antenna was

Fig. 5-13. W. C. Jakes in the control room at the Bell Labs "space station" at Holmdel, New Jersey.

equipped with a second receiver arranged to respond to the cross-polarized component of the incoming signal to obtain more information concerning the transmission properties of the medium.

The balloon was placed in an almost exactly circular orbit with an inclination of 47.3 degrees, which provided periods of mutual visibility up to about 15 minutes from Bell Labs and JPL and 25 minutes from Bell Labs and NRL. The slant range from Holmdel to the balloon varied between 3,000 and 10,000 mi. during a typical pass.

The communication tests were carried out primarily using frequency modulation. The threshold in the Echo demodulators was improved relative to that of conventional frequency modulation by the application of negative feedback to the FM demodulator.[136] Two masers,[137] cooled with liquid helium pumped to very low vapor pressure to get the temperature down to 2 K, were used to receive the two polarizations of the incoming signal. The threshold sensitivity of the Bell Labs receivers was approximately 10^{-18} w. This allowed meaningful measurements of both direct and cross-polarized components of the incoming signal.

5.2.1 Operation of the Echo I Satellite System

After the successful launching of the Echo I balloon on August 12, 1960, operations at the Bell Labs station were carried on for about 1120 passes up to March 1, 1961. Some of the historic events associated with the Echo satellite are noted below:

Pass No.	Date	Event
1	8/10	First demonstration of transmission via the balloon: President Eisenhower's prerecorded message sent from JPL to Bell Laboratories.
11	8/13	First two-way audio transmission between JPL and Bell Labs: prerecorded messages of President Eisenhower and United States Senator L. B. Johnson.
12	8/13	First two-way live voice: W. C. Jakes of Bell Labs and P. Tardani of JPL talked briefly.
21	8/14	Voice received with excellent quality from NRL.
33	8/15	Two-way live voice with JPL using standard outside telephone lines connected to the satellite circuit.
70	8/18	F. R. Kappel, president of AT&T, L. DuBridge, president of JPL, and J. B. Fisk, president of Bell Laboratories, talked between California and the east coast via the satellite.
503	9/22	Demonstration of facsimile picture transmission from NRL.

The Project Echo experiment was essentially completed by the end of 1961. It was a dramatic demonstration that laid the groundwork for the successful deployment of the active satellites that were later accepted as commonplace.

5.3 Active Satellite Systems—Telstar

Following the successful completion of Project Echo, attention turned toward the demonstration of the feasibility of an active satellite repeater. Such a satellite would make the transmission of television bandwidth signals feasible. The Telstar experiment, undertaken exclusively by AT&T with NASA being reimbursed for satellite launch costs and certain tracking and telemetry functions, was designed to demonstrate the operational feasibility of a broadband active repeater in the space environment. Again, a low earth orbit (2000 miles) was chosen, and an omnidirectional antenna was employed to avoid the need for spacecraft attitude control.

The experimental effort that went into Telstar was huge compared with that of Project Echo, involving research and development organizations of Bell Laboratories, which were responsible for the satellite as well as the ground stations.[138]

The first Telstar satellite was launched on July 10, 1962, and soon produced the world's first demonstration of transatlantic television transmission. By demonstrating that spacecraft communications electronics can survive a launch and operate reliably in the space environment, and, by generating valuable data pertaining to the effects of radiation in space, Telstar was a major milestone in the realization of a commercial satellite system. However, the Communications Satellite Act, passed on August 31, 1962, created the Communications Satellite Corporation, which was to be the exclusive American participant in any subsequent international satellite ventures. A second satellite was nevertheless launched to complete the Telstar technical program.

5.3.1 Domestic Satellite Systems

In 1968, Tillotson proposed a model satellite system having the equivalent of 100 million voice circuits, which could be provided by a network consisting of 50 ground stations and 50 active repeater satellites placed in geosynchronous orbit.[139,140] Three frequency band pairs were allocated for commercial communications satellite applications. A bandwidth of 500 MHz was allocated for each of the 4- and 6-GHz and 12- and 14-GHz bands, and a bandwidth of 2500 MHz was allocated for use in the 19- and 28-GHz bands. The lower frequency of each pair was used for the ground-to-satellite up-link, and the upper frequency was used for the satellite-to-ground down-link. The 4- and 6-GHz bands were shared with the terrestrial microwave radio-relay network, and, to prevent potential interference with this network as well as to avoid expected congestion of 4- and 6-GHz satellite systems, the higher bands were emphasized. A given antenna size yields greater gain at higher frequencies, but the propagation of the higher frequencies is adversely affected by rain and means must be provided to maintain service during intense rain events. (See section 3.1.)

Tillotson's system provided for highly directive multibeam antennas stabilized in such a way that the beam would point continuously toward the intended coverage region. Another feature of the proposed satellite system was the use of digital modulation. This would allow the integration of data and image services with voice telecommunications, provide the opportunity to exploit fully the satellite's capabilities, and also interconnect users efficiently.

5.3.2 Spot Beams and Time-Division Multiple Access

As seen from a geosynchronous satellite, the continental United States spans an angular segment approximately 3 degrees by 6 degrees. The gain of a satellite antenna radiating energy confined to this segment is about 30 dB; that is, the flux density within this segment is about 1000 times greater than that produced by an omnidirectional radiator. At higher frequencies, it is quite feasible, however, to deploy antennas with beam widths on the order of a few tenths of a degree, resulting in an antenna gain that is 100 times higher than that produced by an omnidirectional radiator and a coverage area reduced to 1/100. Techniques were invented (see section IV) to form a large number of nonoverlapping spot beams within the 3 degree by 6 degree angular extent of the continental United States. Since these beams are spatially isolated, the allocated spectrum can be reused among the nonadjacent spot beams; i.e., the beams can all carry independent information. The capacity is therefore much higher than can be achieved with a single antenna covering the continental United States.

Model systems with about a dozen spot beams focused on major metropolitan areas were considered for possible telephone trunking applications. Each spot-beam footprint had a diameter of about 200 mi. To permit ground stations located within the various spot-beam regions to communicate with each other, it was proposed to use Satellite Switched/Time-Division Multiple Access (SS/TDMA), an approach that has received considerable attention at Bell Laboratories and elsewhere. The technique requires digital transmission and the transfer of messages between stations in packets. The packet is transmitted so that it arrives at the satellite just as a switch in the satellite connects the receive spot beam to the intended down-link spot beam.

With fixed beam SS/TDMA, service would be restricted to those regions covered by a spot-beam footprint. Although, in principle, the number of beams might be increased, the reuse of a frequency in the same polarization must be separated by a few beam widths to keep interbeam interference sufficiently low. Several techniques were proposed in an attempt to reduce or eliminate the resulting blackout region.[141]

5.3.3 Scanning Spot-Beam Concept

As the number of earth stations in a network grows large, access by frequency division becomes cumbersome because the number of channels needed to connect each pair of users grows as the square of the number of earth stations. Time-sharing a single wideband channel among all earth stations is not only simpler conceptually, but has the added advantage that adjusting the connect time between user pairs to accommodate varying traffic is readily accomplished by changing packet size. The equivalent procedure in frequency division would be varying bandwidth, a difficult chore.

Recognizing that only one pair of users is simultaneously communicating in a TDMA system, Reudink and Y. S. Yeh suggested that high-gain spot antenna beams be used to make the connection, with the resulting power savings of about a factor of 100.[142,143]

They proposed using scanning spot beams in the satellite to interconnect each user pair (one transmitting and one receiving) at different points in time. A satellite capable of forming a pair of rapidly movable spot beams can thereby produce the same accessibility as does the area coverage system, provided the beams are scanned synchronously with the TDMA bursts that interconnect the correct user pairs.

The scanning of the beam was achieved by a phased array antenna. This is an array of many small radiating elements, each of which is preceded by a device that can shift the phase of the microwave signal passed through it. By imparting the appropriate phase to the wave radiating from each element, the superposition creates a beam focused in a particular direction. This direction can be altered by changing the settings of the individual phase shifters, similar to the approach used in the 1930s for the shortwave MUSA array.

The microwave phase shifters should be capable of fast switching, since time lost during a switching operation reduces the number of time slots available for communications. A digital phase shifter module with switching times under 10 nanoseconds (ns) was built by B. S. Glance in support of the scanning-beam concept.[144]

An array controller designed and constructed by W. L. Aranguren and R. E. Langseth provided phase-shifter settings for each position to which the beam must scan.[145] Also the correct sequence of scanning positions was stored. Both of these memories could be updated as the scanning sequence changes in response to changing traffic demand. An automatic cophasing system to measure any drift and report appropriate changes to the array controller was also constructed. The feasibility of the scanning-spot-beam concept was successfully demonstrated using a ground-based transmit array and two receivers. It was shown that, if all of the satellite beams are scannable, the total capacity of the multibeam satellite can be used with an efficiency close to 100 percent.[146,147] To avoid effective power loss due to intermodulation distortion, it was proposed that each beam be scanned only over a limited region.[148] An SS/TDMA switch is used on the satellite to permit interconnection of the various strips. The total number of array elements and phase shifters needed is no greater than that needed to form a single fully scannable beam.

The capacity afforded by a multibeam satellite with frequency reuse is dependent largely on the number of simultaneous noninterfering spot beams that can be formed, and this number is related to the width of each beam, which depends on the size of the satellite antenna. Other factors that influence the usable capacity of the satellite are the available power, the radiation bandwidth, the terrestrial traffic distribution, and the locations of the ground stations.[149] An outer bound on the achievable capacity region has been derived theoretically, providing a yardstick against which the performance of any systems concept can be compared.[150]

5.3.4 Resource Sharing and Coding

Perhaps the most significant research result involving the role of coding in satellite communications is the resource-sharing concept proposed by Acampora.[151] As already mentioned, rain attenuation seriously impairs communications satellites operating at frequencies above 10 GHz. Rather than using larger antennas or site diversity to minimize communication outage, a common pool of resources, shared among all ground stations, is much more efficient. This technique creates a small pool of time slots in each frame that is reserved for use by any ground station experiencing a rain fade exceeding the built-in margin. When a fade occurs at a particular site, time slots are borrowed from the pool to overcome the fade. These extra time slots are used to accommodate the redundancy of a powerful code to provide 8 to 10 dB of additional fade margin. Redundancy provides a method for correcting errors. For example, if a desired bit of information was repeated three times and two out of three of the received bits are the same, the correctness of the result is dramatically increased. Channel errors of one in a thousand are reduced to less than one in a million. Even lower error rates can be achieved by a more complicated combination of several bits. Resource sharing does not require an increase in either radiated power or antenna size. Applying a rain model that provides for diurnal, seasonal, and geographical correlation among rain events, it was found that reserving 6 percent of the time slots would provide an outage of less than 1 hour per year in the 12-GHz band with 9 dB less margin than otherwise needed.

Although channel coding can provide low bit error rates and accommodate more transmission noise, the channel data rate must increase to accommodate the added redundancy.[152] This implies that the required bandwidth must increase, raising a question as to the applicability of coding to band-limited satellite channels. This question was studied extensively, and a receiver structure was derived to optimally decode the data in the presence of band-limiting distortion. It was found that this structure can provide performance within 3 dB of the Shannon limit for certain select codes.

VI. MOBILE RADIO RESEARCH

Motivated by the opportunity to provide communications service for tens of millions of vehicles in the United States, Bell Labs researchers started thinking about the possibility of developing a mobile radio system as early as the early 1930s. Pioneering propagation studies were carried out at microwave frequencies by W. R. Young, Jr., in the early 1950s,[153] but intensive research programs did not get started until the early 1960s.

A broadband mobile telephone system providing greatly expanded service by means of integrated switching and transmission and high-speed common control was advanced by W. D. Lewis in 1960.[154] The situation the researchers faced prior to 1970 was the extremely limited bandwidth available to mobile radio. The frequency space allocated to mobile services was a total of 2 MHz, distributed among bands at 35, 150, and 450 MHz. This bandwidth, which was equivalent to about 33 telephone channels, certainly could not meet the demands of millions of motorists. Moreover, due to interference considerations, these limited channels were spread over adjoining metropolitan areas. The severity of this interference depends on relative signal strengths, which, in turn, depend on the various factors governing radio transmission at these high frequencies. For example, in New York City, with close to eight million people, only 20 mobile telephone conversations could be held simultaneously until service in the UHF band was authorized by the FCC in the early 1980s.

Research in mobile radio communications covered three topics: (1) propagation and antennas, (2) cellular systems, and (3) modulation and diversity combining. These investigations proved the feasibility of microwave mobile radio service and paved the way for the FCC decisions in 1970 to allocate a significant portion of the UHF band, from 806 to 881 MHz, for domestic, public land-mobile service. Immediately following this decision, a full-scale research and development program started at Bell Labs. In the 1970s, research interest focused on efficient use of the mobile radio spectrum, emphasizing advances in digital signal processing capabilities. In 1974, Jakes edited a book, written by several Bell Labs scientists on microwave mobile communications, documenting the research results of the previous decade.[155]

6.1 Mobile Propagation and Orthogonal Antenna System

The direct line-of-sight paths from base station to mobiles are often blocked. The waves arrive at the mobile antenna principally by reflection and diffraction. The multipath phenomenon causes a random distribution of standing-wave patterns along the street. When a single frequency is transmitted from the base station, the motion of the vehicle through these standing-wave patterns causes a rapid fluctuation in both the amplitude and phase of the received signal. The received signal at the base station transmitted from a moving vehicle experiences similar fluctuations. Although the mean value is relatively stable over a short distance, over longer distances it experiences considerable fluctuations because of shadowing by buildings.

A simple model was proposed by R. H. Clarke[156] and further analyzed by Gans to describe the multipath fading.[157] The model assumed (which was reasonable on physical grounds) that, at any point along the street, the received fields are made up of a number of horizontally traveling plane waves with random amplitudes, phases, and angles of arrival. On the basis of this model, many properties of the received signals were theoretically derived and subsequently verified experimentally.

An important finding was that the correlation functions are zero order Bessel functions, and the field components become uncorrelated at the mobile when antennas are separated by about half a wavelength (the wavelength at 900 MHz is about 33 cm). This impacts modulation formats and receiver design. At base stations, the decorrelation distances vary from 10λ to 100λ, depending on the antenna height and local scatterers.[158] It was also established that cross-polarized transmissions will become uncorrelated after passing through the mobile radio environment and that the electric and magnetic field components are independent.[159,160] These independent components are useful for diversity reception systems. It was found that mobile antenna patterns have only a minor effect on the average received power. Horizontal directivity will not increase the average signal strength whereas vertical directivity can increase it. Clarke and Gans showed that the amount of frequency spread depends on the vehicle speed and the directivity of the mobile antenna. Knowledge of the fluctuation rates is important in the design of switch diversity receivers. The power spectra of the signal envelope and phase were extensively studied because these fluctuations cause distortions of the signal modulations.

6.1.1 Effect of Finite Bandwidth

With the statistical properties of single-frequency transmission well understood, the transmission of narrow-band signals (up to perhaps 100 kHz) in either AM, FM, or digital formats could be treated with confidence. As the signal bandwidth increases, as with digital modulations or multiplexed base station transmissions, the narrow band description of the channel is no longer accurate, since each of the multiple paths is associated with a different time delay. This is most easily visualized for pulse transmission, where the time delays cause the received pulses to overlap, impairing or even destroying the original signal.

Extensive broadband probings of the medium were performed by Cox in New York City and its suburbs to characterize delay spreads by cataloging many delay spread distributions.[161] Due to the large number of special cases, a typical delay spread model for the mobile environment does not exist. A less variable parameter, and one which is much easier to determine, is the route-mean-square (rms) value of the delay spread, which was found to change between 0.5 and 5 μsec from suburban to urban environments. Knowing the system performance, the bit error rate for various bandwidth signals could be calculated.

6.1.2 Large City Effects

Reudink [Fig. 5-14] carried out measurements in Philadelphia and New York City[162] with a view toward understanding the peculiar factors influ-

Fig. 5-14. D. O. Reudink, who made fundamental contributions to cellular radio and satellite research.

encing the propagation of mobile radio signals in large cities. Typical findings indicated strong channeling effects of radio signals along the street and also the peaking of signals at street intersections. Measurements were also made on propagation in tunnels with a somewhat surprising result that microwaves propagate quite well in these structures.[163]

6.2 Cellular Systems

To make efficient use of the limited spectrum, a hexagonal cellular frequency reuse concept was proposed as early as 1947 and discussed subsequently in a number of internal Bell Laboratories memoranda. These ideas formed the basis for worldwide cellular radio. The first publication was by H. J. Shulte, Jr., and W. A. Cornell in 1960.[164] In this concept, a metropolitan area is covered by adjoining hexagon cells that cover the whole region. The available mobile telephone channels are divided into distinct groups with each group assigned to particular cells. The same channel group is used in cells separated by an amount (reuse distance) such that cochannel interference in each cell is tolerable. If the traffic distribution is nonuniform, e.g., decreasing traffic demands from the center of the metropolitan area to the outskirts, more channels will be assigned to the high traffic cells.

6.2.1 Dynamic Channel Assignment

Dynamic channel assignment was proposed in 1970 by Cox and Reudink to handle the short-term statistical fluctuations of traffic. The goal was to increase the overall channel-use efficiency with low blocking probability. Computer models were constructed to study dynamic channel assignment.[165] Extensive simulation results were obtained for both one-dimensional and two-dimensional cell layouts.[166] The results indicated significant improvements in service availability using assignments. Typical results showed that, for low blocking probability on call attempts, the dynamic assignment system can handle a higher call attempt rate and allow 50 percent more simultaneous conversations.

Further refinements in dynamic channel assignment result in a strategy combining the high packing density of fixed channel assignment with the flexibility of dynamic channel assignment.[167] In this concept, the available channels are divided into two pools. The first pool of channels is assigned to the service cells as fixed assigned channels that are used first. The second pool of channels is dynamically assigned. These channels are used only when no fixed channels are available. This mixed system, because of its reassignment strategy, was shown to provide even better service availabilities than the earlier dynamic assignment system.

6.2.2 *Modulation and Diversity Combining Techniques*

In parallel with the study of transmission media, diversity combining techniques were developed to reduce signal envelope fluctuations to a range acceptable for efficient voice transmission. The basic idea of diversity is to have one or more versions of the same transmitted signal available to help fill in the missing parts of the original signal. Using space diversity it was observed that even a few diversity branches would improve the signal envelope significantly. For example, without diversity, the envelope is more than 10 dB below its mean value 10 percent of the time, whereas for two antennas combined in a maximal ratio sense, i.e., combining the sum of the squares of the voltages on the two antennas, the output is below this level only 1 percent of the time.[168]

Specific hardware was built to test various promising diversity receiver structures.[169,170] The principal conclusions from the diversity studies were that the differences in quality of the output signal envelope are minor among different diversity combining formats and that diversity not only reduces envelope fading but also reduces the random FM and frequency selective fading.

Another important conclusion from the diversity studies was related to phase conjugate retransmission, as proposed in 1962 by C. C. Cutler,

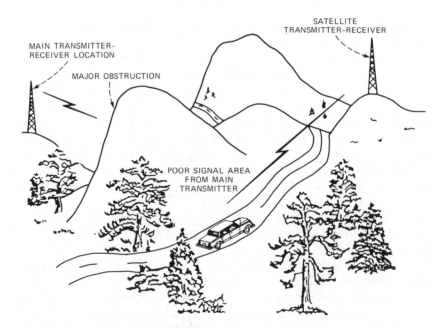

Fig. 5-15.   Use of a satellite base station to fill an area of poor reception. [Jakes et al, *Microwave Mobile Communications* (1974): 378.]

Kompfner, and Tillotson in connection with satellite systems[171] and investigated analytically by S. P. Morgan.[172] If a signal from a mobile travels to two separate base-station antennas, and each of these antennas transmits the complex conjugate of the phase it received, these signals add in-phase on arrival at the mobile antenna. Since both signals fade independently, the chances of nearly always having a good signal are greatly enhanced.[173] [Fig. 5-15] Based on these results, it was concluded that the complex signal processing can be placed at the base stations, thus providing the mobiles with the benefits of diversity, but without any complex hardware.[174,175]

6.2.3 Efficient Spectrum Use

The frequency reuse distance in the cellular layout is a major factor in determining the overall capacity of the mobile radio system. If the reuse interval is large, the total number of mobile channels must be divided into smaller sets such that only a small number of channels is available in each cell. For example, in a 12-channel set system, only 1/12 of the total channels is available in each cell, and the channel-use efficiency is very low, 8-1/3 percent. To increase the total capacity of the system, cells might be divided into even smaller units, but the number of base stations would have to be increased, which is a costly approach.

One attempt to increase the channel-use efficiency and reduce the reuse distance uses a space diversity approach in combination with a new frequency plan. Space diversity smooths the fluctuations in the received signal and reduces the probability of interference. By means of an intracell frequency assignment plan, a majority of the channels are assigned to mobiles near the center of each cell, and the remaining channels are used to cover the interference-prone corner regions. Efficiencies approaching 80 percent were calculated with four branches of space diversity combining.[176]

With advances in digital signal processing capabilities, digital time-division retransmission was proposed in 1981 by P. S. Henry to simplify the mobile receivers.[177] This approach also offers advantages compared to the frequency-division approaches studied earlier in the multiplexing of base station transmitting antennas. Another advantage of digital modulation is the realization that cochannel interference in digital systems may be reduced by carefully planned cell layouts and controlled timing throughout the system.

VII. EPILOGUE

The last half century has seen remarkable progress in radio communications. In the early days, the United States and Europe were served by a few, often unreliable, shortwave circuits. In less than 50 years, the world has been linked by millions of radio circuits worldwide, carrying voice, television, and data. Radio research at Bell Laboratories has made numerous contributions to this rapid evolution in telecommunications. Bell Labs scientists and engineers have participated in nearly every aspect of exploiting this medium, which, in the early 1980s, has carried nearly three-quarters of all the long-distance telecommunications worldwide.

Having ready access to results of research, development, and manufacturing operations, and excellent opportunities to interact with colleagues in electronics and physical and mathematical sciences have been a key to Bell Laboratories leadership in this remarkably fast-growing field. Taking the traveling wave tube and then the transistor from electronics and utilizing mathematical concepts of modulation, noise, and information theory, combined with the traditional radio work of antennas and propagation, have enabled Bell Labs scientists not only to make numerous individual contributions but also to create entirely new system approaches in the fields of satellite, terrestrial point-to-point, and mobile communications.

REFERENCES

1. H. T. Friis, "The Holmdel Laboratory," *Bell Lab. Rec.* **13** (December 1934), pp. 117-121.
2. R. A. Heising, J. C. Schelleng, and G. C. Southworth, "Some Measurements of Short Wave Transmission," *Proc. IRE* **14** (October 1926), pp. 613-647.
3. H. W. Nichols and J. C. Schelleng, "Propagation of Electric Waves Over the Earth," *Bell Syst. Tech. J.* **4** (April 1925), pp. 215-234.
4. A. E. Kennelly, "On the Elevation of the Electrically Conducting Strata of the Earth's Atmosphere," *Elec. World and Eng.* **39** (March 15, 1902), p. 473; O. Heaviside and others, "Telegraphy," in *Encyclopedia Britannica*, 10th ed., **9** (London: Adam and Charles Black, 1902), pp. 213-235.
5. J. C. Schelleng, "Long Waves or Short," *Bell Lab. Rec.* **4** (June 1927), pp. 349-354.
6. C. R. Englund, "Note on the Measurement of Radio Signals," *Proc. IRE* **11** (February 1923), pp. 26-33.
7. H. T. Friis and E. Bruce, "A Radio Field-Strength Measuring System for Frequencies up to Forty Megacycles," *Proc. IRE* **14** (August 1926), pp. 507-519.
8. R. A. Heising, "Experiments and Observations Concerning the Ionized Regions of the Atmosphere," *Proc. IRE* **16** (January 1928), pp. 75-99.
9. J. P. Schafer and W. M. Goodall, "Radio Transmission Studies of the Upper Atmosphere," *Proc. IRE* **19** (August 1931), pp. 1434-1445.
10. W. M. Goodall, "The Ionosphere," *Bell Lab. Rec.* **13** (March 1935), pp. 194-199.
11. K. Bullington, "Radio Propagation Variations at VHF and UHF," *Proc. IRE* **38** (January 1950), pp. 27-32.
12. See entire issue of *Proc. IRE* **43** (October 1955), pp. 1173-1570.
13. H. G. Booker and W. E. Gordon, "A Theory of Radio Scattering in the Troposphere," *Proc. IRE* **38** (April 1950), pp. 401-412.
14. T. J. Carroll and R. M. Ring, "Propagation of Short Radio Waves in a Normally Stratified Troposphere," *Proc. IRE* **43** (October 1955), pp. 1384-1390.
15. H. T. Friis, A. B. Crawford, and D. C. Hogg, "A Reflection Theory for Propagation Beyond the Horizon," *Bell Syst. Tech. J.* **36** (May 1957), pp. 627-644.
16. A. B. Crawford, D. C. Hogg, and W. H. Kummer, "Studies in Tropospheric Propagation Beyond the Horizon," *Bell Syst. Tech. J.* **38** (September 1959), pp. 1067-1178.

17. R. M. Foster, "Directive Diagrams of Antenna Arrays," *Bell Syst. Tech. J.* **5** (April 1926), pp. 292-307.

18. G. C. Southworth, "Certain Factors Affecting the Gain of Directive Antennas," *Proc. IRE* **18** (September 1930), pp. 1502-1536.

19. E. Bruce, "Developments in Short-Wave Directive Antennas," *Proc. IRE* **19** (August 1931), pp. 1406-1433.

20. A. E. Harper, *Rhombic Antenna Design* (New York: D. Van Nostrand Co., 1941).

21. R. Bown, Forward to *Rhombic Antenna Design* by A. E. Harper (New York: D. Van Nostrand Co., 1941), p. VII.

22. J. C. Schelleng, "Some Problems in Short Wave Telephone Transmission," *Proc. IRE* **18** (June 1930), pp. 913-938.

23. H. T. Friis, "Oscillographic Observations on the Direction of Propagation and Fading of Short Waves," *Proc. IRE* **16** (May 1928), pp. 658-665.

24. C. B. Feldman, "Optical Behavior of the Ground for Short Waves," *Proc. IRE* **21** (June 1933), pp. 764-801.

25. C. R. Burrows and E. J. Howard, "Short Wave Transmission to South America," *Proc. IRE* **21** (January 1933), pp. 102-113.

26. H. T. Friis and C. B. Feldman, "A Multiple Unit Steerable Antenna for Short-Wave Reception," *Proc. IRE* **25** (July 1937), pp. 841-917.

27. L. R. Lowry, "The Musa from the Outside," *Bell Lab. Rec.* **16** (February 1938), pp. 203-207.

28. J. B. Johnson, "Thermal Agitation of Electricity in Conductors," *Phys. Rev.* **32** (July 1928), pp. 97-109.

29. H. Nyquist, "Thermal Agitation of Electric Charge in Conductors," *Phys. Rev.* **32** (July 1928), pp. 110-113.

30. H. T. Friis, "Noise Figures of Radio Receivers," *Proc. IRE* **32** (July 1944), pp. 419-422.

31. F. B. Llewellyn, "A Study of Noise in Vacuum Tubes and Attached Circuits," *Proc. IRE* **18** (February 1930), pp. 243-265.

32. C. R. Englund, "The Short Wave Limit of Vacuum Tube Oscillators," *Proc. IRE* **15** (November 1927), pp. 914-927.

33. C. R. Englund, A. B. Crawford, and W. W. Mumford, "Some Results of a Study of Ultra-Short-Wave Transmission Phenomena," *Bell Syst. Tech. J.* **12** (April 1933), pp. 197-227.

34. C. R. Englund, A. B. Crawford, and W. W. Mumford, "Further Results of a Study of Ultra-Short-Wave Transmission Phenomena," *Bell Syst. Tech. J.* **14** (July 1935), pp. 369-397.

35. J. C. Schelleng, C. R. Burrows, and E. B. Ferrell, "Ultra-Short Wave Propagation," *Bell Syst. Tech. J.* **12** (April 1933), pp. 125-161.

36. R. A. Heising, "Radio Extension Links to the Telephone System," *Bell Syst. Tech. J.* **19** (October 1940), pp. 611-645.

37. C. C. Taylor, "Radio Telephone Service in Chesapeake Bay," *Bell Lab. Rec.* **19** (August 1941), pp. 358-362.

38. A. C. Peterson, "Multi-Channel Radio Telephone Spans Chesapeake Entrance," *Bell Lab. Rec.* **22** (May 1944), pp. 387-390.

39. R. Bown, "The Outlook for Radio Relaying," *Bell Lab. Rec.* **23** (October 1945), pp. 365-367.

40. J. C. Lozier, "Spectrum Analysis of Pulse Modulated Waves," *Bell Syst. Tech. J.* **26** (April 1947), pp. 360-387; L. A. Meacham and E. Peterson, "An Experimental Multichannel Pulse Code Modulation System of Toll Quality," *Bell Syst. Tech. J.* **27** (January 1948), pp. 1-43; R. W. Sears, "Electron Beam Deflection Tube for Pulse Code Modulation," *Bell Syst. Tech. J.* **27** (January 1948), pp. 44-57; W. R. Bennett, "Noise in PCM Systems," *Bell Lab. Rec.* **26** (December 1948), pp. 495-499.

41. H. T. Friis, "Microwave Repeater Research," *Bell Syst. Tech. J.* **27** (April 1948), pp. 183-246.

42. W. M. Sharpless, "Measurement of the Angle of Arrival of Microwave," *Proc. IRE* **34** (November 1946), pp. 837-845; A. B. Crawford and W. M. Sharpless, "Further Observations of the Angle of Arrival of Microwaves," *Proc. IRE* **34** (November 1946), pp. 845-848; A. L. Durkee, "Results of Microwave Propagation Tests on a 40-mile Overland Path," *Proc. IRE* **36** (February 1948), pp. 197-205.

43. A. B. Crawford and W. C. Jakes, "Selective Fading of Microwaves," *Bell Syst. Tech. J.* **31** (January 1952), pp. 68-90.

44. O. E. DeLange, "Propagation Studies at Microwave Frequencies by Means of Very Short Pulses," *Bell Syst. Tech. J.* **31** (January 1952), pp. 91-103.

45. A. C. Dickieson, "The TD2 Story: From Research to Field Trial," *Bell Lab. Rec.* **45** (October 1967), p. 285.

46. G. N. Thayer, A. A. Roetken, R. W. Friis, and A. L. Durkee, "A Broad-Band Microwave Relay System Between New York and Boston," *Proc. IRE* **37** (February 1949), pp. 183-188.

47. See reference 45, pp. 282-289.

48. See reference 46, p. 188.

49. J. W. Clark and A. L. Samuel, "A Wide-Tuning-Range Microwave Oscillator Tube," *Proc. IRE* **35** (January 1947), pp. 81-83.

50. J. A. Morton and R. M. Ryder, "Design Factors of the Bell Telephone Laboratories 1553 Triode," *Bell Syst. Tech. J.* **29** (October 1950), pp. 496-530.

51. A. E. Bowen and W. W. Mumford, "A New Microwave Triode: Its Performance as a Modulator and as an Amplifier," *Bell Syst. Tech. J.* **29** (October 1950), pp. 531-552.

52. C. Dragone, "Phase and Amplitude Modulation in High-Efficiency Varactor Frequency Multipliers— General Scattering Properties," *Bell Syst. Tech. J.* **46** (April 1967), pp. 775-796; C. Dragone, "Performance and Stability of Schottky Barrier Mixers," *Bell Syst. Tech. J.* **51** (December 1972), pp. 2169-2196; M. V. Schneider and W. W. Snell, Jr., "Stripline Downconverter With Subharmonic Pump," *Bell Syst. Tech. J.* **53** (July/August 1974), pp. 1179-1183.

53. D. H. Ring, "The Measurement of Delay Distortion in Microwave Repeaters," *Bell Syst. Tech. J.* **27** (April 1948), pp. 247-264.

54. A. G. Fox, S. E. Miller, and M. T. Weiss, "Behavior and Applications of Ferrites in the Microwave Region," *Bell Syst. Tech. J.* **34** (January 1955), pp. 5-103.

55. " 'TJ'— A New Microwave Relay System," *Bell Lab. Rec.* **35** (April 1957), p. 153.

56. C. L. Ruthroff and L. C. Tillotson, "An Experimental 'Short-Hop' Microwave System," *Bell Lab. Rec.* **38** (June 1960), pp. 202-206.

57. J. P. Schafer, "Ferrite Isolators at 11,000 Megacycles," *Bell Lab. Rec.* **33** (October 1955), pp. 385-389.

58. C. L. Ruthroff, "Amplitude Modulation Suppression in FM Systems," *Bell Syst. Tech. J.* **37** (July 1958), pp. 1023-1046.

59. L. C. Tillotson, "Use of Frequencies Above 10 GHz for Common Carrier Applications," *Bell Syst. Tech. J.* **48** (July/August 1969), pp. 1563-1576.

60. Federal Communications Commission, *Rules and Regulations-Part 2: Frequency Allocations and Radio Treaty Matters; General Rules and Regulations*, Vol. II (January 1974), Section 2.106.

61. C. L. Ruthroff, T. L. Osborne, and W. F. Bodtmann, "Short Hop Radio System Experiment," *Bell Syst. Tech. J.* **48** (July/August 1969), pp. 1577-1604.

62. V. K. Prabhu, "Error Rate Considerations for Coherent Phase-Shift Keyed Systems with Co-Channel Interference," *Bell Syst. Tech. J.* **48** (March 1969), pp. 743-767.

63. C. L. Ruthroff and L. C. Tillotson, "Interference in a Dense Radio Network," *Bell Syst. Tech. J.* **48** (July/August 1969), pp. 1727-1743.

64. See reference 61.
65. A. B. Crawford and R. H. Turrin, "A Packaged Antenna for Short-Hop Microwave Radio Systems," *Bell Syst. Tech. J.* **48** (July/August 1969), pp. 1605-1622.
66. T. L. Osborne, "Design of Efficient Broadband Varactor Upconverters," *Bell Syst. Tech. J.* **48** (July/August 1969), pp. 1623-1649.
67. T. L. Osborne, L. U. Kibler, and W. W. Snell, "Low Noise Receiving Downconverter," *Bell Syst. Tech. J.* **48** (July/August 1969), pp. 1651-1663.
68. W. F. Bodtmann and F. E. Guilfoyle, "Broadband 300 MHz IF Amplifier Design," *Bell Syst. Tech. J.* **48** (July/August 1969), pp. 1665-1686.
69. W. F. Bodtmann, "Design of Efficient Broadband Variolossers," *Bell Syst. Tech. J.* **48** (July/August 1969), pp. 1687-1702.
70. R. A. Semplak and R. H. Turrin, "Some Measurements of Attenuation by Rainfall at 18.5 GHz," *Bell Syst. Tech. J.* **48** (July/August 1969), pp. 1767-1787.
71. M. V. Schneider, B. Glance, and W. F. Bodtmann, "Microwave and Millimeter Wave Hybrid Integrated Circuits for Radio Systems," *Bell Syst. Tech. J.* **48** (July/August 1969), pp. 1703-1726.
72. C. L. Ruthroff and W. F. Bodtmann, "A Linear Phase Modulator for Large Baseband Bandwidths," *Bell Syst. Tech. J.* **49** (October 1970), pp. 1893-1903; B. Glance, "Power Spectra of Multilevel Digital Phase-Modulated Signals," *Bell Syst. Tech. J.* **50** (November 1971), pp. 2857-2878; V. K. Prabhu, "Performance of Coherent Phase-Shift-Keyed Systems with Intersymbol Interference," *IEEE Trans. Inform. Theory* **IT-17** (July 1971), pp. 418-431.
73. A. B. Crawford and D. C. Hogg, "Measurement of Atmospheric Attenuation at Millimeter Wavelengths," *Bell Syst. Tech. J.* **35** (July 1956), pp. 907-916.
74. D. C. Hogg, "Millimeter Wave Communication Through the Atmosphere," *Science* **159** (January 5, 1968), pp. 39-46.
75. D. E. Setzer, "Computed Transmission Through Rain at Microwave and Visible Frequencies," *Bell Syst. Tech. J.* **49** (October 1970), pp. 1873-1892.
76. R. A. Semplak and H. E. Keller, "A Dense Network for Rapid Measurement of Rainfall Rate," *Bell Syst. Tech. J.* **48** (July/August 1969), pp. 1745-1756.
77. T. S. Chu and D. C. Hogg, "Effects of Precipitation on Propagation at 0.63, 3.5, and 10.6 Microns," *Bell Syst. Tech. J.* **47** (May/June 1968), pp. 723-759.
78. D. C. Hogg and R. A. Semplak, "The Effect of Rain and Water Vapor on Sky Noise at Centimeter Wavelengths," *Bell Syst. Tech. J.* **40** (September 1961), pp. 1331-1348.
79. D. C. Hogg and T. S. Chu, "The Role of Rain in Satellite Communications," *Proc. IEEE* **63** (September 1975), pp. 1308-1331.
80. R. W. Wilson, "Sun Tracker Measurements of Attenuation by Rain at 16 and 30 GHz," *Bell Syst. Tech. J.* **48** (May/June 1969), pp. 1383-1404.
81. P. S. Henry, "Measurement and Frequency Extrapolation of Microwave Attenuation Statistics on the Earth-Space Path at 13, 19, and 30 GHz," *IEEE Trans. Ant. Propag.* **AP-23** (March 1975), pp. 271-274.
82. D. C. Hogg, "Intensity and Extent of Rain on Earth-Space Paths," *Nature* **243** (June 8, 1973), pp. 337-338.
83. R. H. Dicke, "The Measurement of Thermal Radiation at Microwave Frequencies," *Rev. Sci. Instrum.* **17** (July 1946), pp. 268-275; R. W. DeGrasse, D. C. Hogg, E. A. Ohm, and H. E. D. Scovil, "Ultra-Low-Noise Antenna and Receiver Combination for Satellite or Space Communication," *Proc. Nat. Electron. Conf.* **15,** Chicago (October 12-14, 1959), pp. 370-379.
84. A. A. Penzias and R. W. Wilson, "A Measurement of Excess Antenna Temperature at 4080 Mc/s," *Astrophys. J.* **142** (July 1, 1965), pp. 419-421.
85. R. W. Wilson, "A Three-Radiometer Path-Diversity Experiment," *Bell Syst. Tech. J.* **49** (July/August 1970), pp. 1239-1242.

86. R. W. Wilson and W. L. Mammel, "Results from a Three-Radiometer Path-Diversity Experiment," *IEEE Conf. Propag. Radio Waves at Frequencies above 10 GHz,* London (April 10-13, 1973), pp. 23-27 and Supplementary Notes.

87. A. A. Penzias, "First Result from 15.3-GHz Earth-Space Propagation Study," *Bell Syst. Tech. J.* **49** (July/August 1970), pp. 1242-1245.

88. D. C. Hogg, "Path Diversity in Propagation of Millimeter Waves Through Rain," *IEEE Trans. Ant. Propag.* **AP-15** (May 1967), pp. 410-415.

89. See reference 76.

90. D. A. Gray, "Earth-Space Path Diversity: Dependence on Base Line Orientation," *IEEE 1973 G-AP Int. Symp.,* Boulder, Colorado (August 22-24, 1973), pp. 366-369.

91. T. S. Chu, "Restoring the Orthogonality of Two Polarizations in Radio Communication Systems, I," *Bell Syst. Tech. J.* **50** (November 1971), pp. 3063-3069.

92. T. S. Chu, "Restoring the Orthogonality of Two Polarizations in Radio Communication Systems, II," *Bell Syst. Tech. J.* **52** (March 1973), pp. 319-327.

93. R. A. Semplak, "Effect of Oblate Raindrops on Attenuation at 30.9 GHz," *Radio Sci.* **5** (March 1970), pp. 559-564; R. A. Semplak, "Simultaneous Measurements of Depolarization by Rain Using Linear and Circular Polarizations at 18 GHz," *Bell Syst. Tech. J.* **53** (February 1974), pp. 400-404; O. E. DeLange, A. F. Dietrich, and D. C. Hogg, "An Experiment on Propagation of 60-GHz Waves Through Rain," *Bell Syst. Tech. J.* **54** (January 1975), pp. 165-176.

94. T. Oguchi, "Attenuation of Electromagnetic Wave Due to Rain with Distorted Raindrops," *J. Radio Res. Lab. (Tokyo)* **7** (September 1960), pp. 467-485; T. Oguchi, "Attenuation of Electromagnetic Wave Due to Rain with Distorted Raindrops (Part II)," *J. Radio Res. Lab. (Tokyo)* **11** (January 1964), pp. 19-44; J. A. Morrison and T. S. Chu, "Perturbation Calculations of Rain-Induced Differential Attenuation and Differential Phase Shift at Microwave Frequencies," *Bell Syst. Tech. J.* **52** (December 1973), pp. 1907-1913.

95. T. S. Chu, "Rain-Induced Cross-Polarization at Centimeter and Millimeter Wavelength," *Bell Syst. Tech. J.* **53** (October 1974), pp. 1557-1579; T. S. Chu, "Microwave Depolarization of an Earth-Space Path," *Bell Syst. Tech. J.* **59** (July/August 1980), pp. 987-1007; D. C. Cox, "Depolarization of Radio Waves by Atmospheric Hydrometeors in Earth-Space Paths: A Review," *Radio Sci.* **16** (September/October 1981), pp. 781-812.

96. D. C. Cox, "An Overview of the Bell Laboratories 19- and 28-GHz COMSTAR Beacon Propagation Experiments," *Bell Syst. Tech. J.* **57** (May/June 1978), pp. 1231-1255.

97. A. J. Rustako, Jr., "An Earth-Space Propagation Measurement at Crawford Hill Using the 12-GHz CTS Satellite Beacon," *Bell Syst. Tech. J.* **57** (May/June 1978), pp. 1431-1448.

98. T. S. Chu, R. W. Wilson, R. W. England, D. A. Gray, and W. E. Legg, "The Crawford Hill 7-Meter Millimeter Wave Antenna," *Bell Syst. Tech. J.* **57** (May/June 1978), pp. 1257-1288.

99. H. W. Arnold, D. C. Cox, H. H. Hoffman, R. H. Brandt, R. P. Leck, and M. F. Wazowicz, "The 19- and 28-GHz Receiving Electronics for the Crawford Hill COMSTAR Beacon Propagation Experiment," *Bell Syst. Tech. J.* **57** (May/June 1978), pp. 1289-1329.

100. A. J. Rustako, Jr., "A Measurement of Rain Attenuation and Depolarization of the 12 GHz Communications Technology Satellite (CTS) Beacon Signal—Some Early Results," paper presented at *USNC/URCI Meeting,* Amherst, Massachusetts (October 15, 1976).

101. H. W. Arnold, D. C. Cox, H. H. Hoffman, and R. P. Leck, "Rain Attenuation Statistics from a 19- and 28-GHz COMSTAR Beacon Propagation Experiment: One Year Cumulative Distributions and Relationships Between the Two Frequencies," *IEEE Trans. Commun.* **COM-27** (November 1979), pp. 1725-1728.

102. H. W. Arnold, D. C. Cox, H. H. Hoffman, and R. P. Leck, "Characteristics of Rain and Ice Depolarization for a 19- and 28-GHz Propagation Path from a Comstar Satellite," *IEEE Trans. Ant. Propag.* **AP-28** (January 1980), pp. 22-28.

103. H. W. Arnold, D. C. Cox, H. H. Hoffman, and R. P. Leck, "Ice Depolarization Statistics for 19- and 28-GHz Satellite-to-Earth Propagation," *IEEE Trans. Ant. Propag.* **AP-28** (July 1980), pp. 546-550.
104. D. C. Cox, H. W. Arnold, and R. P. Leck, "Phase and Amplitude Dispersion for Earth-Satellite Propagation in the 20 to 30 GHz Frequency Range," *IEEE Trans. Ant. Propag.* **AP-28** (May 1980), pp. 359-366.
105. T. S. Chu, "Rain-Scatter Interference on Earth-Space Path," *IEEE Trans. Ant. Propag.* **AP-25** (March 1977), pp. 287-288.
106. G. C. Southworth and A. P. King, "Metal Horns as Directive Receivers of Ultra-Short Waves," *Proc. IRE* **27** (February 1939), pp. 95-102.
107. W. E. Kock, "Metal Lens Antennas," *Proc. IRE* **34** (November 1946), pp. 828-836; C. C. Cutler, A. P. King, and W. E. Kock, "Microwave Antenna Measurements," *Proc. IRE* **35** (December 1947), pp. 1462-1471; W. C. Jakes, "Gain of Electromagnetic Horns," *Proc. IRE* **39** (February 1951), pp. 160-162; S. A. Schelkunoff and C. B. Feldman, "On Radiation from Antennas," *Proc. IRE* **30** (November 1942), pp. 511-516; C. C. Cutler, "Parabolic-Antenna Design for Microwaves," *Proc. IRE* **35** (November 1947), pp. 1284-1294.
108. W. D. Lewis and L. C. Tillotson, "Non-Reflecting Branching Filter for Microwaves," *Bell Syst. Tech. J.* **27** (January 1948), pp. 83-95; W. A. Tyrrell, "Hybrid Circuits for Microwaves," *Proc. IRE* **35** (November 1947), pp. 1294-1306; R. W. Dawson, "An Experimental Dual Polarization Antenna Feed for Three Radio Relay Bands," *Bell Syst. Tech. J.* **36** (March 1957), pp. 391-408; W. E. Kock, "Path-Length Microwave Lenses," *Proc. IRE* **37** (August 1949), pp. 852-855.
109. S. A. Schelkunoff and H. T. Friis, *Antennas: Theory and Practice* (New York: John Wiley, 1952).
110. A. B. Crawford, D. C. Hogg, and L. E. Hunt, "Project Echo: A Horn-Reflector Antenna for Space Communication," *Bell Syst. Tech. J.* **40** (July 1961), pp. 1095-1116.
111. See reference 84.
112. G. C. Southworth, U.S. Patent No. 2,206,923; filed September 12, 1934; issued July 9, 1940.
113. C. C. Cutler, U.S. Patent No. 2,659,817; filed December 31, 1948; issued November 17, 1953.
114. C. C. Cutler, U.S. Patent No. 2,912,695; filed December 31, 1948; issued November 10, 1959.
115. C. Dragone and D. C. Hogg, "The Radiation Pattern and Impedance of Off-Set and Symmetrical Near-Field Cassegrainian and Gregorian Antennas," *IEEE Trans. Ant. Propag.* **AP-22** (May 1974), pp. 472-475.
116. T. Li, "A Study of Spherical Reflectors as Wide-Angle Scanning Antennas," *IRE Trans. Ant. Propag.* **AP-7** (July 1959), pp. 223-226.
117. T. S. Chu, R. W. Wilson, R. W. England, D. A. Gray, and W. E. Legg, "The Crawford Hill 7-Meter Millimeter Wave Antenna," *Bell Syst. Tech. J.* **57** (May/June 1978), pp. 1257-1288.
118. E. A. Ohm, "A Proposed Multiple-Beam Microwave Antenna for Earth Stations and Satellites," *Bell Syst. Tech. J.* **53** (October 1974), pp. 1657-1665.
119. E. A. Ohm and M. J. Gans, "Numerical Analysis of Multiple-Beam Offset Cassegrainian Antennas," AIAA Paper No. 76-301, presented at *AIAA/CASI 6th Commun. Satellite Syst. Conf.*, Montreal, Canada (April 5-8, 1976).
120. L. C. Tillotson, "A Model of a Domestic Satellite Communication System," *Bell Syst. Tech. J.* **47** (December 1968), pp. 2111-2137.
121. C. Dragone, "An Improved Antenna for Microwave Radio Systems Consisting of Two Cylindrical Reflectors and a Corrugated Horn," *Bell Syst. Tech. J.* **53** (September 1974), pp. 1351-1377.

122. R. H. Turrin, "A Multibeam, Spherical-Reflector Satellite Antenna for the 20- and 30-GHz Bands," *Bell Syst. Tech. J.* **54** (July/August 1975), pp. 1011-1026.

123. R. A. Semplak, "100-GHz Measurements on a Multiple-Beam Offset Antenna," *Bell Syst. Tech. J.* **56** (March 1977), pp. 385-398.

124. C. Dragone and M. J. Gans, "Imaging Reflector Arrangements to Form a Scanning Beam Using a Small Array," *Bell Syst. Tech. J.* **58** (February 1979), pp. 501-515.

125. T. S. Chu and R. H. Turrin, "Depolarization Properties of Offset Reflector Antennas," *IEEE Trans. Ant. Propag.* **AP-21** (May 1973), pp. 339-345; M. J. Gans, "Cross Polarization in Reflector-Type Beam Waveguides and Antennas," *Bell Syst. Tech. J.* **55** (March 1976), pp. 289-316; C. Dragone, "Characteristics of a Broadband Microwave Corrugated Feed: A Comparison Between Theory and Experiment," *Bell Syst. Tech. J.* **56** (July/August 1977), pp. 869-888.

126. A. S. Acampora, C. Dragone, and D. O. Reudink, "A Satellite System with Limited-Scan Spot Beams," *IEEE Trans. Commun.* **COM-27** (October 1979), pp. 1406-1415.

127. J. R. Pierce, "Orbital Radio Relays," *Jet Propulsion* **25** (April 1955), pp. 153-157.

128. C. E. Shannon, "A Mathematical Theory of Communication," *Bell Syst. Tech. J.* **27** (July 1948), pp. 379-423, and (October 1948), pp. 623-656.

129. B. M. Oliver, J. R. Pierce, and C. E. Shannon, "The Philosophy of PCM," *Proc. IRE* **36** (November 1948), pp. 1324-1331.

130. See reference 30.

131. J. R. Pierce and R. Kompfner, "Transoceanic Communication by Means of Satellites," *Proc. IRE* **47** (March 1959), pp. 372-380.

132. W. C. Jakes, Jr., "Participation of Bell Telephone Laboratories in Project Echo and Experimental Results," *Bell Syst. Tech. J.* **40** (July 1961), pp. 975-1028.

133. J. P. Schafer and R. H. Brandt, "Project Echo: 960-mc, 10-kw Transmitter," *Bell Syst. Tech. J.* **40** (July 1961), pp. 1041-1064.

134. E. A. Ohm, "Project Echo: Receiving System," *Bell Syst. Tech. J.* **40** (July 1961), pp. 1065-1094.

135. A. B. Crawford, D. C. Hogg, and L. E. Hunt, "Project Echo: A Horn-Reflector Antenna for Space Communication," *Bell Syst. Tech. J.* (July 1961), pp. 1095-1116.

136. C. L. Ruthroff, "Project Echo: FM Demodulators with Negative Feedback," *Bell Syst. Tech. J.* **40** (July 1961), pp. 1149-1156.

137. R. W. DeGrasse, J. J. Kostelnick, and H. E. D. Scovil, "Project Echo: The Dual Channel 2390-mc Traveling-Wave Maser," *Bell Syst. Tech. J.* **40** (July 1961), pp. 1117-1127.

138. A. B. Crawford, C. C. Cutler, R. Kompfner, and L. C. Tillotson, "The Research Background of the *Telstar* Experiment," *Bell Syst. Tech. J.* **42** (July 1963), pp. 747-764.

139. A. C. Clarke, "Extra-Terrestrial Relays," *Wireless World* **51** (October 1945), pp. 305-308.

140. See reference 120.

141. A. S. Acampora, "Spectral Sharing in Hybrid Spot and Area Coverage Satellite Systems via Channel Coding Techniques," *Bell Syst. Tech. J.* **57** (September 1978), pp. 2613-2631.

142. D. O. Reudink and Y. S. Yeh, "A Scanning Spot-Beam Satellite System," *Bell Syst. Tech. J.* **56** (October 1977), pp. 1549-1560.

143. D. O. Reudink, "Spot Beams Promise Satellite Communications Breakthrough," *IEEE Spectrum* **15** (September 1978), pp. 36-42.

144. N. Amitay and B. Glance, "Switching Performance of a 12 GHz p-i-n Phase Shifter/Driver Module for Satellite Communication Phased Array," *IEEE Trans. Commun.* **COM-29** (January 1981), pp. 46-50.

145. W. L. Aranguren, R. E. Langseth, and C. B. Woodworth, "Sequencer Designs for Scanning-Beam Satellites," *Bell Syst. Tech. J.* **58** (November 1979), pp. 1999-2011.

146. A. S. Acampora and B. R. Davis, "Efficient Utilization of Satellite Transponders via

Time-Division Multibeam Scanning," *Bell Syst. Tech. J.* **57** (October 1978), pp. 2901-2914.

147. A. S. Acampora, "Digital Error Rate Performance of Active Phased Array Satellite Systems," *IEEE Trans. Ant. Propag.* **AP-26** (November 1978), pp. 833-842.

148. See reference 126.

149. D. O. Reudink, A. S. Acampora, and Y. S. Yeh, "The Transmission Capacity of Multibeam Communication Satellites," *Proc. IEEE* **69** (February 1981), pp. 209-225.

150. A. S. Acampora, "The Ultimate Capacity of Frequency-Reuse Communication Satellites," *Bell Syst. Tech. J.* **59** (September 1980), pp. 1089-1122.

151. A. S. Acampora, "A Shared Resource TDMA Approach to Increase the Rain Margin of 12/14-GHz Satellite Systems," *Bell Syst. Tech. J.* **58** (November 1979), pp. 2097-2111.

152. A. S. Acampora and R. P. Gilmore, "Analog Viterbi Decoding for High-Speed Digital Satellite Channels," *IEEE Trans. Commun.* **COM-26** (October 1978), pp. 1463-1470.

153. W. R. Young, Jr., "Comparison of Mobile Radio Transmission at 150, 450, 900, and 3700 Mc," *Bell Syst. Tech. J.* **31** (November 1952), pp. 1068-1085.

154. W. D. Lewis, "Coordinated Broadband Mobile Telephone System," *IRE Trans. Veh. Commun.* **VC-9** (May 1960), pp. 43-48.

155. W. C. Jakes, Jr., ed., *Microwave Mobile Communications* (New York: John Wiley, 1974).

156. R. H. Clarke, "A Statistical Theory of Mobile-Radio Reception," *Bell Syst. Tech. J.* **47** (July/August 1968), pp. 957-1000.

157. M. J. Gans, "A Power-Spectral Theory of Propagation in the Mobile-Radio Environment," *IEEE Trans. Veh. Tech.* **VT-21** (February 1972), pp. 27-38.

158. W. C. Y. Lee, "An Energy-Density Antenna for Independent Measurement of the Electric and Magnetic Field," *Bell Syst. Tech. J.* **46** (September 1967), pp. 1587-1599.

159. W. C. Y. Lee, "Antenna Spacing Requirement for a Mobile Radio Base-Station Diversity," *Bell Syst. Tech. J.* **50** (July/August 1971), pp. 1859-1876.

160. W. C. Y. Lee and Y. S. Yeh, "Polarization Diversity System for Mobile Radio," *IEEE Trans. Commun.* **COM-20** (October 1972), pp. 912-923.

161. D. C. Cox, "Delay Doppler Characteristics of Multipath Propagation at 910 MHz in a Suburban Mobile Radio Environment," *IEEE Trans. Ant. Propag.* **AP-20** (September 1972), pp. 625-635.

162. D. O. Reudink, "Comparison of Radio Transmission at X-Band Frequencies in Suburban and Urban Areas," *IEEE Trans. Ant. Propag.* **20** (July 1972), pp. 470-473.

163. D. O. Reudink, "Mobile Radio Propagation in Tunnels," paper presented at *IEEE Veh. Tech. Group Conf.*, San Francisco, California (December 2-4, 1968).

164. H. J. Shulte, Jr., and W. A. Cornell, "Multi-Area Mobile Telephone System," *IRE Trans. Veh. Commun.* **VC-9** (May 1960), pp. 49-53.

165. D. C. Cox and D. O. Reudink, "Dynamic Channel Assignment in High-Capacity Mobile Communications Systems," *Bell Syst. Tech. J.* **50** (July/August 1971), pp. 1833-1857.

166. D. C. Cox and D. O. Reudink, "A Comparison of Some Channel Assignment Strategies in Large-Scale Mobile Communications Systems," *IEEE Trans. Commun.* **COM-20** (April 1972), pp. 190-195.

167. D. C. Cox and D. O. Reudink, "Increasing Channel Occupancy in Large-Scale Mobile Radio Systems: Dynamic Channel REassignment," *IEEE Trans. Veh. Tech.* **VT-22** (November 1973), pp. 218-222.

168. M. J. Gans, "The Effect of Gaussian Error in Maximal Ratio Combiners," *IEEE Trans. Commun. Tech.* **COM-19** (August 1971), pp. 492-500; B. R. Davis, "Random FM in Mobile Radio with Diversity," *IEEE Trans. Commun. Tech.* **COM-19** (December 1971), pp. 1259-1267; A. J. Rustako, Jr., "Evaluation of a Mobile Radio Multiple Channel Diversity Receiver Using Pre-Detection Combining," *IEEE Trans. Veh. Tech.* **VT-16**

(October 1967), pp. 46-57; B. R. Davis, "FM Noise with Fading Channels and Diversity," *IEEE Trans. Commun. Tech.* **COM-19** (December 1971), pp. 1189-1200.

169. S. W. Halpern, "The Theory of Operation of an Equal-Gain Predetection Regenerative Diversity Combiner with Rayleigh Fading Channels," *IEEE Trans. Commun.* **COM-22** (August 1974), pp. 1099-1106.

170. A. J. Rustako, Jr., Y. S. Yeh, and R. R. Murray, "Performance of Feedback and Switch Space Diversity 900 MHz FM Mobile Radio Systems with Rayleigh Fading," *IEEE Trans. Commun.* **COM-21** (November 1973), pp. 1257-1268.

171. C. C. Cutler, R. Kompfner, and L. C. Tillotson, "A Self-Steering Array Repeater," *Bell Syst. Tech. J.* **42** (September 1963), pp. 2013-2032.

172. S. P. Morgan, "Interaction of Adaptive Antenna Arrays in an Arbitrary Environment," *Bell Syst. Tech. J.* **44** (January 1965), pp. 23-47.

173. Y. S. Yeh, "An Analysis of Adaptive Retransmission Arrays in a Fading Environment," *Bell Syst. Tech. J.* **49** (October 1970), pp. 1811-1825.

174. M. J. Gans and D. O. Reudink, U.S. Patent No. 3,631,494; filed August 8, 1969; issued December 28, 1971.

175. J. S. Bitler, H. H. Hoffman, and C. O. Stevens, "A Mobile Radio Single-Frequency 'Two-Way' Diversity System Using Adaptive Retransmission from the Base," *IEEE Trans. Veh. Tech.* **VT-22** (November 1973), pp. 157-163.

176. Y. S. Yeh and D. O. Reudink, "Efficient Spectrum Utilization for Mobile Radio Systems Using Space Diversity," *IEEE Trans. Commun.* **COM-30** (March 1982), pp. 447-455.

177. P. S. Henry and B. S. Glance, "A New Approach to High-Capacity Digital Mobile Radio," *Bell Syst. Tech. J.* **60** (October 1981), pp. 1891-1904.

Chapter 6

Waveguide Research

Waveguide research at Bell Laboratories was stimulated by two theoretical predictions that were considered remarkable in their day. The first was that radio waves could propagate in hollow metal tubes with no "return" conductor. The second was that certain waves having a special configuration of electromagnetic fields could propagate through cylindrical metal tubes with attenuations that would approach zero as their frequency was indefinitely increased. The experimental and theoretical explorations that followed were greatly aided by the rapid advance in techniques of generating and detecting ever-higher microwave frequencies. By-products of the developing technology were quickly applied to wartime radar and, subsequently, to microwave radio-relay systems. Eventually much effort was devoted to the realization of the predicted low losses for the circular electric wave. Problems of mode conversion due mainly to random deviations in straightness of waveguides were solved, and the engineering feasibility of ultrabroadband long-distance transmission systems using circular electric waves at millimeter wavelengths was demonstrated.

I. ORIGINS OF WAVEGUIDE RESEARCH

When Bell Laboratories was incorporated in 1925, the only means in common use for sending electric power from one place to another was the parallel wire line. It had been used for many years for guiding dc and ac power, and for telephone and telegraph signals as well. But by the 1920s, considerable interest had developed in radio both for entertainment and for long-distance communication. And it was observed that at these frequencies, the parallel wire lines used to connect the antennas to transmitters and receivers not only leaked power by radiation but also picked up interference from other radio sources. Shielding the lines helped, but the most attractive arrangement was found to be a rigid cylindrical outer sheath with a single return conductor inside, known as a coaxial line. But at that time, the properties of coaxial lines were not fully understood. A small group of engineers under the direction of L. Espenschied devoted

---

Principal authors: A. G. Fox and W. D. Warters.

itself to experimental and theoretical studies of these structures during the latter half of the 1920s, and, by the start of the 1930s, their characteristic impedance and attenuation constant as a function of cross-sectional geometry and frequency were well understood.

In 1931, G. C. Southworth [Fig. 6-1], then employed in the Development and Research Department of the AT&T Company, began experiments that were to blossom into a radically new technique for guiding electromagnetic waves at frequencies orders of magnitude higher than those then in use.[1] This work grew out of some chance observations Southworth made ten years earlier while he was at Yale University. He had set out to measure the dielectric constant of water at radio frequencies using a continuous-wave oscillator, which had recently become available. The oscillator was coupled to a pair of parallel wires, called a Lecher frame, with adjustable reflecting plates at either end. By measuring the wavelength on the frame, first in air, and then when the frame was immersed in a trough of water,

Fig. 6-1.   G. C. Southworth in front of a TE_{01} waveguide transmission line built at Holmdel, New Jersey, in 1935. Southworth holds one of the resonant chambers used for tests of waveguide transmission.

the dielectric constant of water could be deduced. He found, however, that while the standing-wave pattern in air was a simple periodic function of position, the pattern observed in water was sometimes very erratic. This could be explained by the presence of other waves of different wavelengths superimposed on the expected ones. In fact, Southworth found that these spurious waves persisted in the water when he removed the Lecher frame from the trough, leaving only the oscillator and detector connected to the water. And he discovered that their wavelength depended on the transverse dimensions of the water in the trough, which led him to conclude that the water was guiding these waves.

Ten years earlier, a review of a paper by O. Schriever of the University of Kiel appeared in the *Journal Club*. In this paper, waves were described that might be supported on dielectric wires. The similarities to his own observations piqued Southworth's curiosity and created a desire for a chance to investigate this matter further. It was not until 1931 that this finally became possible. In addition to Schriever's work, there had been several other earlier contributions pointing the way to dielectric and hollow-tube waveguides. In a paper written in 1897, Lord Rayleigh had concluded that a number of modes of propagation could exist in such structures and that each of these modes had a lowest possible frequency (cut-off frequency) below which propagation could not exist.[2] None of these earlier publications seems to have been well known, and it is interesting to speculate on the reasons why. The most likely explanation appears to be that although Lord Rayleigh's theoretical predictions were on target, the techniques for experimental verification were essentially nonexistent. The only generators of radio waves were spark sources, and detectors were notoriously insensitive. A secondary reason may have been a lack of interest in a subject that was so remote from any obvious application. At any rate, these early disclosures were apparently filed and forgotten, only to be rediscovered many years later.

By 1931, when Southworth reactivated his investigations, the technology had greatly improved, but skepticism still existed about whether electromagnetic waves could pass through hollow metal tubes and dielectric rods, and whether there was any practical use for them even if they could. On the first point, common teaching held that the flow of power along a transmission line required at least two longitudinal conductors to provide for forward and return current paths. Furthermore, it was known that the space around the conductors contained electric and magnetic fields, but these were regarded as secondary manifestations rather than primary causes of the flow. Small wonder then that many engineers instinctively balked at the notion that a single hollow tube could transmit power. On the second point, common wisdom held that telephones worked very well with twisted pairs, so what excuse could there be for moving to extremely high frequencies where sources were not yet available?

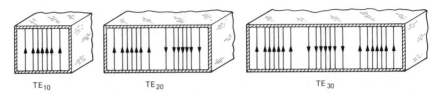

Fig. 6-2.   Electric fields in rectangular waveguide. [Southworth, *Principles and Applications of Waveguide Transmission* (1950): 115.]

As it became well known in the late 1930s, a hollow metal tube is capable of transmitting a number of different waves (i.e., modes of propagation) having unique electric- and magnetic-field patterns. For transverse electric waves (TE_{nm}), the lines of electric force lie entirely in planes transverse to the axis of the tube. [Fig. 6-2] Similarly, for transverse magnetic waves (TM_{nm}), the lines of magnetic force lie in transverse planes, and, in addition, always form closed loops. When these transverse fields are plotted on paper, they form symmetrical contour patterns somewhat resembling the modes of vibration of a drumhead. For propagation to take place, the free-space wavelength must be comparable to the diameter of the tube, or smaller.

II. EARLY WAVEGUIDE EXPERIMENTS AND THEORY

By the middle of 1932, Southworth had set up apparatus enabling him to observe guided waves in water-filled circular metal tubes in a wavelength range from 123 to 200 centimeters (cm). Had they been air-filled, diameters in the range of 200 cm would have been required. But the high dielectric constant of water reduced the effective wavelength by a factor of nine, which allowed Southworth to use tubes that were 15 and 25 cm in diameter. With these he had been able to launch two low-order waves and to measure their phase velocities, and by inserting slender coaxial probes terminating in a tiny dipole or a wire loop, he had determined the field configurations over a transverse plane. Southworth was thus able to identify these two waves as the dominant TE_{11} and the circular magnetic TM_{01}. [Fig. 6-3]

When internal memoranda reported these results, a high-level supervisor with his own lingering doubts felt the need for an independent opinion from one of the company's highly respected mathematicians, who, in due course, reported that the proposed system of transmission was not practicable. For a while, this cast a considerable shadow over the experimental program, which, however, continued to confirm earlier results. Fortunately, the mathematician found an error in his analysis and reported this in a memorandum that cleared the air.

Not long afterwards, Southworth transferred to Bell Laboratories where his waveguide research found a better fit, and he was assured the full

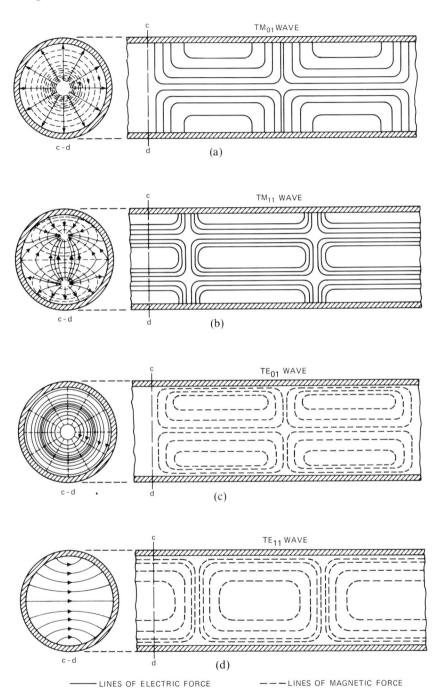

LINES OF ELECTRIC FORCE   — — — LINES OF MAGNETIC FORCE

Fig. 6-3. Electric and magnetic fields in circular waveguide. [Southworth, *Principles and Applications of Waveguide Transmission* (1950): 120.]

Fig. 6-4.   S. A. Schelkunoff, who, along with S. P.
Mead of AT&T, predicted from theoretical considerations that the circular electric wave, transmitted
down a cylindrical waveguide, would exhibit decreasing attenuation with increasing frequency.

support of his supervision. By then J. R. Carson and his assistant, S. P.
Mead, at AT&T were already involved in investigations of waveguide
theory. And independently, S. A. Schelkunoff [Fig. 6-4], a young electromagnetic theorist who had recently joined the Mathematics Department
of Bell Laboratories, had been intrigued by Southworth's memoranda and
was eagerly working on waveguide theory. Thus began a very valuable
interaction in which theoretical predictions helped to explain experimental
observations, and the observations helped point the way for extensions
of theory. By the end of 1932, several experimental and theoretical memoranda had been exchanged, and the reality of guided waves had been
established. Much work remained, however, to demonstrate how useful
these waves might be.

2.1 Circular Electric Waves

By the end of May 1933, both Mead at AT&T and Schelkunoff at Bell
Labs had independently issued memoranda giving for the first time the

attenuations of certain modes of propagation. In June, they apparently talked together, discussing certain differences in their results, and, in early July, within three days of one another issued separate memoranda giving the now-famous result for the attenuation of circular electric waves. Schelkunoff's memorandum abstract, dated July 7, 1933, states it concisely:

> Among several types of electromagnetic waves that can be shot along a hollow cylindrical conductor exists a wave with a circular line of electromotive intensity tangential to the conductor. For sufficiently high frequencies, its attenuation is inversely proportional to the 3/2's power of the frequency.

This astonishing result ran counter to all past experience. All other transmission lines had attenuations that increased with frequency. But this result predicted an attenuation that approached zero with increasing frequency. [Fig. 6-5] Understandably, this could have aroused new misgivings on the part of management regarding the plausibility of the claims being made for waveguides, which might explain why three more years were to pass before papers reporting on research results were released for publication. At the same time, hopes must have been raised for the possibility of a transcendently superior new means of transmission, and this too might have cautioned against haste in announcing results to competitors. In

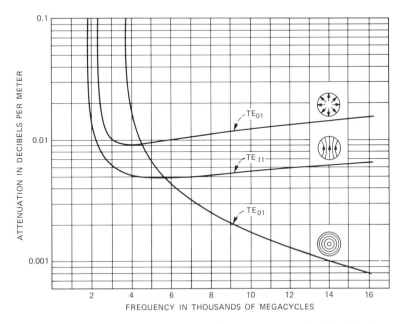

Fig. 6-5.   The attenuation presented by a hollow copper pipe (radius 5 cm) for three waveguide modes. Note the steadily decreasing attenuation of the TE_{01} mode. [Southworth, *Principles and Applications of Waveguide Transmission* (1950): 127.]

either case, it was clearly important to try to obtain experimental confirmation of the theoretical prediction.

Within a few months after Schelkunoff issued his memorandum, Southworth found ways of generating and identifying not only the TE_{01} but also the TM_{11} waves, and he measured their cut-off frequencies and phase velocities in short lengths of water-filled pipe. But there was great skepticism at the time about whether the predicted low attenuation could actually be realized in practice. In fact, many questioned whether any of the waveguide modes would maintain their identity in traveling long distances. Consequently, by late 1933, an air-filled guide 12.7 cm in diameter and 265 meters (m) long was built at a Bell Laboratories location in Netcong, New Jersey, and many tests were run at wavelengths between 16 and 17.5 cm. It was established that energy could be transmitted through a long waveguide without severe attenuation, and, although measurement techniques were still too crude to permit a confirmation of the theoretically predicted TE_{01}-mode attenuation, waveguide transmission over a distance was a demonstrated reality.

III. WAVEGUIDE COMES OF AGE

In 1934, Southworth and his project transferred from the Bell Labs headquarters location at 463 West Street, New York City to the Bell Labs location in Holmdel, New Jersey, where he began a collaborative research program with A. P. King and A. E. Bowen. Over the next four years, this team improved measuring techniques and broadened its understanding of how waveguide discontinuities could be used as lumped circuit elements. A. E. Bowen developed wavemeters, standing-wave detectors, and vacuum-tube oscillators for the 3-gigahertz (GHz) range. King devised small point-contact detectors using silicon with tungsten points that could be mounted inside the waveguides, and he gathered much data on the impedance matching and directional patterns of electromagnetic horns. By the time World War II started, a body of knowledge had been developed that provided strong support for the rapid development of microwave radar.[3]

During 1935, reports drifted in that Professor W. A. Barrow at the Massachusetts Institute of Technology (MIT) was engaged in research similar to the work of the Bell Labs group. In early 1936, Barrow wrote to Southworth announcing his plans to publish a paper on his work. Southworth resurrected his own previously prepared draft and was promptly given publication approval. His paper and Barrow's were both delivered at a joint meeting of the Institute of Radio Engineers and the American Physical Society on April 30, 1936. Southworth's written version of his experimental results[4] was published with a paper by Carson, Mead, and Schelkunoff on theory[5] in the April 1936 issue of the *Bell System Technical Journal*. From this point on, the gauntlet was down and waveguides were to be taken seriously.

As the pace of experimental work increased, Schelkunoff continued to make many important contributions to waveguide theory. For wavelengths of only a few centimeters, ordinary coils, capacitors, and resistors no longer behaved as lumped circuit elements, and alternative methods had to be found using waveguide discontinuities, such as internal irises, metal rods, and wire grids, for providing equivalent impedance transformations. Schelkunoff provided theoretical insights for understanding such structures, determined the directional patterns of electromagnetic horns, and, in general, was of great assistance to the experimenters who were trying to make sense of their observations.

In the years that followed, the waveguide group at Holmdel continued to develop its techniques, gave many lectures, and stimulated much interest in high-frequency research. Other groups at Holmdel were already working on the idea of using radio-relay transmission with directive antennas at the lower frequencies then available (500 megahertz (MHz)). With the new possibility of using waveguides and electromagnetic horns at much higher frequencies, much greater antenna gains could be achieved with smaller structures. This offered an exciting alternative that was more immediately realizable than circular electric wave transmission.

In fact, measurements were made in the late 1930s of the TE_{01}-mode attenuation through a new 1250-foot-long test guide using higher frequency signal sources that had become available at 3.75 GHz, and the loss was disappointingly higher than calculated. Since seamless copper pipe was not commercially available in the 10- and 15-cm diameters needed for the test guides, it had been necessary to build them by hand, wrapping sheet copper around a mandrel and hand-soldering the seam. This seam, which extended more or less parallel to the axis of the pipe, was an obvious crudity, and was blamed for the excessive attenuation. Indeed, as was later discovered, the ability of the TE_{01} wave to propagate with the predicted low attenuation depends on perfection in the waveguide, in circularity of cross section, straightness, and freedom from small dents or patches of different conductivities. The presence of such aberrations can distort the lines of electric field so as to generate components of other waveguide modes. If the aberrations lie above their cut-off frequencies, they can propagate down the waveguide and are capable of bleeding off substantial power from the circular electric mode, causing its attenuation to be substantially higher than predicted. Realizing this, researchers postponed efforts to pursue the lure of TE_{01}-mode transmission in favor of experimental work on waveguide components essential for a microwave radio-relay system operating at 3000 MHz.

3.1 Waveguides in Microwave Radio

By 1940, most of the components needed for a 3000-MHz transmission system had been demonstrated. Multiplexers using frequency-selective waveguide filters, providing bandwidths of from 3 to 20 MHz, had shown the possibility of multichannel transmission. R. S. Ohl of Bell Labs, with his pioneering work on silicon crystals, had provided efficient point-contact detectors and frequency converters. (See another volume in this series, *Physical Sciences (1925-1980)*, Chapter 11, sections II and 8.1.) A microwave amplifier providing 15-decibel (dB) amplification had been built, following the lead set by the invention of the klystron by R. H. and S. F. Varian. And antennas with directive gains of 36 dB had been realized. A demonstration 3000-MHz system at Holmdel included the transmission of three multiplexed channels through a 400-m waveguide to an electro-

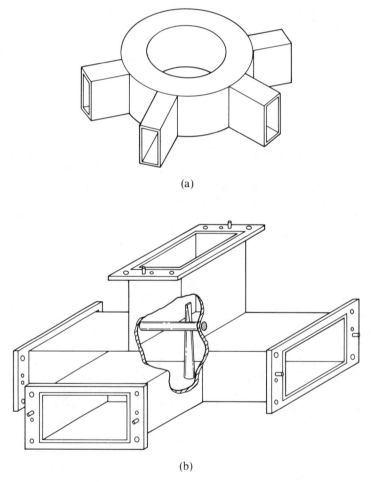

(a)

(b)

Fig. 6-6.   Balanced waveguide circuits: (a) the ring form of waveguide bridge; (b) a matched form of hybrid junction. [Southworth, *Principles and Applications of Waveguide Transmission* (1950): 338, 341.]

magnetic horn antenna that transmitted back, by radio, to a similar horn and receiver.

In 1939 and 1940, the waveguide group grew with the addition of three young engineers, A. G. Fox, S. D. Robertson, and W. A. Tyrrell. Fox developed the concept of simple resonant chambers in a waveguide line into sophisticated multicavity filters that could be designed to have specific desired transmission characteristics.[6] The concept was adapted and refined to such an extent that maximally flat filters could be realized in practice.[7] As an example, a short section of round waveguide equipped with parallel metal rods in an axial plane could be designed to produce a 90-degree retardation for dominant TE_{11} waves polarized parallel to the rods, while having no effect on waves polarized perpendicular to them. For waves polarized at 45 degrees, linear polarization was converted to circular polarization and vice versa. This permitted the building of a rotary joint for the feed line of a radar antenna that would allow the antenna to rotate about an axis. A linear-to-circular polarization converter was used on either side of the joint to produce circular polarization at the joint while maintaining properly oriented linear polarization in the waveguides at either end. Tyrrell invented balanced waveguide circuits,[8] such as the hybrid ring and the hybrid junction (dubbed the "magic tee" by engineers at MIT). These circuits made it possible to combine a received signal with power from a local oscillator to drive a pair of balanced detectors without the loss of any power. [Fig. 6-6] Robertson developed waveguide modulator and demodulator circuitry that later provided rapid progress in raising the frequencies at which measurements could be made.

3.2 Waveguides in Radar

In 1940 and 1941, interest in waveguide work grew rapidly as its possible application to the Allied war effort became evident. In September of 1940, Dr. J. Cockcroft and Dr. E. G. Bowen of Cambridge University visited the Holmdel, New Jersey location of Bell Labs and described the early radars, which operated at moderately low frequencies and used coaxial rather than waveguide techniques. These radars were making a significant contribution to winning the Battle of Britain. It was clear to everyone that much higher frequencies were needed to provide lightweight airborne equipment and much better directional resolution, and that waveguide techniques would be extremely helpful.

Later in 1940, the National Defense Research Committee formed the now-famous Radiation Laboratory at MIT, which soon grew to include several hundred top scientists working on the development of microwave radar. During 1941, the Waveguide Research and Radio Research groups at Holmdel played a vital role in disseminating their waveguide techniques to members of the Radiation Laboratory, as well as to other departments of Bell Laboratories. And for the duration of World War II, they continued to invent and test new waveguide devices needed for military radars. Thus, almost at the moment of its birth, the first proposed peacetime application of waveguide, the radio-relay project, was put aside for more urgent business.

3.2.1 Waveguides for Radar Antennas

Among these wartime contributions were several novel antennas. One of the early submarine radars employed a parabolic reflector illuminated alternately by two slightly off-axis waveguide feeds. This produced a major lobe that jumped between two positions separated by a small angle. By aiming to equalize the target echoes seen by the two beams, the target position could be accurately determined. This required rapid switching of power from one feed to the other by a snap-action switch that minimized the transition time. Fox employed a pair of resonant waveguide cavities through which power could flow to the feeds.[9] [Fig. 6-7] A rapidly rotating metal rod, penetrating first one cavity and then the other, detuned the cavities so that only one could transmit at a time. A later version used a pair of resonant irises with a rotating metal vane to detune them.

As another example, the United States Navy needed a high-resolution scanning antenna for use with a 3-GHz fire-control radar on its heavy ships. C. B. Feldman, relying on his earlier experience with Multiple Unit Scanning Antennas (MUSA), at lower frequencies, laid out a design for

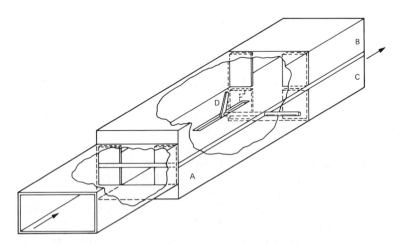

Fig. 6-7.   Snap-action switch used for submarine radar. Microwave energy from *A* is directed at single-cavity filters *B* and *C*, which are alternately detuned by rotating waveguide arm *D*. [Southworth, *Principles and Applications of Waveguide Transmission* (1950): 321.]

the first waveguide adaptation of the MUSA principle. (See Chapter 5, section 1.5.) It called for a broadside array of 42 radiating elements fed through a system of continuously running phase shifters to produce a sharp scanning beam. The radiating elements were required to have end-fire directivity to reduce minor lobes and reduce coupling between elements, and dielectric waveguide launchers were chosen for this purpose. G. E. Mueller, who joined Bell Labs early in the war, undertook the design of these elements that took the form of polystyrene rods, called polyrods, about 5 cm in diameter and 1 m in length. One end of the rods was inserted a short distance inside of the metal waveguide feed, and the projecting portion of the rod was gently tapered to squeeze out the prop-agating wave into the surrounding space while providing a reflectionless termination. The phase shifters, invented by Fox,[10] employed three tandem sections of circular waveguide containing metal rods similar to the wave-guide rotary joint mentioned earlier. [Fig. 6-8] The fixed sections at either end were linear-to-circular polarization converters, and the center section, which was motor driven to rotate at high speed, provided 180 degrees of differential phase shift for two orthogonal polarizations. Radiators near the outer ends of the array were fed through many phase changes, thus providing large phase shifts. Those near the center of the array were fed through few phase shifts. The result was a horizontally sweeping beam that appeared at one side of the field of view and disappeared at the other side, displaying not only the positions of enemy ships, but shell splashes as well. This radar (Mark 8) enabled attacks to be made in total darkness with accuracy, and was responsible for the sinking of many Japanese war-ships in the Pacific. More detail on these and other major wartime efforts

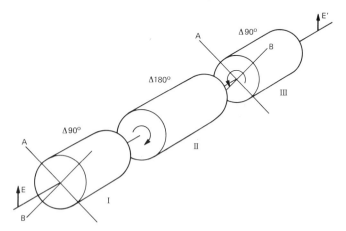

Fig. 6-8. A. G. Fox's adjustable phase changer. The rotating center section provided phase shifts needed to sweep a radar beam for naval fire control. [Fox, *Proc. IRE* **35** (1947): 1496.]

is given in another volume of this series, subtitled *National Service in War and Peace (1925-1975)*.

3.2.2 Waveguides for 24-GHz Radar

The extension of waveguide techniques to ever-higher frequencies had been a long-range goal of the Holmdel scientists and engineers, but now they were being pushed by the wartime need for smaller, more directive antennas, and the work was greatly aided by the cooperation of many other organizations involved in radar research. Starting from a 3-GHz capability in early 1940, higher frequency techniques were developed by a leapfrogging process, using existing microwave signal sources to drive harmonic generators with the aid of Ohl's silicon crystals and Robertson's modulator techniques. The first step was a third-harmonic generator that provided a 9-GHz signal when driven by a 3-GHz (S-band) source. While the signal was too weak for any practical system use, it permitted the laboratory development of essential components, such as attenuators, wavemeters, and standing-wave detectors. These instruments then aided the scientists and engineers of the Electronics Research Laboratory in developing higher-power oscillators such as klystrons and magnetrons, which opened the way for a second generation of radars operating at 9 GHz (X-band). A similar tripling of frequency was obtained from 8 to 24 GHz (K-band), and by the end of the war researchers in the Holmdel location of Bell Labs assembled a 24-GHz experimental radar. This radar was taken to Atlantic Highlands, New Jersey, where it clearly revealed ships 14 miles away in New York Harbor. The last upward step used a 24-GHz klystron supplied by H. V. Neher of the MIT Radiation Laboratory and newly developed crystal rectifiers made by Ohl, and yielded a second harmonic output at 48 GHz. At this point, however, the going became difficult and several years passed before solid progress became visible in this millimeter-wavelength range.

3.3 Nonreciprocal Transmission in Waveguides

For many years, electrical engineers had been taught to respect the reciprocity principle. When a two-port transmission system is made up of linear passive elements, this principle predicts that if a wave traveling through the system from port *A* to port *B* suffers a certain loss in decibels, then a wave traveling in the opposite direction (*B* to *A*) suffers the same loss. However, in 1948, B. D. H. Tellegen at the Philips Research Laboratory in the Netherlands, recognizing that the Faraday rotation of a transverse electromagnetic wave is nonreciprocal, pointed out that it should be possible, in principle, to build passive nonreciprocal transmission line elements.[11] In particular he proposed an ideal two-port device having zero phase delay for propagation in one direction and 180-degree phase delay in the opposite direction. This he named a gyrator because Faraday rotation results from gyromagnetic interactions between a wave and precessing electron spins in the Faraday medium. With the gyrator as a building block, Tellegen believed that a number of useful nonreciprocal devices could be made.

Although Faraday rotation had been known for a long time, it was a weak effect in most transparent media. To obtain substantial rotation of the polarization, the medium must be strongly magnetized in the direction of propagation of the wave. While this is possible in ferromagnetic metals and alloys that have high permeabilities, their high conductivities made it impossible for electromagnetic waves to penetrate them.

Toward the end of 1950, C. L. Hogan in the Physical Research Laboratory at the Murray Hill, New Jersey location of Bell Labs, recognized that a new class of magnetic oxides called ferrites could exhibit strong ferromagnetic resonance effects. (See *Physical Sciences (1925-1980)*, Chapter 1, sections 1.3.1 and 2.3.1.) Because of their low conductivities, the ferrites would allow microwaves to propagate in waveguides containing these oxides. By mounting a ferrite cylinder along the axis of a section of circular waveguide and magnetizing it in an axial direction, Hogan found that X-band dominant waves could be arranged to pass through with a rotation of polarization of 90 degrees. For propagation in the reverse direction, starting from the 90-degree polarization, another 90-degree rotation was added in the same sense. Hence the return trip output had the same polarization angle as the original input, but was reversed in direction, corresponding to a 180-degree phase shift. Thus he had demonstrated a microwave gyrator for the first time.[12] This device immediately captured the interest of many engineers and scientists at Bell Labs and outside. It soon became obvious that there were many avenues open for exploration, both in devising new nonreciprocal waveguide devices and in seeking a better understanding of the physics involved, and, for the next five years, considerable waveguide research effort was devoted to this subject.

Initial difficulties were encountered in obtaining sufficient Faraday rotation in the ferrites without high loss, and the loss varied unpredictably from sample to sample of ferrite. It was found that some of this was due to differences in the chemical composition and homogeneity of the nickel-zinc ferrites used. When the yttrium-iron garnets became available and replaced the ferrites, there was a marked improvement in the rotation-to-loss ratios obtainable. To avoid the propagation of higher-order modes within the ferrite-loaded region, slender ferrite rods occupying only a small part of the waveguide cross section were used, so that only the dominant mode could propagate. Finally, it was found to be important to taper the ends of the rods to avoid reflections of the dominant mode, which could also cause resonances. Because magnetized ferrite inserts strongly perturb the microwave fields in waveguides, no theory adequately predicted the interactions. Without such guidance, the design of all devices depended on extensive experimentation.

3.3.1 Circular Waveguide Nonreciprocal Devices

A number of useful components were invented using Faraday rotation in circular waveguides. Because two orthogonal polarizations could propagate, they may be thought of as two-mode guides. One such device due to S. E. Miller[13] used a 45-degree rotator and two rectangular waveguide ports at each end. [Fig. 6-9] Waves launched at one port were rotated 45 degrees and emerged at a second port. Waves entering the second port did not return to the first port, but instead emerged at a third port. From this port, transmission went to a fourth port, and finally back to the first port, thereby closing the path of circulation. For this reason it was named a circulator.

If, in the above example, matched terminations were connected to the third and fourth ports, forward propagation could pass from the first port to the second port, but no reflections occurring beyond the second port could return to the first port. Such a device was called an isolator because, for the first time, it became possible to protect an oscillator from disturbing reflections caused by mismatched loads without having to suffer the power

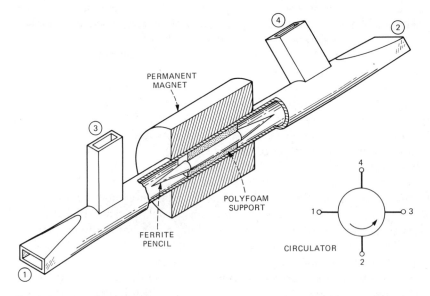

Fig. 6-9. A Faraday rotation circulator. The ferrite pencil rotates the plane of polarization 45 degrees. This allows transmission through the next port in the circular sequence, but not through the other ports.

loss of attenuator pads. A simpler isolator can be made by omitting the rectangular waveguide takeoffs for the third and fourth ports and substituting internal resistance cards in the circular waveguide oriented perpendicular to the electric fields in the first and second ports. Regardless of their construction, isolators have become the most used nonreciprocal devices.

Additionally, directional phase shifters were developed that could produce any arbitrary difference in phase delay for opposite directions of transmission. In the special case of 180 degrees, the device became a gyrator. It is interesting that the gyrator, which Tellegen regarded as a fundamental building block, has not been as useful in circular waveguide as the other devices previously mentioned. Waveguide switches were built that could deliver power to either of two output ports by controlling the magnetic field. And techniques were developed for broadbanding isolators and circulators by including additional Faraday rotation sections.

3.3.2 Rectangular Nonreciprocal Waveguide Devices

Following somewhat later than the Faraday rotation devices, a second family of nonreciprocal devices was developed for rectangular waveguide. Because only one mode of propagation exists in rectangular guide, the principles of operation were fundamentally different from those depending on Faraday rotation. Rather than using longitudinal magnetizing fields, transverse fields were used normal to the broad face of the waveguide. The ferrite, in the form of a thin rectangular plate, was inserted lengthwise in the waveguide with its plane parallel to the narrow faces of the guide. Because the magnetic field of the dominant mode forms closed loops lying in planes parallel to the broad walls, as one looks down on a broad face and observes the propagating electromagnetic wave, the magnetic field appears to rotate clockwise on one side of center and counterclockwise on the other side of center. For the opposite direction of propagation, the sense of rotation on the two sides is reversed. Therefore, by placing the ferrite plate away from the center toward one of the narrow faces, it is exposed to a rotary magnetic field transverse to the axis of magnetization of the ferrite. Under these conditions, the radio frequency (RF) permeability of the ferrite is different for the two directions of propagation, and this produces different phase velocities for oppositely directed waves. The loaded waveguide then becomes a directional phase shifter, with a nonreciprocal phase shift dependent on the dimensions and position of the ferrite. When the shift is 180 degrees, the waveguide becomes a gyrator. With the development of the rectangular waveguide directional phase shifter, it became possible to build a variety of circulators by combining the phase shifter with standard directional couplers.[14]

Other nonreciprocal devices were developed that depended on the fact that a plate of ferrite placed near one of the narrow walls of a rectangular waveguide could strongly perturb the microwave fields, pulling them toward the ferrite for one direction of propagation, and pushing them away for the opposite. By suitably positioning the ferrite and coating the inside surface with a conductive film, the attenuation in one direction could be made very small, while in the other it was very large. Such devices were called field displacement isolators.

Another achievement of the ferrite waveguide research was the demonstration by M. T. Weiss of a ferrite parametric amplifier and oscillator.[15]

In the years since the ferrite work came to a halt at the Holmdel location of Bell Laboratories, nonreciprocal components have been further developed and have found many useful applications. New versions have appeared that incorporate ferrites into microwave printed circuit and strip-line designs, thus resulting in smaller size and lighter weight nonreciprocal devices than the hollow metal waveguide components.

IV. MILLIMETER WAVES IN A CIRCULAR ELECTRIC (TE_{01}) TRANSMISSION SYSTEM

By about 1950, measurements of rain attenuation of radio beams at S-, X-, and K-bands by Robertson, King, and others at the Holmdel location of Bell Laboratories had clearly indicated that a radio-relay system covering long distances could suffer unacceptable attenuation unless the carrier frequency was kept below about 10 GHz. On the other hand, it was becoming clear that with the advent of commercial television and other communication services requiring vastly expanded information capacity, the use of much higher microwave frequencies could hardly be avoided. For these, only waveguides could provide a medium free of atmospheric disturbances and crosstalk problems.

Realizing this, H. T. Friis, then director of radio research, began urging his team of research engineers to devote more time to the development of millimeter-wave techniques. These he regarded as an essential next step toward the realization of a circular electric wave system, which he thought should standardize the use of 5-cm inside-diameter round waveguide operating with frequencies around 60 GHz.

Several researchers at Holmdel had already been exploring millimeter-wave techniques and developing scaled-down versions of TE_{01}-mode components for this frequency range. However, it was evident that much remained to be done before the promise of the TE_{01} mode for long-distance communication could be demonstrated. In 1950, Miller was given responsibility for a group of engineers whose efforts were focused on this goal. And over the next few years, the group was increased in size until it represented a formidable amount of talent.

4.1 Millimeter-Wave Techniques

4.1.1 Millimeter-Wave Homodyne System

As mentioned earlier, low-power oscillators and crystal detectors were already available in the millimeter-wave range. An assortment of small dominant-mode rectangular waveguide components was developed for laboratory measurements. But the range of attenuations that could be measured using direct detection was far too limited. The use of heterodyne detection with intermediate frequency amplification could greatly increase the sensitivity for weak signals, but the oscillators were so unstable that, even with elaborate frequency stabilization systems, measurements were unreliable.

D. H. Ring devised an ingenious solution for measuring attenuation, using a homodyne double detection system.[16] He split the power from a 50-GHz oscillator into two paths. One path included the device whose loss was to be measured. The other path included a continuous phase shifter of the type used on the Mark 8 radar antenna. (See section 3.2.1.) By driving the middle (rotary) section of the phasechanger with a synchronous motor to rotate at 75 revolutions per second, the output frequency was shifted 150 hertz (Hz) from the input frequency. Thus, when the outputs of the two paths were combined at a crystal detector, a difference frequency of 150 Hz was generated, and this was passed through a high-gain audio amplifier with a 30-Hz passband. Even though the signal oscillator might wander in frequency, the output was always 150 Hz and had a good signal-to-noise ratio, providing about 100 dB of loss measuring range. For several years this measuring set was the mainstay for laboratory measurements until improved 50-GHz oscillators became available.

4.1.2 Dielectric Waveguides

Another problem during the early work with millimeter waveguides was the need for flexible patch cords for connections to movable devices. Some 15 years earlier, Southworth had demonstrated propagation in dielectric waveguides, but these were so thick and stiff that they were unattractive as flexible links. However, during the 1940s, considerable progress had been made by chemists in producing low-loss polymers, notably polystyrene and polyethylene, and both of these materials proved to be useful for dielectric waveguides. By extruding them through hot dies, round rods about 4 millimeters (mm) in diameter and 100-m long could be made. And with these slender dimensions they could be easily flexed in bends of about 30-cm radius with low transmission loss. Transitions from metal to dielectric waveguide were made by tapering and shaping the end of a dielectric rod so it could slip snugly inside the metal tube.

In addition, a small conical horn, about 2.5 cm in diameter and 2.5 cm long, placed on the end of the metal guide decreased stray radiation and gave a good impedance match. However, it was found that with a dominant TE wave launched on a round rod, the wave soon became depolarized by any bends or irregularities in cross section. The problem was easily avoided by drawing the rods through dies of rectangular or elliptical cross section, guaranteeing that the phase velocities for the two principal polarizations were sufficiently different to minimize power transfer from one polarization to the other. Such dielectric patch cords proved very popular in millimeter-wave measuring equipment.

The dielectric rods did not have sharp cut-off frequencies, and the wave energy propagated along the rods, partly inside and partly in the space immediately outside. It was therefore necessary to maintain a clear region of several centimeters around a rod to avoid scattering energy and causing attenuation. As an interesting by-product of this behavior, it was found that shrinking the cross section of a rod caused more of the wave energy to be carried outside and less inside. And since the major loss was due to the dielectric, this served to reduce the attenuation.

A number of experiments were carried out on 100-m lengths of dielectric waveguide suspended by looped threads at frequent intervals. It was found that attenuations considerably lower than that of the rectangular silver waveguide used for local plumbing were easily obtained. However, the lower the loss in the rod, the weaker was its control of the wave, and to avoid radiation loss at a bend, the bends had to be very gradual. This, together with the inconvenience of having to suspend a rod in a clear region, discouraged thoughts about low-loss dielectric rods as long-distance waveguides. At that time, the idea of cladding dielectric waveguides, as became common practice with optical fibers, had not been born. Even if it had been, a cladding would probably have resulted in a rod with a diameter of about one inch, which would have made it too bulky and stiff to be practical. On the other hand, the presence of the external field turned out to be a great convenience in making directional couplers.

4.1.3 Directional Couplers

For a number of years, directional couplers had been in common use for measuring reflections in metal waveguides, sampling power flowing in both directions, and combining signals from two sources. The simplest versions employed two sections of rectangular metal waveguide placed together in parallel so as to share a common wall. [Fig. 6-10] Two small openings were placed in the common wall a quarter wavelength apart in the direction of propagation. The leakage components from the first guide into the second guide via the two holes add in the forward direction and cancel in the backward direction, but only at the correct wavelength.

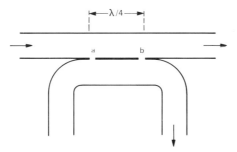

Fig. 6-10. A simple form of directional coupler. Two openings, *a* and *b*, placed a quarter wavelength apart, allow transmission in the forward direction and cancellation in the backward direction. [Southworth, *Principles and Applications of Waveguide Transmission* (1950): 346.]

However, by using a series of holes properly spaced and with the proper openings, much broader operating bandwidths could be obtained.[17] Still later designs used continuous coupling from a long slot in the common wall parallel with the axis of the waveguides, and the slot was usually provided with a fine wire grid to reduce the leakage per unit length to a suitable low level. Miller studied this weak continuous coupling case and developed an analysis that predicted the necessary conditions (length and coupling strength) for any desired power division between the two waveguides.[18]

With this work as an inspiration, Fox experimented with wave coupling between two parallel dielectric waveguides. By flexing one rod in a gentle arc and moving it toward the second rod until the center of the arc penetrated the zone of external field of the other rod, very good power transfers could be obtained.[19] Supporting the rods in low-density Styrofoam* provided a permanent directional coupler with any desired power division.

4.2 The Circular Electric Wave in a Long-Distance Transmission System

4.2.1 The TE_{11}-to-TE_{01} Mode Converter

One of the essential components developed at an early stage was a TE_{11}-to-TE_{01} converter that could accept millimeter waves from the dominant-mode rectangular guide used for local RF plumbing and convert them into circular electric waves in a circular-metal waveguide with an inside diameter of 1 cm. The converter was fabricated starting with the

---

* Trademark of Dow Chemical Co.

internal cross section of the 1/2-cm-wide rectangular guide. One narrow wall was slowly tapered to zero height, while the opposite wall was expanded in a circular arc that closed on itself to form the 1-cm-diameter circular waveguide at the opposite end. The total length of the taper was about 15 cm. Since it is impossible to drill such a complex hole, some clever tricks had to be used in constructing the device. These involved machining multipart steel mandrels, electroforming copper walls around them to form two lengthwise-split half-sections, removing the mandrels, and brazing the halves together in accurate alignment.

Another required component was a taper from the 1-cm round waveguide up to the 5-cm round waveguide that had been chosen for the final transmission medium. First attempts made use of linear tapers that, however, had to be made excessively long to keep conversion to unwanted modes suitably low.

H. G. Unger developed a theoretical analysis that showed that by using a unique nonlinear taper, the required performance could be obtained with sections only about a meter in length. Such tapers had their greatest rate of expansion near the small diameter end, after which the rate fell slowly over the remaining major portion of the length.[20]

4.2.2 Mode Filters

While the mode converter and taper put most of the power into the desired wave, some unwanted modes were generated by the imperfections of the guide, and these required elimination using mode filters. A number of filter designs were tried, all based on the fact that only the circular electric modes have electric fields that form closed circular loops in the transverse plane, and therefore produce no longitudinal wall currents. All other modes, both TE and TM, have longitudinal wall currents. Consequently, if the walls of a circular waveguide are corrugated or cut transverse to its axis, this will not interfere with transverse wall currents induced by circular electric waves, but it will interfere with the longitudinal wall currents of all other waves. Experimental guides with alternating brass and polystyrene washers were effective in discriminating against unwanted modes. However, loss was incurred by power radiating between the conducting washers to the exterior of the guide, making the behavior sensitive to nearby objects. This was subsequently avoided by using spaced metal washers bound together by a graphite-loaded plastic sheath that not only provided rigidity but effectively absorbed the leakage radiation. These proved very useful in the experimental program.

The best design of all, however, came sometime later with the invention of the "helix guide." For this, fine enameled copper wire was continuously wound close-spaced on a 5.1-cm-diameter steel cylinder, one layer deep.

Outside of this was a layer of conductively loaded plastic. And this assembly was inserted in a heavy-walled steel tube that provided the protective armor and straight alignment for the helix. Finally the steel mandrel was removed. The enamel on the wire provided the separations between adjacent turns needed for the radiation of unwanted mode power. The small diameter of the wire was advantageous because it permitted a turn spacing that was small compared to a wavelength, which was helpful in avoiding resonance effects. Three-meter lengths or six-meter lengths of this helix guide became the preferred form of mode filter for the TE_{01} transmission system.[21]

4.2.3 Bends in Waveguide for TE_{01} Transmission

From the start, bends were a problem. A pure TE_{01} wave entering a gently curved bend immediately began coupling to unwanted modes. The total power lost to other modes depended in a complex way on the length of bend and on the radius of curvature. From the start of the bend, loss increased with total angle traversed, but beyond a certain point the losses could actually decrease. This was because the TE_{01} and TM_{11} modes in straight guide have the same phase velocity. A bend causes continuous coupling between them, and as a result the waveguide acts like a directional coupler with the radius determining the coupling strength. Consequently, power is converted from the TE_{01} mode continuously until all of the power is in the TM_{11} mode. Beyond this point, conversion takes place back into the TE_{01} mode. The remedy for this was to avoid the velocity degeneracy of the two modes. By placing a thin dielectric lining on the inside wall of the waveguide, the TM_{11} wave was slowed down while the TE_{01} wave was hardly affected. This proved to be the best solution for the bend problem.[22]

4.2.4 Cross-Section Circularity and Straightness of Waveguide

Even in nominally straight sections of waveguide, it was found that there was a slow build-up of unwanted mode power with distance. This was eventually traced by H. E. Rowe and W. D. Warters to small deviations from circularity of cross section, to small deviations in straightness, and sometimes to blemishes on the inside surface of the copper tube.[23] Such random defects produced no reflections but coupled power from the TE_{01} mode into other modes traveling only in the forward direction. Through improvement in manufacturing techniques, these defects were essentially eliminated. Straightness defects, while greatly reduced, remained the principal cause of residual mode conversion. These not only caused power to be coupled out of the TE_{01} mode, but also could cause reconversion from other modes back into the TE_{01} mode. And depending on the spacing of these defects, reconverted fields could distort the original signal. The antidote was to absorb the unwanted modes either by using a continuous helix guide or by inserting sections of helix guide.[24]

4.2.5 Measurement Techniques in TE_{01} Propagation

To carry out the search for the causes of loss and mode conversion, sophisticated measurement techniques had to be developed. One of these, called the shuttle-pulse technique, was first used by A. C. Beck in the late 1940s. Using a high-power pulsed magnetron at 9 GHz, he injected a 0.1-microsecond pulse through a small iris at the end of a 150-m length of waveguide with a 12.7-cm diameter. This pulse traveled to the far end where it was reflected by a metallic plate and continued to bounce back and forth between the iris and the end reflector as it died away. By extracting a small sample through the iris, the pulse was monitored by a receiver at every transit. From the observed rate of decay over a number of transits representing a travel distance up to 65 kilometers (km), the attenuation per kilometer could be deduced. In addition, one could observe that the initial pulse energy was distributed among a number of high-order modes traveling with different velocities. Among these, one mode was found to have the lowest attenuation of between 1.6 and 2.0 dB/km. Only the TE_{01} mode, whose theoretical attenuation was 1.2 dB/km, could explain the observation. And this represented the long-sought confirmation of the unusual low-loss properties of the TE_{01} mode. These and related results were reported in 1953 by Miller and Beck,[25] and in 1954 by Miller.[26] Later, the shuttle-pulse technique was used with short pulses injected in only the TE_{01} mode. With successive transits, it could be observed that the pulses broadened due to conversion into higher-order modes whose pulses traveled at different velocities and sometimes separated from the original TE_{01} pulse. This gave valuable information on bandwidth and information capacity of the waveguide.

Because shuttle-pulse tests used only a small fraction of the initial pulse energy, they required high-power oscillators. A more sensitive technique was devised by J. A. Young and D. Marcuse,[27] which used a section of waveguide to be tested as part of a resonator. By observing the sharpness of resonance over a range of frequencies and also as a function of position of the end reflectors, the position of defects in the waveguide could be determined and their coupling to higher-order modes estimated.

4.2.6 System Consideration in TE_{01} Transmission

With the properties of the all-important transmission medium understood and under good control, attention shifted to more system-oriented problems that would require solution. New forms of branching filters for frequency multiplexing were devised, and some attention was given to repeater designs.[28] In the mid-1960s, the TE_{01}-waveguide-system activity was transferred to an experimental development organization charged with refinement, manufacture, and installation of a system of considerable length that could be used in a field trial for final evaluation of its practicality.

This evaluation was completed in 1975, and the verdict was that the TE_{01} system was a success. It had the predicted low losses, only 5 percent above Schelkunoff's theoretical heat loss based on dc conductivity of copper. And it could handle ultrabroadbands of information (from 38 to 120 GHz). But like a jumbo jet airplane, it was efficient only if heavily loaded. Moreover, the technological competitor on the horizon at that moment was the optical fiber, which could be economical on low-traffic routes and easily augmented to handle the full range of communications needs in a more flexible and cost-efficient way.

REFERENCES

1. G. C. Southworth, *Principles and Applications of Waveguide Transmission* (New York: D. Van Nostrand Co., 1950).
2. Lord Rayleigh, "On the Passage of Electric Waves Through Tubes, or the Vibrations of Dielectric Cylinders," *Phil. Mag.* **43** (February 1897), pp. 125-132.
3. Bell Telephone Laboratories, *Radar Systems and Components* (New York: D. Van Nostrand Co., 1949).
4. G. C. Southworth, "Hyper-Frequency Wave Guides—General Considerations and Experimental Results," *Bell Syst. Tech. J.* **15** (April 1936), pp. 284-309.
5. J. R. Carson, S. P. Mead, and S. A. Schelkunoff, "Hyper-Frequency Wave Guides—Mathematical Theory," *Bell Syst. Tech. J.* **15** (April 1936), pp. 310-333.
6. A. G. Fox, U.S. Patent No. 2,396,044; filed December 10, 1941; issued March 5, 1946.
7. W. W. Mumford, "Maximally-flat Filters in Waveguide," *Bell Syst. Tech. J.* **27** (October 1948), pp. 684-713.
8. W. A. Tyrrell, "Hybrid Circuits for Microwaves," *Proc. IRE* **35** (November 1947), pp. 1294-1306.
9. A. G. Fox, U.S. Patent No. 2,438,119; filed November 3, 1942; issued March 23, 1948.
10. A. G. Fox, "An Adjustable Waveguide Phase Changer," *Proc. IRE* **35** (December 1947), pp. 1489-1498.
11. B. D. H. Tellegen, "The Gyrator, A New Electric Network Element," *Philips Res. Rep.* **3** (April 1948), pp. 81-101.
12. C. L. Hogan, "The Ferromagnetic Faraday Effect at Microwave Frequencies and its Applications, The Microwave Gyrator," *Bell Syst. Tech. J.* **31** (January 1952), pp. 1-31.
13. A. G. Fox, S. E. Miller, and M. T. Weiss, "Behavior and Applications of Ferrites in the Microwave Region," *Bell Syst. Tech. J.* **34** (January 1955), pp. 5-103.
14. See reference 13.
15. M. T. Weiss, "A Solid-State Microwave Amplifier and Oscillator Using Ferrites," *Phys. Rev.* **107** (July 1, 1957), p. 317.
16. D. H. Ring, "Single-Oscillator Microwave Measuring System," *Bell Lab. Rec.* **34** (December 1956), pp. 465-468.
17. W. W. Mumford, "Directional Couplers," *Proc. IRE* **35** (February 1947), pp. 160-165.
18. S. E. Miller and W. W. Mumford, "Multi-Element Directional Coupler," *Proc. IRE* **40** (September 1952), pp. 1071-1078.

19. A. G. Fox, U.S. Patent No. 2,794,959; filed March 1, 1952; issued June 4, 1957.
20. H. G. Unger, "Circular Waveguide Taper of Improved Design," *Bell Syst. Tech. J.* **37** (July 1958), pp. 899-912.
21. E. A. Marcatili, "Mode-Conversion Filters," *Bell Syst. Tech. J.* **40** (January 1961), pp. 149-184.
22. S. E. Miller, "Notes on Methods of Transmitting the Circular Electric Wave Around Bends," *Proc. IRE* **40** (September 1952), pp. 1104-1113.
23. H. E. Rowe and W. D. Warters, "Transmission in Multimode Waveguide with Random Imperfections," *Bell Syst. Tech. J.* **41** (May 1962), pp. 1031-1170.
24. H. E. Rowe and W. D. Warters, "Transmission Deviations in Waveguide Due to Mode Conversion: Theory and Experiment," *Proc. IEEE* **106,** Part B, Supplement 13 (September 1959), pp. 30-36.
25. S. E. Miller and A. C. Beck, "Low-Loss Waveguide Transmission," *Proc. IRE* **41** (March 1953), pp. 348-358.
26. S. E. Miller, "Waveguide as a Communication Medium," *Bell Syst. Tech. J.* **33** (November 1954), pp. 1209-1265.
27. J. A. Young and D. Marcuse, "Waveguide Measurements in Multimode Cavities," *Proc. Symp. Millimeter Waves* **9,** New York (March 31–April 2, 1959), pp. 513-533.
28. S. E. Miller, "Coupled Wave Theory and Waveguide Applications," *Bell Syst. Tech. J.* **33** (May 1954), pp. 661-719; E. A. Marcatili, "A Circular-Electric Hybrid Junction and Some Channel-Dropping Filters," *Bell Syst. Tech. J.* **40** (January 1961), pp. 185-196; E. A. Marcatili and D. L. Brisbee, "Band-Splitting Filter," *Bell Syst. Tech. J.* **40** (January 1961), pp. 197-212; W. M. Hubbard, J. E. Goell, W. D. Warters, R. D. Standley, G. D. Mandeville, T. P. Lee, R. C. Shaw, and P. L. Clouser, "A Solid-State Regenerative Repeater for Guided Millimeter-Wave Communications Systems," *Bell Syst. Tech. J.* **46** (November 1967), pp. 1977-2018.

Chapter 7

Lightwave Communications

The use of light in communications received its greatest impetus from two fundamental technological developments: the invention of the laser in the late 1950s and the attainment of ultralow-loss glass in fibers suitable for optical waveguides in the late 1960s. Soon after the laser became a reality, Bell Labs scientists conducted studies on lightwave coherence, with particular emphasis on heterostructure ultrashort-pulse lasers. In the mid-1960s, glass lenses and gas lenses were proposed for guided optical transmission, but interest soon shifted to the study of lightwave propagation properties of glass fibers. Contributions were made to lightwave modulation techniques, photodiodes, and lightwave repeaters. Research on integrated optics, dealing with miniature forms of laser beam circuitry, fabricated by lithographic techniques on planar surfaces, received special attention. The guiding of laser beams around waveguide bends and the making of needed connections between various optical components were investigated. This included the invention of the prism coupler for coupling between a free-space laser beam and any mode of dielectric waveguide as well as studies of the techniques of coupling light from one waveguide to another.

I. INTRODUCTION

The idea of using light for communication dates back at least as far as the invention of smoke signals. However, the small bandwidth of smoke signals restricted their application to societies having very little information to transmit. In 1880, a few years after inventing the telephone, Alexander Graham Bell invented the photophone. This device employed a mirrored diaphragm to convert acoustic waves directly into a modulated beam of light. At the receiving end, a selenium photocell, connected to a telephone headset, served to reconvert the light into acoustic waves. While Bell was able to demonstrate speech transmission over distances of several hundred feet, his idea never attained practical importance because the only transmission medium then available was open air, which is notoriously inhospitable to lightwaves.

Principal authors: A. G. Fox and I. P. Kaminow.

From the early days of Bell Laboratories, light and vision were studied in connection with sound movies and the transmission of television pictures over electrical cables. However, the use of light itself to transmit wide bands of information over long distances seems not to have been seriously considered until R. V. L. Hartley wrote an unpublished memorandum in 1945 in which he examined in detail the possibilities for guiding beams of light through transparent rods, internally reflecting pipes, and sequences of lenses. He concluded that transparent rods had too much loss, that pipes were too intolerant of bends, and that the near-field diffraction of lenses was too poorly understood to predict their behavior. Somewhat later, in a memorandum dated March 1951, W. A. Tyrrell pointed out the advantages of using optical frequencies over microwave frequencies (for example, providing more highly directional beams from much smaller antennas), but he noted the lack of coherent radiation sources at optical frequencies (see section II below). These would be needed to realize the high directivity possible with the shorter wavelength. He emphasized that coherent optical sources would open up an entirely new approach to optics. Thus, while the idea of using light for communications had been around for a long while, it was the lack of coherent sources, low-loss transmission media, and related supporting technologies that had prevented practical applications.

The proposal by A. L. Schawlow and C. H. Townes for an optical maser in 1958 and the experimental demonstration of several such devices in the early 1960s (see Chapter 5 in the *Physical Sciences (1925-1980)* volume of this series) had a tremendous impact on the field of optics and stimulated new efforts to develop lower-loss transmission media and supporting device technology. Within 15 years of the demonstration of the first laser in 1960, optical waveguides in the form of glass fibers having losses of a few decibels per kilometer (dB/km)—and subsequently a fraction of a dB/km—had become available (see Chapter 13 in the volume, *Physical Sciences (1925-1980)*), a rather complete understanding of the modes of these fibers and their effect on the dispersion of short light pulses had been developed, and the devices were at hand for assembling sophisticated, ultra-wideband optical communications links. This required the efforts of many people of many disciplines, and in all areas, Bell Labs scientists were in the forefront of contributors.

II. RADIATION SOURCES AND COHERENCE

For a better understanding of the advantages of coherent light for communications, we should consider briefly the disadvantages of incoherent sources—the only kind we had before the laser was invented. When such sources are raised to a sufficiently high temperature by electrical or thermal energy, their atoms emit short bursts of light randomly in time and in random directions. Moreover, there is no correlation between the emissions of the many atoms taking part. This results in two important disadvantages. First, the directional incoherence means that there is no way to form the emitted power into a highly directional beam other than by passing the light through a series of apertures that block the light going in unwanted directions. Thus, most of the light is wasted. Second, the temporal incoherence means that the radiated power is spread over a broad frequency spectrum and that power received at a detector fluctuates rapidly. Thus, any useful signal modulation must compete with a high intrinsic noise level.

In contrast, the coherent sources used at radio and microwave frequencies emit an essentially continuous sine wave with negligible amplitude and phase fluctuation. When a useful signal is modulated on this carrier, it is not polluted by fluctuation noise, and the signal-to-noise ratio of the emitted power can be orders of magnitude greater than for an incoherent source. Also, the emitted waves are spatially highly ordered and can be focused into beams of extremely high directivity without wasting most of the power.

Two classes of light sources, having different degrees of coherence, have been considered for optical communications: lasers and light-emitting diodes (LEDs). The term coherence describes the degree of correlation between the light field sampled at two different points in space or in time. Spatial coherence indicates how far apart two points may be spaced while still allowing the light, sampled at these points, to interfere. Temporal coherence can be described similarly with time replacing the spatial coordinate. However, temporal coherence is also related to the spectral width of the light source. A perfectly (temporally) coherent source has vanishing spectral width. An imperfectly coherent source is associated with a finite spectral width.

The heterostructure semiconductor injection lasers typically used in optical communications systems are not as coherent as gas lasers, but their degree of coherence is much higher than that of the LEDs. Lasers can be used as sources for any type of fiber system, single mode or multimode (see section 3.2.2), while the use of LEDs is limited to multimode fiber systems. This difference is caused by the fact that the (spatially) more highly coherent light of lasers can be focused to a smaller spot with a small angular spread and thus can be launched more effectively into the small core of a single-mode fiber. Laser light can, of course, also be injected into multimode fibers. However, lasers tend to be more complicated than LEDs and require more careful control of their drive currents and temperatures. For these reasons and because multimode fibers are also easier to splice, LEDs coupled to multimode fibers may be preferable for some communications systems.

2.1 Modes of Oscillation in a Laser Resonator Structure

In their classic paper, Schawlow and Townes predicted in 1958 that the spectral width of a laser oscillator could compare favorably with the best microwave generators.[1] Although a laser amplifier would have a very high noise temperature, the achievable amplifier noise figure (defined as the signal-to-noise ratio at the amplifier input divided by the signal-to-noise ratio at its output) could be as low as or lower than that of the best microwave amplifier. For a resonator containing the gain medium, they proposed a pair of plane-parallel mirrors that could be many wavelengths in size and still provide essentially monochromatic output in the form of plane waves, many wavelengths across. Therefore, the output would appear as a sharply directional beam. Only power emitted along the axis normal to the mirrors would be trapped between them and would serve to stimulate other atoms to emit coherently into the lowest-order mode of the resonator. Alternatively, this can be taken to mean that the wave bouncing back and forth between the mirrors passes through the gain medium many times and is therefore amplified to high intensity, while waves directed even at small angles with respect to the mirror axis leave the resonator without

Fig. 7-1. A. G. Fox (left) and T. Li, who were the first to establish the existence of laser resonator modes by performing calculations on a digital computer and by confirming the theoretical prediction experimentally with a helium-neon laser.

further amplification, and therefore are very weak. Schawlow's and Townes's resonator design has been adopted in almost all lasers.

In 1960, as interest began to build up among Bell Labs researchers who were striving to make an operational laser along the lines envisioned, it became clear that the most likely candidates for the gain medium of a laser were unlikely to provide more than a fraction of a dB of amplification per pass between mirrors. Consequently, it was important to keep the resonator loss as low as possible if there was to be a reasonable hope of attaining net gain. Good data were available on the reflection loss of high-quality mirrors, but it was not known what to expect for the diffraction loss due to spill-over around the output mirror or aperture. This would depend upon the exact electromagnetic-field distribution over the mirrors for the expected mode of oscillation, and that too was not known. Some rough estimates were disturbingly high. However, there were grounds for doubt, at least in the minds of A. G. Fox and T. Li [Fig. 7-1], about the reasonableness of the assumptions underlying the estimates. To throw further light on the problem they decided to use a computer to simulate what would happen to a wave bouncing back and forth between mirrors.[2,3] Although a strictly analytical solution was not possible for their plane-parallel-mirror configuration, they were able to obtain computer results leading to predictions, which they confirmed experimentally with a helium-neon laser, that the losses would be much smaller than the original estimates indicated. Their results are discussed in some detail in Chapter 5, section 2.2, of the *Physical Sciences (1925-1980)* volume of this series.

2.2 Quantum Nature of Light and a Beam's Information-Carrying Capacity

Another important theoretical question was raised as to whether the quantum nature of light would seriously limit the information-carrying capacity of a beam. In the early 1960s, J. P. Gordon studied this matter and demonstrated that, in the range of fairly large signal-to-noise ratios, C. E. Shannon's formula for the capacity of a communication channel (see Chapter 1, section 8.2 in this volume) was still valid, with quantum noise replacing thermal noise.[4,5] This result offered further encouragement that wideband lightwave communications could become practicable.

2.3 Lasers for Optical Communications—The Heterostructure Laser

During the early 1960s, an extensive research and development program devoted to lasers was mounted at Bell Labs and elsewhere. While a wide variety of media (crystals, gases, and semiconductors) provide laser action, it is the heterostructure laser invented by I. Hayashi and M. B. Panish that is of primary interest for communications, because of its small size, low voltage, and high efficiency.[6] For a detailed discussion of the evolution of the gallium aluminum arsenide heterostructure laser and its performance characteristics, see Chapter 5, section 3.1 in the *Physical Sciences (1925-1980)* volume of this series.

2.3.1 The Nd:YAG Laser

The neodymium-doped yttrium aluminum garnet (Nd:YAG) laser, invented by J. E. Geusic and L. G. Van Uitert, is another potential source for lightwave communications systems.[7] It can be made to operate at either 1.06 or 1.31 micrometers (μm), where fiber lightguides have particularly low losses, and its narrow spectral width is important for use in very-high-capacity systems. Moreover, by coincidence, it has a strong pumping band in the 0.8-μm region, where (Ga,Al)As and Ga(As,P) LEDs have emission peaks (see Chapter 5, section 4.1 of the *Physical Sciences (1925-1980)* volume of this series). In 1969, F. O. Ostermayer at Bell Labs, collaborating with researchers at Texas Instruments Company, succeeded in using a Nd:YAG laser that was side-pumped with an array of LEDs. However, this laser was only barely operable at room temperature because the light from the LEDs, entering the YAG rod from the side, is strongly absorbed near the surface and consequently provides less energy along the rod axis where it is needed to pump the laser beam.

J. Stone, C. A. Burrus, and their coworkers overcame this problem in 1974 with the use of single-crystal fibers of Nd:YAG only 50 to 75 μm in diameter, obtained by pulling a seed crystal from the melt. These produced a laser appropriate in size for coupling to glass transmission fibers. Furthermore, they injected the pumping light through an end face of the crystal fiber where it would be most effective in interacting with the laser beam. In this way, they were able to obtain continuous laser output at room temperature, at both 1.06 μm and 1.3 μm (using a single LED of their own construction), with low enough pumping power to be attractive for communication applications.[8,9] [Fig. 7-2] However, unlike an injection laser, which can be turned on and off rapidly by modulating the injection current, the YAG laser requires an external modulator. This, and the fact that subsequently developed heterostructure injection lasers can operate in the same infrared range, made the injection laser the preferred choice for communications by optical fibers.

2.3.2 Ultrashort-Pulse Laser

To test lightguide components, it is desirable to have lasers that produce very short pulses (but not necessarily at high repetition rates). In 1980, Stone, Burrus, and J. C. Campbell designed a laser to meet this need.[10] Thin GaAs films were epoxied between suitable dielectric mirrors aligned

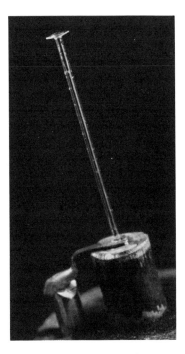

Fig. 7-2. Experimental LED-pumped Nd:YAG single-crystal fiber laser. The laser is composed of an Nd:YAG fiber grown at 75-μm diameter with heat from a CO_2 laser, a glass support tube, a 150-μm square output mirror, which is visible at the end of the fiber, and a similar input mirror in the well of the Burrus-LED pump. The LED operated near the 0.8-μm wavelength, and the 1.03-μm output of the laser was about a 1-milliwatt continuous wave. [Stone and Burrus, *Fiber Integrated Opt.* **2** (1979): 36.]

to form a cavity only a few micrometers long, with the semiconductor film serving as the active laser medium. When optically pumped in a small region by the focused beam of a suitable dye laser, laser action is initiated and short pulses at wavelengths characteristic of the GaAs film are emitted. These pulses, only a few picoseconds in length and of significant power output, can be used to test the time response of components, such as photodetectors and transmission lines. The technique was later extended to use very thin semiconductor films of various compositions grown by liquid-phase epitaxy, so that 1 to 10 picosecond (psec) pulses at many wavelengths between about 0.75 and 1.6 μm could be generated with relative ease from films in the Ga-In-As-P system.

2.4 Light-Emitting Diodes for Optical Communications

Although the early forms of the LED, which operate in the visible region of the electromagnetic spectrum, have had important applications, they are not very useful for single-fiber optical transmission lines. Both the Ga(As,P) LED, invented by R. A. Reuhrwein[11] of the Monsanto Company (and used in displays), and Bell Labs GaP LED[12] (used in telecommunications equipment) have large emitting areas (not well matched to optical fiber cross sections) and have to operate at low input power to avoid overheating.

In 1968, Burrus designed a small-area, high-radiance LED specifically for use as a source compatible with the glass fiber lightguide.[13] [Fig. 7-3] This LED, which has commonly been referred to as the Burrus diode, emits light from a small active spot approximately the size of the fiber (about 15- to 100-μm diameter). It is configured to have the light-emitting area at the bottom of a well etched in the diode chip so that the fiber can be attached very close to the emitting area. Collection of light by the fiber is therefore more complete than from the earlier large-area devices, and the heat-transfer is also better, so that high current densities—several thousands of amperes per square centimeter—and high radiance are possible. With this diode, useful power can easily be coupled into a single fiber.

A somewhat different LED, having properties between those of a surface-emitting LED and a laser, is known as a superluminescent LED (SLED). Such a diode was first fabricated as a double-heterostructure device and studied in 1972 and 1973 for possible usefulness in lightwave communications by T. P. Lee, Burrus, and B. I. Miller.[14] In structure it is a double-heterostructure laser in which lasing action is suppressed by lowering the Q of the cavity, as, for example, by introduction of added cavity loss. The resulting diode has moderate optical gain with somewhat narrower spectral bandwidth and somewhat narrower output beam width than exhibited by a simple LED. Both of these properties are advantageous in the coupling and transmission of optical signals in fiber lightguides. Originally, the SLED appeared destined to remain a pulsed device due to the high current density then required in its operation. Later, however, advances in the technology permitted its fabrication as a continuous wave device, and it was advocated as an alternative to the LED.

The original Burrus LED was a gallium arsenide homostructure diode—i.e., a simple p-n junction without reflective layers. However, in 1970, soon after the demonstration by Hayashi and Panish of the importance of using heterostructures for lasers (see section 2.3 above and Chapter 5, section 3.1 in the *Physical Sciences (1925-1980)* volume of this series), where such configuration provides for confinement of both the light and the

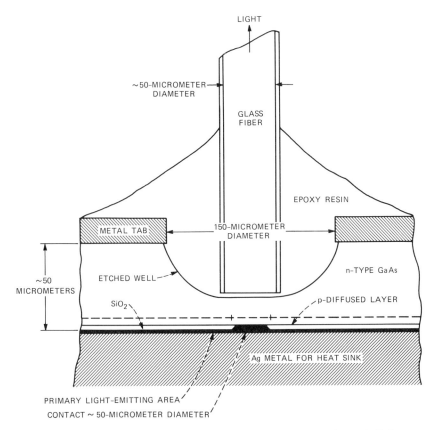

Fig. 7-3. Early version of the first LED designed by C. A. Burrus (about 1969) for use with optical fibers. Light emission was from a small region, defined by the electrical contact, which was approximately equal to the area of a fiber core. Later versions were more complicated double-heterostructure designs with several grown layers replacing the simple p-n junction. [Burrus and Dawson, *Appl. Phys. Lett.* **17** (1970): 97.]

injected electrons to the active region, Burrus adopted this idea for LEDs. In the LED, however, the optical confinement is of little importance, but the confinement of the electrons leads to conversion of an increased fraction of the injected current into photons, and thus to increased optical output. It was observed in practice that the grown-junction double-heterostructure gallium aluminum arsenide LEDs had as much as six-times-greater power efficiency than the simple diffused gallium arsenide p-n junction LED. As expected, power output at the highest modulation rate is reduced compared to operation at lower rates. By the late 1970s, Burrus diodes were being made by several domestic and foreign firms in both homo- and heterostructure versions. They have been modulated at rates up to nearly 300 megabits per second (Mb/sec). Like the injection laser, the LED can be modulated directly by varying the injection current; no external modulator is required.

Compared with the heterostructure laser, the LED is simpler to make and thus is less expensive. However, the LED radiates with much greater spectral width: about 300 angstroms (Å) compared with 20 Å for a gallium arsenide laser. The LED also radiates light over wider angles than the laser and, largely for this reason, it cannot couple as much power into a fiber lightguide as a laser. Certain types of LEDs were shown to be extremely reliable; extrapolated operating lifetimes on the order of 10^9 hours were achieved. GaAs LEDs proved to be particularly useful in relatively low-data-rate applications over relatively short distances, such as within buildings, ships, aircraft, and central offices. The longer wavelength heterostructure LEDs, operating in a region where fiber transmission loss is low, promised to be useful at much higher modulation rates and greater distances.

III. LIGHTWAVE TRANSMISSION

Even clear atmosphere has thermal gradients that distort light in various ways. More important, however, is the absorption due to precipitation of water as fog, rain, or snow. Bell Labs scientists studied these effects extensively and showed that the idea of long-distance transmission through the atmosphere at wavelengths in the visible or near infrared region is not feasible when reliable transmission is needed (see also Chapter 5, section 3.1 of this volume).

3.1 Glass Lenses and Gas Lenses in Guided Optical Transmission

In 1965, O. E. DeLange designed an experiment that consisted of bouncing a laser beam back and forth between two curved mirrors housed in an above-ground aluminum pipe 100-meters (m) long.[15] The object was to avoid the vagaries of the weather and to simulate guided transmission of light over long distance. Although the losses were low enough to be acceptable, the presence of temperature gradients strongly distorted the 'aser beam. To eliminate such distortions and the consequent beam spreading, D. Gloge used a sequence of glass lenses located 120 m apart in an iron pipe 800-m long buried 1.5-m deep in the ground.[16] He demonstrated the feasibility of transmission of light over long distance, with a power loss of only 3 dB in 20 km.

A logical extension of the sequence of glass-lenses concept was the sequence of gas lenses invented and investigated experimentally and theoretically in the mid-1960s by Bell Labs scientists.[17] Each lens consisted of a heated metallic tube inside of which cool gas circulated. The cooler gas in the center had a higher index of refraction than the hotter gas at the periphery. Such a focusing medium offered the possibility of more nearly continuous guidance of the beam without subjecting it to the reflection and scattering losses of solid lenses.

The expensive installations needed by the sequences of glass or gas lenses made these transmission media economically attractive only for very wideband (perhaps a million voice circuits or equivalent bandwidths of video or data) communication systems. In the meantime, it became clear that the dielectric waveguides, particularly the low-loss optical fibers, would be cheaper and simpler to make, would have smaller cross sections, and would permit the fabrication of multifiber cables capable of practically satisfying any foreseeable bandwidth need.

3.2 Glass Fibers for Guided Optical Transmission

John Tyndall, the famous British physicist, demonstrated the basic principle of the dielectric waveguide in 1870 by showing that light moving through a medium with a higher index of refraction and striking an interface with a lower index of refraction at a sufficiently small glancing angle is totally reflected as though the interface were a perfect mirror. By the 1950s, the light pipe principle was being applied in medical instrumentation using glass-fiber bundles. By that time, methods had been developed for making what became known as a clad fiber—a core of glass of one refractive index surrounded by a glass cladding of lower index to isolate the core from its environment. However, the losses in these fibers were so high that their use was restricted to transmission over a few meters at most.

Reasonable estimates in the 1960s suggested that for an economically viable long-haul lightwave communications system, losses as low as 20 dB/km (one percent of the input power arriving at the end of one kilometer) would be needed. In those days the best optical glasses had losses of about 1000 dB/km, which were caused by impurities present even in the best available raw materials and in the crucibles used to melt them.

Early evidence that silica could indeed be made with optical loss sufficiently low for a communications system was advanced in 1966 by K. C. Kao and colleagues at the Standard Telecommunications Laboratories in England. In fact, they measured commercially available bulk silica with losses as low as a few dB/km.[18] During the period between 1965 and 1970, research aimed at obtaining lower-loss fibers began in Japan, in England, and in the United States at Bell Laboratories and at Corning Glass Works. Kao and G. A. Hockham had speculated that glass fibers with losses as low as 20 dB/km should be achievable,[19] and materials experts agreed that the possibility justified an exploration. For a detailed discussion of the research activities and achievements of Bell Labs scientists in low-loss fiber glass see Chapter 13, section 2.1.1 in the *Physical Sciences (1925-1980)* volume.

3.2.1 Fiber Structures

A number of different fiber structures have been made and studied over the years. The simplest is a solid dielectric fiber of a single material, with air being the surrounding medium or cladding. This structure is unsatisfactory, however, because the optical field extends beyond the surface of the core and can be disturbed by proximity to material objects with resulting loss of power.

The simplest practical fiber has a core of one glass and cladding of another with a lower refractive index. As indicated earlier, this structure, the step-index type, has long been known. A variation on the step-index fiber was the liquid-core design, first proposed by A. A. Ashkin and E. P. Ippen[20] in 1970 and reduced to practice in 1972 by Stone.[21] The fiber consisted of a slender glass tube filled with tetrachloroethylene, and for a time it exhibited lower losses than all-glass fibers.

Another novel fiber structure was the single-material fiber, invented in 1973 by S. E. Miller.[22,23] In this structure the glass core was supported along the axis of an air-filled glass tube by a thin glass septum extending across the tube. The air in the tube thus served as the cladding, and the septum was made thin enough to minimize the power leak from the core. Using such fibers, P. Kaiser achieved optical transmission with power loss as low as 3 dB/km at 1.1 μm.[24] Like the liquid-core fiber, the single-material structure became less interesting because of spectacular progress in reducing the losses of solid-glass types that permit parabolic radial variation of the index of refraction.

3.2.2 Single-Mode and Multimode Propagation

Optical fibers may be classified as either single-mode or multimode according to whether they transmit light in one or many characteristic waves. The single-mode fiber has a very small core and a small difference between the indices of refraction of core and cladding.[25] As a result, the electromagnetic fields extend into the cladding for a considerable distance from the core; and, to keep them from reaching the outer surface of the cladding, it is necessary to make the cladding very thick relative to the core. Typically, the core might be 10 μm in diameter, with an overall fiber diameter of 100 to 150 μm. By 1975, excellent single-mode fibers were made with a borosilicate cladding and a borosilicate core of slightly different composition. Fibers with such small cores are difficult to splice. However, single-mode fibers are essential in systems where the enormous theoretical capacity of lightwave communications is to be realized.

Multimode fibers, in contrast, employ large-diameter cores and a relatively large difference between the indices of refraction of core and cladding. Many modes of propagation are permitted and, except for those close to cutoff, their fields extend only a short distance into the cladding. Thus the cladding can be made quite thin; typical dimensions for multimode fibers are 60 μm for the core diameter and 100 to 150 μm for the outside diameter. The outside diameters are thus about the same for the multimode as for the single-mode fibers. Although multimode fibers do not have the enormous capacity of the single-mode fibers, they can nevertheless be made with a bit-rate-distance product of 1 gigabit per kilometer, which is clearly large compared with a coaxial system.

Initially, multimode fibers appeared to have limited usefulness for communications applications because velocity differences among the various modes can distort the information traveling down the fiber. Usually, the information is in the form of pulses. The energy in each input pulse is distributed among many modes, and the modal velocity differences cause the pulse to spread out in time as it propagates. An extensive research program was launched at Bell Labs to increase the understanding of light propagation in these fibers and possibly to alleviate the intermodal-dispersion problem. In 1971, Gloge started with a simplified theory of light propagation in fibers with a uniform core refractive index.[26] [Fig. 7-4] S. D. Personick showed that intermodal dispersion could be reduced by introducing slowly varying perturbations along the fiber that continuously redistribute energy among the various modes and effectively average their velocities.[27] However, these perturbations involve a small loss penalty,

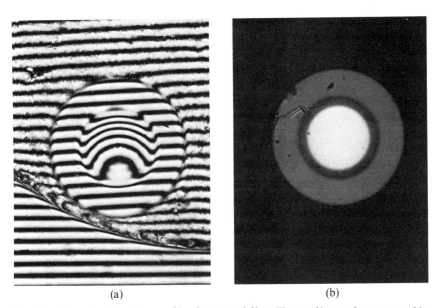

(a)   (b)

Fig. 7-4. The refractive-index profile of an optical fiber. This profile was first measured by interference microscopy on wafer-thin, cut and polished fiber samples. (a) The displacement of a fringe is proportional to the refractive-index value at the measured point. (b) The fiber sample is shown by ordinary microscopy. The core (about 50 μm in diameter) is the bright central region, surrounded by a barrier layer and the cladding.

which tends to increase with increasing perturbations, as was shown in 1972 by D. Marcuse.[28] In 1973, A. Hasegawa and F. Tappert investigated theoretically the nonlinear transmission of light for the different modes through the fiber and its effect on pulse dispersion.[29]

A more effective method for reducing modal dispersion was suggested by S. E. Miller. It involves the use of fiber with a cross section such that the refractive index is made to vary parabolically with the fiber radius.[30] In 1973, Gloge and E. A. J. Marcatili [Fig. 7-5] proposed an improved index profile (departing slightly from parabolic), which could potentially increase the bandwidth 1000-fold over that of a step-index fiber.[31] They realized that such an improvement is hard to achieve in practice and estimated the tolerances that must be adhered to by the manufacturer. The best fibers fabricated in the mid-1970s[32] exceeded the bandwidth of the step-index fiber by a factor of 75, while fibers produced in a pilot manufacturing process have yielded a bandwidth improvement of about 20.

Marcuse combined Personick's perturbation idea with the graded-index theory and computed the resulting multimode-fiber capacity, which can be quite large for tolerable loss penalties.[33] Another perturbation observed

Fig. 7-5.   D. Marcuse, E. A. J. Marcatili, and D. Gloge, who made extensive contributions to the theory of lightwave transmission on fibers.

in fibers, more rapidly varying and unintended in nature, became known as microbends. These were microscopic kinks that could result from pressing the fiber against a rough surface. Microbends can cause significant radiation losses in fiber cables. Gloge developed a theoretical understanding of the mechanisms involved and developed guidelines for the design of suitable fiber jackets and sheaths.[34,35]

A concurrent measurement program provided early evidence of the effectiveness of the velocity equalization approaches and helped in analyzing early single-mode and multimode fiber designs. The measurement showed another, and not unexpected, fundamental capacity limitation later known as chromatic dispersion, arising from the fact that the phase velocity of an electromagnetic wave in glass fibers varies with wavelength.[36,37] Thus, the various spectral components constituting a light pulse propagate at different velocities, causing the pulse to spread out in time even if there is only one mode present. The effect is critical for LEDs with their wide spectral distribution, and it also places an important limitation on the capacity of laser-operated single-mode systems. In single-mode fibers, the total chromatic dispersion has two components—one due to the variation in phase velocity caused by the variation in the index of refraction of the glass with wavelength and the other due to a waveguiding effect, wherein the phase velocity varies with wavelength even if the index of refraction is constant over the entire spectral distribution of the pulse. For fused silica-based fibers at wavelengths near 0.85 μm, the glass dispersion dominates and is relatively large—about 200 picoseconds per kilometer of fiber and per nanometer (psec/km $\cdot$ nm) of source spectral width. However, at wavelengths near 1.3 μm, the silica-glass dispersion becomes much smaller (a few psec/km $\cdot$ nm), and fortunately also the loss goes to zero (due to the λ^{-4} decrease of Rayleigh scattering). This provided a major motivation for developing LEDs, lasers, detectors, and fibers optimized for the 1.3- to 1.6-μm wavelength region. A pioneering demonstration of this low-dispersion, low-loss fiber capability was made by W. M. Muska, T. Li, and A. G. Dentai.[38] LED-based optical-fiber systems operating at 1.3 μm were, by the early 1980s, installed worldwide for short-haul applications that include interoffice trunks, subscriber loops, and on-premises data links. [Fig. 7-6]

3.2.3 Splicing Optical Fibers

At an early stage of the fiber research program, it was realized that fibers would have to be connected by unskilled personnel and that fiber cable would have to be spliced in the field under adverse conditions. In 1971, D. L. Bisbee was the first to demonstrate that well-prepared fiber ends joined end-to-end and fused at a high temperature offered the possibility of a permanent splice with excellent transmission characteristics.[39]

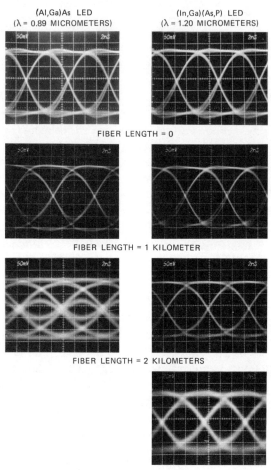

FIBER LENGTH = 0

FIBER LENGTH = 1 KILOMETER

FIBER LENGTH = 2 KILOMETERS

FIBER LENGTH = 3 KILOMETERS

Fig. 7-6.   Experimental results obtained with the first optical-fiber data-link experiment, operating at wavelengths longer than 0.9 μm and transmitting data at fairly high speeds, e.g., 137 Mb/sec, as performed by W. M. Muska, T. Li, T. P. Lee, and A. G. Dentai in 1977. The photographs above show eye diagrams of the received signal using LEDs of two different wavelengths as sources. It is clear from the data that with the (Al,Ga)As LED emitting radiation at 0.89 μm, transmission at a distance of 2 km is not possible. However, with the (In,Ga)(As,P) LED emitting at 1.20 μm, transmission even beyond 3 km is feasible. [Muska, Li, and Dentai, *Electron. Lett.* **13** (1977): 606.]

GOOD (< 0.1 DECIBELS) POOR (≈ 0.5 DECIBELS)

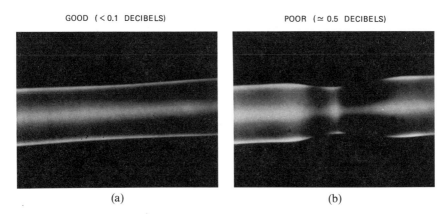

(a) (b)

Fig. 7-7. Fusion splice of silica optical fibers, as obtained in 1975 by D. L. Bisbee, with an electric arc, a technique that has found worldwide commercial use. The photographs show (a) A good splice, with a loss of less than 0.1 dB. [Bisbee, *Appl. Opt.* **15** (1976): 797.] (b) A poor splice, with a loss over 0.5 dB. The latter was obtained when the fiber ends were not in intimate contact over the entire surface.

[Fig. 7-7] R. D. Standley introduced the concept of arranging fibers in flat-cable subgroups, called ribbons, which permit rapid splicing of fiber groups in one operation.[40] Gloge and P. W. Smith found a way of preparing flat, perfectly smooth fiber ends by a controlled breaking technique that exploits the fracture process in brittle materials like glass.[41,42] [Fig. 7-8] Grooved capillaries and substrates with etched or embossed precision grooves have eliminated earlier microscope-aided alignment steps in all of Bell Labs single- or group-slicing operations. Research on rearrangeable fiber terminations resulted in an injection-molded plastic fiber connector. P. K. Runge, who designed the connector, was able to demonstrate unimpaired precision alignment after thousands of connect-disconnect operations.[43] Further development in the Atlanta, Georgia laboratories produced a 144-fiber cable consisting of a stack of 12 ribbons, each bearing 12 fibers. In addition, an array-splicing method was developed for permanently joining lengths of cable as needed.

IV. LIGHTWAVE MODULATION

There are a number of methods of modulating light sources. The simplest is direct modulation of the injection current, either in the LED or the laser, to produce a train of digital light pulses. This method was studied extensively at Bell Labs during the 1960s and 1970s and was used in the 1976 Atlanta experimental system.[44] Burrus-type LEDs were directly modulated at rates up to about 250 megabits per second (Mb/sec), but material dispersion in fibers at 0.8 to 0.9 μm, in combination with the LED's spectral

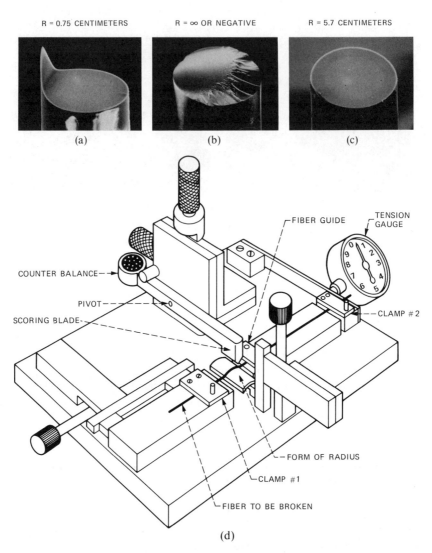

Fig. 7-8. Glass fiber ends. Glass fibers fracture in such a way that the ends resemble one of the three types shown in the top figure. To avoid the undesirable surfaces shown in (a) and (b) and consistently achieve the "mirror" surface (c), D. C. Gloge and coworkers proposed to bend the fiber over a form of suitable curvature radius R while simultaneously applying tension. If the radius is much larger than 5.7 cm, a "hackle" zone (b) forms; too small a radius causes the lip formation (a). To obtain reproducible fractures, they constructed the machine shown in the bottom figure (d).

width, limited the modulation to lower rates for transmission over kilometer distances. (Later work with fibers and LEDs in the 1.3-μm region made possible long-span high-bit-rate LED systems.) The gallium aluminum arsenide laser was modulated at rates up to 2.3 gigabits per second.

For greater bandwidths (or higher bit rates) external modulation—modulation of the light after it leaves the source—is required. Some devices, such as the Nd:YAG laser, can only be internally modulated at very low rates. Three principal physical effects that have long been known can be used for modulating light externally. In each case, modulation results from a change in the refractive index of a modulator material. The corresponding three phenomena involved are the electro-optic, acousto-optic, and magneto-optic effects. Bell Labs researchers have worked on all three.

4.1 Electro-Optic Modulation

The electro-optic effect—changing the refractive index of a material by varying an electric field applied to it—has received the most attention. In 1961, I. P. Kaminow made a microwave light modulator operating at 10 gigahertz (GHz) with a bandwidth of 40 megahertz (MHz) that used a potassium dihydrogen phosphate crystal to rotate the polarization of an optical beam.[45] [Fig. 7-9] Since relatively high modulating power was required, attention turned to a search for more efficient electro-optic materials. Of many materials investigated, lithium niobate and lithium tantalate were the best for the visible and near-infrared regions. Techniques for growing lithium niobate and lithium tantalate were developed by A. A. Ballman, K. Nassau, and coworkers.[46,47] In 1974, F. S. Chen and W. W. Benson reported a lithium tantalate modulator operating at 1.06 μm at a speed of 70 Mb/sec.[48]

4.2 Acousto-Optic and Other Lightwave Modulators

The acousto-optic effect refers to a change in the refractive index of a material produced by an acoustic strain wave. Thus a train of acoustic waves produces a traveling index grating, which can deflect power from an optical beam. Acousto-optic devices were explored extensively at Bell Labs during the 1960s by E. I. Gordon, R. W. Dixon, and L. G. Cohen.[49] This work resulted in the identification of appropriate modulator materials[50] and in the fabrication of efficient light modulators.[51] In 1973, A. W. Warner and D. A. Pinnow reported on a modulator developed specifically for use with fiber lightguides at a wavelength of 1.06 μm.[52] This modulator used arsenic selenide glass as the acousto-optic material. Warner and Pinnow also worked with germanium arsenide selenide glass and crystalline gallium arsenide. Lithium niobate and lithium tantalate have good acousto-optic as well as electro-optic properties and have been used with acousto-optic modulators.

Some work was also done with magneto-optic modulators. Early work was reported by R. C. LeCraw.[53] S. H. Wemple and coworkers demonstrated a modulator made from an iron-garnet crystal in 1973, operating at a wavelength of 1.52 μm.[54]

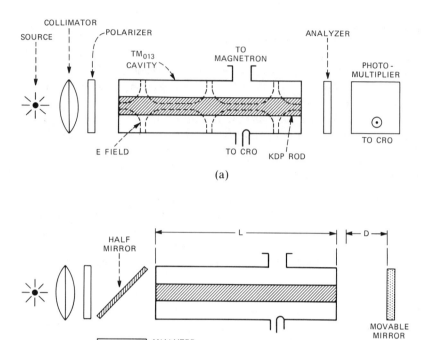

Fig. 7-9.   Microwave light modulator. (a) Traveling wave light modulator used the electro-optic crystal KDP (KH_2PO_4) and operated at 9.25 GHz. The refractive index in the crystal changes in proportion to an applied electric field. Thus, the microwave in the cavity, in synchronism with the optical wave, modulates the optical-phase retardation. The polarizer and analyzer convert the modulated retardation into intensity-modulated light. (b) Since no continuous-wave laser was readily available in 1961, a white-light source was employed and, since no high-speed optical detector was available, a movable mirror scheme (that showed a periodic behavior with mirror displacements equal to the microwave half-wavelength) was used. [Kaminow, *Phys. Rev. Lett.* **6** (1961): 528.]

Considerable progress was made in improving the efficiency of light modulators by employing a waveguide configuration to confine the light to a narrow interaction region. This concept was first developed in 1964 by D. F. Nelson and F. K. Reinhart,[55,56] who demonstrated electro-optic modulation in GaP p-n junction waveguides that was superior to that of bulk modulators based on special electro-optic materials.[57,58]

Another interesting physical effect, somewhat different from the three discussed so far, is the change in the optical absorption of a semiconductor material with an applied electric field. Reinhart demonstrated this effect with gallium aluminum arsenide in 1973, achieving modulation at a wavelength of 0.9 μm.[59]

V. PHOTODETECTORS

When light is incident on the p-n junction of a semiconductor such as silicon and the photon energy exceeds the energy gap of the semiconductor, the light creates electron-hole pairs. Under the influence of a reverse-biased electric field, current flows in an external circuit in proportion to the intensity of light. This is the basic principle of photodetection in semiconductor photodiodes as proposed by W. Shockley in the late 1940s. However, prior to 1941, R. S. Ohl had discovered experimentally that a p-n junction in silicon was photovoltaic, and, during the late 1940s, he learned how to produce consistently photocells of high sensitivity by ion bombardment. These early works were soon followed by the invention of the phototransistor by J. N. Shive.[60]

5.1 Photodiodes

F. M. Smits proposed the use of a layer of intrinsic (undoped) material to increase the efficiency and speed of photodiodes. The addition of the intrinsic region between the p and n layers (p-i-n) effectively increases the width of the junction so that more light is absorbed; the resulting photogenerated electron-hole pairs traverse the high-field junction region at the saturated velocity, increasing the speed of collection of the carriers. The first in-depth theory of the p-i-n diode was given by W. T. Read, Jr., in 1956[61] (see also Chapter 2, section 2.4 in the *Physical Sciences (1925-1980)* volume). In 1962, R. P. Riesz constructed the first high-speed silicon p-i-n photodiode.[62] Further theoretical study of the frequency response and noise characteristics of the p-i-n photodiode was conducted by M. DiDomenico, Jr., and O. Svelto in 1964.[63] Very-high-speed germanium point-contact photodiodes with frequency response in the millimeter-wave region were constructed by L. U. Kibler in 1962[64] and W. M. Sharpless in 1964.[65] Similar high-speed silicon photodiodes were made by DiDomenico, Sharpless, and J. J. McNicol in 1965,[66] and planar germanium photodiodes by Burrus and Sharpless in 1970.[67]

With the advent of work in the so-called long-wavelength region—i.e., 1- to 1.6-μm wavelength—a need arose for simple photodetectors responsive at these wavelengths. In 1979, Burrus, Dentai, and Lee fabricated a novel back-illuminated p-i-n photodiode[68] made in the In-Ga-As-P system; in it the illumination enters through the InP substrate to a p-n junction in an epitaxially grown (In,Ga)As or (In,Ga)(As,P) layer. This is possible because InP is transparent to the radiation to be absorbed in the active region located in the epitaxially grown material. Such a structure offers several significant advantages over the more conventional front-illuminated germanium photodiodes (which are responsive in the same wavelength region, but in which the radiation is incident through a very thin, highly absorbing surface layer of the same semiconductor in which the active p-n junction is located). The back-illuminated structure provides in one device essentially uniform response over the entire 1- to 1.6-μm wavelength range at external quantum efficiencies approaching the theoretical maximum. In addition, the inherent properties of the material provide orders of magnitude less dark current at ordinary temperatures than does germanium. By 1981, this back-illuminated detector design for long wavelengths was extended both to extremely small (20-μm diameter) areas with response times as short as 30 psec[69] and to large area (1-millimeter diameter) units for general use,[70] and found use as a signal detector and monitor in both terrestrial and undersea lightwave applications, as well as in testing and evaluation of long-wavelength lasers and LEDs.

5.1.1 Avalanche Photodiodes

An improvement on the p-i-n structure is the avalanche photodiode (APD), which incorporates current gain in the device. Internal current gain increases the optical-receiver sensitivity by overcoming the thermal noise of the preamplifier that follows the detector. However, the avalanche-gain mechanism also introduces some excess noise. The physics of the avalanche mechanism were first explored by K. G. McKay and K. B. McAfee in 1953.[71] Avalanche diodes were first studied in the mid-1950s for use as microwave detectors but proved too noisy for that application. High-speed germanium APDs for lightwave communications were fabricated by H. Melchior and W. T. Lynch in 1966.[72] In the following years, noise properties of the APDs became better understood as a result of the work of scientists at Bell Labs and at other institutions. A silicon APD detector developed by Melchior and A. R. Hartman[73] provided near-optimal performance in an experimental optical-fiber system—above 90 percent efficiency at 0.85 μm, with less than 1 nanosecond rise time, and an excess-noise factor of 4 at a current gain of 100, which is about 10 dB better than a p-i-n detector.

For operation at wavelengths above 1 μm, where silicon becomes transparent, materials other than silicon have to be employed for photodetectors. Although germanium APDs can be used, their large dark current and high excess noise make them less sensitive than their silicon counterparts (at $\lambda = 0.85$ μm). In 1975, Lee and his coworkers made a high-speed Schottky-barrier photodiode using (In,Ga)As.[74]

5.1.2 Phototransistors

In 1980, Campbell and his coworkers, following a suggestion by J. A. Copeland, designed a back-illuminated heterojunction phototransistor in the (In,Ga)As/InP system for use in the 1- to 1.6-μm wavelength region.[75] This device had higher gain and far higher sensitivity (gain at low light levels) than had been reported for any phototransistor previously.

During the following year, a small-area (15- to 20-μm diameter) version was constructed, having, simultaneously, high sensitivity and high gain; its gain-bandwidth product was in excess of 1.7 GHz.[76] Phototransistors of this type may provide a practical alternative to front-end devices (such as a p-i-n photodiode in tandem with a field-effect-transistor (FET) amplifier) in long-wavelength lightwave receivers.

VI. LIGHTWAVE REPEATERS

Just as in any other transmission system, repeaters are needed to boost and regenerate the signal that is transmitted in an optical-fiber system. The repeater for optical-fiber transmission has a photodetector that converts the received optical pulses into electrical pulses for subsequent filtering, amplification, and regeneration; it also has a laser or LED that converts the regenerated pulses back to optical pulses for transmission.

The first experimental repeater designed specifically for fiber application, using a silicon APD and (Ga,Al)As LED, was built by J. E. Goell[77] in 1972; it operated at 6.3 Mb/sec. In 1973, he built an experimental repeater that operated at 274 Mb/sec.[78] In 1974, Runge built one that operated at 50 Mb/sec;[79] this was the forerunner of the repeater used in the Atlanta experiment.[80] During the same period, Personick provided a basic theory and design of optical receivers for digital communications.[81] The performances of the optical receivers in the experimental repeaters described above were found to agree very closely with those predicted by Personick's theory. Further contributions to the theory, design, and packaging of optical repeaters made possible the design of optical-fiber prototype repeaters for large-scale systems experiments such as the Atlanta experiment in 1976.

VII. INTEGRATED OPTICS

During the 1960s, essentially all research on lasers and their applications was carried out on optical benches using techniques largely carried over from the older classical optics. Freely propagating beams were sent through the air from component to component, and lenses and mirrors were used to prevent excessive beam divergence, to change beam size, and to change beam direction. Typical separations between components ranged from a few centimeters (cm) to 30 cm. The resulting apparatus was sensitive to ambient temperature gradients, to absolute temperature changes, to airborne acoustical effects, and to mechanical vibrations of the separately mounted parts. To overcome these problems, S. E. Miller [Fig. 7-10] proposed, in 1969, a miniature form of laser-beam circuitry to be formed by lithography on planar surfaces.[82] Simultaneous construction of complex circuit patterns

Fig. 7-10.   S. E. Miller, who for over 20 years led
the Bell Labs Crawford Hill, New Jersey, research
on fibers, lightwave sources and detectors, and system explorations. He made important contributions
to integrated optics, new fiber structures, and coupled-wave theory.

was proposed. It was shown that dielectric waveguides employing index
differences on the order of 10^{-2} yielded guided laser beams approximately
10-μm wide and that the needed waveguide bends between components
could be in the order of a 15-mm radius. This triggered more exact analysis
and proposals for novel forms of optical circuitry suitable for fabrication
in the integrated form.[83,84,85] Much innovation remained to be done; but
the prospect excited many researchers, and the activity proliferated.

Even before integrated optics systems were proposed, related research
was carried out by many Bell Labs scientists. One motivation had been
to enhance certain nonlinear and linear optical effects by concentrating
the lightwave field in a small cross section. For example, in 1962, Ashkin
and M. Gershenzon observed reflection and guiding of light at p-n semiconductor junctions,[86] and, in 1964, Nelson and Reinhart demonstrated
modulation of light in a GaP p-n junction.[87] Other early work was basic
science relating to lightwave guidance and coherent wave analysis. For

example, in 1968, R. E. Schineller and colleagues reported the formation of optical waveguides by proton irradiation of fused silica.[88] In 1968, P. K. Tien invented the prism coupler, which made possible coupling between a free-space (laser) beam and any mode of a dielectric waveguide.[89,90] High modulation rates, as proposed by Ashkin and Gershenzon, were demonstrated in GaP in 1968 by Reinhart[91] and in (Al,Ga)As/GaAs heterostructures in 1972 by Reinhart and B. I. Miller.[92]

7.1 Waveguides for Integrated Optics

In 1969, a comprehensive fundamental paper giving a tractable theory for dielectric waveguides applicable to integrated optics was published by Marcatili.[93] The ideas developed in that paper have constituted the foundation for most of the approximate techniques developed ever since for calculating the guiding properties of active and passive dielectric guides of rectangular cross section. The computer analysis of rectangular dielectric waveguides published by Goell in 1969 complemented Marcatili's theory and provided pictures of the lightwave intensity in a transverse plane for both the dominant and higher-order modes.[94] Also in 1969, sputtered-glass waveguides 0.3 μm by 20 μm on a glass substrate were reported by Goell and Standley to have losses less than 1 dB/cm, a very satisfactory value.[95] Organo-silicon waveguides were made by G. Smolinsky, Tien, and R. J. Martin in 1972.[96,97]

In the early 1970s, Tien [Fig. 7-11] and his associates developed laboratory techniques and investigated the fundamental physics relevant to thin-film waveguides. Tien was among the first to recognize that the large power densities achievable at low absolute power levels in thin-film waveguides could give rise to useful nonlinear effects. Optical second-harmonic generation in a thin ZnS film was reported in 1970 by Tien, R. Ulrich, and Martin.[98] Most famous perhaps is Tien's prism-film coupler,[99] a laboratory component widely used for transferring a freely propagating laser beam into either a planar or a three-dimensional waveguide. The prisms were combined with a planar iron-garnet film to produce a magneto-optic light-beam deflector, which might prove useful as a switch or modulator.[100] In other contributions Tien collaborated in showing ways to form dielectric waveguides for coupling different optical components on the same substrate[101] or possibly to connect a planar dielectric waveguide to a fiber.[102] Magneto-optic waveguides made from single-crystal garnet films were reported by Tien and his associates in 1972.[103,104] Rib waveguides formed by etching GaAs/(Al,Ga)As heterolayers were made by Reinhart, R. A. Logan, and Lee in 1974.[105]

Crystalline LiNbO$_3$ and LiTaO$_3$ have been used widely as hosts for integrated optical waveguides. In 1973, Kaminow and J. R. Carruthers

Fig. 7-11.   P. K. Tien, who made fundamental contributions
to integrated optics, including the prism-film coupler.

formed increased refractive-index layers in these crystals by out-diffusion
of lithium,[106] and R. V. Schmidt and Kaminow devised a technique for
creating an increase in the index of refraction by in-diffusing titanium or
various other metals into $LiNbO_3$.[107] Thus, a thin film of Ti could be
evaporated on the $LiNbO_3$ crystal's surface, and a pattern of the desired
optical circuit could be formed using conventional photolithographic techniques. After a diffusion cycle, the increased index region becomes the
optical circuit.[108,109] This technique was widely adopted both by workers
developing communications devices (reported below) and by outside groups
producing information-processing devices for defense applications.

7.1.1 Single-Mode Transmission Waveguides

When lasers are used as the sources for optical communications, it is
important that they radiate in a single mode. To achieve this, the lasers
should have the structure of a thin- and narrow-channel waveguide in
which only one waveguide mode can propagate. The first single-mode

laser, which had a rib-waveguide structure, was made in 1975 by Lee, Burrus, B. I. Miller, and Logan.[110] In 1976, Lee and A. Y. Cho reported a single-transverse-mode laser that has an embedded stripe layer grown by molecular beam epitaxy.[111] In 1978, a strip buried-heterostructure laser, which exhibited stable fundamental transverse-mode operation, with excellent linearity in light versus current characteristics, was reported by W. T. Tsang, Logan, and M. Ilegems.[112]

7.1.2 Diffraction Gratings in Waveguides

The use of diffraction gratings as Bragg reflectors in waveguides was proposed by S. E. Miller in 1969,[113] and then as lightwave couplers by Ashkin and Ippen in 1972.[114] Waveguides with a grating formed either on the top surface or at the film-substrate interface are called corrugated waveguides. Such waveguides with the period of corrugation as small as

Fig. 7-12.   H. Kogelnik, who was coinventor of the distributed-feedback laser and the optical $\Delta\beta$ switch. He made fundamental contributions to integrated optics.

0.1 μm were reported by C. V. Shank and Schmidt in 1973.[115] In 1974, D. C. Flanders, H. Kogelnik, Schmidt, and Shank published a paper describing a grating filter with a bandwidth of 0.1 Å.[116] Based upon the principles of the coupled waves in periodic structures, Kogelnik [Fig. 7-12] and Shank invented in 1971 the distributed-feedback laser that made it possible for a laser to be incorporated in an integrated optical-circuit planar structure without the need for conventional mirrors.[117]

Further development on this subject is the curved-line gratings proposed by Tien for simultaneously reflecting and focusing light in waveguides and also for forming near-confocal resonators in thin films.[118,119] Experiments using this type of grating have been described by R. J. Capik and Tien.[120]

7.1.3 Theoretical Developments

Early in 1969, Marcatili computed field patterns for the modes in optical waveguides,[121] and, at the same time, Tien provided a zigzag wave model for thin waveguides,[122] which has been used extensively for device analysis. Later in 1969, Marcuse developed a theory on the radiation modes and computed for the first time scattering losses in waveguides.[123,124] Kogelnik and Shank[125] developed a coupled-mode theory of corrugated waveguides, which has been used extensively for the analysis of Bragg reflectors, optical filters, and distributed-feedback lasers.

7.2 Modulators, Switches, Filters, Directional Couplers, and Other Components

As integrated optics gradually grew toward maturity, Bell Labs scientists started intensive research for forming integrable optical components such as modulators, switches, filters, and directional coupler switches. As mentioned earlier, experiments on modulation of light in semiconductor p-n junctions were started in the 1960s. An (Al,Ga)As/GaAs modulator with a potential bandwidth of 4 GHz was built by Reinhart and B. I. Miller in 1972. An electroabsorption modulator made of the same material system by Reinhart achieved 90 percent amplitude modulation.[126] An electro-optic phase modulator was demonstrated by I. P. Kaminow and associates[127] and a three-dimensional ridge-waveguide modulator using out-diffused LiNbO$_3$ was reported in 1974.[128] Efficient acousto-optic modulators were also reported at about that time.[129]

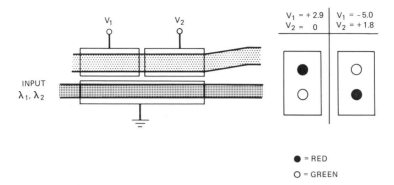

Fig. 7-13. Schematic drawing of the tunable, wavelength-selective directional coupler switch made with Ti:LiNbO$_3$ waveguides. Experimental results are shown for light of two colors (red and green) incident in the lower waveguide. Upon application of appropriate voltages to electrodes over the waveguides, the coupler is phase matched at the red wavelength, which crosses to and exits from the upper waveguide. The coupler is mismatched at the shorter wavelength and, as a result, the green light exits from the lower waveguide. By changing the applied voltages, the situation is reversed as shown. Crosstalk in both cases is −17 dB. The split electrode is required to achieve complete crossover at the phase-matched wavelength.

The first wideband thin-film magneto-optic switch using epitaxial iron-garnet films was reported by Tien and colleagues.[130,131] An optical switch as a bistable device, reported by P. W. Smith and E. H. Turner in 1977, involves an electro-optic element in an interferometer.[132] Bistable operation is obtained when the output of the interferometer is detected and used to drive the electro-optical element. Such bistable switches have been successfully demonstrated in diffused LiNbO$_3$ waveguides.[133,134] An optical switch with 110-psec response time was produced by R. C. Alferness, N. P. Economou, and L. L. Buhl.[135]

Representative of the communications devices coming out of the Ti:LiNbO$_3$ technology were the filters produced by Alferness and his associates. A tunable wavelength-multiplexing filter was reported by Alferness and Schmidt in 1978.[136] [Fig. 7-13] In 1981, Alferness and Buhl designed a device capable of transforming any polarization of input wave into any chosen polarization of output wave.[137] The device is electrically controllable and could be part of a servocontrol of lightwave in either a device or in a transmission-line configuration to correct for other component or trans-

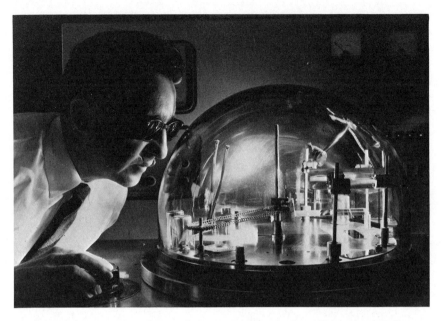

Fig. 7-14. R. V. Schmidt, who was coinventor of the optical $\Delta\beta$ switch. He is shown here regulating the rate of vacuum deposition of contacts to a 7-GHz silicon transistor used in his integrated-optics experiments.

mission line aberrations. Another achievement in 1981 was a wavelength-multiplexing filter capable of accepting any polarization of input wave, thereby removing polarization-stability requirements from the single-mode fiber of a long-distance transmission system.[138]

Directional couplers for coupling light from one waveguide to another may be fabricated by bringing two guide regions within 1 μm of each other. When these couplers are made of an electro-optic material such as Ti-diffused $LiNbO_3$, they perform as the switches. A novel concept is a directional coupler employing phase-constant-mismatch reversal or $\Delta\beta$ reversal. It was introduced for integrated optics by Schmidt [Fig. 7-14] and Kogelnik in 1976 when available fabrication tolerances were too coarse to permit fabricating synchronous-velocity directional couplers.[139,140] The $\Delta\beta$-reversal technique employs a cascaded two-section coupler with intentional phase-constant (β) mismatch that is reversed in one section relative to the other. Electrical control of the βs allows adjustment of the finished device to compensate for fabrication errors. This concept can be very valuable for realizing practical devices. These switches have been built with crosstalk as small as −30 dB. In 1976, Schmidt and Buhl assembled five of these switches in a single substrate to form an integrated optical network, which could switch any of four optical inputs to any of four outputs.[141]

7.3 Integrated Optics for Transmission Systems

7.3.1 Monolithic Integrated Optics—(Al,Ga)As/GaAs Technology

In the mid-1970s, interest developed among Bell Labs scientists in designing an integrated-optics system with the optical components made from a single-material system, so that they can be processed simultaneously on a common substrate. The material chosen for developing such monolithic integrated optics was the (Al,Ga)As/GaAs system, since GaAs technology had already been well established at that time in connection with the development of light-emitting diodes and heterostructure lasers. Based on this concept, distributed-feedback lasers and Bragg-reflector lasers were made from (Al,Ga)As/GaAs heterostructures by H. C. Casey, S. Somekh, and M. Ilegems,[142] by Reinhart, Logan, and Shank[143] and by Tsang, Logan, and L. F. Johnson.[144] Techniques were also developed in this material system by Logan (using liquid phase epitaxy)[145] and by Cho (using molecular beam epitaxy)[146] for forming tapered-film couplers and other structures for integrated optics. With these techniques, simple monolithic circuits containing lasers and modulators were constructed by Reinhart and Logan.[147]

An integrated detector-FET combination was reported by R. F. Leheny and associates in 1980,[148] and a wavelength-multiplexed AND gate was reported by Copeland and coworkers in 1981.[149] The goal of these studies was to produce integrated electrical and optical circuits that could be used in logic devices as well as in communications repeaters.

7.3.2 Multiplexing in Integrated Optics

The rapid maturing of lightwave technology has led to proposals for increasing the transmission capacity of each lightguide by transmitting signals simultaneously at different wavelengths. In 1979, J. C. Campbell and colleagues proposed the use of a single LED, emitting simultaneously at multiple wavelengths and coupled to a single fiber, and a single p-i-n photodiode, capable of simultaneously detecting and demultiplexing (separating) the different wavelengths at the receiving end. They demonstrated

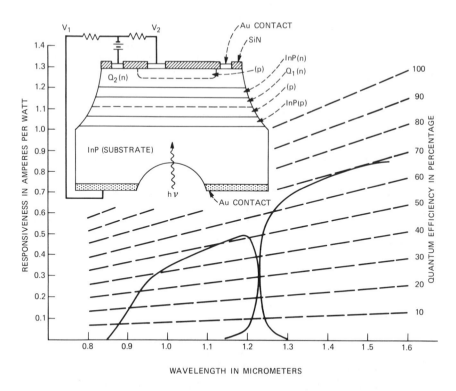

Fig. 7-15.   Early demultiplexing long-wavelength photodetector made by liquid-phase epitaxy. Layers Q_1 and Q_2, of different semiconductor compositions, are sensitive to separate wavelengths, as shown in the responsiveness curve; each wavelength provides a separate output voltage V_1 and V_2. Thus signals carried by two separate wavelengths, entering the detector together, are separated. [Campbell, Dentai, Lee, and Burrus, *IEEE J. Quantum Electron.* **QE-16** (1980): 601, 602.]

a two-wavelength demultiplexing detector for the 1-μm to 1.6-μm wavelength region.[150] [Fig. 7-15] A two-wavelength LED was demonstrated in 1980 for use in the same wavelength region by Lee, Burrus, and Dentai.[151] [Fig. 7-16] These two devices were combined by K. Ogawa and associates in 1981 into a 33-Mb/sec systems-type demonstration, using wavelengths of 1.03 μm and 1.28 μm.[152] For many applications, multiplexing with such multiple-wavelength active devices appears to be potentially simpler and cheaper than the use of separate passive devices. By the early 1980s, lightwave communications was beginning to dominate the design of new guided transmission systems.

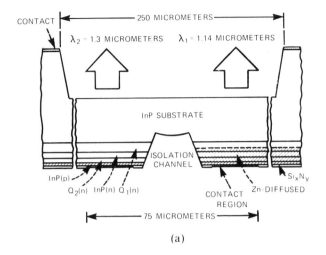

(a)

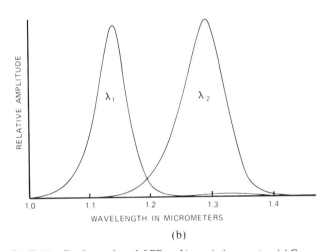

(b)

Fig. 7-16. Dual-wavelength LED and its emission spectra. (a) Cross-sectional view of a dual-wavelength LED composed of two independently driven p-n junction diodes in a single semiconductor chip; it can emit two wavelengths (e.g., 1.14 μm and 1.3 μm) simultaneously. Such a device is useful for a light source in a wavelength-division-multiplexed lightwave system. The first active layer (Q_1) of $In_{0.77}Ga_{0.23}As_{0.5}P_{0.5}$ is separated from a second active layer (Q_2) of $In_{0.66}Ga_{0.34}As_{0.75}P_{0.25}$ by a thin InP barrier layer. All layers were grown by liquid-phase epitaxy onto an InP substrate, and p-n junctions were formed by a deep Zn-diffusion in the Q_1 layer and by a grown p-InP layer on the top Q_2 layer. Electrical isolation is accomplished by a chemically etched deep channel between the two junctions. (b) The emission spectra of the dual-wavelength LED. The electrical crosstalk between the two wavelengths was measured to be about -24 dB. [Lee, Burrus, and Dentai, *Electron. Lett.* **16** (1980): 845, 846.]

REFERENCES

1. A. L. Schawlow and C. H. Townes, "Infrared and Optical Masers," *Phys. Rev.* **112** (December 1958), pp. 1940-1949; A. L. Schawlow and C. H. Townes, U. S. Patent No. 2,929,922; filed July 30, 1958; issued March 22, 1960; J. P. Gordon, H. J. Zeiger, and C. H. Townes, "Molecular Microwave Oscillator and New Hyperfine Structure in the Microwave Spectrum of NH_3," *Phys. Rev.* **95** (July 1, 1954), pp. 282-284.

2. A. G. Fox and T. Li, "Resonant Modes in an Optical Maser," *Proc. IRE* **48** (November 1960), pp. 1904-1905.

3. A. G. Fox and T. Li, "Resonant Modes in a Maser Interferometer," *Bell Syst. Tech. J.* **40** (March 1961), pp. 453-488.

4. J. P. Gordon, "Quantum Effects in Communications Systems," *Proc. IRE* **50** (September 1962), pp. 1898-1908.

5. J. P. Gordon, "Quantum Noise in Communication Channels," in *Quantum Electronics* **1**, ed. P. Grivet and N. Bloembergen (New York: Columbia University Press, 1964), pp. 55-64.

6. M. B. Panish, I. Hayashi, and S. Sumski, "A Technique for the Preparation of Low-Threshold Room-Temperature GaAs Laser Diode Structures," *IEEE J. Quantum Electron.* **QE-5** (April 1969), pp. 210-211; I. Hayashi, M. B. Panish, and P. W. Foy, "A Low Threshold Injection Laser," *IEEE J. Quantum Electron.* **QE-5** (April 1969), pp. 211-251; M. B. Panish and S. Sumski, "Ga-Al-As: Phase, Thermodynamic and Optical Properties," *J. Phys. Chem. Solids* **30** (January 1969), pp. 129-137; I. Hayashi, M. B. Panish, P. W. Foy, and S. Sumski, "Junction Lasers which Operate Continuously at Room Temperature," *Appl. Phys. Lett.* **17** (August 1, 1970), pp. 109-111.

7. J. E. Geusic and L. G. Van Uitert, U. S. Patent No. 3,252,103; filed May 14, 1964; issued May 17, 1966.

8. J. Stone, C. A. Burrus, A. G. Dentai, and B. I. Miller, "Nd:YAG Single-Crystal Fiber Laser: Room-temperature cw Operation Using a Single LED as an End Pump," *Appl. Phys. Lett.* **29** (July 1, 1976), pp. 37-39.

9. C. A. Burrus, J. Stone, and A. G. Dentai, "Room Temperature 1.3 μm C. W. Operation of a Glass-Clad Nd:Y.A.G. Single-Crystal Fibre Laser End Pumped with a Single L.E.D.," *Electron. Lett.* **12** (October 28, 1976), pp. 600-602.

10. J. Stone, C. A. Burrus, and J. C. Campbell, "Laser Action in Photopumped GaAs Ribbon Whiskers," *J. Appl. Phys.* **51** (June 1980), pp. 3038-3041.

11. R. A. Reuhrwein, U. S. Patent No. 3,218,205; filed July 13, 1962; issued November 16, 1965.

12. A. A. Bergh and P. J. Dean, *Light-Emitting Diodes* (Oxford: Clarendon Press, 1976).

13. C. A. Burrus and R. W. Dawson, "Small-Area High-Current-Density GaAs Electroluminescent Diodes and a Method of Operation for Improved Degradation Characteristics," *Appl. Phys. Lett.* **17** (August 1, 1970), pp. 97-99.

14. T. P. Lee, C. A. Burrus, and B. I. Miller, "A Stripe-Geometry Double-Heterostructure Amplified-Spontaneous-Emission (Superluminescent) Diode," *IEEE J. Quantum Electron.* **QE-9** (August 1973), pp. 820-828.

15. O. E. DeLange, "Losses Suffered by Coherent Light Redirected and Refocused Many Times in an Enclosed Medium," *Bell Syst. Tech. J.* **44** (February 1965), pp. 283-302.

16. D. Gloge, "Experiments with an Underground Lens Waveguide," *Bell Syst. Tech. J.* **46** (April 1967), pp. 721-735.

17. D. W. Berreman, "A Lens or Light Guide Using Convectively Distorted Thermal Gradients in Gases," *Bell Syst. Tech. J.* **43** (July 1964), pp. 1469-1475; D. Marcuse and S. E. Miller, "Analysis of a Tubular Gas Lens," *Bell Syst. Tech. J.* **43** (July 1964), pp. 1759-1782; E. A. J. Marcatili, "Modes in a Sequence of Thick Astigmatic Lens-Like Focusers," *Bell Syst. Tech. J.* **43** (November 1964), pp. 2887-2904; P. Kaiser, "An Improved Thermal

Gas Lens for Optical Beam Waveguides," *Bell Syst. Tech. J.* **49** (January 1970), pp. 137-153.

18. M. W. Jones and K. C. Kao, "Spectrophotometric Studies of Ultra Low Loss Optical Glasses II: Double Beam Method," *J. Sci. Instrum.*, Series 2, **2** (April 1969), pp. 331-335.

19. K. C. Kao and G. A. Hockham, "Dielectric-Fibre Surface Waveguides for Optical Frequencies," *Proc. Inst. Elec. Eng. London* **113** (July 1966), pp. 1151-1158.

20. A. Ashkin and E. P. Ippen, U.S. Patent No. 3,793,541; filed December 21, 1970; issued February 19, 1974.

21. J. Stone, "Optical Transmission in Liquid-Core Quartz Fibers," *Appl. Phys. Lett.* **20** (April 1, 1972), pp. 239-240.

22. S. E. Miller, U. S. Patent No. 3,813,141; filed November 22, 1972; issued May 28, 1974.

23. P. Kaiser, E. A. J. Marcatili, and S. E. Miller, "A New Optical Fiber," *Bell Syst. Tech. J.* **52** (February 1973), pp. 265-269.

24. P. Kaiser and H. W. Astle, "Low-Loss Single-Material Fibers Made From Pure Fused Silica," *Bell Syst. Tech. J.* **53** (July/August 1974), pp. 1021-1039.

25. W. G. French and G. W. Tasker, "Fabrication of Graded Index and Single Mode Fibers with Silica Cores," *Proc. Topical Meeting Optical Fiber Transmission*, Williamsburg, Virginia (January 7-9, 1975), pp. TuA2-1—TuA2-3.

26. D. Gloge, "Weakly Guiding Fibers," *Appl. Opt.* **10** (October 1971), pp. 2252-2258.

27. S. D. Personick, "Time Dispersion in Dielectric Waveguides," *Bell Syst. Tech. J.* **50** (March 1971), pp. 843-859.

28. D. Marcuse, "Pulse Propagation in Multimode Dielectric Waveguides," *Bell Syst. Tech. J.* **51** (July/August 1972), pp. 1199-1232.

29. A. Hasegawa and F. D. Tappert, "Transmission of Stationary Non-Linear Optical Pulses in Dispersive Dielectric Fibers. I. Anomalous Dispersion," *Appl. Phys. Lett.* **23** (August 1, 1973), pp. 142-144.

30. S. E. Miller, "Light Propagation in Generalized Lens-Like Media," *Bell Syst. Tech. J.* **44** (November 1965), pp. 2017-2064.

31. D. Gloge and E. A. J. Marcatili, U. S. Patent No. 3,823,997; filed June 18, 1973; issued July 16, 1974.

32. W. G. French, G. W. Tasker, and J. R. Simpson, "Graded Index Fiber Waveguides with Borosilicate Composition: Fabrication Techniques," *Appl. Opt.* **15** (July 1976), pp. 1803-1807.

33. D. Marcuse, "Losses and Impulse Response of a Parabolic Index Fiber with Random Bends," *Bell Syst. Tech. J.* **52** (October 1973), pp. 1423-1437.

34. D. Gloge, U. S. Patent No. 4,000,936; filed July 30, 1974; issued January 4, 1977.

35. D. Gloge, "Optical-Fiber Packaging and Its Influence on Fiber Straightness and Loss," *Bell Syst. Tech. J.* **54** (February 1975), pp. 245-262.

36. D. Gloge and E. L. Chinnock, "Fiber-Dispersion Measurements Using a Mode-Locked Krypton Laser," *IEEE J. Quantum Electron.* **QE-8** (November 1972), pp. 852-854.

37. L. G. Cohen, "Pulse Transmission Measurements for Determining Near Optimal Profile Gradings in Multimode Borosilicate Optical Fibers," *Appl. Opt.* **15** (July 1976), pp. 1808-1814.

38. W. M. Muska, T. Li, and A. G. Dentai, "Material-Dispersion-Limited Operation of High-Bit-Rate Optical-Fibre Data Links Using L.E.D.s," *Electron. Lett.* **13** (September 1977), pp. 605-607.

39. D. L. Bisbee, "Optical Fiber Joining Technique," *Bell Syst. Tech. J.* **50** (December 1971), pp. 3153-3158.

40. R. D. Standley, "Fiber Ribbon Optical Transmission Lines," *Bell Syst. Tech. J.* **53** (July/August 1974), pp. 1183-1185.

41. D. Gloge, P. W. Smith, and E. L. Chinnock, U. S. Patent No. 3,934,773; filed November 2, 1973; issued January 27, 1976.

42. D. Gloge, P. W. Smith, D. L. Bisbee, and E. L. Chinnock, "Optical Fiber End Preparation for Low-Loss Splices," *Bell Syst. Tech. J.* **52** (November 1973), pp. 1579-1588; D. Gloge, P. W. Smith, and E. L. Chinnock, U. S. Patent No. 4,027,814; filed October 24, 1975; issued June 7, 1977.

43. P. K. Runge, L. Curtis, and W. C. Young, "Precision Transfer Molded Single Fiber Optic Connector and Encapsulated Connectorized Devices," *Proc. Topical Meeting Optical Fiber Transmission,* Williamsburg, Virginia (February 22-24, 1977), pp. WA4-1– WA4-4.

44. See entire issue of *Bell Syst. Tech. J.* **57** (July/August 1978), pp. 1717-2312.

45. I. P. Kaminow, "Microwave Modulation of the Electro-optic Effect in $KH_2 PO_4$," *Phys. Rev. Lett.* **6** (May 15, 1961), pp. 528-530.

46. A. A. Ballman, "Growth of Piezoelectric and Ferroelectric Materials by the Czochralski Technique," *J. Amer. Ceram. Soc.* **48** (February 1965), pp. 112-113.

47. K. Nassau, H. J. Levinstein, and G. M. Loiacono, "Ferroelectric Lithium Niobate. 1. Growth, Domain Structure, Dislocations and Etching," *J. Phys. Chem. Solids* **27** (June/ July 1966), pp. 983-988; K. Nassau, H. J. Levinstein, and G. M. Loiacono, "Ferroelectric Lithium Niobate. 2. Preparation of Single Domain Crystals," *J. Phys. Chem. Solids* **27** (June/July 1966), pp. 989-996.

48. F. S. Chen and W. W. Benson, "A Lithium Niobate Light Modulator for Fiber Optical Communications," *Proc. IEEE* **62** (January 1974), pp. 133-134.

49. R. W. Dixon, "The Acoustooptic Interaction," in *The Physics of Opto-Electronic Materials,* ed. W. A. Albers, Jr. (New York: Plenum Press, 1971), pp. 131-149.

50. R. W. Dixon, "Photoelastic Properties of Selected Materials and Their Relevance for Applications to Acoustic Light Modulators and Scanners," *J. Appl. Phys.* **38** (December 1967), pp. 5149-5153.

51. D. A. Pinnow and R. W. Dixon, "Alpha-Iodic Acid: A Solution-Grown Crystal with a High Figure of Merit for Acousto-Optic Device Applications," *Appl. Phys. Lett.* **13** (August 15, 1968), pp. 156-158.

52. A. W. Warner and D. A. Pinnow, "Miniature Acoustooptic Modulators for Optical Communications," *IEEE J. Quantum Electron.* **QE-9** (December 1973), pp. 1155-1157.

53. R. C. LeCraw, "Wide-Band Infrared Magneto-Optic Modulation," *IEEE Trans. Magn.* **MAG-2,** Abstract (September 1966), p. 304.

54. S. H. Wemple, J. F. Dillon, Jr., L. G. Van Uitert, and W. H. Grodkiewicz, "Iron Garnet Crystals for Magneto-Optic Light Modulators at 1.064 μm," *Appl. Phys. Lett.* **22** (April 1, 1973), pp. 331-333.

55. D. F. Nelson and F. K. Reinhart, "Light Modulation by the Electro-Optic Effect in Reverse-Biased GaP P-N Junctions," *Appl. Phys. Lett.* **5** (October 1, 1964), pp. 148-150.

56. F. K. Reinhart, "Reverse-Biased Gallium Phosphide Diodes as High-Frequency Light Modulators," *J. Appl. Phys.* **39** (June 1968), pp. 3426-3434.

57. See references 55 and 56.

58. F. K. Reinhart and B. I. Miller, "Efficient $GaAs-Al_xGa_{1-x}As$ Double-Heterostructure Light Modulators," *Appl. Phys. Lett.* **20** (January 1, 1972), pp. 36-38.

59. F. K. Reinhart, "Phase and Intensity Modulation Properties of $Al_yGa_{1-y}As-Al_xGa_{1-x}As$ Double Heterostructure p-n Junction Waveguides," *Topical Meeting Integrated Optics Tech. Digest,* New Orleans, Louisiana (January 21-24, 1974), pp. WA6-1—WA6-6.

60. J. N. Shive, "The Properties of Germanium Photo-transistors," *J. Opt. Soc. Amer.* **43** (April 7, 1953), pp. 239-244.

61. W. T. Read, Jr., "Theory of the Swept Intrinsic Structure," *Bell Syst. Tech. J.* **35** (November 1956), pp. 1239-1284.

62. R. P. Riesz, "High-Speed Semiconductor Photodiodes," *Rev. Sci. Instrum.* **33** (September 1962), pp. 994-998.

63. M. DiDomenico, Jr., and O. Svelto, "Solid-State Photodetection: A Comparison Between Photodiodes and Photoconductors," *Proc. IEEE* **52** (February 1964), pp. 136-144.

64. L. U. Kibler, "A High-Speed Point Contact Photodiode," *Proc. IRE* **50** (August 1962), pp. 1834-1835.

65. W. M. Sharpless, "Cartridge-Type Point-Contact Photodiode," *Proc. IEEE* **52** (February 1964), pp. 207-208.

66. M. DiDomenico, Jr., W. M. Sharpless, and J. J. McNicol, "High-Speed Photodetection in Germanium and Silicon Cartridge-Type Point-Contact Photodiodes," *Appl. Opt.* **4** (June 1965), pp. 677-682.

67. C. A. Burrus and W. M. Sharpless, "Planar p-n Junction Germanium Photodiode for Use at Microwave Modulation Frequencies," *Solid-State Electron.* **13** (September 1970), pp. 1283-1287.

68. C. A. Burrus, A. G. Dentai, and T. P. Lee, "InGaAsP PIN Photodiodes with Low Dark Current and Small Capacitance," *Electron. Lett.* **15** (September 1979), pp. 655-657.

69. T. P. Lee, C. A. Burrus, K. Ogawa, and A. G. Dentai, "Very-High-Speed Back-Illuminated InGaAs/InP PIN Punch-Through Photodiodes," *Electron. Lett.* **17** (June 11, 1981), pp. 431-432.

70. C. A. Burrus, A. G. Dentai, and T. P. Lee, "Large-Area Back-Illuminated InGaAs/InP Photodiodes for Use at 1.0 to 1.6 μm Wavelength," *Opt. Commun.* **38** (July 15, 1981), pp. 124-126.

71. K. G. McKay and K. B. McAfee, "Electron Multiplication in Silicon and Germanium," *Phys. Rev.* **91** (September 1, 1953), pp. 1079-1084.

72. H. Melchior and W. T. Lynch, "Signal and Noise Response of High-Speed Germanium Avalanche Photodiodes," *IEEE Trans. Electron Dev.* **ED-13** (December 1966), pp. 829-838.

73. H. Melchior and A. R. Hartman, "Epitaxial Silicon n^+-p-π-p^+ Avalanche Photodiodes for Optical Fiber Communications at 800 to 900 Nanometers," *IEEE Int. Electron Dev. Meeting Tech. Digest,* Washington, D.C. (December 6-8, 1976), pp. 412-414.

74. T. P. Lee, C. A. Burrus, M. A. Pollack, and R. E. Nahory, "High-Speed Schottky-Barrier Photodiode in LPE $In_xGa_{1-x}As$ for 1.0 μm to 1.1 μm Wavelength Region," *IEEE Trans. Electron Dev.* **ED-22** (November 1975), p. 1062.

75. J. C. Campbell, A. G. Dentai, C. A. Burrus, and J. F. Ferguson, "High Sensitivity InP/InGaAs Heterojunction Phototransistor," *Electron. Lett.* **16** (August 28, 1980), pp. 713-714.

76. J. C. Campbell, C. A. Burrus, A. G. Dentai, and K. Ogawa, "Small-Area High-Speed InP/InGaAs Phototransistor," *Appl. Phys. Lett.* **39** (November 15, 1981), pp. 820-821.

77. J. E. Goell, "A Repeater with High Input Impedance for Optical-Fiber Transmission Systems," *IEEE/OSA Conf. Laser Eng. Appl. Tech. Digest,* Washington, D.C. (May 30-June 1, 1973), pp. 23-24.

78. J. E. Goell, "A 274-Mb/s Optical-Repeater Experiment Employing a GaAs Laser," *Proc. IEEE* **61** (October 1973), pp. 1504-1505.

79. P. K. Runge, "A 50-Mb/s Repeater for a Fiber Optic PCM Experiment," *IEEE Int. Conf. Commun.,* Minneapolis, Minnesota (June 17-19, 1974), pp. 17B-1—17B-3.

80. See reference 44.

81. S. D. Personick, "Receiver Design for Digital Fiber Optic Communication Systems, I and II," *Bell Syst. Tech. J.* **52** (July/August 1973), pp. 843-886.

82. S. E. Miller, "Integrated Optics: An Introduction," *Bell Syst. Tech. J.* **48** (September 1969), pp. 2059-2069.

83. E. A. J. Marcatili, "Bends in Optical Dielectric Guides," *Bell Syst. Tech. J.* **48** (September 1969), pp. 2103-2132.

84. E. A. J. Marcatili, "Dielectric Rectangular Waveguide and Directional Coupler for Integrated Optics," *Bell Syst. Tech. J.* **48** (September 1969), pp. 2071-2102.
85. A. Ashkin and M. Gershenzon, "Reflection and Guiding of Light at p-n Junctions," *J. Appl. Phys.* **34** (July 1963), pp. 2116-2119.
86. See reference 85.
87. See references 55 and 56.
88. E. R. Schineller, R. P. Flam, and D. W. Wilmot, "Optical Waveguides Formed by Proton Irradiation of Fused Silica," *J. Opt. Soc. Amer.* **58** (September 1968), pp. 1171-1176.
89. P. K. Tien, R. Ulrich, and R. J. Martin, "Modes of Propagating Light Waves in Thin Deposited Semiconductor Films," *Appl. Phys. Lett.* **14** (May 1, 1969), pp. 291-294; P. K. Tien, U.S. Patent No. 3,584,230; filed January 24, 1969; issued June 8, 1971.
90. P. K. Tien and R. Ulrich, "Theory of Prism-Film Coupler and Thin-Film Light Guides," *J. Opt. Soc. Amer.* **60** (October 1970), pp. 1325-1337.
91. See reference 56.
92. F. K. Reinhart and B. I. Miller, "Efficient GaAs-$Al_xGa_{1-x}As$ Double-Heterostructure Light Modulators," *Appl. Phys. Lett.* **20** (January 1, 1972), pp. 36-38.
93. See reference 84.
94. See reference 85.
95. J. E. Goell and R. D. Standley, "Sputtered Glass Waveguide for Integrated Optical Circuits," *Bell Syst. Tech. J.* **48** (December 1969), pp. 3445-3448.
96. P. K. Tien, G. Smolinsky, and R. J. Martin, "Thin Organosilicon Films for Integrated Optics," *Appl. Opt.* **11** (March 1972), pp. 637-642.
97. P. K. Tien, G. Smolinsky, and M. J. Vasile, U.S. Patent No. 3,822,928; filed May 29, 1973; issued July 9, 1974.
98. P. K. Tien, R. Ulrich, and R. J. Martin, "Optical Second Harmonic Generation in Form of Coherent Cerenkov Radiation from a Thin-Film Waveguide," *Appl. Phys. Lett.* **17** (November 15, 1970), pp. 447-450.
99. See reference 90.
100. P. K. Tien, R. J. Martin, R. Wolfe, R. C. LeCraw, and S. L. Blank, "Switching and Modulation of Light in Magnetic-Optic Waveguides of Garnet Films," *Appl. Phys. Lett.* **21** (October 15, 1972), pp. 394-396.
101. P. K. Tien, R. J. Martin, and G. Smolinsky, "Formation of Light-Guiding Interconnections in an Integrated Optical Circuit by Composite Tapered-Film Coupling," *Appl. Opt.* **12** (August 1973), pp. 1909-1916.
102. P. K. Tien and R. J. Martin, "Experiments on Light Waves in a Thin Tapered Film and a New Light-Wave Coupler," *Appl. Phys. Lett.* **18** (May 1, 1971), pp. 398-401.
103. P. K. Tien, R. J. Martin, S. L. Blank, S. H. Wemple, and L. J. Varnerin, "Optical Waveguides of Single-Crystal Garnet Films," *Appl. Phys. Lett.* **21** (September 1972), pp. 207-209.
104. S. L. Blank, R. C. LeCraw, H. J. Levinstein, P. K. Tien, L. J. Varnerin, Jr., S. H. Wemple, and R. Wolfe, U.S. Patent No. 3,764,195; filed February 2, 1972; issued October 9, 1973.
105. F. K. Reinhart, R. A. Logan, and T. P. Lee, "Transmission Properties of Rib Waveguides Formed by Anodization of Epitaxial GaAs on $Al_xGa_{1-x}As$ Layers," *Appl. Phys. Lett.* **24** (March 15, 1974), pp. 270-272.
106. I. P. Kaminow and J. R. Carruthers, "Optical Waveguiding Layers in $LiNbO_3$ and $LiTaO_3$," *Appl. Phys. Lett.* **22** (April 1, 1973), pp. 326-328.
107. R. V. Schmidt and I. P. Kaminow, "Metal-Diffused Optical Waveguides in $LiNbO_3$," *Appl. Phys. Lett.* **25** (October 15, 1974), pp. 458-460.
108. I. P. Kaminow, L. W. Stulz, and E. H. Turner, "Efficient Strip-Waveguide Modulator," *Appl. Phys. Lett.* **27** (November 15, 1975), pp. 555-557.
109. R. V. Schmidt and I. P. Kaminow, "Acoustooptic Bragg Deflection in $LiNbO_3$ Ti-Diffused Waveguides," *IEEE J. Quantum Electron.* **QE-11** (January 1975), pp. 57-59.

110. T. P. Lee, C. A. Burrus, B. I. Miller, and R. A. Logan, "Al$_x$Ga$_{1-x}$As Double-Heterostructure Rib Waveguide Injection Laser," *IEEE J. Quantum Electron.* **QE-11** (July 1975), pp. 432-435.

111. T. P. Lee and A. Y. Cho, "Single-Transverse-Mode Injection Lasers with Embedded Stripe Layer Grown by Molecular Beam Epitaxy," *Appl. Phys. Lett.* **29** (August 1, 1976), pp. 164-166.

112. W. T. Tsang, R. A. Logan, and M. Ilegems, "High-Power Fundamental-Transverse-Mode Strip Buried Heterostructure Lasers with Linear Light-Current Characteristics," *Appl. Phys. Lett.* **32** (March 1, 1978), pp. 311-314.

113. S. E. Miller, "Integrated Optics: An Introduction," *Bell Syst. Tech. J.* **48** (September 1969), pp. 2059-2069.

114. A. A. Ashkin and E. P. Ippen, U.S. Patent No. 3,674,335; filed May 25, 1970; issued July 4, 1972.

115. C. V. Shank and R. V. Schmidt, "Optical Technique for Producing 0.1μ Periodic Surface Structures," *Appl. Phys. Lett.* **23** (August 1, 1973), pp. 154-155.

116. D. C. Flanders, H. Kogelnik, R. V. Schmidt, and C. V. Shank, "Grating Filters for Thin Film Optical Waveguides," *Appl. Phys. Lett.* **24** (February 1974), pp. 194-196.

117. H. Kogelnik and C. V. Shank, "Stimulated Emission in a Periodic Structure," *Appl. Phys. Lett.* **18** (February 1971), pp. 152-154.

118. P. K. Tien, "Method of Forming Novel Curved-Line Gratings and Their Use as Reflectors and Resonators in Integrated Optics," *Opt. Lett.* **1** (August 1977), pp. 64-66.

119. P. K. Tien, U.S. Patent No. 3,948,583; filed December 9, 1974; issued April 6, 1976.

120. R. J. Capik and P. K. Tien, "Use of Curved-Line Gratings for Diffraction of Light in an Optical Waveguide," paper presented at *1977 Ann. Meeting Opt. Soc. Amer.*, Toronto, Canada (October 1977).

121. See reference 84.

122. P. K. Tien, "Light Waves in Thin Films and Integrated Optics," *Appl. Opt.* **10** (November 1971), pp. 2395-2413.

123. D. Marcuse, "Radiation Losses of Dielectric Waveguides in Terms of the Power Spectrum of the Wall Distortion Function," *Bell Syst. Tech. J.* **48** (December 1969), pp. 3233-3242.

124. D. Marcuse, "Mode Conversion Caused by Surface Imperfections of a Dielectric Slab Waveguide," *Bell Syst. Tech. J.* **48** (December 1969), pp. 3187-3216.

125. H. Kogelnik and C. V. Shank, "Coupled-Wave Theory of Distributed Feedback Lasers," *J. Appl. Phys.* **43** (May 1972), pp. 2327-2335.

126. F. K. Reinhart, "Electroabsorption in Al$_y$Ga$_{1-y}$As-Al$_x$Ga$_{1-x}$As Double Heterostructures," *Appl. Phys. Lett.* **22** (April 15, 1973), pp. 372-374.

127. I. P. Kaminow, V. Ramaswamy, R. V. Schmidt, and E. H. Turner, "Lithium Niobate Ridge Waveguide Modulator," *Appl. Phys. Lett.* **24** (June 15, 1974), pp. 622-624.

128. I. P. Kaminow, L. W. Stulz, and E. H. Turner, "Efficient Strip Waveguide Modulator," *Appl. Phys. Lett.* **27** (November 15, 1975), pp. 555-557.

129. R. V. Schmidt, I. P. Kaminow, and J. R. Carruthers, "Acousto-optic Diffraction of Guided Optical Waves in LiNbO$_3$," *Appl. Phys. Lett.* **23** (October 15, 1973), pp. 417-419.

130. See reference 100.

131. See reference 104.

132. P. W. Smith and E. H. Turner, "A Bistable Fabry-Perot Resonator," *Appl. Phys. Lett.* **30** (March 15, 1977), pp. 280-281.

133. P. W. Smith, I. P. Kaminow, P. J. Maloney, and L. W. Stulz, "Integrated Bistable Optical Devices," *Appl. Phys. Lett.* **33** (July 1, 1978), pp. 24-26.

134. P. W. Smith, I. P. Kaminow, P. J. Maloney, and L. W. Stulz, "Self-Contained Integrated Bistable Optical Devices," *Appl. Phys. Lett.* **34** (January 1, 1979), pp. 62-65.

135. R. C. Alferness, N. P. Economou, and L. L. Buhl, "Fast, Compact Optical Waveguide Switch/Modulator," *Appl. Phys. Lett.* **38** (February 15, 1981), pp. 214-217.

136. R. C. Alferness and R. V. Schmidt, "Tunable Optical Waveguide Directional Coupler Filter," *Appl. Phys. Lett.* **33** (July 15, 1978), pp. 161-163.

137. R. C. Alferness and L. L. Buhl, "Waveguide Electro-Optic Polarization Transformer," *Appl. Phys. Lett.* **38** (May 1, 1981), pp. 655-657.

138. R. C. Alferness and L. L. Buhl, "Polarization-Independent Optical Filter Using Inter-waveguide TE↔TM Conversion," *Appl. Phys. Lett.* **39** (July 15, 1981), pp. 131-134.

139. H. Kogelnik and R. V. Schmidt, "Switched Directional Couplers with Alternating $\Delta\beta$," *IEEE J. Quantum Electron.* **QE-12** (July 1967), pp. 396-401.

140. R. V. Schmidt and H. Kogelnik, "Electro-Optically Switched Coupler With Stepped $\Delta\beta$ Reversal Using Ti-Diffused LiNbO$_3$ Waveguides," *Appl. Phys. Lett.* **28** (May 1, 1976), pp. 503-506.

141. R. V. Schmidt and L. L. Buhl, "Experimental 4 × 4 Optical Switching Network," *Electron. Lett.* **12** (October 28, 1976), pp. 575-577.

142. H. C. Casey, Jr., S. Somekh, and M. Ilegems, "Room-Temperature Operation of Low-Threshold Separate-Confinement Heterostructure Injection Laser with Distributed Feedback," *Appl. Phys. Lett.* **27** (August 1, 1975), pp. 142-144.

143. F. K. Reinhart, R. A. Logan, and C. V. Shank, "GaAs-Al$_x$Ga$_{1-x}$As Injection Lasers with Distributed Bragg Reflectors," *Appl. Phys. Lett.* **27** (July 1, 1975), pp. 45-48.

144. W. T. Tsang, R. A. Logan, and L. F. Johnson, "GaAs-Al$_x$Ga$_{1-x}$As Strip-Buried-Heterostructure Lasers with Lateral-Evanescent-Field Distributed Feedback," *Appl. Phys. Lett.* **34** (June 1, 1979), pp. 752-755.

145. R. A. Logan, "Integrated Optical Circuits Grown by Liquid Phase Epitaxy," *Topical Meeting Integrated Optics Tech. Digest*, Salt Lake City, Utah (January 12-14, 1976), pp. TuC1-1—TuC1-4.

146. A. Y. Cho and J. R. Arthur, "Molecular Beam Epitaxy," in *Progress in Solid-State Chemistry* **10**, ed. J. O. McCaldin and G. Somorjai (New York: Pergamon Press, 1975), pp. 157-191.

147. F. K. Reinhart and R. A. Logan, "Monolithically Integrated AlGaAs Double Heterostructure Optical Components," *Appl. Phys. Lett.* **25** (November 15, 1974), pp. 622-624; F. K. Reinhart and R. A. Logan, "Integrated Electro-optic Intracavity Frequency Modulation of Double-Heterostructure Injection Laser," *Appl. Phys. Lett.* **27** (November 15, 1977), pp. 532-534; F. K. Reinhart and R. A. Logan, "GaAs-AlGaAs Double Heterostructure Lasers with Taper-Coupled Passive Waveguides," *Appl. Phys. Lett.* **26** (May 1, 1975), pp. 516-518.

148. R. F. Leheny, R. E. Nahory, M. A. Pollack, A. A. Ballman, E. D. Beebe, J. C. DeWinter, and R. J. Martin, "Integrated In$_{0.53}$Ga$_{0.47}$As *p-i-n* FET Photoreceiver," *Electron. Lett.* **16** (May 8, 1980), pp. 353-355.

149. J. A. Copeland, J. C. Cambell, A. G. Dentai, and S. E. Miller, "Wavelength-Multiplexed AND Gate: A Building Block for Monolithic Optically Coupled Circuits," *Appl. Phys. Lett.* **39** (August 1, 1981), pp. 197-199.

150. J. C. Campbell, T. P. Lee, A. G. Dentai, and C. A. Burrus, "Dual-Wavelength Demultiplexing InGaAsP Photodiode," *Appl. Phys. Lett.* **34** (March 15, 1979), pp. 401-402.

151. T. P. Lee, C. A. Burrus, and A. G. Dentai, "Dual Wavelength Surface Emitting InGaAsP L.E.D.'s," *Electron. Lett.* **16** (October 23, 1980), pp. 845-846.

152. K. Ogawa, T. P. Lee, C. A. Burrus, J. C. Campbell, and A. G. Dentai, "Wavelength Division Multiplexing Experiment Employing Dual-Wavelength LED's and Photodetectors," *Electron. Lett.* **17** (October 29, 1981), pp. 857-859.

Chapter 8

Switching Research

After early research on circuits and mechanisms in the 1930s, research in switching carried out in the 15 years following World War II was aimed mainly at designing experimental systems that exploited the potentials of high-speed electronics. Three research switching systems made use of electron tubes, gas tubes, magnetic drums, and transistors for experimenting with new configurations of internal system control and operation. Line scanning, use of bulk memory, electronic logic, repertory dialing, time-division switching, and other advanced techniques were demonstrated in these early systems. This research led ultimately to the development of the 4ESS* switching system, a digital, time-division electronic switching system. Later research emphasized ring switching methods, local-area digital switching networks, digital signal encoding, and digital signal detection. These techniques subsequently took on aspects of research in computer science and computer technology.

I. SWITCHING TECHNOLOGY AND SWITCHING RESEARCH

The impact of switching research on switching systems at Bell Laboratories has been somewhat different from that of research leading to new transmission media and transmission systems. For the latter, the power of the scientific method and the importance of enlisting scientists to work on fundamental problems relevant to communications was recognized very early in the 20th century. (See the first volume of this series, *The Early Years (1875-1925)*, Chapter 10.) Surface studies leading to the historic C. J. Davisson and L. H. Germer experiment, Johnson noise and its impact on information transmission as elucidated by H. Nyquist, and the search for a fundamental understanding of the magnetic behavior of materials of importance to loading coils are but a few outstanding examples of the early realization of the potential importance of new science to communications. (See another volume in this series, *Physical Sciences (1925-1980)*.) In contrast, the switching and signaling systems described in *The Early*

Principal authors: G. D. Bergland, W. A. Malthaner, and H. S. McDonald.

* Trademark of AT&T Technologies, Inc.

Years (1875-1925), Chapter 6, made use of existing technology, with inventions aimed at improving the speed, reliability, and interconnections of the rapidly increasing number of telephones, leading to highly sophisticated switching systems. The remotely controlled switch and signal generator to direct the step-by-step switching operations by the customer, an invention of one of the customers, A. B. Strowger, is an excellent example of such switching systems.

In the *Switching Technology (1925-1975)* volume of this series, prepared primarily by A. E. Joel, Jr., there are a number of examples of switching systems that have benefited from research carried on in the switching research organization or in other parts of Bell Labs research areas, such as C. E. Shannon's work on information theory, or the research on the transistor and gas diodes. Even though no single complete system described in that volume can be said to have been taken over from a single system experiment within the research area, the experimental research systems to be described in this chapter deal with new switching ideas that had a technical or conceptual influence on the first Bell System trial electronic central office, the first electronic line concentrator, and, in turn, on the 1ESS switching system, the 101ESS switching system-private branch exchange (PBX), and other systems. These ideas also stirred interest in digital time switching systems, such as the 4ESS switching system (see *Switching Technology (1925-1975)*, Chapter 12) and, in many other ways, impacted the developing switching technology.

II. EARLY SWITCHING RESEARCH

The earliest publication on a fundamental approach to switching at Bell Labs was by T. C. Fry in his book on *Probability and its Engineering Uses*, published in 1928.[1] The first specific research effort directed at switching and switching systems came in July 1934 with the establishment in the Authorization for Work of official objectives and budgets for "general and experimental study of signaling circuits and mechanisms with the object of arriving at better engineering methods for design and development work . . . applied to specific problems such as dial interference and pulsing . . . that lead to more efficient signaling circuits with less degradation to the associated speech transmission circuits."

Research in the years prior to World War II was mostly on circuits and mechanisms for switching rather than on systems organization or theory. Experimental studies were pursued on dialing and supervision for toll circuits as well as on multifrequency key pulsing for use by operators and subscribers, either by means of plucked tuned reeds or keyed oscillators. These studies resulted eventually in the currently used toll dialing and supervision arrangements and the Touch-Tone subscriber subset with the plucked reeds of the original subscriber sets replaced by transistor oscillators.

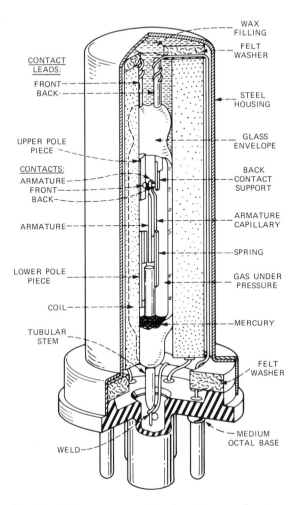

Fig. 8-1. The mercury contact relay. It is one of various switching devices that have benefited from fundamental research at Bell Laboratories.

Research studies on mechanisms produced fundamental knowledge of physical and chemical phenomena that led later to several new types of relays: sealed relays with the contact parts wetted with mercury[2] [Fig. 8-1]; glass-sealed, dry-contact, magnetic-reed relays;[3] and wire spring relays with the wire contact assemblies and armature stock molded in plastic subunits. Extensive studies produced special cold-cathode gas tubes, some with multielectrode configurations with properties of lock-out and logic useful for switching, and others having low noise, low distortion, and negative ac resistance insertion-gain useful as talking path contacts.

III. RESEARCH SYSTEMS EXPERIMENTS

When Bell Labs scientists resumed regular switching research activities after World War II, the emphasis was on the development of new devices, tools, and techniques, and the incorporation of these in experimental systems for automatic switching. Many of the ideas applying electronics to switching and studies by research scientists resulted in new system proposals. Models of some of these were constructed, and the three that included the most promising concepts are discussed in this section. These three research telephone switching systems, constructed and studied from about 1946 to 1961, were: (1) the electronically controlled automatic switching system (ECASS), (2) the drum information assembler and dispatcher (DIAD) system, and (3) the experimental solid-state exchange (ESSEX). These research experiments were carried out under the direction of W. A. MacNair, director of switching research, and his successor, W. D. Lewis.

3.1 Electronically Controlled Automatic Switching System (ECASS)

A laboratory experiment was initiated in 1946 by A. W. Horton, Jr., and colleagues to determine the advantages of applying faster operating electronic techniques to switching systems and using higher-speed systems to test some previously unexplored philosophies in switching and signaling. A new electronically controlled automatic switching system was constructed, which came to be known by its acronym, ECASS, using such basic tools as dry-reed relays, mercury relays, multielement cold-cathode gas tubes, cold-cathode gas diodes, and thermionic electron tubes. [Fig. 8-2] An experimental subscriber's telephone set, incorporating a preset dial mechanism with circuits for generating dialing signals of a new form, together with suitable signal receivers for the central office, was designed. The system incorporated a novel type of switching network with its control circuits. A basic aim of the experiment was to design the various control circuits of the central office so that each was fast enough to accept and process all the calls received, one call at a time. In such a system, only one active control circuit of each type would be required.

3.1.1 System Organization

The most modern switching centers in use at the time, notably the crossbar switch family, included shared circuits known as common control circuits. Many registers, senders, and markers were required to set up the conversational paths. Related functions were grouped together in a particular type of control circuit, and a sufficient number of each type of

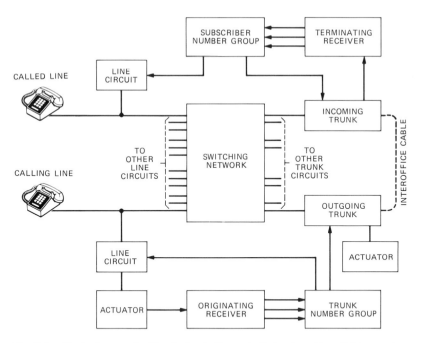

Fig. 8-2. Block diagram for the electronically controlled automatic switching system (ECASS). The subscriber presets the number desired on the telephone set before picking up the handset. An actuator in the office causes the number of the desired exchange to be sent in a high-speed signaling format. The single electronic trunk number group applies voltage marks to the line and trunk terminals of the reed-diode switching network for instantaneous selection and operation of crosspoints in a path from the subscriber to the terminating office. The called line number now is rapidly transmitted by an actuator at the outgoing trunk directly from the subscriber's preset telephone to the possibly distant office. As a terminating office, ECASS uses the electronic subscriber number group to voltage mark the network for the final part of the subscriber-to-subscriber path.

control circuit was provided to handle the expected traffic. These control circuits and associated connectors embraced a considerable fraction of the space and cost of the telephone exchange.

The new ECASS system, in a design worked out by W. A. Malthaner, H. E. Vaughan, and their associates, required only a single control circuit of each kind.[4] Each group of functions was performed at high speed for all the expected traffic on a one-call-at-a-time basis by the corresponding single control circuit. This operational philosophy was to be accomplished by a fresh approach to system design using developments in high-speed components. In addition to the high speed in the common control units, it was necessary to have fast switches, since the operating time of a switching network is part of the total holding time of the control circuit operating the network. Accordingly, a network of high-speed switches with a high-speed control circuit was included. Similarly, since the signaling time is part of the holding time of the control circuit that receives and registers the signals, some form of high-speed signaling was required. It was also essential that individual subscribers should have no direct control of the holding time of any common control circuit. The great reduction in the number of common control circuits and connectors was designed to reduce the size and cost of a central office even if the individual control circuits were somewhat more expensive. Furthermore, a speed permitting one-at-a-time operation also could result in faster service for the subscriber.

Available, inherently high-speed elements, such as cold-cathode gas tubes and thermionic electron tubes, were adopted for the system. A network of high-speed switches with a high-speed control circuit was designed. A preset-dialing device in the subscriber telephone set (subset), with transmission of dialing signals to the central office under control of common equipment in the office, was selected as a means of eliminating the direct influence of subscribers on the holding time of control circuits. A code of high-speed signals, suitable for transmission over all existing types of telephone facilities, with means for customer preselection and office-controlled generation of telephone numbers, was designed into the subset. Such a subset is necessarily complex, since it becomes a form of manually operated register that stores all digits of a number before transmission to the central office. Circuits to control the generation of subset signals from the central office and receiver circuits to decode and register the signals were constructed.

3.1.2 Vacuum Tubes and Relays in ECASS

Cold-cathode, gas-filled diode or triode tubes had already found wide telephone application. Special types were designed to have special characteristics for switching use. Three new tubes were used—a diode at each crosspoint of the switching network, a screen-grid pentode for the path selection processes, and an octode for miscellaneous purposes in the line, trunk, number group, and other circuits. The dry-reed switch, which was used as the contact element in many fast relays as well as in the metallic talking path through the office, consisted of two permalloy rods sealed in opposite ends of a small glass tube that is filled with an inert gas. The overlapping ends of the rods were rhodium-plated and normally adjusted to have a small gap between them. The application of a magnetic field coaxial with the reeds magnetizes the rods and causes them to pull together and close a metallic path from one rod to the other. The dry-reed switch has an extremely small operate and release time and provides a highly reliable, dirt-free contact for low-current applications. Descendants of this dry-reed switch became well known and were used in most metallic contact switching networks as well as throughout the computer and industrial control industry. Mercury contact relays of a sealed construction were used in ECASS where fast operation at heavier currents was required. These relays were later widely used in other applications.

3.1.3 Preset Pulse-Position-Dialing Telephone Set

To eliminate direct control by the subscriber and to reduce the holding time of dialed information receiving circuits, D. B. Parkinson, J. F. Muller, K. S. Dunlap, and Malthaner designed a preset telephone set.[5,6] Physical aspects of the telephone set were designed by Parkinson and Muller. The internal circuits of the set were conceived by Dunlap and Malthaner. H. E. Hill assisted in the detailed mechanical design and construction. The number to be called was set up before the handset was removed from its cradle. To place a call the subscriber positioned each of the eight finger wheels so that the desired number could be read on the edge numbers immediately above the lower edge of the finger-wheel frame. A new, high-speed form of subscriber signaling, called pulse-position dialing, was invented for this system. [Fig. 8-3] In operation, the number was rapidly transmitted to the central office when a receiving circuit had been connected.

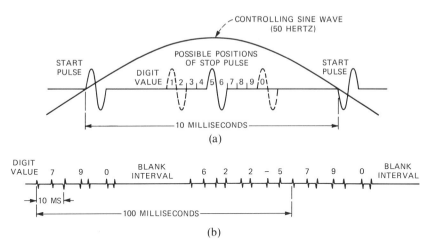

Fig. 8-3. ECASS pulse-position dialing. (a) Called-number signals at about 50 times the speed of conventionally dialed digits were sent from the ECASS telephone under control of 50-hertz simplex power sent from the central office. These signals, called pulse-position dialing, consisted of two pulses per digit: a start pulse at each zero-crossing of the 50-hertz control wave and some time later in the 10 millisecond half-cycle interval, a stop pulse. Each digit pulse was approximately a single cycle of a 1000-hertz sine wave and the interval between a start pulse and its following stop pulse was identified with an associated digit value. The digit pulses in consecutive intervals were of opposite polarity. (b) Compressed time scale. An interval of at least 3.2 milliseconds was provided after each pulse for possible transient lengthening in the transmission medium. A silent interval of two digits was provided between the automatic repetition of the entire dialed number.

Eight digits were sent for a complete local-area directory number and repeated as many times as necessary for establishing the call.

Although the use of a preset telephone set was not adopted for general use specifically to reduce the holding time of central office control circuits, the availability of low-cost, large-scale integrated solid-state circuits has led to terminals with the same internal functions providing storage of telephone number(s) and automatic dialing or pulsing as a customer convenience.

A receiver was designed to operate with the signals generated by the telephone sets described above. The dialing system, pulse form, digit code, and number format used in ECASS with its generating and receiving circuits were the results of transmission investigations started as early as 1946 by Malthaner, N. D. Newby, and Vaughan.[7,8]

3.1.4 *The Switching Network in ECASS*

To provide a switching network with the high operating speed required, a new crosspoint and new path-selecting arrangement was devised by E. Bruce and N. I. Hall employing cold-cathode gas diodes and dry-reed relays.[9] In addition, this switching arrangement had other desirable properties: (1) The idle-path testing and selection functions were incorporated in the internal controls of the network. (2) Busy sections of the network were automatically isolated from the sections tested for subsequent calls. (3) Selection of a trunk within a trunk group or subgroup occurred as part of the internal controls of the network. (4) Selection of an idle trunk and idle switch path in combination reduced blocking. These internal selection controls eliminated many of the connector contacts that would have otherwise been required between the switches and external common control circuits.

The network was operated in a novel self-selecting process known as end marking. Voltages, called marks, are applied by a number group to the line and to the trunk between which a talking path is desired. These marks, in conjunction with permanently wired, high-impedance bias voltages on the primary-secondary switch links, caused the cold-cathode tubes of associated idle paths to fire and conduct at low current. The essentially constant voltage drop characteristic of gas diodes caused the voltage on the primary-secondary switch links to shift, thereby marking one input lead to each secondary switch of the marked frames. [Fig. 8-4]

In each control lead connection between line and trunk frames was a junctor circuit. Gas diodes between marked secondary switch links and idle junctors fired, thereby marking all available junctors. In each junctor, a five-element, cold-cathode gas tube was used for path detection and selection with a circuit arrangement common to all junctors serving the same line frame, automatically ensuring the selection of a single path.[10]

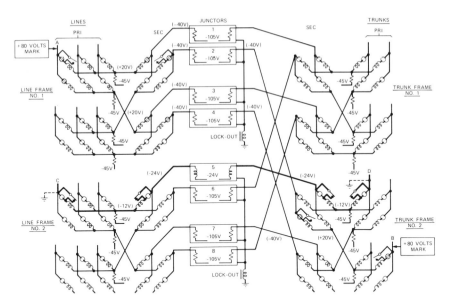

Fig. 8-4. ECASS switching network schematic. In the ECASS high-speed switching network, a cold-cathode gas diode and a dry-reed relay formed the crosspoint. Two of the relay contacts are shown in the talking path, and the third is associated with the sleeve or control path. The network was operated in a self-selecting process known as end marking. Voltages, called marks, were applied to the line and to the trunk or trunks between which a talking path was desired. These marks caused the gas tubes of all available paths to conduct. The five-element, cold-cathode tube in each control junctor at the center of the network was arranged as a lock-out circuit so that only one junctor of those serving the line frame could conduct at higher current. The higher current operated the relays along the selected path to complete the talking connection. The other relays were held at lower current and voltage.

If a conduction region through such a negative-resistance gas tube was provided with a load impedance of proper value, which was common to a similar conduction path through one or more similar gas tubes, only one tube ionized and remained ionized, even if firing potentials were applied to several tubes either simultaneously or in sequence. This functional arrangement, known as a lock-out circuit, dealt with the simultaneous requests for the use of several junctors. The one junctor in which the gas tube conducted in its main anode gap effectively first shorted out the bias resistors in its voltage supply leads. This permitted a higher value of current to flow through the gas diodes along the selected path and caused the operation of the reed contacts associated with the crosspoint relay windings, which were in series with the diodes. The control lead contact at each of these crosspoints shorted out the gas diodes; with the diodes shorted out, a further increase in the current operated relays in the line and junctor circuits. These relays caused the high-voltage supplies in the associated junctor to be replaced by lower-voltage sources and the voltage marks on the line and trunk terminals to be replaced by ground. This shift of power sources permitted the gas diodes, along paths marked but not selected for this call, to extinguish but hold the crosspoints at low power level along the selected path. With all diodes extinguished, the switching network was ready for the next path-selection operation. In this arrangement, the average holding time for the network control circuits was about 40 milliseconds, ten times faster than older systems. Removal of the ground at the end of conversation resulted in complete release of the associated operated crosspoints and junctor.

Glass-sealed, dry-reed switches were used for the first time in a switching network in ECASS. Subsequently, many commercial networks, including non-Bell systems, were built using these switches. Some of these employed a control (or sleeve) lead through the network and a control contact per crosspoint for holding the connection.

3.2 Drum Information Assembler and Dispatcher (DIAD) System

In 1948, C. E. Brooks, C. A. Lovell, and Parkinson suggested the use of magnetic drums as code or data translators and as dial-pulse registers. Malthaner and Vaughan then expanded this idea into a design for a complete telephone switching system, constructed in 1952, that used magnetic drums for memory elements and various electronic devices for data processing and control elements. In this system, information from customer dialing and on equipment availability and call status was assembled on the magnetizable areas of the surface of a rotating drum and dispatched from the drum surface to fast control circuits for the various call functions, such as the establishment of conversational paths through the switching network. In this way, many customers shared control circuits and memory common to the entire system. From this arrangement of common control, the system derived its name DIAD. Malthaner and Vaughan [Fig. 8-5], who formulated the overall plan for the system organization and operation and designed many of the electronic information processing circuits,[11] continued the philosophy of a one-at-a-time operation in which a single circuit is fast enough to serve all the customers one after another for a selected group of functions.

The DIAD was designed as a heavy-traffic, 10,000-line telephone office. Time studies were made to be sure that each common control unit would handle the information offered to it in the busy hour. The working laboratory system was skeletonized to 27 lines and 12 trunks. A single magnetic drum functionally divided into two sections to serve as line drum and trunk drum was used together with about 2200 germanium diodes and 1100 electron tubes, since reliable transistors were not then available in sufficient quantities or types.

Fig. 8-5. W. A. Malthaner (left) and H. E. Vaughan discussing a drum information assembler and dispatcher (DIAD) circuit in front of the line and trunk bays. The proliferation of electron tubes indicates that the era of solid-state devices had not yet arrived.

3.2.1 *Scanning, Signal Distribution, and Time-Shared Control*

The DIAD experiment was a significant step in the development of switching systems. It included and demonstrated for the first time many new concepts in the application of electronics to switching. Such applications were first motivated by the idea of a single, high-speed control that would be fast enough to process all calls in a common control system on a one-at-a-time basis. This would eliminate connector circuits and contention between markers for access to the switching network and also require only one place where changes in call processing and traffic routing need be made. DIAD was the first system to demonstrate the feasibility of this concept.

Prior to DIAD, the common control portions of systems were accessed through space-division connectors or links. DIAD used the concept of scanning for access to the line and trunk periphery of the system. [Fig. 8-6] This implemented the concept of time division as applied to the system control. Each line and trunk was examined periodically at a rate higher than the shortest expected signal to learn of call requests and dialed digits

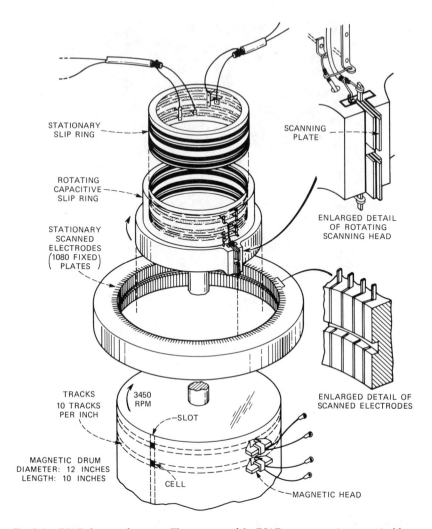

STATIONARY
SLIP RING

SCANNING
PLATE

ROTATING
CAPACITIVE
SLIP RING

STATIONARY
SCANNED
ELECTRODES
(1080 FIXED
PLATES)

ENLARGED DETAIL
OF ROTATING
SCANNING HEAD

TRACKS
10 TRACKS
PER INCH

3450
RPM

SLOT

ENLARGED DETAIL OF
SCANNED ELECTRODES

MAGNETIC DRUM
DIAMETER: 12 INCHES
LENGTH: 10 INCHES

CELL

MAGNETIC HEAD

Fig. 8-6. DIAD drum and scanner. The memory of the DIAD system was in magnetizable cells on the surface of rotating drums. Rotating on the same shaft was a capacitively coupled scanning head used as a synchronized input path from lines and trunks. The 1080 electrodes of the stationary section of the scanner defined an equal number of axial areas or slots on the drum surface, each assigned to a corresponding line or trunk. All permanent and temporary data for the line or trunk were "remembered" in the magnetic cells of the associated slot and were read, and the call-related information was altered as required by the system program. The program itself was recorded in call-progress marks.

and to detect busy-idle conditions. The control functions were divided into small steps, and decisions were made on each change of state of the line or trunk. The steps were applied to each decision point in the logic in much the same manner as in modern action translator or table look-up systems. Signals originating in the control and sent out over trunks were processed by periodically sampling the signals and distributing them to the individual trunks represented by slots on the drum.

These techniques, used for the first time in DIAD, were the forerunners of the modern electronic controls of switching systems that take advantage of speed by time-sharing. Even the name time slot, widely used in time-division systems, originated with this application.

3.2.2 Operation of Magnetic Drum and Associated Circuits

A capacitive scanner was used as a time-division connector from customers' lines to the magnetic drum and its associated circuits. The drum

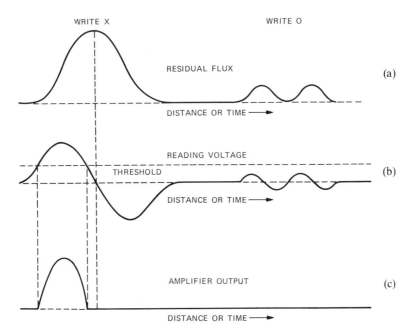

Fig. 8-7. DIAD read/write waveform diagram. Economical operation of the DIAD memory system was based on the ability to alter the information in the cells of a drum slot while these cells were still under the same heads just used for reading. This single pass operation was possible because the residual flux (a) in a recorded cell produced a output reading voltage (b) a short time before the cell reached the point at which writing (or erasing) must take place. High-speed logic circuits using the information in a combination of cells in the same slot together with any other sources of information can cause the magnetic state of any cells in that slot to be "immediately" altered (c) as required by the system program. [McGuigan, *Proc. IRE* **41** (1953): 1439.]

provided for the storage of both temporary and permanent information. The magnetic drum and scanner circuits were designed by W. A. Cornell,[12] Newby,[13] J. H. McGuigan,[14] and O. J. Murphy.[15] One section of the drum memory was associated with the customer lines and the other section with the output side of the switching network, that is, with the trunks. On each call, complete information was finally assembled in the trunk section of the drum memory and retained there for the duration of the call. A built-in program directed the processing of information. Program sequence was controlled by a series of call-progress marks. Each time a new stage in the program was reached, the call-progress mark in the associated drum slot was updated. Information dispatched from the trunk drum directed the operation of the switching network and the signaling to other offices. Each group of information, which formed an item of control data, was entered on or read from the drum in parallel channels rather than serially in time from one channel.

Each customer was assigned a fixed plate on a line scanner, and the line drum slot was indexed by this plate. The scanner inspected each line drum slot, as indexed by this plate, about 60 times a second with an interval of 16 microseconds for each inspection. All the information recorded in the associated slot on the drum was available for reading and alteration during each inspection period. Operation of the memory system was based on being able to alter the information in the cells of a drum slot while these cells were still under the same heads used for reading—called single-pass operation.[16] [Fig. 8-7]

A single-pass method of operation was possible because the reading output from a cell was available a short time before the cell reached the center point where writing was to take place. Thus it was possible to read the information in a given cell, or in a combination of cells in the same slot, to determine on the basis of this information, together with the program or logic of the system and any other available input information, whether the information read should be altered. If so, the information was altered as the slot passed once under the head, thus reducing the size and complexity of the memory control system.

Single-pass operation was important because it offered economies in building data processing systems to handle large amounts of information rapidly. Estimates indicated that to do parts of the DIAD tasks without single-pass operation would have required twice as many drum tracks and amplifiers and four times as many read/write heads.

The operation of the DIAD may be visualized by tracing a call through the system. [Fig. 8-8] As a customer dialed, the scanning and dialing assembler control circuit registered the dialed digits in the drum slot allotted to the originating line. After dialing was completed, information was dispatched from the drum memory to control the switching network and to

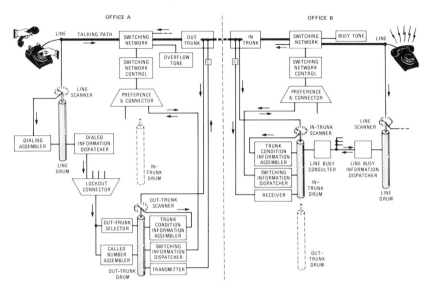

Fig. 8-8.   Block diagram showing DIAD operation. In a DIAD system, the customer picked up the handset of the telephone and after hearing the dial tone dialed the number of the telephone he/she wished to reach. The digits were assembled on a magnetic drum that served lines in an area parallel to the axis of the drum and permanently assigned to the specific line. After collection, the dialed number was transferred to the outgoing trunk drum that sent orders to the switching network to set up a conversational path to a trunk to the called office. The called-line-number information was passed over the trunk to the in-trunk drum in the called office, which completed the connection to the called line.

send the called line number to the terminating office, where, by similar operations, a network path was set up to the called customer.

The switching network used reed-diode crosspoints in a four-stage array quite similar to the network for the ECASS system. (See section 3.1.4.) However, a path selection and detection control circuit was not provided in every junctor path, but using an economically important suggestion of S. T. Brewer,[17,18] a much smaller number of control circuits, called "mactors," were electronically activated in the particular set of junctors involved when a path selection operation took place. In addition, the establishment of a path was reported to and recorded on the magnetic drum, and the path could be released at the end of conversation only by orders originating at the trunk drum.

3.2.3 *Information Transfer*

In DIAD, information from an external source had to be recorded at a particular address on a drum. Information had to be dispatched from a drum to a system control circuit, and, in some cases, from one drum location to another. The process was similar in all cases.

Information was taken from the drum on recognition of a call-progress word, and was checked and dispatched to the proper destination. In the case of transfer to another drum location, for example, part of the data registered was used as an address. The address data was applied to one side of a match circuit. Possible addresses, one of which identified the slot to which the data was to be transferred, were read from the drum and applied to the other side of the match circuit. When the address in the register and one from the drum corresponded, a match pulse was generated that wrote the information on the drum. A new call-progress mark was written at the same time as the transferred data in a single-pass operation. [Fig. 8-9]

3.2.4 Related Innovations

Two other switching-related suggestions of interest explored the application of bulk memory. They were centralized repertory dialing and

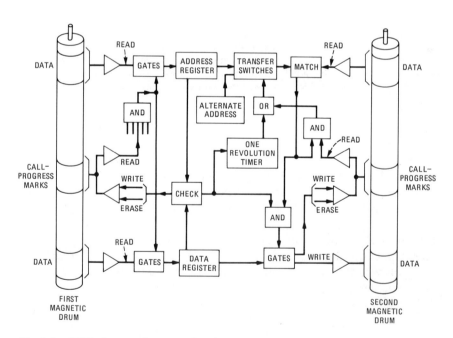

Fig. 8-9. DIAD drum-to-drum transfer of data. In DIAD operations, information was assembled in the slots of the first magnetic drum (left), dispatched to control registers and transferred to the second magnetic drum (right) under the control of the logic section shown between the two drums. The logic section was driven by the information in the call-progress marks on the two drums. [Malthaner and Vaughan, *IRE Trans.* **EC-4** (1955): 25.]

semiautomated directory assistance. The first of these was made a direct adjunct to the DIAD system described in the preceding sections. Provisions were made by Malthaner and Vaughan for a centralized repertory-dialing service in which the customer could produce, alter, check, and call into use a list of frequently called telephone numbers.[19] In the checking process, numbers previously placed in repertory memory with its short identifying number were audibly read aloud to the customer on demand. This was a precursor of services that came into use in the early 1980s. Such services used spoken language responses to telephone inquiries on stock prices, airline schedules, and other information from computer-controlled data storage.

In the semiautomated directory-assistance service, designed by D. W. Hagelbarger, W. G. Hall, and Malthaner, an information retrieval system was provided in which a plurality of operators obtained access to a machine-readable storage file on a time-sharing basis.[20] To reduce the time required for searching through the file, indexing arrangements were provided so that request information (name, address, type of business, etc.) from different operators was compared as accumulated character by character with index information until the location of the requested telephone number was identified with sufficient precision for the display of a short list of numbers to the requesting operator. Further exploratory efforts eventually resulted in the use of computerized directory-assistance systems. Later exploratory developments were undertaken on time-shared information retrieval systems. (See *Switching Technology (1925-1975)*, Chapter 11, section 2.7.2.)

3.3 Experimental Solid-State Exchange (ESSEX)

In theory, both transmission and switching may be space-, frequency-, or time-divided. All three of these methods have been used for transmission systems. Frequency-divided switching has been explored but has always been more costly than the other alternatives. Time-division techniques, on the other hand, have received extensive attention throughout the world with the advent of high-speed, solid-state devices. Research at Bell Labs on time-division switching, then called time-separation switching, was started in 1949. In 1976, the Bell System started the first commercial use of digital time division in toll switching offices. This was made possible by research and the advances of the preceding decade in solid-state technology and time-division techniques.

An example of time-division switching at Bell Laboratories was the experimental model of a communication system called ESSEX. This system for the first time applied new design concepts that integrated and solved simultaneously the fundamental problems of digital telephone switching and transmission. Extensive use was made of discrete transistors for logic, memory, and gating functions for the first time. This experiment was devised by Malthaner, Vaughan, and their associates.[21]

3.3.1 ESSEX System Concepts

There were four important, interrelated points involved in the ESSEX concept. The first was that line concentrators were used near the customers' premises with only a few efficiently used wires connecting the concentrator to the central office. Second, switching at a concentrator—between the many customer lines and the fewer pairs to the central office—was time divided. During a conversation, users shared in rapid succession a single transmission path to the central office, and each caller used the path repetitively at a rate high enough that the interruptions for other callers were unnoticed. Third, the high speed of the switching elements permitted the use of coded digital transmission between the concentrator and the central office. Voice-frequency signals were sampled, and each amplitude sample was coded into a group of binary pulses identifying the amplitude. This is called pulse-code modulation (PCM). The coded group of pulses was then sent over the transmission medium. Control pulse groups of the same form, transmitted from the central office to the concentrator, determined which user was connected in each interval. The fourth point in the ESSEX plan was that the PCM signals were connected directly through the central office by time-division switches. Voice-frequency signals existed in analog form only in the user's telephone and the serving concentrator, not more than a few hundred yards away. At the concentrator, the voice was sampled many times per second, and each sample was switched to a coder shared by all the telephones served by the concentrator. The voice then remained in coded form to the office, through the office, and to the concentrator serving the called telephone. There, it was reconverted to a voice-frequency analog signal for delivery to the called telephone. The switches in time-division systems operate faster than those used in a space-separation switching network. They operate at each time slot. Solid-state switches, circa 1959, were sufficiently fast that speed was no problem in the ESSEX demonstration.

The line-concentrator arrangements in ESSEX used the multiplexed trunk transmission parameters of a PCM transmission system, T1 carrier, then being developed.[22,23] Basic designs of the coding, decoding, and companding equipment were supplied by H. M. Straube, C. P. Villars, and their associates in the Bell Labs Transmission Development Department. In addition to reducing the amount of equipment and number of cable conductors required, a uniform-quality, fixed-loss path was achieved between voice-frequency terminals, independent of the distance and number of switching points between them. The effects of crosstalk and noise buildup were removed by regeneration of the coded signals. Since the code specifies the volume and quality, these are independent of distance.

3.3.2 *The Remote Concentrator*

A concentrator module consisted of a remote unit and a central unit. In the remote part of the concentrator, as many as 225 voice-frequency lines were switched to three cable pairs that carried digital signals to and from the central unit. One pair took PCM signals to the central unit. The second brought PCM signals from the central unit. And the third brought control words from the memory in the central unit. Each line required a line circuit, which contained a gate and a filter. The line circuit was the lowest order module in the system, and these circuits were added only as customers were connected to the concentrator. The ensemble of line circuit packages made up a switching stage that was controlled by a selector and used resonant transfer of voltage amplitude samples, as invented independently by Lewis[24] [Fig. 8-10] and by H. B. Haard and C. G. Syala of L. M. Ericsson.[25] The output of this stage was a two-wire pulse-amplitude-modulation (PAM) bus with 23 time slots or channels for use on links to the central office. The memory controlling the selection of the gates was located at the central point. The information was sent over the control

Fig. 8-10.   W. D. Lewis, who made fundamental contributions to microwave and mobile radio research, and provided leadership in electronic switching research.

pair of wires as an eight-bit word in each time slot. Each word designated to the selector a line gate number and selected one of 255 gates.

The two directions of PAM transmission on the time-divided bus must be separated so that the signals can be handled in each direction on the proper PCM pair. This conversion was accomplished by a circuit called a time-division hybrid.[26,27] It permitted a signal to pass from a line to a send bus or from a receive bus to a line but never permitted a direct connection between the send bus and the receive bus. PAM signals on the send bus were coded into seven-bit PCM signals and sent to the central point. Incoming PCM signals were decoded and presented to the two-wire bus and, in turn, to a voice-frequency line. The line circuit was a passive circuit, and all the signal power needed was supplied by the common receiving amplifier in the receive bus. Timing signals needed for the operation of the remote unit were generated by a local clock slaved to a master clock at the central switching point. Whenever there was a choice between locating equipment in the concentrator or in the controller, the controller was chosen, since, being at the central point, it would be both in a more controlled environment and more accessible for maintenance.

3.3.3 The Concentrator Central Unit

The unit in the central office for the concentrator module was made up of digital circuits that included the memory to control both remote and central switches. [Fig. 8-11] Three recirculating serial memory units were used in each controller, each circulating 192 bits or 8 bits for each of the 24 channels. One memory unit stored the list of active line gate numbers for operation of the remote line unit. One stored words to control the operation of the central switch gates associated with the same concentrator. In addition, the third memory unit stored code words, called call-progress words, concerning the states of the calls being handled. The complete memory could be searched every 125 microseconds to determine which channels were busy or idle or to obtain any other pertinent information.

Binary-coded pulses were transmitted through a magnetostrictive delay line memory. Each line was a 3-mil Supermendur wire (see *Physical Sciences (1925-1980)*, Chapter 12, section 1.1.4) with a solenoid around one end as an input transducer and a similar solenoid at the other end as an output transducer. Electrical impulses were impressed magnetostrictively on the line in acoustic form. The magnetostrictive effect was used at the output solenoid to convert back to electrical impulses. The output of the delay line connected to the first stage of a shift register, and the last stage of the shift register fed pulses back into the delay line to complete the memory loop. These magnetostrictive ultrasonic delay lines were the responsibility of D. A. Aaronson and D. B. James,[28] with mechanical design by Muller.

The most complex part was the logic, which controlled the generation,

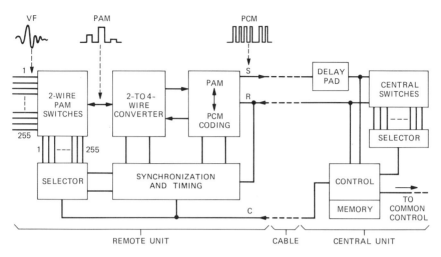

Fig. 8-11. Experimental solid-state exchange (ESSEX) concentrator. It enabled 255 telephone lines to access 23 pulse-code-modulation (PCM) channels to the central unit. In the remote unit of an ESSEX concentrator, speech samples of a group of lines were scanned at an 8-kilohertz rate and pulse-amplitude samples of up to 23 active conversations were interleaved or pulse amplitude modulated on a common bus. Each line delivered, in turn, an outgoing speech sample and received a sample it was to hear. On the shared communication medium to the distant central office, each speech sample appeared as a train of pulses representing in binary code the amplitude of the corresponding speech sample. Separate pairs carried the sent (S) and received (R) codes for amplification and regeneration as required enroute. Timing and control information needed for operation of the remote unit were transmitted on a third pair (C) in similar PCM form from the central unit to the concentrator.

interpretation, and modification of call-progress marks. Some of these marks were operating orders to and from the common control. Supervisory information from the remote unit was held in the circulating delay-line memory, and logical operations were performed on this information when necessary. Control of ringing, supervisory tones, and answer indications were handled in this section.

3.3.4 Central Stage Switches

The central stage switches or junctor gates were simple AND gates that passed digital signals unilaterally. This was another advantage gained by the use of PCM.[29,30] The gate handled low power; and the selector, which used a five-bit input to mark one of 32 pairs of switches, was simple. The central switches for each concentrator were connected to the central switches of all other concentrators by junctors on a space-separation basis. Thus, each concentrator had access to all other concentrators and trunk units, called trunkors, that interfaced the internal digital signals to analog voice frequency trunks and to junctors to other office modules over 32 separate space paths in any of the 23 time slots. A call from one concentrator to another used the same time slot in each concentrator. The switching plan had four stages, one stage in each remote unit and one for each associated central unit. [Fig. 8-12] A two-stage switching plan for the central unit was selected principally because it permitted intermodule and intramodule calls to be handled in almost the same way and permitted a convenient arrangement of the central switch control memory.

Some blocking occurred because of the concentration to 23 channels and because of time-slot mismatch. To obtain practically high enough usage with reasonable avoidance of blocking when calls are routed through many stages of time-division switching, means had to be provided for

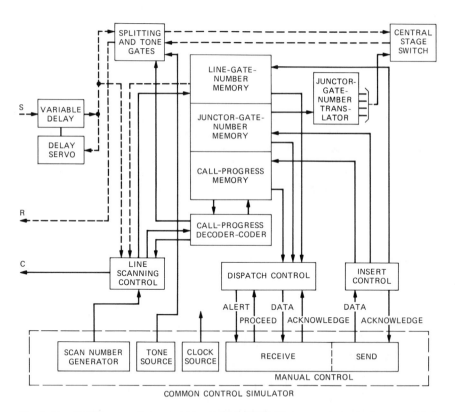

Fig. 8-12. ESSEX concentrator central unit. Each ESSEX line concentrator had an associated central unit with three memory sections, each recirculating a serial pulse train of binary-coded words. The line-gate-number memory stored the list of active line gate numbers for operation of the remote line unit. The junctor-gate-number memory stored words to control the operation of the central stage switch gates associated with the same concentrator. The call-progress memory stored code words concerning the states of the calls being handled. Words in the memories could be used for control in parallel or serial form and could also be received or transmitted in either fashion.

changing the time slot occupied by a call as it proceeded through the system. There were a number of ways of providing time-slot interchange. In one method, a delay line or clocked shift register one frame long with taps at time-slot intervals was added at a switching point as a junction in the transmission path. Gates provided at each tap for extending the transmission path were controlled by tap gate numbers stored in memory.

The time-slot interchange was one of the basic switching principles required for time-division switching to realize the benefits of synergy with time-division transmission. While on leave from the University of Tokyo, H. Inose, working with J. P. Runyon, conceived the idea of time-slot interchange for time multiplex switching. This invention, like many other concepts in ESSEX, has become one of the basic ingredients of all subsequent digital, time-division systems.[31] Later, Inose calculated the benefits derived from this concept[32] and, while under contract with Bell Laboratories, he and his students made a number of other research contributions to switching.

3.3.5 *Supervision, Dialing, and Ringing*

The handling of telephone calls requires many auxiliary functions. Detection of on-hook and off-hook line conditions to determine the start or end of customer calls was done by scanning. The central control sent out a line number code in the 24th time slot, which was reserved for this interrogating purpose. Every fourth frame, a new number was sent to the remote unit, so that 255 lines in each concentrator were scanned in about one-eighth of a second. If action was called for, the result of the scan was stored in the call-progress-mark section of the memory.

All tones and signals originating at the central unit were generated directly in digital form as PCM codes. Digital ringing signals at voice power levels were applied through a separate gate for each concentrator receive pair, and audible ring in digital form was applied through a separate gate for return to the originating end of the circuit, providing full access to all 23 channels. Conventional 20-hertz ringing was possible by adding circuit elements in the line package capable of passing the higher power levels. Busy and other tones in PCM form were switched in the same way. Trunk splitting was also accomplished by proper operation of these time-shared gates. The simplicity of this arrangement for applying special tones and gaining access to link connections is one more advantage of digital time-division switching demonstrated by the ESSEX experiment.

3.3.6 *Delay, Synchronization, and Timing*

Synchronization of digital offices and their transmission lines is a subject that engaged the attention of many Bell Labs researchers during the early days of digital, time-division switching. In 1969, J. R. Pierce discussed the problem of synchronization in digital networks and concluded that with good clocks, buffers, and delay lines, there should be no trouble in synchronizing a nationwide network.[33]

The synchronization of a point-to-point, four-wire, PCM transmission system was relatively straightforward. A clock timed the sending end, and the receiving end was slaved to it. The same operation was used in the opposite direction. Synchronization between the two directions was not required. In the ESSEX system, which extended the PCM signals to the two-wire switching points at the remote terminals, overall synchronization was necessary. Unless all switches operated at the proper time, chaos would have reigned. The transmission delay, about 7 microseconds per mile for cable pairs, complicated the problem. Since the junctor gates for a particular conversation operated once per frame, PCM signals from a concentrator had to arrive at the central stage switch at the same time as PCM signals being sent to the concentrator; signals in the two directions had to pass each other at the junctor. If the loop transmission delay was one frame (or an integral multiple of frames) long, this phase requirement was met. The loop transmission delays of remote concentrators at different distances from the switching centers varied accordingly. These delays could be made an integral multiple of frames and maintained continuously by the insertion of an adjustable delay pad in the appropriate lead, one of several synchronization solutions proposed by M. Karnaugh. A magnetostrictive delay line was used for this purpose, and its effective length was servocontrolled by comparing the output of the delay line to the master clock and generating error signals, which caused the input transducer to be physically moved along the magnetostrictive wire. [Fig. 8-13]

The clock at the remote unit was a crystal-controlled unit slaved to the master clock at the office module. Counting circuits in the remote unit produced timing pulses at submultiples of the clock frequencies. Once every 125 microseconds, a framing signal was sent in the 24th time slot on the receive pair to the remote unit. When this signal was recognized, all counting circuits were checked, and, if out of frame, they were reframed.

3.3.7 Impact of ESSEX on Switching Technology

The ESSEX experiment engaged the attention of those throughout the world interested in developing systems to be implemented with only solid-state devices using digital, time-division techniques. The articles about the ESSEX system are among the most quoted in switching literature. By the late 1960s, the further research, planning, and exploratory development of the concepts triggered by ESSEX reached a point at which development of the first stored-program-controlled, digital, time-division switching system became a reality.

In 1966, Vaughan, one of the principal architects of the ESSEX program, transferred to the switching development area and assumed responsibility

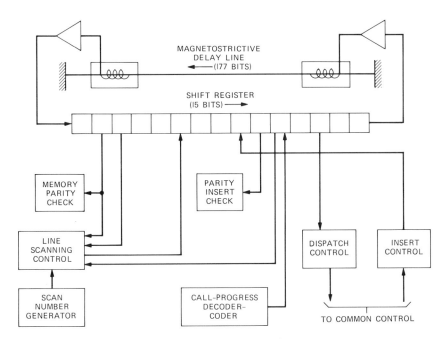

Fig. 8-13. Magnetostrictive delay line. Memory units, such as the line-gate-number memory, in the ESSEX system were magnetostrictive delay lines that held serial pulse trains of binary-coded words. Together with a 15-stage shift register, a recirculating loop operating at the clock rate of the system was formed for 24 words of 8 bits each. The information in the shift register could be examined and transmitted to external circuits in serial form as line gate numbers to the remote unit or in parallel form to the call-progress decoder-coder. Parity check circuits checked for data errors.

for completing part of the development of the stored-program-controlled 1ESS switching system. (See *Switching Technology (1925-1975)*, Chapter 12, section I.) By 1969, switching was well along toward developing a space-division system. By stimulating vigorous exploratory development of digital, time-division switching, Vaughan was able to turn the proposed development towards digital, time-division switching as originally proposed in ESSEX. This led to the realization in 1976 of the first commercial, digital, time-division switching system employing stored-program control. It provided the very large initial capability for serving 107,000 trunk circuits and for the processing of 550,000 calls per hour.

IV. DIGITAL SWITCHING RESEARCH

With the advent of the batch manufacture of integrated circuits, resulting in a drastic reduction of the cost of electronic equipment, the design of switching systems utilizing digital rather than analog components became very attractive. This was enhanced by the fact that digital circuits operate with less stringent requirements than linear analog circuits. In addition, digital circuits are useful in large arrays. Switching researchers began to investigate the possible advantages of using digital methods to perform all of the functions of communication system elements that were commonly done with more conventional analog electronic circuits. These system elements included networks, filters, signaling detectors for dial pulses, Touch-Tone, single-frequency and multifrequency signals, tone generators, and code converters. Moreover, minicomputers, microprocessors, and inexpensive digital logic memory provided new means for implementing digital controls and networks, which stimulated the study of such topics as the switching of data and large-bandwidth signals as well as digitized voice. Digital signal-processing units were constructed that were programmable to allow any of a large variety of tasks on demand and that could be multiplexed by time-sharing the circuitry to perform several of these tasks simultaneously. The multiplexed use of a single conductor by many signals and the implementation of hundreds of gates on a single integrated-circuit chip so reduced the complexity of the central switch network elements and junctors that they were no longer the dominant cost components of switching systems. The attention of researchers turned to exploring new ways to interface the analog signals of the outside telephone plant to the digital world of the low-cost switch built from integrated circuits. New architectures for networks and their control emerged. New concepts were experimented with, such as systems combining switching and transmission functions, systems switching both voice and data signals, and sophisticated loop and packet systems.

4.1 The Digital Wire Center

Research models of several switching systems were constructed by H. S. McDonald and J. H. Condon and their associates in the mid-1970s to prove the feasibility of the newest digital techniques for subscriber switches.[34] One system plan was the Digital Wire Center, which performed all of the functions of call switching, patching, maintenance access, and testing for the wire center. All of the connections between the lines were to be done with a single digital switching fabric and controlled by a master common control. The digital remote switch unit of the Digital Wire Center was built to explore the technology of interfacing the subscriber plant to the digital network. The remote switch unit was designed to provide full subscriber service to a small number of lines (less than 2000) with equipment located near the subscribers, as in a shopping center or housing complex. It constituted most of a complete switching system except that it relied on a remote common control for path finding, translation, and record keeping. To reduce the controller data rate, the remote switching unit contained an autonomous scanner and service circuits controlled by small computers that also performed digits analysis and network control operations. The scanner was connected to the line interface units via a path through the network, as was the control for ringing and testing. The service circuits used a programmable digital processor designed by H. G. Alles.[35] A small switching system was proposed for economics studies, using the results of the remote-switch-unit hardware experiments but not encompassing all of the nonswitching functions of the complete Digital Wire Center version, such as managing the transmission terminal equipment. This system was called the small digital switch (SDS).

The research switching systems incorporated an interface unit for each pair of wires homing in on a node (wire center) with the functions required to terminate the line or trunk pair on the switch units. They contained per-line analog-to-digital and digital-to-analog converters with associated low-pass filters and digital multiplexing circuits. Much of the cost of the switching system resided in these plug-in interface units, and their cost was critical to the economics justifying digital local switching. To reduce the cost of the interface units, a very simple analog-digital codec (coder/decoder) was used.[36] Its simplicity was achieved at the expense of a high data rate (288 kilobits/second). By encoding first into delta modulation and then converting into a 32-kilohertz (kHz) differential PCM, the precision low-pass filters were greatly simplified, and complex analog components such as sample and hold circuits were eliminated.

While the DIAD experiment (see section 3.2) pioneered in time-shared controls, the Digital Wire Center introduced a very important concept in control access beyond DIAD scanning and signal distribution. In the Digital Wire Center, these functions take place using the same time-division network used for the PCM speech paths. The Digital Wire Center system experiments also introduced digital signal processing into the signaling generators and detectors. These experiments demonstrated that if digital techniques are used and large-scale integrated circuits are applied to telephone switching, significant reductions in wire, space, power, and equipment were possible. In 1975, an internal cost study showed the viability of the SDS approach[37,38] (in the reference, the SDS system is referred to as the research switch) and played a significant role in the decision to build the 5ESS switching system. The introduction of the 5ESS switching system and many other digital local switches confirmed the conclusions arrived at in this work.

4.2 The Experimental Digital Switch (XDS)

As the issue of the economic justification of digitally implemented local switches was resolved, the research effort was directed toward the new services that might result from digital networks having new architectures

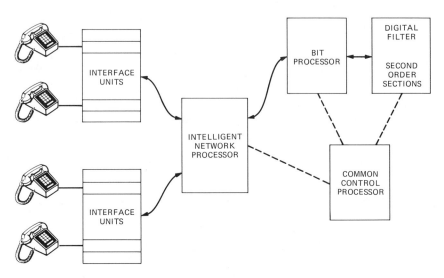

Fig. 8-14.   The Experimental Digital Switch (XDS) architecture. This system incorporated a unique intelligent network processor at its heart, which performed the switching function by executing pairs of memory-to-memory transfer instructions. Two line interface units are shown. The bit processor and digital filter performed the scanning, tone detection, and tone generation functions. The call processing program resided in the common control processor.

and capabilities. Alles, C. Christensen, R. W. Lucky, and their associates constructed a digital system prototype, called XDS (Experimental Digital Switch), that merged processing logic and interconnection logic to form a new type of network that had capabilities for providing new types of communications services.[39] The network became much more than an interconnection medium that supported similar paths carrying speech signals. Each path could be different in bandwidth and could contain processing for conferencing or data analysis. [Fig. 8-14] This prototype system provided telephone service for a small group of researchers at Bell Labs during 1979 through 1981. The design of an enhanced multiple XDS module architecture with the capacity to switch more than 100,000 data and voice lines was reported in a 1981 publication by R. D. Gordon, Alles, and G. D. Bergland.[40]

4.2.1 Systems Concepts in XDS

The unique feature of the experimental digital switch system was the intelligent network processor.[41] This specialized high-speed processor performed all the required switching functions. Data moving into and out of the network appeared at fixed memory locations within the address space of the network processor. This specialized central processing unit accomplished the switching function by executing load and store operations to establish the required connections. Other instructions could process the data as it moved through the network to provide services such as conferencing, companded/linear conversions, data switching, and programmable gain adjustment.

The flexibility of the programmable network allowed all of the control and status information to be collected from the individual line interface units and presented as one composite digital signal to a special bit processor. The bit processor generated or received status and control information such as scanning, line supervision, and ringing control. This programmable processor could gather and monitor 128 digital data streams and generate 128 digital control streams at the system's 8-kHz sampling rate.

4.2.2 Intelligent Network Processor

All data flowing into and out of the XDS system was switched through the intelligent network processor, which was composed of memory, logic, and input-output, all of which were tailored to the job of processing hundreds of signals simultaneously. Within the address space of this processor were dedicated locations, each receiving the data flowing into the system from a specific line unit. These memory locations received an 8-bit appropriately coded PCM sample developed by the line interface unit, referred to as the "mouth" sample data, along with up to 8 bits of additional status and signaling information. For each line interface unit, there was a second dedicated location into which the network stored 16 bits of data to be delivered to the line interface unit. The 8 bits of outgoing PCM data within this 16-bit word was referred to as "ear" sample data. During one sample period, the network completely executed a 1500-word program that contained the required load and store instructions. The memory locations that actually provided and received the mouth and ear samples were double buffered so that the information remained static for the complete sample time. The instruction repertoire of the network processor was designed so that a pipelined execution scheme could be efficiently employed. [Fig. 8-15]

Of the 16 bits of data flowing from and to the line interface units through the intelligent network, only 8 bits were used for voice data. The other 8 bits could be used for control, signaling, and digital data to and from the customer's facility. This digital stream could support many independent data paths, multiplexed and demultiplexed at the customer's facility and at the line interface unit. In particular, one such data path could be a burglar-alarm security bit transmitted at a very low rate.

The conference calls feature enabled three or more customers to be connected simultaneously so that each could hear and talk with the others. While providing such a service was straightforward in analog networks,

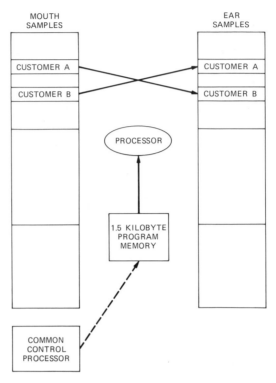

Fig. 8-15. Intelligent network processor. The fabric of the XDS network differed substantially from previous electronic switching systems. It performed the switching function by executing a series of computer instructions on a high-speed network processor instead of closing metal contacts or filling time slots.

it was more difficult in digital networks because arithmetic must be performed on the many PCM voice samples at the sampling rate. One type of network instruction was used to fetch the 8-bit specially coded PCM voice sample and convert it into a 13-bit linear digital representation, which was added to an accumulator in the processor. This instruction was applied to the mouth sample of each participant. A second instruction distributed the accumulated value. That instruction must again fetch the mouth sample of the participant, convert it to a 13-bit linear sample, subtract it from the accumulated value, convert the difference to the 8-bit specially coded PCM voice sample, and store the result in the ear buffer location of the participant. The introduction of loss and scaling was also accomplished during this operation.

The packet mode of operation was introduced to increase the utilization of allocated channel bandwidth for applications that were delay tolerant and presented a bursty communication load. The intelligent network processor and a programmable list processor supported the base-level packet protocol. Complete packets received from the subscriber by the subscriber's link interface were prefixed with the packet length, queued, and subsequently transmitted to the network processor over the allocated packet mode channel. The network processor switched all of the bytes received over the subscriber's packet mode channel to a list processor channel that had been configured to collect nonidle characters in a buffer. Once a number of nonidle bytes equal to the prefixed packet length had been received, a packet arrival interrupt was generated. When a packet was transmitted to a subscriber, it was transmitted one byte at a time by a list processor channel. The list processor fetched each byte from the buffer at a rate that matched the allocated packet channel bandwidth and presented it to the intelligent network processor. The network processor switched the data to the destination subscriber's output memory locations. After the entire packet had been transmitted, a packet departure interrupt was generated. The feature processor then prepared the next queued packet for transmission to the subscriber.

4.2.3 *Multiple Module Networks*

When the switching capacity of one intelligent network processor is exceeded and it is no longer possible to find a free instruction within the network's switching program, it becomes desirable to provide a large XDS switching network by interconnecting multiple modules, using a time-division multiplexed space switch. A network system was constructed in which each module consisted of an intelligent network processor, list processor, and central processing unit. The space switch provided each module with 512 output memory locations whose contents were broadcast at the end of each sample period over a bus dedicated to the module. All other modules in the network could listen to this bus (or the bus dedicated to any other module) and latch one or more samples from the other modules into the 512 input memory locations connected to the space switch. [Fig. 8-16]

Each module did not need to be loaded with a complete repertoire of feature software packages. Although frequently accessed software applications would be loaded into each module, less often accessed features could be provided in as few as two modules. When a line required a service that was not provided by the software loaded into the module to which it was connected, a simple path was established through the space switch to a module that had the required feature software. All of the status

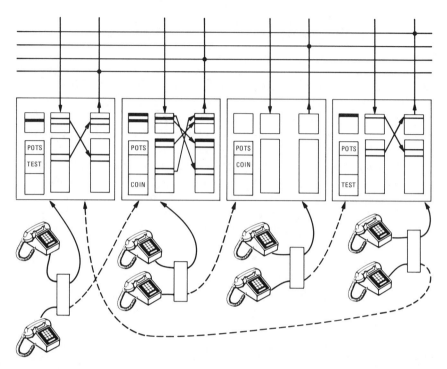

Fig. 8-16. The multiple module XDS system architecture. Up to 100 individual XDS modules could be interconnected using a large time-division multiplexed switch. Each module controlled and transmitted information on its own bus and received information from any of the other buses. Programs could be stored in separate modules and yet be used by all modules. For example, the Plain Old Telephone Service (POTS) feature is shown in all modules; the coin telephone program (COIN) is only shown in two modules but could be used by any of the modules.

and control information associated with the communication link could be switched through the space switch so that the remote module could perform all of the needed control and signaling operations without having to generate and send control packets to the module physically connected to the link. The switched appearance of the line was functionally identical to the line's appearance within the first module.

4.2.4 *Impact of XDS on Switching Technology*

The designers of the XDS architecture foresaw the utility and economic feasibility of having dedicated-line interface units for passing control and voice information through the network together, and of a multimodule construction that would provide both $n + 1$ sparing and modular growth. They foresaw the advantages of digital voice, synchronous data, and packet data in the same network fabric to provide a wide variety of experimental data and voice services.

The intelligent network concept found its way into new PBX systems because it provided a reasonable way of providing digital conferencing. The idea of having load and store operations serve as the network fabric, instead of crosspoints or time slots, provided tremendous versatility for providing services beyond Plain Old Telephone Service.

The problems of economically switching very low data rate, long holding-time calls were solved effectively in the XDS architecture. Using the sub-rate switching schemes developed by Gordon[42] and R. A. Thompson,[43] 24-hour-per-day holding-time calls of very low bit rates became economical. This meant that fire- and burglar-alarm lines could be switched automatically instead of manually at the mainframe. This would be a major benefit in areas experiencing congestion in main distribution frames.

The modular expansion architecture of XDS permitted an effective partitioning of both hardware and software functions. Modules could be specialized to provide certain functions, and traffic from other modules could be switched to that module through the intermodule communication network.

The XDS architecture gracefully handles data and voice traffic together. The convenience of this combination became very clear during experiments with data/voice services.

4.3 Data Switching Experiments

While the experimental digital telephone systems were being built, work was underway on studying the effect of low-cost logic and memory on new ways of communicating signals, especially digital signals. Research was done on ring-type switching-transmission schemes that showed promise of efficiently handling a wide variety of digital communication signals by collecting bits into a packet and preceding them with an identifying header so packets could be merged onto a shared, high-speed digital highway. Although the schemes originated with early proposals made in an unpublished internal memorandum in the 1960s by a research study group led by Lewis, the first experiment to demonstrate what has come to be known as Local Area Networks (LANs) was performed by W. D. Farmer and E. E. Newhall in 1970.[44] Subsequently, Pierce proposed a data ring in which data blocks are inserted into vacant time slots as these occur on a synchronous transmission ring.[45] The system topology was that of a dual-redundant ring closed at a central office that served a number of such rings. A "Pierce ring" was implemented by C. H. Coker in 1971 for interconnecting a series of computers used in speech research.[46]

Several experimental systems were built and found practical use for communications within Bell Laboratories. One by D. R. Weller operated at 3 megabits per second and used central pooling for control. It served as a peripheral bus to interconnect a large number of terminals and small computers to a larger central computer.[47] A second interbuilding system called Spider was constructed by A. G. Fraser and was used for computer-to-computer communications at high data rates over distances of many miles.[48] It used T1 carrier links, and each terminal supported many virtual circuits so many different processes could use the same port. The Spider system contained a microprogrammed controller providing many maintenance and administrative functions as well as controlling the basic multiplexing.

In these early data switching experiments, the switching research was mostly concerned with dynamic multiplexing to use the transmission medium more efficiently rather than to provide access to many other subscribers. To provide a very large number of interconnections, Fraser extended the control concepts demonstrated in the Spider system into a packet switching system that had extended growth capabilities and was adaptable to many types and rates of transmission links. The system, called DATAKIT* packet switching apparatus because of its modular nature and expandability, capitalized on low-cost memory and logic to build queueing elements in the line and trunk interfaces. The switching information was contained as an address in the header portion of a data packet. As the switches routed the data, this address information was updated in order to steer the data along the route until, when the packet was delivered to the final destination, the address identified the sender. The switching module operated in a high-speed serial mode processing data at 7 megabits per second. The centralized common control negotiated with a port for the connection information and then down-loaded a route for the virtual circuit into the appropriate switching modules.

4.4 Digital Switching and Computer Science

Switching research has had a large impact on the technology of modern telephony, starting with the concept of digital, time-division switching that led to the 4ESS switching system. Research demonstrated techniques of signal encoding, digital signal detection, and digital switching architecture that have become important in local digital switching systems and modern PBXs. Large switching systems and the functions of these systems have become more computer-like and more software driven. This trend is expected to continue until computer and switching system technology become indistinguishable. Switching research has turned into computer science and computer technology.

---

* Trademark of AT&T.

REFERENCES

1. T. C. Fry, *Probability and its Engineering Uses* (New York: D. Van Nostrand Co., 1928).
2. J. T. L. Brown and C. E. Pollard, "Mercury Contact Relays," *Elec. Eng.* **66** (November 1947), pp. 1106-1109.
3. W. B. Ellwood, "Glass-Enclosed Reed Relay," *Elec. Eng.* **66** (November 1947), pp. 1104-1106.
4. W. A. Malthaner, U.S. Patent No. 2,620,399; filed June 29, 1948; issued December 2, 1952; W. A. Malthaner and H. E. Vaughan, U.S. Patent No. 2,655,559; filed September 16, 1949; issued October 13, 1953; W. A. Malthaner and H. E. Vaughan, "An Experimental Electronically Controlled Automatic Switching System," *Bell Syst. Tech. J.* **31** (May 1952), pp. 443-468.
5. K. S. Dunlap and W. A. Malthaner, U.S. Patent No. 2,672,523; filed September 16, 1949; issued March 16, 1954.
6. W. A. Malthaner and H. E. Vaughan, U.S. Patent No. 2,713,613; filed July 10, 1952; issued July 19, 1955.
7. W. A. Malthaner, N. D. Newby, and H. E. Vaughan, U.S. Patent No. 2,615,971; filed December 30, 1948; issued October 28, 1952.
8. W. A. Malthaner, N. D. Newby, and H. E. Vaughan, U.S. Patent No. 2,658,188; filed June 29, 1948; issued November 3, 1953.
9. E. Bruce and N. I. Hall, U.S. Patent No. 2,582,959; filed October 29, 1947; issued January 22, 1952.
10. N. I. Hall, U.S. Patent No. 2,350,888; filed November 21, 1941; issued June 6, 1944.
11. W. A. Malthaner and H. E. Vaughan, "An Automatic Telephone System Employing Magnetic Drum Memory," *Proc. IRE* **41** (October 1953), pp. 1341-1347; W. A. Malthaner and H. E. Vaughan, "Control Features of a Magnetic-Drum Telephone Office," *IRE Trans.* **EC-4** (March 1955), pp. 21-26; W. A. Malthaner, U.S. Patent No. 2,723,311; filed March 5, 1953; issued November 8, 1955.
12. W. A. Cornell, U.S. Patent No. 2,691,729; filed March 5, 1953; issued October 12, 1954; N. D. Newby, U.S. Patent No. 2,679,551; filed September 21, 1950; issued May 25, 1954; N. D. Newby, U.S. Patent No. 2,675,427; filed December 21, 1951; issued April 13, 1954.
13. N. D. Newby, U.S. Patent No. 2,739,183; filed April 15, 1952; issued March 20, 1956.
14. J. H. McGuigan, "Combined Reading and Writing on a Magnetic Drum," *Proc. IRE* **41** (October 1953), pp. 1438-1444.
15. J. H. McGuigan and O. J. Murphy, U.S. Patent No. 2,723,312; filed September 15, 1954; issued November 8, 1955; J. H. McGuigan, O. J. Murphy, and N. D. Newby, U.S. Patent No. 2,700,148; filed December 16, 1950; issued January 18, 1955; W. A. Cornell, J. H. McGuigan, and O. J. Murphy, U. S. Patent No. 2,845,610; filed August 29, 1952; issued July 29, 1958.
16. See reference 15.
17. S. T. Brewer, U.S. Patent No. 2,668,195; filed December 29, 1949; issued February 2, 1954.
18. S. T. Brewer and E. Bruce, U.S. Patent No. 2,686,837; filed September 16, 1949; issued August 17, 1954.
19. W. A. Malthaner and H. E. Vaughan, U.S. Patent No. 2,951,908; filed August 5, 1957; issued September 16, 1960.
20. D. W. Hagelbarger, W. G. Hall, and W. A. Malthaner, U.S. Patent No. 3,242,470; filed August 21, 1962; issued March 22, 1966; Re-issue No. 26,919; filed August 21, 1962; issued June 23, 1970.
21. W. A. Malthaner and H. E. Vaughan, U.S. Patent No. 2,951,908; filed August 5, 1957; issued September 6, 1960; D. B. James, J. D. Johannesen, M. Karnaugh, and W. A. Malthaner, U.S. Patent No. 2,957,949; filed September 11, 1958; issued October 25,

1960; H. E. Vaughan, "Research Model for Time-Separation Integrated Communication," *Bell Syst. Tech. J.* **38** (July 1959), pp. 909-932; W. A. Malthaner, "ESSEX: A New Concept in Telephone Communications," *Bell Lab. Rec.* **39** (February 1961), pp. 43-47.

22. W. A. Malthaner and J. P. Runyon, "Controller for a Remote Line Concentrator in a Time-Separation Switching Experiment," *Bell Syst. Tech. J.* **39** (January 1960), pp. 59-86.

23. D. B. James and J. D. Johannesen, "Remote Line Concentrator for a Time-Separation Switching Equipment," *Bell Syst. Tech. J.* **39** (January 1960), pp. 31-57.

24. W. D. Lewis, U.S. Patent No. 2,936,337; filed January 9, 1957; issued May 10, 1960.

25. H. B. Haard and C. G. Svala, U.S. Patent No. 2,718,621; filed March 11, 1953; issued September 20, 1955.

26. D. B. James and H. E. Vaughan, "ESSEX—A Continuing Research Experiment in Time-Separation Communication," *Proc. Inst. Elec. Eng.* **107,** Part B, Supplement 20 (November 1960), pp. 330-335.

27. W. A. Malthaner, "Circuit Techniques in an All Solid-State Telephone Exchange," paper presented at *IRE Symp. Transistor Applications,* New York (April 28, 1962).

28. D. A. Aaronson and D. B. James, "Magnetostrictive Ultrasonic Delay-Lines for a PCM Communication System," *IRE Trans. Electron. Comput.* **EC-9** (September 1960), pp. 329-332.

29. M. R. Aaron, "PCM Transmission in the Exchange Plant," *Bell Syst. Tech. J.* **41** (January 1962), pp. 99-141.

30. H. Mann, H. M. Straube, and C. P. Villars, "A Companded Coder for an Experimental PCM Terminal," *Bell Syst. Tech. J.* **41** (January 1962), pp. 173-226.

31. J. P. Runyon and H. Inose, U.S. Patent No. 3,172,956; filed April 27, 1960; issued March 9, 1965.

32. H. Inose, "Blocking Probability and Junctor Efficiency of a Three-Stage Time-Division Switching Network," *Electron. Commun. Japan* **44** (June 1961), pp. 935-941.

33. J. R. Pierce, "Synchronizing Digital Networks," *Bell Syst. Tech. J.* **48** (March 1969), pp. 615-636.

34. H. S. McDonald, "An Experimental Digital Local System," *Proc. Int. Switching Symp.,* Munich (September 9-13, 1974), pp. 212/1-212/5.

35. H. G. Alles, J. H. Condon, W. C. Fischer, and H. S. McDonald, "Digital Signal Processing in Telephone Switching," *Proc. IEEE 1974 Int. Conf. Commun.,* Minneapolis, Minnesota (June 17-19, 1974), pp. 18E-1—18E-2.

36. J. H. Condon and H. T. Breece, III, "Low Cost Analog-Digital Interface for Telephone Switching," *Proc. IEEE 1974 Int. Conf. Commun.,* Minneapolis, Minnesota (June 17-19, 1974), pp. 13B-1—13B-4.

37. J. C. Lawson and K. G. Oza, "The Evaluation of Integrated Digital Switching and Transmission for Local Networks," *Proc. 2nd Int. Symp. Subscriber Loops Serv.,* London (May 3-7, 1976), pp. 158-162.

38. J. C. Lawson, W. D. Miller, G. P. McNamara, K. G. Oza, and G. Ryva, "The Impact of Potential New Telecommunications Services on the Structure of the Local Network," *Proc. Int. Symp. Subscriber Loops Serv.,* Atlanta, Georgia (March 20-24, 1978), pp. 116-120.

39. R. W. Lucky, "A Flexible Experimental Digital Switching Office," *Proc. IEEE 1978 Int. Sem. Digital Commun.,* Zurich, Switzerland (March 7-9, 1978), pp. A4.1-A4.4.

40. R. D. Gordon, H. G. Alles, and G. D. Bergland, "An Experimental Digital Switch for Data and Voice," *Proc. 1981 Int. Switching Symp.,* Montreal (September 21-25, 1981), pp. 21B-3-1—21B-3-7.

41. H. G. Alles, "An Intelligent Network Processor for a Digital Central Office," *Proc. IEEE 1978 Int. Sem. Digital Commun.,* Zurich, Switzerland (March 7-9, 1978), pp. A5.1-A5.6.

42. R. D. Gordon, "Providing Multiple-Channel Communication Using the Experimental Digital Switch," *IEEE Trans. Commun.* **COM-30** (June 1982), pp. 1409-1416.

43. R. A. Thompson, "Experimental Multiple-Channel Circuit-Switched Communications," *IEEE Trans. Commun.* **COM-30** (June 1982), pp. 1399-1409.

44. W. D. Farmer and E. E. Newhall, "An Experimental Distributed Switching System to Handle Bursty Computer Traffic," *Proc. ACM Symp. on Problems in Optimization of Data Commun. Syst.*, Pine Mountain, Georgia (October 13-16, 1969), pp. 1-33.

45. J. R. Pierce, "Network for Block Switching of Data," *Bell Syst. Tech. J.* **51** (July/August 1972), pp. 1133-1145.

46. C. H. Coker, "An Experimental Interconnection of Computers Through a Loop Transmission System," *Bell Syst. Tech. J.* **51** (July/August 1972), pp. 1167-1175.

47. D. R. Weller, "A Loop Communication System for I/O to a Small Multi-User Computer," *Proc. 5th Ann. IEEE Int. Comput. Soc. Conf.*, Boston (September 22-24, 1971), pp. 49-50.

48. A. G. Fraser, "SPIDER— An Experimental Data Communications System," *Proc. IEEE 1974 Int. Conf. Commun.*, Minneapolis, Minnesota (June 17-19, 1974), pp. 21F-1—21F-10.

Chapter 9

Computer Science

Bell Laboratories work on computers grew naturally out of the technologies of telephone switching (for digital computers) and transmission (for analog computers). Notable early achievements were the Complex Number Computer, a relay digital machine conceived in 1937, and the M-9 analog computer, used effectively for antiaircraft gun control during World War II. The invention of the transistor at Bell Laboratories in 1947 launched the solid-state revolution in device electronics that led directly to modern computers. As attention to software grew, Bell Laboratories people originated a series of languages and operating systems, including SNOBOL string manipulation language, the C programming language, and the UNIX* operating system. In other areas of computer science, contributions ranged from techniques for processing text and speech to new computer networking arrangements, combinatoric algorithms, and studies of computational complexity.

I. INTRODUCTION

Basically there are two varieties of modern computers, analog and digital, corresponding respectively to the much older slide rule and abacus. Analog computers deal with continuous information, such as real numbers and waveforms, while digital computers handle discrete information, such as letters and digits. An analog computer is limited to the approximate solution of mathematical problems for which a physical analog can be found, while a digital computer can carry out any precisely specified logical procedure on any symbolic information, and can, in principle, obtain numerical results to any desired accuracy at a very rapid speed. For these reasons, digital computers have become the focal point of modern computer science, although analog computing facilities remain of great importance, particularly for specialized applications.

It is no accident that Bell Labs was deeply involved with the origins of both analog and digital computers, since it was fundamentally concerned

---

Principal authors: W. S. Brown, B. D. Holbrook, and M. D. McIlroy.

* Trademark of AT&T Bell Laboratories.

351

with the principles and processes of electrical communication. Electrical analog computation is based on the classic technology of telephone transmission, and digital computation on that of telephone switching. Moreover, from its very inception, Bell Labs found itself with a rapidly growing load of design calculations, performed partly with slide rules but mainly with desk calculators. The magnitude of this load of tedious routine computation and the necessity of carefully checking it indicated a need for new methods. In 1928, a design department, heavily burdened with calculations on complex numbers, specifically asked the Mathematical Research Department to suggest possible improvements in computational methods. (See Chapter 1, section 1.1.) At that time, however, no useful suggestions could be made.

II. EXPEDIENTS FOR COMPUTING WITHOUT COMPUTERS

By 1928, the Bell Labs Accounting Department was making extensive use of punched-card equipment for cost accounting. This mechanical equipment was, from time to time, used by technical departments with extensive statistical jobs; in addition, members of the Mathematical Research Department made valiant efforts to use it for more purely mathematical problems, but with little success. The then-available logical capabilities of such calculators were too limited.

In some cases, the necessity of obtaining computed answers to important problems required technical departments to improvise special-purpose methods. In one example, described in an unpublished memorandum of November 1937, C. A. Lovell and L. E. Kittredge solved traffic-congestion problems for the first crossbar switching system by statistical simulation, or throwdown, as Monte Carlo experiments were then called. They used punched-card equipment for much of their work, but to handle the crucial link-matching phase of their job, they had to build a large mechanism that included two or more Monroe desk calculators and some moving belts whose motion was tied to the calculators. A number of clerks moved counters onto and off the belts and transferred numbers between counters and calculators. With this partly analog mechanism for a basically digital problem, Lovell and Kittredge provided the information required to engineer early crossbar systems.

The probability studies needed for initial engineering of the early multichannel telephone transmission systems provide a second example of special-purpose methods improvised to compute answers. The distribution of instantaneous voltages in the speech of individual channels was known, mainly by the use of sampling equipment developed by H. K. Dunn of the Bell Labs Acoustic Research Department. To obtain the distribution for multichannel speech as a function of the number of channels, B. D. Holbrook recorded telephone speech on high-quality phonograph records, and used simple electrical analog adders to combine the output of such records and rerecord the sum.[1] By repeating this process to obtain sufficient samples, and using the original sampling equipment to measure the distributions for various numbers of speakers, he made it possible to design economical multichannel amplifiers with adequate load-carrying capacity. His procedure, of course, amounted to the use of an analog computer, built of necessity out of components that were then readily available.

An early suggestion for doing arithmetic by electrical methods came from S. B. Wright and E. R. Taylor of the Development and Research Department of AT&T.[2] (This department became part of Bell Labs in 1934.) They were not at all concerned with computational problems, but rather with the mechanization of the control of transatlantic radiotelephone facilities. Here it was necessary to adjust the gain of certain sections of the transmission paths to ensure that the actual radio links were used at their maximum capacity, but without permitting overloading if either the speech volume or the noise level changed substantially; heretofore this had been done manually by technical operators observing suitable meters. Wright and Taylor's mechanism was basically an analog adder that used the algebraic sum of the route-mean-square values of several rapidly varying waveforms to effect the necessary control. It took some time for this idea to be widely used, and then it took rather a different form from the initial proposal; the delay was essentially because the invention was a bit ahead of the state of the art.

III. ELECTRICAL ANALOG COMPUTERS

Since useful analog computers could be built without modern electronic technology, they were in constant, though limited, use long before the digital computer. In many fields they were very valuable, for instance, in cases where mechanical models of continuously changing problems could be set up on a machine in scale-model form. Lord Kelvin's ball-and-disk integrator, for example, was the heart of "the great brass brain," a machine that predicted the tides for any port for which the tidal constituents were known—not merely the times and heights of high water, but also the depth of water at any and every instant for a year or more in advance.[3]

The potential for accurate electrical analog computers was enhanced by H. S. Black's invention of the feedback amplifier in 1927.[4] H. W. Bode subsequently developed mathematical methods for designing feedback amplifiers to specified tolerances. As a consequence, it became possible to design reliable vacuum-tube circuitry suitable for precision applications.[5] These developments also permitted the development of servomechanisms of comparable accuracy.

During the early 1930s, Vannevar Bush at the Massachusetts Institute of Technology (MIT) greatly increased the flexibility of the analog computer by applying electrical control and drive equipment; the computation itself was still based on an improved mechanical integrator. At about the same time, comparable mechanical analog computers, with electrical follow-up servos, were beginning to be used by the United States Army and Navy, particularly the latter. These computers notably improved the performance of their medium and heavy guns.

Bell Labs scientists and engineers made some use of the Bush equipment, and also built some small analog computers for special purposes. One was an isograph,[6,7] a mechanical, two-dimensional analog of the one-dimensional harmonic synthesizer invented around the turn of the century by A. A. Michelson and S. W. Stratton. It was designed to find the complex roots of polynomials, a necessary step in the design of many types of filters and networks. The isograph did its job, but not well enough to compete successfully with desk calculators. During World War II, it was given to Princeton University for instructional use but became a victim of wartime scheduling difficulties. It was shipped by rail to Princeton and left overnight on a railway platform without a protective cover. During the night a heavy rain fell; rust made the isograph no longer a precision instrument.

3.1 Analog Computers for Military Applications

The pressing need for better control of antiaircraft guns led—just before this country entered World War II—to the development by Bell Labs of a pioneering electrical analog computer, conceived in 1940 by D. B. Parkinson and Lovell. This computer used shaped wire-wound potentiometers and vacuum-tube amplifiers to perform standard arithmetic operations; it led directly to the M-9 gun director, which became the Army's mainstay for fire control of heavy antiaircraft guns.[8] The first production M-9 was delivered to the Army on December 23, 1942, and others followed rapidly. These gun directors did yeoman service on many fronts; their finest achievements were against the German V-1 buzz bombs during the Second Battle of Britain. During the month of August 1944, over 90 percent of the buzz bombs aimed at London were shot down over the cliffs of Dover; in a single week in August, the Germans launched 91 V-1s from the Antwerp area, and heavy guns controlled by M-9s destroyed 89 of them.

A number of other fire-control computers for antiaircraft guns and one for control of coast-defense artillery were built during the war. While none of these computers was placed in regular operation, their development led to further advances in the technology of electrical analog computers. A more detailed account is given in the second volume in this series, *National Service in War and Peace (1925-1975)*, Chapter 3.

3.2 Analog Computers for Solving Mathematical Problems

All of these military analog computers were designed to perform elaborate, but very specific, computing tasks. After the war, a need was felt for computers that could solve a variety of mathematical problems, particularly those beyond the capabilities of the first relay computers. To find a way of solving the growing number of problems not amenable to other methods of computation, Bell Labs engineers, like other members of the technical community, soon turned to the computer. In addition to relay computers, they developed a general-purpose analog computer (GPAC).[9] Nicknamed Gypsy, the computer was designed by E. Lakatos of the Mathematical Research Department. [Fig. 9-1] Many leftover parts from uncompleted wartime computers were used to construct it.

Like the military analog computers, the Gypsy computer used electronic circuits to perform addition, subtraction, multiplication, division, integration, and differentiation. Unlike the military computers, its circuit configurations were readily changed from problem to problem, which made it much more flexible to use. Its normal output mechanism was a precise electrically driven plotting board developed in connection with wartime gun-director work. Although its accuracy was only in the range of 0.1 to 1 percent, this was adequate for many engineering applications, especially

Fig. 9-1. R. W. Hamming setting up a problem on the general-purpose analog computer, Gypsy, which was designed by E. Lakatos and placed in service in 1949. Gypsy was relatively easy to change from problem to problem; output normally appeared on an electrically driven plotting board.

since some of the problems that Gypsy was able to solve, such as nonlinear differential equations for relay design, were otherwise so extremely laborious to handle that without such a computer only very rough approximations were available.

The first Gypsy was placed in service in 1949 and proved so useful that a duplicate was built a few years later. The two machines were arranged so that they could be used independently for small problems and could be coupled together for large ones. In 1960, they were replaced with a more modern commercial analog computer; the Gypsies were given to the Polytechnic Institute of Brooklyn for educational use.

IV. DIGITAL COMPUTERS

The history of large-scale digital circuitry in the Bell System may conveniently be dated from E. C. Molina's 1906 invention of the relay translator to automatically convert phone numbers into routing instructions; this invention triggered the development of the panel dial telephone switching system.[10] Engineers learned how to use relays to handle all kinds of duties that had previously required the attention of an operator, and, by about 1930, the design of relay circuits had become a sophisticated art. It was, however, an art difficult to teach to novices. But, in 1937, C. E. Shannon, then a student at MIT, showed how to use Boolean algebra for the synthesis, analysis, and optimization of relay circuits. Shannon's discovery raised the art to a science that could be taught as a straightforward engineering discipline,[11] because it provided a set of mathematical tools for dealing with binary logical states (i.e., "true" and "false") in terms that are equivalent to the "open" and "closed" states of a switch or relay.

4.1 The Complex Number Computer

In 1937, G. R. Stibitz [Fig. 9-2], a Bell Labs research mathematician, was well aware of the growing need for improvements in numerical computation and also of the logical capabilities of relay circuits. Since he saw both the need and a practicable means of satisfying it, he proceeded to sketch out a preliminary design for the first binary relay calculator. His initial plan consisted of a machine that worked internally in the binary system, with decimal input either from a keyboard or teletypewriter paper tape, and decimal output either on paper tape or a teleprinter. Relay circuitry would take care of binary-decimal conversion in either direction. His plan also provided for internal memory (relay registers) and for teletypewriter tape facilities to handle programs and subroutines and to provide additional external memory. The machine would be constructed from existing telephone components: relays, sequence switches, and standard teletypewriter equipment. A careful examination of the possible uses of such a machine

Fig. 9-2. Inventor G. R. Stibitz in the early 1940s. The Bell Laboratories Model I computer, conceived by Stibitz in 1937, was in continuous service from 1940 to 1949. [Tropp, *IEEE Spectrum* **11** (1974): 70.]

resulted in a decision to build first a smaller and simpler machine that would try out most of the essential features; the resulting experience would be of great value in the design of a second and more elaborate machine.

At the time Stibitz was working on his computer, there was a great need for improvements in means for accurately performing standard arithmetic operations on complex numbers. Three computing groups at Bell Labs were spending a large proportion of their time doing such calculations on desk calculators, a job that could be handled by a relatively simple machine of the type envisioned by Stibitz. This machine was designed by Stibitz, and engineered and constructed during 1938 and 1939 under the direction of S. B. Williams, an experienced relay-system design engineer, together with E. G. Andrews.[12,13] Because of the time needed for relay circuitry to do extensive binary-decimal conversion for input and output, Stibitz revised his initial proposal in favor of operating throughout on a binary-coded decimal basis, using four relays per decimal digit.

The computer consisted of a standard relay rack, on which 450 relays and ten crossbar switches were mounted. There were two separate calculator units, one to handle the real parts of complex numbers, the other for the imaginary parts. Input and output could handle numbers of up to eight decimal digits, with two extra internal digits to minimize round-off errors. The computer itself was locked up in a large closet, which was opened only for maintenance. Its users were provided with three operator stations, each with a keyboard for input and a standard teletypewriter for output. The keyboards controlled the complex-number arithmetic operations to be performed. The multiplication and division keys invoked what would later be called hardware subroutines of about a dozen steps.

The three operator stations were installed on different floors of the Bell Labs building on West Street in New York City, each close to one of the three groups expected to make the most use of the computer. [Fig. 9-3] Although the complex computer was not time-shared, these multiple operator stations presaged a style of computer access that would not become common for another quarter of a century.

The machine was completed in October 1939, and, after thorough testing for performance in actual operation, it was placed in routine service on January 8, 1940. It remained in service until 1949, continuously performing

Fig. 9-3.   One of three operator stations for the Model I, also known as the complex number computer. [Tropp, *IEEE Spectrum* **11** (1974): 70.]

accurate and rapid calculations. During World War II, the great increase in the work load of the network design groups, its principal users, kept it almost continuously busy from 8:00 AM to 9:00 PM, six days a week. Since the machine had been built as a demonstration model before the war, it was not equipped with many of the self-checking and contact-protection facilities that were standard in dial-control central offices; and the war prevented design and construction of the second and more elaborate machine that was initially envisioned. As a result, it became necessary, late in the war, to take it out of service for two days, while special mainte-nance tools (developed by Western Electric for the relief of central offices with similar complaints) were used to strip the badly worn contacts from the computer's relays and replace them with new metal.

Thus, Stibitz's original complex number computer, later known as the Model I, remained in service for over nine years, until replaced by the Model VI. It was the first electric digital computer to be placed in routine operation for general use, and the first with either remote or multistation terminal facilities.

The complex computer was demonstrated on September 11, 1940, before a meeting of the American Mathematical Society at Hanover, New Hamp-shire, where its operation was observed by Professor N. Wiener of MIT among others. One of the operator consoles from the West Street building, modified to communicate with the computer over a standard long-distance teletypewriter circuit instead of the multiconductor cable used locally, was installed in the lecture room at Hanover, and members of the audience were invited to use the keyboard to give the computer problems involving addition, subtraction, multiplication, or division of complex numbers.[14] The circuits transmitted the input to the computer's relay equipment in New York and the results back to the Hanover teletypewriter; the answers returned in less than a minute. This remote-control operation, not to be duplicated anywhere for ten years, foreshadowed the use of telephone and radio circuits for computer data transmission. This became commercially important in the mid-1960s and thereafter showed almost explosive growth.

4.2 Relay Digital Computers in World War II

The successful development of electrical analog computers for gunfire-control purposes triggered a demand for a great deal of highly routine computation. Initially, this computation was used in the performance tests of gunfire-control equipment as the equipment came off the production line, and later in the investigation of the effects of new enemy tactics on the behavior of available equipment and the value of possible design modifications as countermeasures. The required computing was almost always within the scope of desk calculators, but the load was immediately seen to be much greater than could be handled with available personnel,

COMPUTER
TABLE NO. 1

KEY AND
LAMP PANEL

REGISTER FRAMES

MASTER CONTROL FRAME

CALCULATOR FRAMES

FRAME EQUIPMENT WITH COVERS REMOVED

Fig. 9-4.   Model III relay computer. This ballistic computer was completed in June 1944 and served defense needs until 1958.

equipment, and methods of system organization. The digital techniques provided by Stibitz and Williams were therefore applied, and, as a result, Bell Labs engineers developed three additional digital relay computers during the war.[15] These were designed as special-purpose machines to meet very specific needs, but turned out to be sufficiently flexible to handle many other types of problems. These machines are described in more detail in *National Service in War and Peace (1925-1975)*, Chapter 3.

All three of these computers used punched paper tape for data input and output, and also for program input. Frequently used subroutines were punched on looped tapes so that they could be called from the main program as needed. The Model II relay computer contained 440 relays and five teletypewriter machines. It was designed to perform linear iterative operations on numbers obtained from an input data tape. The Model III [Fig. 9-4] and Model IV relay machines were designed for Army and Navy use, respectively, and were much larger and more powerful than the Model II. Each contained about 1400 relays, ten storage registers, and seven teletypewriter machines. All three machines had the standard dial-system features needed for reliability and maintainability.

The Model II machine was placed in service in September 1943, the Model III in June 1944, and the Model IV in March 1945. All of them operated regularly seven days and nights a week, usually unattended, and together they did the work of at least 100 desk calculators. All were later modified to extend their capabilities, and they remained in service for 13 to 15 years after the war—several years after much faster commercial electronic computers were readily available.

4.3 Model V Relay Computers

In 1946, Bell Labs delivered a Model V relay computer to the National Advisory Committee for Aeronautics (NACA) at Langley Field, Virginia.[16] [Fig. 9-5] In the following year, a duplicate Model V was delivered to the Army's Ballistic Research Laboratory at Aberdeen, Maryland. Each used about 9000 relays. The machines were, to use modern terminology, multiprocessors with multiple access and hardware scheduling. Designed to accommodate a maximum of six processors, each was actually built with two. One of the machines had three problem positions; the other had four. While a machine was in continuous operation, a new problem could be loaded on an unused position and be picked up automatically when a processor was free to handle it. Each of the problem positions had a tape

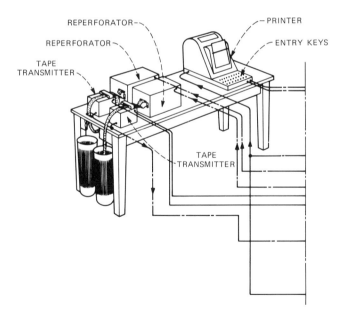

Fig. 9-5. Principle of control used in Model V computers, from Stibitz's US Patent 2,666,579. Of the two tape transmitters on the table, the one at left is reading a continuous loop of paper tape. In the tape transmitter at right, the tape contains additional instructions, data, and blank spaces for recording intermediate results.

reader for input data, as many as five readers for programs, and up to six readers for tabular data. As in the wartime machines, subroutines were punched on looped tape so that they could be repeatedly called from the main program as needed, and the tape devices for intermediate or tabular data were arranged to permit both forward and backward searching to find required locations in storage as rapidly as possible. Such searching could go on independently of calculation.

Since processing was handled on telephone relays, with operating times measured in milliseconds, there was excellent speed-matching between internal operations, storage, and input and output facilities. The machines were almost completely self-checking; if a single failure occurred, the computer stopped, sounded an alarm, and gave the maintenance personnel useful and fairly detailed information as to where to look for the trouble. Among the novel features introduced in the Model V computers were the capability of recognizing most indeterminate operations, the capability of rounding off digits, and the provision for elaborate discriminatory controls (which came to be called conditional calculations).

Each Model V could handle a load equivalent to 200 to 250 desk calculators, and since they worked essentially around the clock, they competed successfully for some years with the early electronic computers. The machines often ran completely unattended for long periods; there were a good many weeks when one or the other computer worked 167 out of a possible 168 hours, a record seldom equaled in the next 25 years. When their self-checking circuitry stopped them, their diagnostic facilities permitted minor repairs or adjustments to be made very quickly.

After years of service at Aberdeen, one of the Model V computers was transferred to Fort Bliss, Texas. This machine was later given to New Mexico State University at Las Cruces for educational and research programs, and remained in service at least until 1965.

4.4 Model VI Relay Computer

Experience with the Model I computer and its successors—particularly the versatile Model V machines—led Bell Labs engineers to design the Model VI computer for internal use in a variety of research and development applications.[17] [Fig. 9-6] It went into regular use in November 1950, after extensive testing, and provided far better computing facilities than the Model I. A somewhat simplified version of the Model V, the Model VI had only a single processor and a smaller number of problem positions. However, it had new and interesting features of its own, notably fast internal storage for several hundred semipermanent subroutines. The read-only memory for these subroutines was a Dimond-ring translator, invented by T. L. Dimond and used in the No. 5 crossbar dial system to provide rapid conversion from the code describing the mainframe location of a

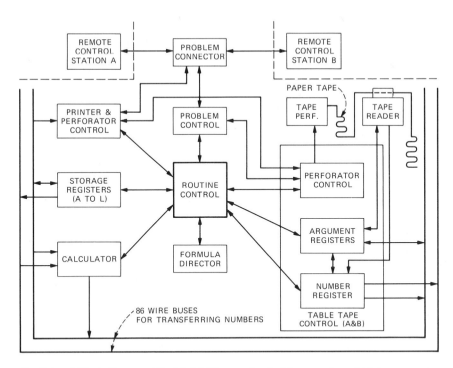

Fig. 9-6. A block diagram of the Model VI computer. In this computer, which began service at Bell Laboratories in 1950, the problem connector (middle top) responded to a tape at a remote station by delegating control to the routine control (center), which directed the actions of the other elements of the system. The formula director (lower middle) held up to 200 subroutines. [Andrews, *Elec. Eng.* **68** (1949): 753.]

calling line to the caller's number as listed in the telephone directory.[18] This translator consisted of about 80 air-core coils, each of which would trigger an associated gas tube when a suitable current pulse flowed in any one of the wires threading that particular coil. In the computer application, a subroutine was programmed in by threading a wire loosely from a numbered pulse terminal through an appropriate subset of the available coils to a common return terminal. This library of subroutines operated at six levels of precedence. The highest level was called by an order punched on a program tape, and each level could call in sequence several subroutines at lower levels. The bottom level, of course, consisted of the basic instructions built into the hardware of the machine. These extremely flexible subprogramming facilities avoided the cumbersome tape handling required in the earlier Bell Labs relay computers, and thus made program preparation for the Model VI a great deal easier.

The Model VI also had a second-trial feature, which operated automatically when the control circuit failed to receive the usual signal indicating satisfactory execution of the instruction or operation called for. Experience on previous relay computers had shown that a sizable proportion of machine stoppages resulting from relay-contact troubles would clear themselves when the relay at fault operated again. This automatic second trial proved effective in permitting much longer periods of uninterrupted computer operation. In addition, if the machine was operating unattended and the second trial failed, the problem was abandoned, and the master tape searched for the beginning of the next problem, which was then loaded. When work was available, it was customary to load the machine late every afternoon with enough problems to keep it busy until morning; on Friday afternoons enough could be loaded to occupy it until Monday morning. In these circumstances, the machine was started, the room lights turned off, and the door locked. Sometimes one or two of the problems would be found abandoned in the morning, but they could then be rerun, perhaps after some maintenance.

Models V and VI represented the high point of the relay-computer art; their successors almost all used electronic rather than electromagnetic apparatus to permit higher speed. The Bell Labs machines were equipped with very dependable heavy-duty relays perfected for telephone-switching applications; the use of such relays, together with the provision of extensive self-checking features, resulted in high availability and high accuracy. In fact, during their entire working lives, only two errors due to machine failures were reported from all three Model V and VI machines. Their operating times were, however, quite slow—it took about a second to perform a multiplication, 2.7 seconds for division, 4.5 seconds for a square root, and as much as 15 seconds to calculate a logarithm. But reliability and accuracy were the main objectives, not speed. And the reliability of these plodding, meticulous computers was truly remarkable.

The Model VI remained in service at Bell Labs in Murray Hill, New Jersey until 1956, when it was replaced by a much faster commercial electronic computer. It was then given to the Polytechnic Institute of Brooklyn, where it was used for both instructional and research purposes. There it operated reliably and with negligible difficulty until March 1960, when it was finally given to the University of Bihar in India.

4.5 Relay Computers for Telephone Accounting

The successful and reliable operation of the Model I through Model V relay computers was influential in determining the course of development of the accounting center equipment for automatic telephone message accounting. This system mechanized most of the operations involved in billing telephone subscribers. The information needed for billing was collected automatically (initially only in the local dial central offices; after about 1953, also in tandem or toll offices). Then, from this data, the billing was assigned to the correct customer, printed out, and delivered.

The first such accounting center was opened in 1948, coincident with the cutover of the first No. 5 crossbar office, which was equipped for this type of operation.[19] Early accounting centers depended heavily on re-punching paper tape for much of their operation, but relay computers were used for doing the necessary arithmetic. Later, improved assembler-computers were installed that used relay-computer technology for sorting calls by customer's numbers as well as for the arithmetic needed for determining charges. About a hundred of the combined assembler-computers were built, and together with their simpler predecessors, they provided reliable and accurate billing facilities until the relay-computer accounting center facilities were gradually replaced (mostly in the 1960s) by electronic computers of standard commercial types. These accounting centers represented by far the major application of relay-computer techniques in this country.

To wrap up the story of relay digital computing techniques, we note that the type of traffic problem investigated for the No. 1 crossbar system by Lovell and Kittredge in the mid-1930s was, 15 years later, handled for the No. 5 crossbar by G. R. Frost, W. Keister, and A. E. Ritchie, who built for this purpose a specialized relay computer.[20] This essentially used relay circuitry to do what Lovell and Kittredge had done by punched-card methods, but it is interesting to note that it was still necessary to use human operators to handle the link-matching job.

4.6 From Relays to Electronics

The relay computers were soon eclipsed by electronics. Vacuum tubes, used first in the Electronic Numerical Integrator and Calculator (ENIAC), built for the Aberdeen Proving Ground under the direction of J. W. Mauchly and J. P. Eckert of the University of Pennsylvania Moore School of Electrical Engineering, operated faster than, if not as reliably as, relays.[21] The decade of relay computers had started the computer revolution, but electronics pointed the way to the future. Vacuum-tube computers would hold sway for another decade until the maturation of the transistor opened the limitless vistas of modern computers.

V. THE TRANSISTOR REVOLUTION

The great size and heavy power drain of vacuum-tube digital computers like ENIAC and its immediate successors could have severely limited their growth in complexity and efficiency. As it happened, the expanding computer art paralleled an equally dramatic growth in solid-state technology in the early 1950s. This trend first became evident in the growing use of solid-state passive devices for doing many of the necessary internal operations in a computer: bistable magnetic cores for fast, compact, relatively cheap, random-access memory, and crystal diodes for handling most of the detailed logical operations needed in calculation and control. Two of the most-used diode logic circuits, the AND gate[22] and the OR gate,[23] had been invented by W. H. T. Holden and A. W. Horton at Bell Labs in connection with exploratory work on new dial-switching techniques. The magnetic core and the diode still required use of vacuum-tube pulse amplifiers to restore signal levels, but the total number of vacuum tubes was greatly reduced, together with the power requirements and the physical size of the tubes. As a result, computers became smaller while their performance became substantially better. The commercial computers of the latter 1950s were typically based on this use of solid-state logic with vacuum-tube amplification.

In late 1947, J. Bardeen, W. H. Brattain, and W. Shockley at Bell Labs invented the transistor. (See another volume in this series, *Physical Sciences (1925-1980)*, Chapter 2.) Just as vacuum-tube technology had ended the day of the relay computer, this discovery foreshadowed the end of vacuum tubes in digital computers. The new technology took over a decade to come to fruition—it was first necessary to learn how to manufacture reliable transistors in adequate quantities and to suitable specifications. Nevertheless, the transistor made possible the all-solid-state computers of the 1960s.

Probably the first use of transistor circuits in digital computers were those in a transistor gating matrix built by W. H. MacWilliams, Jr., in 1949 as a small part of a simulated-warfare computer.[24] Two general-purpose, all-solid-state digital computers, Transistor Digital Computer (TRADIC) and the more advanced model called Leprechaun, as well as a large special-purpose machine for a Naval gunfire-control system, were developed at Bell Labs between 1952 and 1959. These and other defense-related computer projects are described in *National Service in War and Peace (1925-1975)*, Chapters 10, 11, and 13.

With the advent of electronic computers in the commercial marketplace, Bell Labs engineers ceased to design machines for routine engineering, commercial, or scientific computation, but continued to be involved in the design of computers for special purposes, notably telephone switching, where extraordinary reliability was required, and military command and control, where the processing of input data at high speed was crucial.

VI. THE GROWTH OF COMPUTATION AND THE RISE OF THE UNIX OPERATING SYSTEM

As we have seen, engineers' work required a sizable supporting effort in computation. In the early 1950s, more than 60 people were employed full time doing engineering calculations. These workers were usually female and well trained in mathematics but not engineering. When they began using computers, their classification changed from computress to the more esteemed title of programmer.

Computing expertise diffused throughout the company wherever it was needed. This arrangement, which differed markedly from what evolved in most commercial establishments, and even in some other research labs, sprang directly from the historically collaborative environment of Bell Labs. It derived also from the fact that computing began under the auspices of research personnel, who wished to transfer operations responsibilities to others as quickly as possible.

6.1 Commercial Computers for Bell System Needs—Bell Operating System (BESYS)

Through the 1950s, a succession of commercial computers went into use at Bell Labs. The IBM Card Programmed Calculator (CPC), installed in 1952, was in logical terms far less sophisticated than the relay computers, but did arithmetic at electronic speed. It did floating-point operations about as fast as a modern hand-held calculator, had no subroutines, and performed loops only by manual transfer of program cards from the stacker to the feed. The IBM 650 (1955) was internally programmed, with a magnetic drum for main memory. The IBM 704 (1958) had magnetic core memory and magnetic tape input-output. An open shop for scientific computing, available to all comers, evolved around these machines. R. W. Hamming's epigrams, "It is better to do the right problem the wrong way than to do the wrong problem the right way," and "The purpose of computing is insight, not numbers," which stressed the role of computing as a servant to science, gained universal assent.[25]

Implicit in the widespread use of computers was the need to make programming a manageable task, and to make operation effective: it would not do to dissipate hours of machine time on set up and debugging for computer runs that needed only minutes of computer time. Programming the relay computer or the CPC had not been too different from operating a hand calculator, except that one had to plan ahead. Subsequent computers, though, were stored-program binary machines, where the hardware was not prepared to respond directly to a series of arithmetic instructions on decimal data. For the IBM 650, V. M. Wolontis and D. C. Leagus devised L1, a higher level language that handled floating point, looping, indexing, and storage allocation for variables.[26] L1 and its successor, L2, became the workhorses for scientific computation throughout the life of the 650 at Bell Labs. [Fig. 9-7] They set the research tradition of system programming at Bell Labs, which has consistently sought simultaneously to simplify and to generalize the methodologies of computing.

Calculate $S_j = \sum_{i=1}^{10} a_{ji} x_i$ for $j = 1,2,3,4,5$.

		A	B	C
	SETA	-	q	a
	SETC	-	r	s
p:	MOVE	-	0	t
q:	MPY	[]	x	0
	ADD	0	t	t
	LOOPAB	-	10	q
r:	MOVE	-	t	[]
	ADDA	-	q	10
	ADDC	-	r	1
	TRC	r	s+5	p

The meanings of selected instructions are:

SETA	Set the A-address at the instruction in location q to a.
MPY	Multiply the quantity in the location designed by the supplied A-address by the quantity in location x.
LOOPAB	Go to location q until 10 repetitions are complete, and at each repetition add the repeat count to A- and B-addresses that denote locations.
ADDA	Add 10 to the A-address in location q.
TRC	Transfer to location p if the C address in location r is less than s+5.

Before a program could be punched into cards for the computer to read, it had to be translated into numbers because the computer could not read letters. The instruction code translated into a sign and one digit, plus a possible extension into an unused A-address. With the example program in locations 101-110, t in 400, $s_1, ..., s_5$ in 701-705, $a_{11}, a_{12}, ..., a_{21}, ...$ in 811, 812, ..., 821, and $x_1, ..., x_{10}$ in 901-910, the program becomes:

+	0	500	104	811
+	0	005	107	701
+	9	000	500	400
-	3	000	901	000
+	1	000	400	400
+	0	110	010	104
+	9	000	400	000
+	0	600	104	010
+	0	006	107	001
+	8	107	706	103

Fig. 9-7.   Example of a calculation in L1, known outside Bell Laboratories as the Bell 1 interpreter. A, B, and C are addresses; p, q, and r are locations. More than half of all IBM 650s operated under L1 or its successor, L2. [Wolontis, *A Complete Floating-Decimal Interpretive System for the IBM 650 Magnetic Drum Calculator* (1956): 21.]

L1 and the 650s served Bell Labs scientists and engineers well for several years. The operating procedures were straightforward: a user's program and data were keypunched and proofread, then the card deck, preceded by an interpreter, was read into the computer, and the output appeared at the other end of the machine, also punched into cards. The output deck was then printed for the user on a tabulator. If errors were suspected, a program could be run in tracing mode to obtain a complete listing of executed instructions. Clean decks were run by an operator without the user being present. During the last year of use of the 650s, the machines ran almost around the clock; on each of the second and third shifts, one operator ran two machines with no trouble.

Released outside Bell Labs, L1 became known as the Bell 1 interpreter. It was soon joined by the L2, or Bell 2 interpreter, by Hamming and R. A. Weiss. Eventually more than half of the IBM 650s in the world operated under one or the other. Reimplemented for other hardware, Bell interpreters survived at some non-Bell installations well into the 1960s, to become perhaps the first instance of a successful language being sustained in the name of compatibility far beyond its rational life span.

When the main computer at Bell Labs was replaced by an IBM 704, the monumental new language FORTRAN (Formula Translation) was to be the principal programming vehicle, but no effective way to run small jobs was available. This need was met by G. H. Mealy and G. J. Hansen, who, in the months prior to delivery, constructed a computer operating system that would run jobs sequentially on-line or off-line, off-line input and output being mediated by magnetic tape. Neither the first nor the last operating system for the 704, the Mealy-Hansen system, known as the Bell Operating System (BESYS), was one of the more influential and longest-lived. Mealy's control-card scheme, modeled after the Share Assembly Program (SAP), proved to be easily augmented to keep abreast of changing hardware facilities. The resident monitor program included a control card interpreter, a loader, and input-output routines. Nonresident code kept on a magnetic tape included the FORTRAN compiler, the SAP assembler, and a back-up copy of the monitor. Much of the code had been obtained from IBM or the Share users' group, but all components had to be modified substantially to work together under operating system control. The effectiveness of that control is told by the normal picture of computer operation; users seldom approached the machine, and the console operator had little to do but punch a time clock—computers did not then have their own—at the beginning and end of jobs, which typically lasted about a minute.

By 1960, several hundred people were regularly involved in scientific computation. Though computing represented less than five percent of the company budget at that time, Hamming predicted that one day half the resources of Bell Labs would go into computers and people directly involved with them. Few listeners, if any, believed such hyperbole, but time proved him right some 20 years later.

With the steady spread of expertise, and the increasing dependence of already confirmed users upon computers, computing capacity grew exponentially with a doubling time of less than two years. Innovations in BESYS kept pace. BESYS2, which followed very soon upon the installation of the 704, incorporated FORTRAN II. BESYS3 through BESYS7 for the IBM 7090 and 7094, largely the work of R. E. Drummond and Hansen, provided memory protection, source language debugging, and a blocked-and-buffered input-output system that integrated magnetic tape, unit-record equipment, and permanent files on disk store. Although it is difficult to assign priority to advances in that era of rapid evolution and free interchange among programmers nationwide, certainly Bell Labs was at the forefront of operating system technology. The combination of features just mentioned was in place a year or two ahead of comparable software from the manufacturer. And BESYS innovations were worked out with a degree of coherence and simplicity that was unrivaled at the time and that was still far from universal in the industry two decades later.

Users and creators of BESYS worked on the same computer using the same software. To help the most people get the most work out of a computing system, the creators consistently strove to build a simple, intelligible extended machine. So well did they succeed that users seldom had to become aware of mechanisms that were employed for efficiency, but which played no role in problem specification.

Between creators and users a lively dialogue developed. Many computing innovations originated with the clients, among the more influential of whom were users from the Visual and Acoustics Research Center led by E. E. David. Their speech-processing work stretched the normal limits of scientific computing. Attaching an amplifier to one bit of the central processor, they were able to generate tones on line. When one day the computer began suddenly to repeat aloud, "Help, I'm caught in a loop," in the Texas drawl of J. L. Kelly, Jr., all work stopped in the computer center as operators and programmers gathered around in amazement. (The use of computers in acoustical research is more fully treated in Chapter 2 of this volume.) Acoustics researchers often suffered a wearisome cycle of interaction with the computer: acoustic recording, analog-to-digital conversion, computer processing, digital-to-analog conversion, and finally audio playback, plus carrying of magnetic tapes among pieces of equipment located all over Murray Hill. To shorten the cycle Kelly, H. S. McDonald, and E. N. Pinson connected a small Packard-Bell 250 computer that controlled audio and graphical equipment directly to the IBM 7094 machine. This foreshadowed a coming era when dedicated "intelligent" peripherals to control experiments to gather data, prepare computer jobs, and display results would appear in departmental laboratories all over Bell Labs. Through such experiments minicomputers gained a foothold among the growing stable of mainframes.[27] They were an ingredient in the ferment that fostered the UNIX operating system.

6.2 From BESYS to the UNIX System and Tool Building

Time-sharing, promoted at MIT by J. McCarthy and pioneered there by F. Corbato in the Compatible Time-Sharing Service (CTSS), carried open-shop computing another step.[28] In time-sharing, the services of a large computer rotated among several users, each with his/her own teletypewriter terminal. With the disparity between electronic and human speeds absorbed by somebody else's computing, each person could be afforded direct interaction with the expensive computer.

In 1964, Bell Laboratories joined with MIT and General Electric to create a successor to both BESYS and CTSS. Envisioned as an information utility, the new MULTICS (Multiplexed Information and Computing Service) system centered on a radically organized file system, in which segments of information were to be linked into the address space of each computing process as needed. (The term process, coined for MULTICS by V. A. Vyssotsky, has since become a standard term of art.) Segments were collected in logical groupings into directories, which were themselves segments, and so on hierarchically. A hierarchical system of access permissions allowed users to collaborate, maintain complete privacy, or share information to varying degrees. Data files, traditionally accessed piecemeal by input-output operations, would be directly addressable within a program's address space. Programming distinctions between main and secondary memory had to disappear; this consolidation was accomplished by adopting an operating algorithm called paged virtual memory, originally invented for the ATLAS (Automated Testing and Load Analysis System) computers at the University of Manchester, England.[29] Data segments, which had to grow independently of each other, constituted a second dimension above and beyond the usual linearly addressed computer memory. The operating system was a collection of program segments linked like any other segments into the address space of each running process. Conceptually no different from user code, system routines were written in the same principal programming language PL/I and called just like any other subroutines. The extra privileges necessary for system code were obtained by a mechanism of protection rings whereby access rights differed among code segments.[30]

Arising as it did in a large project that telescoped research and development from several disparate organizations, MULTICS eventually turned out to be a somewhat heavy product, from which Bell Labs dissociated itself in 1969 after four years' work. Nevertheless, MULTICS caught the imagination of the computing community and exerted enormous influence. Virtual memory, segmented address spaces, and hierarchical file systems became commonplace in the industry. MULTICS survived as a product of Compagnie Bull in France. And Bell Labs participants in the MULTICS project went on to conceive the UNIX System.

Upon the abandonment of MULTICS, K. Thompson [Fig. 9-8], like everybody else involved, was thrown back on his own resources. The conventional time-sharing system then deployed in the computer center did not live up to his conception of an ideal environment for program development. He envisioned a far less rigid model of a computing job, and far fewer special arrangements to cater to jobs of different preconceived categories. He envisioned, too, a simpler file system abstracted from the hierarchical file system of MULTICS. In fact, a paper design for such a file system had emerged from discussions with D. M. Ritchie and R. H. Canaday. Accordingly, he seized on a disused Digital Equipment Corporation PDP*7 and proceeded to construct a simple but powerful computing environment to his own taste from the ground up. The goal was to enable the easy combination of programs and the easy use of programs to build larger programs. This operating system, christened UNIX in a

Fig. 9-8.   K. Thompson, who, in 1969, devised a computing environment, christened the UNIX system, complete with file system, multiple processes, and time-sharing between two users.

---

* Trademark of Digital Equipment Corporation.

reaction to the gigantism of MULTICS, became fully self-supporting in just a few months of 1969, complete with a file system, multiple processes, and even time-sharing between two users. The minuscule PDP7 (8K 18-bit words of main memory and 256K words of disk memory) became a home not only for the graphics applications for which it had originally been intended, but also for major software work. No fewer than three compilers for radically different languages were constructed there during its brief life.

Overcoming management reluctance to risk extensive operating system research so soon after the demise of MULTICS, Thompson, J. F. Ossanna, Jr., and D. M. Ritchie were able to obtain better, but still small, equipment to expand the UNIX system from an experiment into a vehicle for serious software research. Ritchie collaborated with Thompson on the operating system proper; many others contributed novel software.[31,32]

Visitors flocked to the attic room where the UNIX system machines were housed. Because the UNIX system was the first, and also the most capable, operating system then running on the popular Digital Equipment Corporation PDP11 minicomputer family, other projects in Bell Labs, the Bell System, and universities adopted it straight from the laboratory. By 1972, UNIX systems were doing word processing in the patent division and work scheduling in the AT&T Long Lines test room in Charlotte, South Carolina, and handling trouble-reports for No. 5 crossbar systems in the Pacific Telephone and Telegraph Company.[33] None of these applications took more than three months to develop and install. The burden of supporting the UNIX system in the Bell System was assumed by development groups in 1973, and external licensing under Western Electric auspices began in 1975. By the early 1980s, UNIX systems had become ubiquitous, running in the Bell System and throughout the world on thousands of machines from dozens of manufacturers ranging in size from mainframes to microcomputers.

The success of the UNIX systems stemmed directly from the original purpose: to be a flexible, productive home for software experimentation and development within which programs work smoothly together. Among the key design principles that achieve the purpose, all manifest by 1972, were (1) a single, undifferentiated file format that allowed most programs to use most data; (2) pipes, conceived by M. D. McIlroy, that made programs easy to combine by connecting the output of one directly to the input of another running simultaneously; (3) device-independent input-output that worked identically with files, pipes, terminals, or any other peripheral equipment; (4) a homogeneous, extensible file system with a simple permission mechanism that rationalized access to data and programs; (5) an aliasing technique patented by D. M. Ritchie that allowed one user's permissions to be extended to selected programs working on behalf of other users;[34] and (6) a control program, called the shell, that started other programs and connected them to input-output destinations at users' requests. [Fig. 9-9] The shell, although seen by most users as the gateway to the UNIX system, occupied no privileged position; any program could control the execution of any other.

A matter of taste as well as technique, the UNIX system was born in fertile territory. Computing expertise was ubiquitous at Bell Labs, and style was widely regarded as important; it had been learned the hard way that complex, crabbed programs were a liability, prone to error, and unmaintainable in the field. By providing a clear model for programming in the expressive C language (see section 7.1), the UNIX system answered the need for better style. Running on affordable minicomputers, it could be adopted incrementally and prove its worth project by project. Finally, in its effective suite of utility programs, the UNIX system illustrated the power of small means suitably deployed. Users met in the UNIX system "features seldom found even in much larger operating systems."[35]

The command ls

ordinarily lists, on the typewriter, the names of the files in the user's current directory. The command

ls > there

creates a file called "there" and places the listing there. On the other hand:

ed

ordinarily enters the editor, which takes requests from the user via the user's keyboard. The command

ed < script

interprets "script" as a file of editor commands; thus control can be turned over to a canned procedure.

Output can be directed not only to files, but also, via a piping facility, directly from one command to the input of another.

Thus the command line

ls | pr | opr

ls lists the names of the files in the correct directory. Its output is piped to "pr," which paginates its input, thence to "opr" for off-line printing. This procedure would have been carried out more clumsily in earlier systems by a sequence such as

ls > temp1
pr < temp1 > temp2
opr < temp2

Fig. 9-9. Example of how the UNIX shell introduces notation for switching standard input-output assignments away from a user's terminal printer or keyboard and for piping one command directly to another. [Thompson and Ritchie, *Commun. ACM* **17** (1974): 371.]

The UNIX system fostered a philosophy of software design that was soon popularized by B. W. Kernighan and P. J. Plauger in their book, *Software Tools*: seek to construct applications out of well-defined program modules, each with a single purpose; expect the output of programs to be read by programs as well as by people; identify generic computing tasks and address them with reusable code; and use programs to write programs.[36,37] Utility programs for sorting, searching, combining, and rearranging text and data became the archetypical program tools. Frequently, as in the so-called "grep" family of pattern-matching programs or the "diff" differential file comparator, these utilities embodied the latest fruits of theoretical computer science to achieve remarkable speed and capacity.[38,39,40]

Progress in computing illustrates the Bell Labs philosophy of managing research by generously nurturing, but not rigidly directing, individual creativity. Repeatedly since Stibitz's complex-number computer, through Wolontis's L1, Mealy's BESYS, Thompson's UNIX operating system, and D. M. Ritchie's C language, individuals have addressed their imaginations and energies to a perceived need. Their solutions have reverberated through Bell Labs and beyond, shaped and amplified by the talents of the entire technical community.

VII. PROGRAMMING LANGUAGES

Starting with L1, Bell Labs researchers created a succession of programming languages to make computers easier to use in the open shop, better matched to requirements of particular applications, and more productive for their own use. McIlroy and D. E. Eastwood, in 1959, introduced conditional and recursive macro instructions into a standard assembler for the IBM 704 and first described how macros (i.e., tailored sequences of computer instructions) could be used to extend any programming language to meet users' own special requirements.[41] Macros made possible the implementation of qualitatively different languages as extensions of assembly language. Among these were an optimizing list processing (LISP) compiler (which converted LISP into assembly language) by McIlroy, the highly optimized network simulation program, Toll Network Simulator (TOLL-SIM), by P. J. Burke and R. Bennett, consultant,[42] and K. C. Knowlton's list-processing language L6.[43] Knowlton's language introduced modern pointer-chasing notation and buddy-system storage allocation.[44] Macros became the basis of the SWAP (Switching Assembly Program) family of assemblers for electronic switching machines and other computers.[45,46] In a thoroughgoing use of macros, B. N. Dickman created the higher-level language Centran in which the Safeguard missile defense system was programmed.[47] A later free-text style of macroprocessor, M6 by McIlroy, R. Morris and A. D. Hall, Jr., was a key implementation tool for the ALTRAN computer algebra system.

Special classes of problems fostered special languages. Signal processing needs of acoustic research inspired Kelly, C. Lochbaum, and Vyssotsky to create the Block Diagram (BLODI) compiler, which produced efficient code for simulating sample-data systems from their block diagrams. In BLODI, which would now be called a data-flow language, each circuit element, such as an amplifier or a delay line, was specified on a punched card together with its connections. The compiler used graph-theoretic techniques to arrange the code in a suitable order for simulation.[48] Also arising from acoustic research was a series of languages for musical composition by M. V. Mathews, which culminated in Music V; its notation was still in use in the 1980s.[49] (See Chapter 2, section 2.4.4, in this volume.)

Taking off from experimental string-processing programs by C. Y. Lee, the team of D. J. Farber, R. E. Griswold, and I. P. Polonsky invented the very-high-level SNOBOL (string oriented symbolic language) based on pattern-matching and associative storage of character strings. Radically different from other programming languages, even other symbol-manipulating languages, SNOBOL made light work of text processing and proved to be extremely useful for experimentation with new languages, for data laundry, and for high-level presentation of algorithmic ideas in classrooms.[50] Its mature incarnation, SNOBOL4, incorporated advanced data types and pattern-matching techniques and set a new standard for language portability. Implemented in macro instructions, SNOBOL4 has been transported to more than 50 different kinds of computers worldwide, because its instructions can be realized on most computers as simple macro calls.[51,52] In an interesting variant, J. F. Gimpel added a block data type, two-dimensional arrays of characters with operators for combining blocks hierarchically. The blocks language provided a suggestive calculus for rectangular computer graphics and typesetting, including justification operators for fitting stretchable blocks together.[53]

In the early 1960s, W. S. Brown with B. A. Tague and J. P. Hyde created Algebra Package (ALPAK), a set of routines for symbolic mathematics capable of manipulating very large rational algebraic expressions, such as those that arise in physics, elasticity, queueing theory, and other branches of applied math.[54] A simple FORTRAN-style interface implemented in SNOBOL and macros was ultimately succeeded by ALTRAN, a highly portable implementation of both algorithms and compiler. Created by W. S. Brown, Hall, S. I. Feldman, and D. M. Ritchie, ALTRAN included algorithmic advances in the handling of multivariate polynomials and macro generation to tailor FORTRAN code to make full use of the characteristics of particular hardware. Its features included a run-time environment with dynamic storage allocation, recursion, symbolic dumping, and error handling.[55] Portability was assured by mechanically verifying that the entire suite of FORTRAN programs stayed within a safely portable subset of American National Standard FORTRAN, known as portable

FORTRAN (PFORT). The verifier, defined by Hall and implemented by B. G. Ryder, has served as a standard of acceptability for algorithms published by the Association for Computing Machinery.[56] ALPAK and ALTRAN helped mathematicians and scientists do theoretical analysis in communications, queueing, coding, materials, fluids, relativity, and other fields.[57]

Computers multiplied the possibilities for Monte Carlo experiments. In addition to Burke's TOLLSIM simulator, J. P. Runyon, D. L. Dietmeyer, G. Gordon, and Tague designed Sequence Diagram Simulator (SDS) in the early 1960s, and R. F. Grantges and N. R. Sinowitz designed Network Analytical Simulator (NEASIM), all of which were applied to traffic and congestion problems.[58]

7.1 C Language and UNIX

The UNIX operating system owes its success in no small part to the general-purpose language C in which it and most of its associated software are written. C is one of what might be called the international style of programming languages conceived by C. Strachey, P. Landin, and others in the tradition of the algorithmic language ALGOL 60. The immediate ancestors of C were BCPL (Basic Combined Programming Language) by M. Richards at Cambridge,[59] and the unpublished language B by Thompson at Bell Labs. In designing C, D. M. Ritchie [Fig. 9-10] sought to match the expressive capability of the international style as closely as possible to the hardware capabilities of real machines, and to match the flexibility of assembly language with the abstract diction of higher level languages. The characteristic contributions of C are (1) a coherent model of pointers and arrays that corresponds to machine addresses, yet maintains machine independence, (2) a rich set of operators that correspond to typical computer instructions, and (3) a terse syntax that makes programs compact and readable.[60] [Fig. 9-11] From its inception in 1973, C grew by 1980 to be the prime programming language of Bell Laboratories, working on diverse hardware. Software tools written in C propagated to many computing environments, from microcomputers to switching machines to supercomputers.

The parsimonious but expressive syntax of C spawned imitators, notably Kernighan's Rational FORTRAN (RATFOR) preprocessor, which adapted the structured style of C to the ubiquitous FORTRAN language. RATFOR became a vehicle for spreading the software tools outlook beyond the UNIX system.[61]

In an unusual synthesis of theory, programming, and human engineering, B. S. Baker created a program "struct," which converted programs in FORTRAN to RATFOR, thereby retrieving the essential logical structure that FORTRAN had obscured. Baker showed that the structure of a FORTRAN program was unique in a particular sense, the naturalness of which

Fig. 9-10. D. M. Ritchie, who, in 1973, designed
the C programming language, in which most UNIX
system associated software is written. C quickly developed into the prime programming language at
Bell Laboratories.

was attested to by the fact that programmers preferred the rearranged
RATFOR text to their own original code.[62]

Certain Bell Labs innovations in compiler technique have had lasting

```
for (j = 1; j <= 5; j++){
    s[j] = 0;
    for (i = 1; i <= 10; i++)
        s[j] += a[j][i]* x[i];}
```

Here i++ means add 1 to i; the first "for" statement means do the enclosed
code with j starting with 1, repeated, while j is less than or equal to 5,
adding 1 to j after each repetition; $s[j]$ += ⋯ means add ⋯ to $s[j]$.

Fig. 9-11. The program of Fig. 9-7 written in the C language. This example
indicates something of C's compactness and flexibility not its full expressive
power.

influence. In 1961, Vyssotsky used bit-vector techniques for data-flow analysis to provide flow-based diagnostics in FORTRAN. Vyssotsky's un-published methods were to be generalized a decade later in the works of J. Cocke at IBM, J. T. Schwartz at New York University (NYU), and G. A. Kildall at the Naval Postgraduate School.[63,64] M. S. Hecht and J. D. Ullman later found efficient ways to order the iterative steps that the methods involve.[65] In 1969, at Bell Labs, R. Sethi and Ullman, starting from work by J. Nievergelt in Zurich, demonstrated an algorithm to generate provably optimal code to evaluate mathematical expressions on simple register machines.[66,67] Shortly after, S. G. Wasilew invented an enumerative technique to optimize code for the elaborate instruction set of the 1A ESS* switching equipment. Building on the methods of Sethi, Ullman, and Wasilew, A. V. Aho and S. C. Johnson subsequently presented a widely applicable dynamic programming technique that handled multiple registers, temporary storage, and a mix of instruction forms.[68,69] The stan-dard textbook methods of flow analysis and code optimization in use in the 1980s can be traced to these origins.

VIII. COMPUTERS FOR THE TRANSMISSION AND STORAGE OF INFORMATION

8.1 Data Transmission Between Computers

Stibitz's complex number computer had been introduced in 1940 to the scientific community over the first computer data link, a teletypewriter connection. (See section 4.1.) By the mid-1950s, it was apparent that elec-tronic computers would require much higher-speed data transmission than could be provided by standard teletypewriter equipment. Bell Labs ac-cordingly demonstrated in 1956 the use of standard switched telephone circuits to provide direct magnetic-tape to magnetic-tape transmission of digital data at a speed of 600 baud (60 characters per second), or about ten times that of standard teletypewriters. The data were protected by parity checks, and records showing parity errors were automatically re-transmitted. This demonstration was not, in fact, hooked up to a computer. Since there was at that time no agreement as to computer magnetic-tape formats, an ad hoc arrangement of the magnetic tape was used, which was prepared and printed out, at much lower speed, on standard off-line printing equipment. The demonstration did, however, show that tape-to-tape transmission of digital data could be achieved—at speeds reasonably matched to the computers of the time—over normal long-distance tele-phone connections dialed at random.

---

* Trademark of AT&T Technologies, Inc.

In the early 1960s, transmission facilities similar to those used in the 1956 demonstration were used to provide several Bell Labs branches with entry to the major computing centers in New Jersey. This enabled the branch labs to resolve problems beyond the capability of their own modest computing facilities. The transmission facilities normally used voice-grade telephone circuits, usually those provided for interlocation telephone traffic. The detailed arrangements depended on the specific equipment available at the remote location.

In early 1972, A. R. Breithaupt and N. A. Martellotto proposed connecting the large IBM batch-processing systems at Holmdel, Whippany, and Indian Hill. Connections were made via Telpak-A data links, and IBM's Associated Support Processor (ASP) was expanded considerably to support ASP-to-ASP communications.[70] By June 1976, the resulting Bell Labs Interlocation Computing Network, which had become fully operational and generally available in 1974, included three centers and over a dozen satellite locations across the country. If desired, a user at one site could run a job at a second site and direct the output to a third site.

By the late 1960s, work was progressing on techniques for forming networks of cooperating computers. In 1968, W. D. Farmer and E. E. Newhall demonstrated an experimental loop system for interconnecting digital devices.[71] In 1970, J. R. Pierce proposed a hierarchial interconnecting loop network for high-speed data communications, with users responsible for their own signaling and error handling.[72] At about the same time, A. G. Fraser proposed and started constructing an experimental, high-speed, packet-switched network known as Spider, in which a central mini-computer acts as a switch and provides error-control and flow-control services for computers and terminals that are connected by the network.[73] By 1976, several minicomputers in the Bell Labs acoustics research group had been connected by a loop system following Pierce's ideas, and Spider had grown into an internal network supporting about a dozen minicomputers with various services, including a network file-storage facility, a network printer, and access to the Honeywell 6070 computer in the Murray Hill computation center.

Pierce loops and Spider were two of many packet network experiments in the world at the time, the best known of which was ARPANET, sponsored by the Defense Advance Research Projects Agency.[74] In such networks, a shared high-speed transmission medium carries packets of data from many sources, each packet being tagged with identifying information to get it to the proper destination. In a small loop network, receivers simply grab from one shared loop the packets destined for them. In a larger Pierce network or in the ARPANET, packets may travel by stages, relying on intermediate receivers to forward them towards their ultimate destinations; routing is a time-consuming, packet-by-packet activity. The overhead of routing was greatly simplified by Fraser's idea of virtual circuits, first demonstrated in Spider and its successor network, DATAKIT* virtual circuit switch.[75] (See Chapter 8, section 4.3.) In these networks, as in the voice telephone network, a route is set up in advance for each call; however, no circuit space is dedicated to any individual call. The packets of a call identify only the call, not its destination, and switches along the route keep simple tables that specify the next link of the route for each call in progress. As its name implied, the DATAKIT virtual circuit switch was designed as a modular switching system that could gracefully expand into a large-scale communication network.[76] The DATAKIT virtual circuit switch demonstration eventually led to Bell System data-switching products.

8.2 Information Transfer Between Computers and People

Computer scientists have long been concerned with the transfer of information between computers and people, and between people and people. Although information transfer, viewed broadly, was the entire mission of the Bell System, we shall exclude telephony from the present discussion and focus on the parts that belong properly to computer science.

8.2.1 Computer Movies

For communication between computers and people, words and numbers may be sufficient, yet for many applications, a graphical or pictorial representation may be much more informative. To provide this type of output, Bell Labs installed a Stromberg-Carlson 4020 microfilm printer at Murray Hill in 1961. This device converted information from a computer-generated magnetic tape to 35-millimeter film. In the first large-scale application of the facility, W. L. Brown and J. D. Gabbe generated several thousand plots from hundreds of thousands of measurements of the earth's radiation belts made by the Telstar satellites.[77,78] [Fig. 9-12]

The low cost of film production on the Stromberg-Carlson recorder suggested using it for movies. R. M. McClure made the first computer movie at Bell Labs, a classified film of a cloud of incoming ballistic missiles and decoys. J. B. Kruskal, Jr., made a moving display of the iterations of his algorithm for multidimensional scaling, and E. E. Zajac conveyed the results of a computer simulation of satellite motion as a movie of a gyrating and tumbling box.[79] [Fig. 9-13] A. M. Noll made a stereographic three-dimensional movie, and F. W. Sinden illustrated the educational potential of computer movies.[80,81] Interested in the artistic potential of computer

---

* Trademark of AT&T.

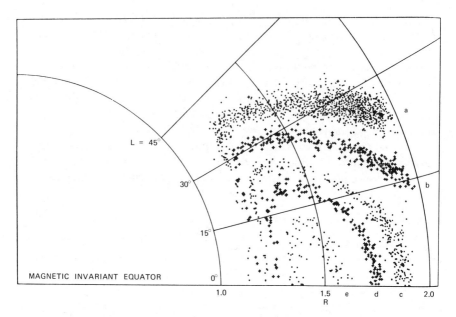

Fig. 9-12. High-energy proton data from the Telstar I satellite. *R* is earth radii and *L* is magnetic latitude. Computer-generated plot shows five bands of flux, labeled *a* through *e*, in the earth's inner radiation belt. The several thousand plots generated from Telstar data would have been exceedingly difficult if not impossible to prepare manually.

animation, Knowlton introduced a movie-making language called Beflix, with which several award-winning scientific and artistic films were produced.[82] Several computer-generated stereoscopic films were made on such topics as the motion of an inner ear component.

In the mid-1960s, W. H. Ninke and collaborators developed a series of satellite processors for interactive graphics. Graphic 1 and Graphic 2 incorporated minicomputers and vector display-processing hardware with graphic subroutine capabilities.[83] These powerful terminals represented a remarkable advance over the simple teletypewriter used by Stibitz in 1940 to demonstrate his complex number computer. (See section 4.1.) The Graphic 2, later manufactured for Bell Labs and Western Electric by the Digital Equipment Corporation, saw wide use in computer-aided design of printed-wiring boards, logic schematic drawings, and office-equipment layouts.

8.2.2 *Computers in Data-Base Applications*

Data-base applications burgeoned throughout Bell Laboratories and the Bell System from the mid-1960s onward, from enormous inventory-control

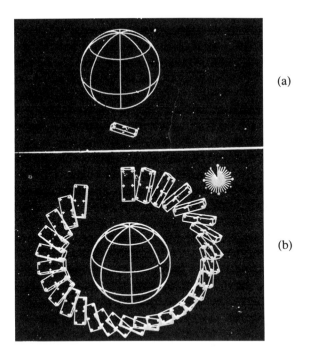

(a)

(b)

Fig. 9-13. Computer-generated movie frame showing a satellite tumbling in orbit around earth. (a) Single frame. (b) A composite of several frames. A clock drawn at the upper right of each frame counted the orbits. [Zajac, *Commun. ACM* **7** (1964): 170.]

systems to relatively small ad hoc surveys. To support the myriad smaller data management applications, Sinowitz at Bell Labs developed an interactive information retrieval system called Dataplus.[84] T. A. Gibson, B. W. Puerling, J. T. Roberto, and others provided further automated tools.[85,86] With their Off-the-Shelf System, the construction of hierarchical data bases including data-gathering, inquiry, and summary facilities that worked in the terms of an application became a matter of little work beyond that of defining the task in the first place.[87] This system proved particularly valuable in preparing Bell System surveys with nationwide input.

In an unusual experimental information service, M. E. Lesk developed a directory-assistance system for Bell Labs telephones. A caller would type the name and initials of a fellow employee on his Touch-Tone telephone and receive the called party's number by recorded voice.[88] A recorded voice would ask further questions to resolve ambiguities. Despite the confounding of three letters on each button of a Touch-Tone phone, the rate of unresolvable ambiguities was under one percent.

8.2.3 *Computer-Aided Distribution in Libraries*

To help get Bell Labs papers promptly to the employees who needed them, W. S. Brown and J. F. Traub conceived the Mercury computer-aided distribution system.[89] Using subject codes from a hierarchical vocabulary, together with organization and project numbers and individual names, authors described the readers they wished to reach, and readers described the papers they wished to receive. These descriptions were matched by a computer, which printed a distribution list and addressing labels for each paper. Developed in 1966 in cooperation with the Bell Labs library, Mercury was just one of many computer applications to help the libraries locate and disseminate information for the benefit of technical people at Bell Labs. Other applications included keeping on-line circulation records, preparing the union catalogue, constructing specialized indexes and bibliographies, keeping business records, and disseminating awareness bulletins about current literature.[90,91]

8.2.4 *Computer Preparation of Documents*

With the advent of interactive computing, research people began preparing manuscripts on computers. Starting from the model of Runoff by J. Saltzer at MIT, a succession of text-formatting programs culminated in the early 1970s with Ossanna's "troff" (pronounced "tee-roff").[92] Troff drove a commercial phototypesetter directly from a computer rather than from punched paper tape as was customary in the industry. Combining familiar formatting capabilities with programmability—macros, traps that could be set to perform arbitrary actions at particular positions on a page, and "diversions" to capture already formatted text for repositioning on the page—troff was capable of setting pages of a complexity that would normally have had to be set by hand. Troff strove for generality, not simplicity, and "penalty copy," such as mathematics, was painful to get right. But in the tool-building environment of UNIX, troff could be exploited by other programs. Kernighan and L. L. Cherry used the YACC (yet another compiler-compiler) compiler-writing system to create eqn, a remarkably natural language for setting mathematics, which could be translated automatically into troff.[93] [Fig. 9-14] Lesk supplied a set of macros that divorced the logical content of a document from the physical shape of the page. By the mid-1970s, it became possible to run off a typewritten draft, a typeset internal memorandum, and finally camera-ready copy in the style of a particular journal from one and the same text file.[94] Troff and related programs propagated throughout Bell Labs, to Western Electric for the production of Bell System Practices, to the *Physical Review*, and elsewhere, fostering radical changes in job descriptions and altering the traditional division of labor among technical, secretarial, and clerical personnel. Though computerized typesetting did not originate with troff, only with troff did

$$x \text{ sup 2 over a sup 2 } \sim = \sim \text{ sqrt } \{pz \text{ sup 2} + qz + r\}$$

$$\frac{x^2}{a^2} = \sqrt{pz^2+qz+r}$$

$$\text{roman erf } (z) \sim = \sim \text{ 2 over sqrt pi}$$
$$\text{int sub 0 sup z e sup -t sup 2 dt}$$

$$\text{erf}(z) = \frac{2}{\sqrt{\pi}} \int_0^z e^{-t^2} dt$$

Fig. 9-14. Mathematical typesetting by eqn. The two typed equations, which closely imitate spoken mathematics, produce the two typeset versions.

it become established as a widely accessible facility, giving substance to and enlarging upon Charles Babbage's 19th century dream that the product of automatic computation might one day be printed without the intervention of human labor and human error.[95]

Text in a computer was available for analysis as well as for typesetting.[96] Using data gleaned from a million words of text at hand in 1973, Morris conceived an ingenious approach to detecting typing errors based on the statistical likelihood of the appearance of three-letter groups in English.[97] The UNIX program that implemented the idea also performed the neat trick of counting logarithmically to compress the storage needed for frequency counts.[98]

IX. COMPUTING AND MATHEMATICS

9.1 Mathematical Foundations of Computing

Theory preceded practice in computers. In the 1930s, A. M. Turing, at Cambridge, had outlined ultimate limitations on computability and had propounded a compelling thesis of universality: aside from efficiency considerations, whatever one computer can calculate, all computers can.[99] The mathematical methods, which the first computers were designed to carry out, were also classical. And Shannon's application of Boolean algebra to the design and analysis of logic circuits reached maturity with the publication of the book *Design of Switching Circuits* by three Bell Labs authors, Keister, A. E. Ritchie, and S. H. Washburn.[100] (Ritchie's son, Dennis, would later participate in the creation of the UNIX system and the C language.) Nevertheless, the actual presence of machines gave new impetus, and altered emphasis, to the applicable mathematical disciplines.

During the 1950s, switching theory flowered into automata theory, with contributions from many quarters. Particularly influential were the methods of D. A. Huffman (MIT) for synthesizing sequential circuits and of M. O. Rabin and D. Scott (IBM) for deciding equivalence.[101,102] Formal models of finite-state automata, known by their author's names, were formulated by E. F. Moore and Mealy of Bell Labs.[103,104] These models decomposed sequential circuits into a combinatorial, or Boolean part, and a memory part. Combinatorial synthesis by prime implicant analysis—a way of minimizing the size of Boolean equations—was studied by M. Karnaugh, whose name became enshrined in Karnaugh maps.[105] Researchers, particularly D. B. Armstrong, A. D. Friedman, and P. R. Menon, became proficient in devising effective design methodologies to re-express Boolean expressions in various forms that corresponded to realistic circuit technologies: restricted depth, restricted fanout, NAND-NOR circuits, exclusive OR circuits, programmed logic arrays, etc.[106]

Automata theorists also turned their attention to the important but forbidding task of diagnosing faulty digital circuits. Fortunately circuits typically failed digitally: it was plausible to model single errors as certain wires being stuck at 0 or stuck at 1. Then the diagnostic problem became one of formulating efficient sets of test vectors, or inputs that would elicit distinctive syndromes, whereby offending circuit elements could be identified. Armstrong proposed a method of path sensitization to establish the external visibility of errors internal to a circuit.[107] Diagnostic techniques were codified in the book *Fault Detection in Digital Circuits* by Friedman and Menon.[108]

As theoretical understanding of logic circuits advanced, formal techniques were adapted into computer programs to help design these circuits. As early as 1958, the logical design of processors for the Nike X missile defense system, later known as Safeguard, was expressed in logical equations from which wiring diagrams and physical layouts were generated automatically. (See *National Service in War and Peace (1925-1975)*.) By the late 1960s, methods of automata theory became an indispensable tool for major hardware design projects. The Logic Analyzer for Maintenance Planning (LAMP) was developed to aid in the design and verification of the 1A ESS switching equipment.[109] Another example is the Finite State Support Software (FS^3) system, which was developed to provide a uniform system of machine-aided tools to support an orderly method of software design and development. It was designed in 1972 by L. L. Crume to support the mobile radio cellular processing system and described in an internal publication in 1976. The ultimate infusion of automata theory into development projects happened at the instigation of development departments, which could not hope to accomplish their complex undertakings without computer assistance. Research interest, inspired indeed by the real world of digital hardware, provided the confident basis of understanding that undergirded the technology.

About a decade after founding switching theory, Shannon announced the fundamental theorem of information theory[110] (see Chapter 1, section VIII) and established as the elementary unit of information the binary digit, dubbed bit by J. W. Tukey. The use of this term became widespread throughout the computer and communications industries to specify storage capacities and information content. Information theory quantifies the limits of performance of communications systems. Successful performance in the face of random errors is secured by adjusting the degree of redundancy in messages.

Introduced about 1938 into telephone switching equipment by R. E. Hersey, error-correcting codes were first employed in computers by Stibitz in his design for the Model II relay machine. In 1948, R. W. Hamming showed a systematic and optimal way to make correctable any single-bit error in a block of data. The coding technique that bears his name has been widely used in computer memories.[111] Error-correcting codes that cope with bursts of errors, devised by D. W. Hagelbarger in 1959, have commonly been employed to enhance the reliability of disk memories.[112] Related work in the development of algebraic coding theory by D. Slepian and others is discussed in Chapter 1, section 8.6 of this volume.

Deepened mathematical study of automata theory was fueled by fascinating speculation: J. von Neumann at the Institute for Advanced Study suggested self-reproducing automata as a model of organic existence.[113] His idea was to be vivified by Moore at Bell Labs, who imagined a population explosion of floating factories that he called "artificial living plants."[114] Moore's ideas, as well as the related work on how machines might be made to play chess by Shannon,[115] and by J. H. Condon and Thompson,[116] are discussed in Chapter 1, section 9.3 of this volume.

Automata theory has roots in mathematical logic and linguistics as well as switching theory. The capabilities of state machines relate directly to the richness of the languages, or sets of symbol strings, that they produce or recognize. The hierarchy of language families characterized in the mid-1950s by the MIT linguist N. Chomsky was seen to unify known logical systems and automata models.[117] The abstract linguistic viewpoint fostered an explosive growth of understanding to which Ullman and Aho at Bell Labs contributed heavily. From the study of formal languages and their processors grew a scientific basis for the technology of programming languages. Chomsky's syntactic formalisms, further propagated by the report on ALGOL 60, almost immediately suggested mechanical means of creating language parsers.[118,119] Among these was the TMG (Transmogrifier) compiler generator, which originated with McClure at Southern Methodist University, and was elaborated on by McIlroy at Bell Labs. The TMG became the basis for the PL/I compiler with which MULTICS was implemented.[120,121] From the flood of parsing models there eventually emerged, the eminently practical left-to-right (LR) methods originated by D. E. Knuth at California Institute of Technology.[122] Aho, S. C. Johnson, and Ullman discovered how, in the LR framework, to cope with simplified, formally ambiguous grammars.[123] Johnson implemented these ideas in the YACC compiler generator. One of the most powerful of the UNIX system tools, YACC produced professional-quality parsers from do-it-yourself specifications. Complex YACC-based processors for the C and FORTRAN programming languages, typesetting (see section 8.2.4 in this chapter), and many other purposes have seen extensive use throughout Bell Labs and the Bell System.[124] Such was the leverage of this one product of research in automata and formal languages that most YACC-based compilers and programs were constructed by only one or two individuals.

9.2 Complexity in Computing

The speed of computing depends not only on the speed of hardware but also on the computational complexity of computing processes. As computers grew in size and speed, larger problems were attempted, and the scaling of solution time with problem size became a matter of concern. For example, early methods of sorting n items of data stored in a computer memory took time proportional to n^2. This made little practical difference when computer memories were small. It seldom mattered whether a job ran for a second or a minute. But, by the late 1950s, computer memories could hold more than 10,000 items; then the discovery of a method of internal sorting, in which the running time grew only as $n\log n$, spelled the difference between a minute and an hour of computing.[125]

A heuristic argument that $n\log n$ was the best guarantee that could be made for the time to sort n items was finally made rigorous in 1969 by Morris.[126] His result took the number of comparisons as a measure of time. Aho, J. E. Hopcroft, and Ullman later showed that if comparisons themselves take time proportional to the amount of store occupied by the items being compared, sorting can be accomplished in time proportional to the total amount of store occupied.[127] (There is no conflict with Morris's result: n items, all different, must occupy at least $n\log_2 n$ bits of store.)

As illustrated by the analysis of sorting, complexity theory involves (1) models of computation and the costs of computation, (2) upper bounds, that is, achievable costs for classes of problems, and (3) lower bounds, that is, costs that cannot uniformly be bettered for a given class of problems in a given model of computation. Among the models of computation are models of automata theory; complexity theory intertwines naturally with automata and formal language theory. In an application to library work, Aho and M. J. Corasick, knowing that texts in regular languages could be analyzed in time proportional to the length of the text, were led to devise a literature search program that could spot any of 100 or more keywords in a bibliographic file as quickly as it could spot one.[128] Their method reduced search time from being proportional to the product of the sizes of the bibliographic file and the list of keywords to search time proportional to the sum; this achieved a speedup of a factor of 50 in typical cases.

The algorithm used for pattern-matching by Aho and Corasick was deterministic, i.e., it was designed for one processor to carry out sequentially. Since it gets only one look at each symbol of the file, it must encode history in an internal state, and the number of states may be exponentially large in the size of language specification. An alternative nondeterministic model of computation due to R. W. Floyd of Stanford required only a linear number of states and used backtracking, or parallel computation, to follow a multiple path.[129] Thompson devised an elegant linear-space way to carry all the parallel paths forward simultaneously on a single processor.[130] Thompson's algorithm made elaborate pattern-searching facilities possible in text-editing programs on even the smallest minicomputers.

Sorting and searching are examples of discrete or combinatoric problems, which have been elevated to prominence by the advent of computers, bringing graph theory and finite groups into the tool kit of computer scientists on an equal footing with linear algebra and probability. Combinatoric problems had long concerned Bell Labs scientists studying network problems. (See Chapter 1, section 3.4 in this volume.) Naturally computers were soon brought to bear on them.

In 1956, Kruskal, who later joined Bell Labs, found an efficient method for the minimum spanning tree problem—finding a set of links that connects all points of a network and uses a minimum amount of wire—and the following year, R. C. Prim of Bell Labs found an alternative method particularly suited to networks with many edges per vertex.[131,132] (See Chapter 1, section 3.4 in this volume.) Z. A. Melzak showed that a related problem posed by J. A. Steiner in the 19th century—finding the minimum spanning tree in a plane network given the freedom to introduce new internal vertices—is also discrete; only a finite number of points are candidates for introduction.[133]

Prim's and Kruskal's methods were disarmingly simple to understand and could be carried out for a network of n points in time at most proportional to n^2. This time bound is dramatically better than that for the naive method of simply trying all of the at most n^{n-2} spanning trees, each of size $n - 1$. On the other hand, even with Melzak's reduction, the Steiner problem remained much harder, and had no known method of solution guaranteed to be dramatically superior to enumeration.

The two spanning tree problems illustrate an important dichotomy in combinatorics, polynomial-time versus NP-complete problems. First recognized by S. A. Cook of Toronto, NP-completeness became a lively topic of study at Bell Labs, epitomized in the treatise *Computers and Intractability* by M. R. Garey and D. S. Johnson.[134,135] (See Chapter 1, section 9.4.1.) NP-complete problems studied at Bell Labs included wire routing,[136] process scheduling,[137,138] bin packing,[139] and graph partitioning.[140] Though compelling evidence suggests that NP-complete problems have no solution methods that uniformly require less than exponential time, excellent approximate solutions may often be found more rapidly. So it was with S. Lin's approach to the traveling salesman problem, to find the shortest closed route that visits every one of n cities.[141] Lin's techniques worked essentially perfectly on 50-city problems. (Curiously, the Bell System was sometimes required by law, as well as by engineering needs, to solve the minimum spanning tree, Steiner, and traveling salesman problems. In certain jurisdictions network rates have been based on these criteria.)

In another dramatic illustration of the potential gains from reduced time complexity, the FFT algorithm for finite Fourier transforms burst into the collective consciousness of scientists who had ignored a half-century of precursors. (See Chapter 1, section 12.4 in this volume). Because of computers, the time was right for its rediscovery by J. W. Cooley of IBM and Tukey of Bell Labs in 1965.[142] By achieving a factor of $n/\log n$ speed up, the FFT made digital signal processing much more widely affordable than before, and spurred the development of special digital signal processors. A cascade architecture by G. D. Bergland and R. Klahn followed almost immediately in 1966.[143] Then, in 1967, R. R. Shively and his associates completed the first sequential FFT processor, which was used for research in digital signal processing.[144] Two years later, Bergland and D. E. Wilson introduced a new version of the FFT, suitable for implementation on computers employing multiple processors in parallel.[145]

9.3 Numerical Analysis and Computing

Numerical analysis antedated computers by more than a century. Indeed, the first computers were built to cope with problems in numerical analysis, and their spectacular successes reinvigorated the field. The very scale of problems that could be attacked made new approaches necessary. For example, traditional methods of filter design, stretched to their limits, entailed calculations to 40 decimal digits in order to get three- or four-digit accuracy. New design techniques became necessary. The filtering process itself could be carried out numerically, which led to more problems of design and analysis that were pursued by J. F. Kaiser and others.[146,147] (See Chapter 1, section 3.3.) Digital filters not only became a computational tool but also were deployed in telephone transmission, radar, and other operational systems. And the study of filters fed back into classical numerical analysis as Hamming applied insights from signal processing to the question of stability of quadrature methods.[148]

Hamming frequently articulated the difference in interests, tastes, and objectives between practicing numerical analysts and most other mathematicians.[149] Those differences were already in mind when he participated in the creation of the Association for Computing Machinery (ACM) in 1948—almost before there were any computing machines—and when he gave the ACM Turing Award lecture in 1968.[150] With time, however, computing so invaded the domain of applied mathematics, and mathematical reasoning proved so valuable in all of computer science, that the fields came to enrich each other. Indeed, researchers in foundations, particularly logic and complexity, identified themselves as mathematicians or computer scientists more by will than by reason.

The possibility of doing math mechanically intrigued scientists long before computers were developed. Turing intended his machine model to be a model of formal mathematics, and through it showed that mathematics is inherently incomplete: it must always be possible to pose undecidable problems. Undecidability, however, is a property of an infinite class of problems; even in undecidable domains, individual problems may very well be decidable. Thus H. Wang was able to show that in mathematical logic undecidability is confined to formulas of certain special types.[151] In a decidable subdomain of logic, Wang used the IBM 704 to prove, in 8.4 minutes, all the theorems of propositional calculus in A. N. Whitehead and B. Russell's *Principia Mathematica*.[152] Encouraged by the work of Wang at Bell Labs and of Loveland at IBM, M. Davis of NYU conceived and McIlroy programmed a theorem prover for the predicate calculus. Capable of proving elementary theorems in group theory or number theory *ab initio*, the theorem prover was too feeble to help in the everyday work of practicing mathematicians. Far more knowledge of techniques for specific problem domains would be required to do real mathematics on a computer.

ALTRAN (see section VII above) mounted just such a specialized attack in the domain of multivariate rational functions. In addition to being a large undertaking, ALTRAN posed a significant computational challenge in the essential matter of finding multivariate greatest common divisors. Classical generalizations of Euclid's algorithm had intolerable exponential time and memory requirements, which were finally overcome by W. S. Brown and Traub.[153] Similar obstacles to polynomial factoring were ameliorated by a fundamental algorithm devised by E. R. Berlekamp.[154] Thus in symbolic algebra, as in many other areas of computing, the implementation on computers of well-known mathematics led to the augmentation of that very knowledge.

REFERENCES

1. B. D. Holbrook and J. T. Dixon, "Load Rating Theory for Multi-Channel Amplifiers," *Bell Syst. Tech. J.* **18** (October 1939), pp. 624-644.
2. S. B. Wright and E. R. Taylor, U.S. Patent No. 1,927,999; filed December 10, 1930; issued September 26, 1933.
3. W. Thomson, Baron Kelvin, *Mathematical and Physical Papers*, Vol. 6 (Cambridge: Cambridge University Press, 1911), pp. 285-290.
4. H. S. Black, "Stabilized Feedback Amplifiers," *Bell Syst. Tech. J.* **13** (January 1934), pp. 1-18.
5. H. W. Bode, *Network Analysis and Feedback Amplifier Design* (New York: D. Van Nostrand Co., 1945).
6. R. L. Dietzold, "The Isograph—A Mechanical Root-Finder," *Bell Lab. Rec.* **16** (December 1937), pp. 130-134.
7. R. O. Mercner, "The Mechanism of the Isograph," *Bell Lab. Rec.* **16** (December 1937), pp. 135-140.
8. C. A. Lovell, "Continuous Electrical Computation," *Bell Lab. Rec.* **25** (March 1947), pp. 114-118.
9. A. A. Currie, "The General Purpose Analog Computer," *Bell Lab. Rec.* **29** (March 1951), pp. 101-108.
10. E. C. Molina, U.S. Patent No. 1,083,456; filed April 20, 1906; issued January 6, 1914.
11. C. E. Shannon, "A Symbolic Analysis of Relay and Switching Circuits," *Trans. Amer. Inst. Elec. Eng.* **57** (December 1938), pp. 713-723.
12. E. G. Andrews, "Bell Laboratories Digital Computers," *Bell Lab. Rec.* **35** (March 1957), pp. 81-84.
13. G. R. Stibitz and E. Loveday, "The Relay Computer at Bell Labs," *Datamation* **13** (April 1967), pp. 35-44.
14. S. B. Williams, U.S. Patent No. 2,434,681; filed February 13, 1943; issued January 20, 1948.
15. E. G. Andrews, "Telephone Switching and the Early Bell Laboratories Computers," *Bell Syst. Tech. J.* **42** (March 1963), pp. 341-353.
16. F. L. Alt, "A Bell Telephone Laboratories' Computing Machine," *Math. Tables Aids Comput.* **3** (1948), pp. 1-13 and pp. 69-84.
17. E. G. Andrews, "The Bell Computer, Model VI," *Elec. Eng.* **68** (September 1949), pp. 751-756.
18. T. L. Dimond, "No. 5 Crossbar AMA Translator," *Bell Lab. Rec.* **29** (February 1951), pp. 62-68.
19. A. E. Joel, Jr., *A History of Engineering and Science in the Bell System: Switching Technology (1925-1975)*, ed. G. E. Schindler, Jr. (Bell Telephone Laboratories, 1982).
20. G. R. Frost, W. Keister, and A. E. Ritchie, "A Throwdown Machine for Telephone Traffic Studies," *Bell Syst. Tech. J.* **32** (March 1953), pp. 292-359.
21. H. H. Goldstine and A. Goldstine, "The Electronic Numerical Integrator and Computer (ENIAC)," *Math. Tables Aids Comput.* **2** (April 1946), pp. 97-110.
22. W. H. T. Holden, U.S. Patent No. 2,299,898; filed October 16, 1941; issued October 27, 1942.
23. A. W. Horton, U.S. Patent No. 2,244,700; filed September 21, 1939; issued June 10, 1941.

24. W. H. MacWilliams, Jr., "A Transistor Gating Matrix for a Simulated Warfare Computer," *Bell Lab. Rec.* **35** (March 1957), pp. 94-99.

25. R. W. Hamming, *Numerical Methods for Scientists and Engineers* (New York: McGraw-Hill, 1962).

26. V. M. Wolontis, *A Complete Floating-Decimal Interpretive System for the IBM 650 Magnetic Drum Calculator*, IBM Applied Science Division Technical Newsletter No. 11 (March 1956).

27. M. V. Mathews, "Choosing a Scientific Computer for Service," *Science* **161** (July 5, 1968), pp. 23-27.

28. F. J. Corbató, M. M. Daggett, and R. C. Daley, "An Experimental Time-Sharing System," *Proc. Amer. Federation Inform. Process. Soc. Spring Joint Comput. Conf.* **21**, San Francisco (May 1-3, 1962), pp. 335-344.

29. T. Kilburn, "One-Level Storage System," *IRE Trans. Electron. Comput.* **EC-11** (April 1962), pp. 223-235.

30. "A New Remote Accessed Man-Machine System," *Proc. Amer. Federation Inform. Process. Soc. Fall Joint Comput. Conf.* **27**, Part 1, Session 6 (1965), pp. 185-247.

31. K. Thompson and D. M. Ritchie, "Unix Time-Sharing System," *Commun. ACM* **17** (July 1974), pp. 365-375.

32. See special Unix issue, *Bell Syst. Tech. J.* **57** (July/August 1978), pp. 1897-2312.

33. S. P. Morgan, "Minicomputers in Bell Laboratories Research," *Bell Lab. Rec.* **51** (July/August 1973), pp. 194-201.

34. D. M. Ritchie, U.S. Patent No. 4,135,240; filed July 9, 1973; issued January 16, 1979.

35. See reference 31.

36. F. D. Brown, V. J. Calderbank, and M. D. Poole, "Some Comments on the Portability of a Large ALGOL Program—The Implementation of SID on KDF9," *Software Pract. Exper.* **1** (October-December 1971), pp. 367-371.

37. B. W. Kernighan and P. J. Plauger, *Software Tools* (Reading, Massachusetts: Addison-Wesley, 1976).

38. A. V. Aho and M. J. Corasick, "Efficient String Matching: An Aid to Bibliographic Search," *Commun. ACM* **18** (June 1975), pp. 333-340.

39. K. Thompson, "Regular Expression Search Algorithm," *Commun. ACM* **11** (June 1968), pp. 419-422.

40. J. W. Hunt and M. D. McIlroy, *An Algorithm for Differential File Comparison*, Comput. Sci. Tech. Rep. No. 41, 1976 (Murray Hill, New Jersey: Bell Laboratories).

41. M. D. McIlroy, "Macro Instruction Extensions of Compiler Languages," *Commun. ACM* **3** (April 1960), pp. 214-220.

42. P. J. Burke, "Automatic Overload Controls in a Circuit-Switched Communications Network," *Proc. Nat. Electron. Conf.* **24**, Chicago (December 9-11, 1968), pp. 667-672.

43. K. C. Knowlton, "A Programmer's Description of L⁶," *Commun. ACM* **9** (August 1966), pp. 616-625.

44. K. C. Knowlton, "A Fast Storage Allocator," *Commun. ACM* **8** (October 1965), pp. 623-625.

45. N. A. Martellotto, H. Oehring, and M. C. Paull, "PROCESS III—A Compiler-Assembler for No. 1 ESS," *Bell Syst. Tech. J.* **43** (September 1964), pp. 2457-2481.

46. M. E. Barton, "The Macro Assembler, SWAP—A General-Purpose Interpretive Processor," *Proc. Amer. Federation Inform. Process. Soc. Fall Joint Comput. Conf.* **37**, Houston, Texas (November 17-19, 1970), pp. 1-8.

47. B. N. Dickman, "CENTRAN—A Case History in Extendible Language Design," *Bell Syst. Tech. J.* **54**, SAFEGUARD Special Supplement (1975), pp. S161-S172.

48. J. L. Kelly, Jr., C. Lochbaum, and V. A. Vyssotsky, "A Block Diagram Compiler," *Bell Syst. Tech. J.* **40** (May 1961), pp. 669-676.

49. M. V. Mathews, *The Technology of Computer Music* (Cambridge, Massachusetts: MIT Press, 1969).
50. D. J. Farber, R. E. Griswold, and I. P. Polonsky, "SNOBOL, A String Manipulation Language," *J. ACM* **11** (January 1964), pp. 21-30.
51. R. E. Griswold, J. F. Poage, and I. P. Polonsky, *The SNOBOL 4 Programming Language*, 2nd ed. (Englewood Cliffs, New Jersey: Prentice-Hall, 1971).
52. R. E. Griswold, "A History of the SNOBOL Programming Languages," *Proc. ACM/SIGPLAN History of Programming Languages Conf.*, Los Angeles (June 1-3, 1978), pp. 601-645.
53. J. F. Gimpel, "Blocks—A New Datatype for SNOBOL 4," *Commun. ACM* **15** (June 1972), pp. 438-447.
54. W. S. Brown, "The ALPAK System for Nonnumerical Algebra on a Digital Computer—I: Polynomials in Several Variables and Truncated Power Series with Polynomial Coefficients," *Bell Syst. Tech. J.* **42** (September 1963), pp. 2081-2119; W. S. Brown, J. P. Hyde, and B. A. Tague, "The ALPAK System for Nonnumerical Algebra on a Digital Computer—II: Rational Functions of Several Variables and Truncated Power Series with Rational-Function Coefficients," *Bell Syst. Tech. J.* **43** (March 1964), pp. 785-804; J. P. Hyde, "The ALPAK System for Nonnumerical Algebra on a Digital Computer—III: Systems of Linear Equations and a Class of Side Relations," *Bell Syst. Tech. J.* **43** (July 1964), pp. 1547-1562.
55. A. D. Hall, Jr., "The Altran System for Rational Function Manipulation—A Survey," *Commun. ACM* **14** (August 1971), pp. 517-521.
56. B. G. Ryder, "The PFORT Verifier," *Software Pract. Exper.* **4** (October-December 1974), pp. 359-377.
57. W. S. Brown, *ALTRAN User's Manual* (Murray Hill, New Jersey: Bell Laboratories, 1977).
58. R. F. Grantges and N. R. Sinowitz, "NEASIM: A General-Purpose Computer Simulation Program for Load-Loss Analysis of Multistage Central Office Switching Networks," *Bell Syst. Tech. J.* **43** (May 1964), pp. 965-1004.
59. M. Richards and C. Whitby-Strevens, *BCPL: The Language and Its Compiler* (New York: Cambridge University Press, 1979).
60. B. W. Kernighan and D. M. Ritchie, *The C Programming Language* (Englewood Cliffs, New Jersey: Prentice-Hall, 1978).
61. B. W. Kernighan, "Ratfor—A Preprocessor for a Rational Fortran," *Software Pract. Exper.* **5** (October-December 1975), pp. 395-406.
62. B. S. Baker, "An Algorithm for Structuring Flowgraphs," *J. ACM* **24** (January 1977), pp. 98-120.
63. J. Cocke and J. T. Schwartz, *Programming Languages and Their Compilers* (New York: New York University Press, 1970).
64. G. A. Kildall, "A Unified Approach to Global Program Optimization," *Proc. ACM Symp. Principles Program. Lang.*, Boston (October 1-3, 1973), pp. 194-206.
65. M. S. Hecht and J. D. Ullman, "Analysis of a Simple Algorithm for Global Data Flow Problems," *Proc. ACM Symp. Principles Program. Lang.*, Boston (October 1-3, 1973), pp. 207-217.
66. J. Nievergelt, "On the Automatic Simplification of Computer Programs," *Commun. ACM* **8** (June 1965), pp. 366-370.
67. R. Sethi and J. D. Ullman, "The Generation of Optimal Code for Arithmetic Expressions," *J. ACM* **17** (October 1970), pp. 715-728.
68. S. G. Wasilew, "A Compiler Writing System with Optimization Capabilities for Complex Object Order Structures," Ph.D. Dissertation, Northwestern University (1971).
69. A. V. Aho and S. C. Johnson, "Optimal Code Generation for Expression Trees," *Proc. 7th Ann. ACM Symp. Theory Comput.*, Albuquerque, New Mexico (May 5-7, 1975), pp. 207-217.

70. A. R. Breithaupt, "Project Viperidae: A Bell Labs Computing Network," *COMPCON '73 Digest of Papers, IEEE Comput. Soc. Int. Conf.*, San Francisco (February 27-March 1, 1973), pp. 235-238.

71. W. D. Farmer and E. E. Newhall, "An Experimental Distributed Switching System to Handle Bursty Computer Traffic," *Proc. ACM Symp. Problems in Optimization of Data Commun. Syst.*, Pine Mountain, Georgia (October 13-16, 1969), pp. 1-33.

72. J. R. Pierce, "Network for Block Switching of Data," *Bell Syst. Tech. J.* 51 (July/August 1972), pp. 1133-1145.

73. A. G. Fraser, *Spider—A Data Communications Experiment*, Comput. Sci. Tech. Rep. No. 23, December 1974 (Murray Hill, New Jersey: Bell Laboratories).

74. L. G. Roberts and B. D. Wessler, "Computer Network Development to Achieve Resource Sharing," *Proc. Amer. Federation Inform. Process. Soc. Spring Joint Comput. Conf.* 36, Atlantic City, New Jersey (May 5-7, 1970), pp. 543-549.

75. A. G. Fraser, U.S. Patent No. 3,749,845; filed August 27, 1971; issued July 31, 1973.

76. A. G. Fraser, "Datakit—A Modular Network for Synchronous and Asynchronous Traffic," *Proc. Int. Conf. Commun.*, Boston (June 10-13, 1979), pp. 20.1.1-20.1.3.

77. W. L. Brown and J. D. Gabbe, "The Electron Distribution in the Earth's Radiation Belts during July 1962 as Measured by Telstar," *J. Geophys. Res.* 68 (February 1, 1963), pp. 607-618.

78. J. D. Gabbe, M. B. Wilk, and W. L. Brown, "Statistical Analysis and Modeling of the High-Energy Proton Data Telstar® I Satellite," *Bell Syst. Tech. J.* 46 (September 1967), pp. 1301-1450.

79. E. E. Zajac, "Computer-Made Perspective Movies as a Scientific and Communication Tool," *Commun. ACM* 7 (March 1964), pp. 169-170.

80. A. M. Noll, "Computer-Generated Three-Dimensional Movies," *Comput. Automation* 14 (November 1965), pp. 20-23.

81. F. W. Sinden, "Synthetic Cinematography," *Perspective* 7 (1965), pp. 279-289.

82. K. C. Knowlton, "Computer-Produced Movies," *Science* 150 (November 1965), pp. 1116-1120.

83. W. H. Ninke, "GRAPHIC I: A Remote Graphical Display Console System," *Proc. Amer. Federation Inform. Process. Soc. Fall Joint Comput. Conf.* 27, Las Vegas, Nevada (December 1965), pp. 839-846.

84. N. R. Sinowitz, "Dataplus: A Language for Real Time Information Retrieval from Hierarchical Data Bases," *Proc. Amer. Federation Inform. Process. Soc. Spring Joint Comput. Conf.* 32, Atlantic City, New Jersey (April 30-May 2, 1968), pp. 395-401.

85. T. A. Gibson and P. F. Stockhausen, "MASTER LINKS—A Hierarchical Data System," *Bell Syst. Tech. J.* 52 (December 1973), pp. 1691-1724.

86. B. W. Puerling and J. T. Roberto, "The Natural Dialogue System," *Bell Syst. Tech. J.* 52 (December 1973), pp. 1725-1741.

87. L. E. Heindel and J. T. Roberto, "The Off-The-Shelf System—A Packaged Information Management System," *Bell Syst. Tech. J.* 52 (December 1973), pp. 1743-1763.

88. See reference 33.

89. W. S. Brown and J. F. Traub, "MERCURY: A System for the Computer-Aided Distribution of Technical Reports," *J. ACM* 16 (January 1969), pp. 13-25.

90. W. K. Lowry, "Use of Computers in Information Systems," *Science* 175 (February 25, 1972), pp. 841-846.

91. R. A. Kennedy, "Bell Laboratories Library Real-Time Loan System (BELLREL)," *J. Lib. Automat.* 1 (June 1968), pp. 128-146.

92. B. W. Kernighan, M. E. Lesk, and J. F. Ossanna, Jr., "Document Preparation," *Bell Syst. Tech. J.* 57 (July/August 1978), pp. 2115-2135.

93. B. W. Kernighan and L. L. Cherry, "A System for Typesetting Mathematics," *Commun. ACM* 18 (March 1975), pp. 151-157.

94. See reference 92.

95. C. Babbage, "On the Mathematical Powers of the Calculating Engine (1837)," in *The Origins of Digital Computers: Selected Papers*, 2nd ed., ed. Brian Randell (New York: Springer-Verlag, 1975), pp. 17-52.

96. L. E. McMahon, L. L. Cherry, and R. Morris, "Statistical Text Processing," *Bell Syst. Tech. J.* **57** (July/August 1978), pp. 2137-2154.

97. R. Morris and L. L. Cherry, "Computer Detection of Typographical Errors," *IEEE Trans. Professional Commun.* **PC-18** (March 1975), pp. 54-56.

98. R. Morris, "Counting Large Numbers of Events in Small Registers," *Commun. ACM* **21** (October 1978), pp. 840-842.

99. A. M. Turing, "On Computable Numbers, with an Application to the Entscheidungs-problem," *Proc. London Math. Soc.*, Series 2, **42** (November 12, 1936), pp. 230-265.

100. W. Keister, A. E. Ritchie, and S. H. Washburn, *Design of Switching Circuits* (Princeton, New Jersey: D. Van Nostrand Co., 1951).

101. D. A. Huffman, "The Synthesis of Sequential Switching Circuits," *J. Franklin Inst.* **257** (March 1954), pp. 275-303.

102. M. O. Rabin and D. Scott, "Finite Automata and Their Decision Problems," *IBM J. Res. Develop.* **3** (April 1959), pp. 114-125.

103. E. F. Moore, "Gedanken-Experiments on Sequential Machines," in *Automata Studies*, ed. C. E. Shannon and J. McCarthy (Princeton, New Jersey: Princeton University Press, 1956), pp. 129-153.

104. G. H. Mealy, "A Method for Synthesizing Sequential Circuits," *Bell Syst. Tech. J.* **34** (September 1955), pp. 1045-1079.

105. M. Karnaugh, "Map Method for Synthesis of Combinational Logic Circuits," *Trans. Amer. Inst. Elec. Eng.*, Pt. 1—*Commun. Electron.* **72** (November 1953), pp. 593-598.

106. A. D. Friedman and P. R. Menon, *Theory and Design of Switching Circuits* (Rockville, Maryland: Computer Science Press, 1975).

107. D. B. Armstrong, "On Finding a Nearly Minimal Set of Fault Detection Tests for Combinational Logic Nets," *IEEE Trans. Electron. Comput.* **EC-15** (February 1966), pp. 66-73.

108. A. D. Friedman and P. R. Menon, *Fault Detection in Digital Circuits* (Englewood Cliffs, New Jersey: Prentice-Hall, 1971).

109. H. Y. Chang, G. W. Smith, Jr., and R. B. Walford, "LAMP: System Description," *Bell Syst. Tech. J.* **53** (October 1974), pp. 1431-1449.

110. C. E. Shannon, "A Mathematical Theory of Communication," *Bell Syst. Tech. J.* **27** (July 1948), pp. 379-423, and (October 1948), pp. 623-656.

111. R. W. Hamming, "Error Detecting and Error Correcting Codes," *Bell Syst. Tech. J.* **26** (April 1950), pp. 147-160.

112. D. W. Hagelbarger, "Recurrent Codes: Easily Mechanized, Burst-Correcting, Binary Codes," *Bell Syst. Tech. J.* **38** (July 1959), pp. 969-984.

113. J. von Neumann, "The General and Logical Theory of Automata," in *Cerebral Mechanisms in Behavior*, ed. L. A. Jeffress (New York: John Wiley, 1951), pp. 1-41.

114. E. F. Moore, "Artificial Living Plants," *Sci. Amer.* **195** (October 1956), pp. 118-126.

115. C. E. Shannon, "Programming a Computer for Playing Chess," *Phil. Mag.*, Series 7, **41** (March 1950), pp. 256-275.

116. J. H. Condon and K. Thompson, "Belle Chess Hardware," in *Advances in Computer Chess 3*, ed. M. R. B. Clarke (Oxford, England: Pergamon Press, 1982), pp. 45-54.

117. N. Chomsky, "Three Models for the Description of Language," *IRE Trans. Inform. Theory* **IT-2** (September 1956), pp. 113-124.

118. ACM Committee on Programming Languages and the GAMM Committee on Programming, "Report on the Algorithmic Language ALGOL," *Numerische Math.* **1** (January 1959), pp. 41-60.

119. E. T. Irons, "A Syntax Directed Compiler for ALGOL 60," *Commun. ACM* **4** (January 1961), pp. 51-55.
120. R. M. McClure, "TMG—A Syntax Directed Compiler," *Proc. 20th ACM Nat. Conf.* (August 25, 1965), pp. 262-274.
121. R. R. Fenichel and M. D. McIlroy, "TMGL," Section BN.4.02 in *MULTICS System—Programmers' Manual* (Cambridge, Massachusetts: MIT Press, 1967), pp. 1-38.
122. D. E. Knuth, "On the Translation of Languages from Left to Right," *Inform. Contr.* **8** (December 1965), pp. 607–639.
123. A. V. Aho, S. C. Johnson, and J. D. Ullman, "Deterministic Parsing of Ambiguous Grammars," *Commun. ACM* **18** (August 1975), pp. 441-458.
124. S. C. Johnson, *YACC: Yet Another Compiler-Compiler*, Comput. Sci. Tech. Rep. No. 32, July 31, 1978 (Murray Hill, New Jersey: Bell Laboratories).
125. P. Hildebrandt and H. Isbitz, "Radix Exchange: An Internal Sorting Method for Digital Computers," *J. ACM* **6** (April 1959), pp. 156-163.
126. R. Morris, "Some Theorems on Sorting," *SIAM J. Appl. Math.* **17** (January 1969), pp. 1-6.
127. A. V. Aho, J. E. Hopcroft, and J. D. Ullman, *The Design and Analysis of Computer Algorithms* (Reading, Massachusetts: Addison-Wesley, 1974).
128. See reference 38.
129. R. W. Floyd, "Nondeterministic Algorithms," *J. ACM* **14** (October 1967), pp. 636-644.
130. See reference 39.
131. J. B. Kruskal, Jr., "On the Shortest Spanning Subtree of a Graph and the Traveling Salesman Problem," *Proc. Amer. Math. Soc.* **7** (February 1956), pp. 48-50.
132. R. C. Prim, "Shortest Connection Networks and Some Generalizations," *Bell Syst. Tech. J.* **36** (November 1957), pp. 1389-1401.
133. Z. A. Melzak, "On the Problem of Steiner," *Can. Math. Bull.* **4** (May 1961), pp. 143-148.
134. S. A. Cook, "The Complexity of Theorem-Proving Procedures," *Proc. 3rd Ann. ACM Symp. Theory Comput.* (New York: Association for Computing Machinery, 1971), pp. 151-158.
135. M. R. Garey and D. S. Johnson, *Computers and Intractability: A Guide to the Theory of NP-Completeness* (San Francisco: W. H. Freeman, 1979).
136. A. V. Aho, M. R. Garey, and F. K. Hwang, "Rectilinear Steiner Trees: Efficient Special-Case Algorithms," *Networks* **7** (Spring 1977), pp. 37-58.
137. R. L. Graham, "Bounds for Certain Multiprocessing Anomalies," *Bell Syst. Tech. J.* **45** (November 1966), pp. 1563-1581.
138. M. R. Garey, D. S. Johnson, and R. Sethi, "The Complexity of Flowshop and Jobshop Scheduling," *Math. Operations Res.* **1** (May 1976), pp. 117-129.
139. D. S. Johnson, A. Demers, J. D. Ullman, M. R. Garey, and R. L. Graham, "Worst-Case Performance Bounds for Simple One-Dimensional Packing Algorithms," *SIAM J. Comput.* **3** (December 1974), pp. 299-325.
140. B. W. Kernighan and S. Lin, "An Efficient Heuristic Procedure for Partitioning Graphs," *Bell Syst. Tech. J.* **49** (February 1970), pp. 291-307.
141. S. Lin and B. W. Kernighan, "An Effective Heuristic Algorithm for the Traveling-Salesman Problem," *Operations Res.* **21** (March/April 1973), pp. 498-516.
142. J. W. Cooley and J. W. Tukey, "An Algorithm for the Machine Calculation of Complex Fourier Series," *Math. Comput.* **19** (April 1965), pp. 297-301.
143. G. D. Bergland and R. Klahn, U.S. Patent No. 3,544,775; filed December 29, 1966; issued December 1, 1970.
144. R. R. Shively, "A Digital Processor to Generate Spectra in Real Time," *IEEE Trans. Comput.* **C-17** (May 1968), pp. 485-491.
145. G. D. Bergland and D. E. Wilson, "A Fast Fourier Transform Algorithm for a Global,

Highly Parallel Processor," *IEEE Trans. Audio Electroacoust.* **AU-17** (June 1969), pp. 125-127.

146. J. F. Kaiser, "Digital Filters," in *System Analysis by Digital Computer*, ed. F. F. Kuo and J. F. Kaiser (New York: John Wiley, 1966), pp. 218-285.
147. I. W. Sandberg, "A Theorem Concerning Limit Cycles in Digital Filters," *Proc. 7th Ann. Allerton Conf. Circuit Syst. Theory*, Monticello, Illinois (October 8-10, 1969), pp. 63-68.
148. R. W. Hamming, "Stable Predictor-Corrector Methods for Ordinary Differential Equations," *J. ACM* **6** (January 1959), pp. 37-47.
149. R. W. Hamming, "Numerical Analysis vs. Mathematics," *Science* **148** (April 23, 1965), pp. 473-475.
150. R. W. Hamming, "One Man's View of Computer Science," *J. ACM* **16** (January 1969), pp. 3-12.
151. H. Wang, "Proving Theorems by Pattern Recognition—II," *Bell Syst. Tech. J.* **40** (January 1961), pp. 1-41.
152. H. Wang, "Proving Theorems by Pattern Recognition I," *Commun. ACM* **3** (April 1960), pp. 220-234.
153. W. S. Brown and J. F. Traub, "On Euclid's Algorithm and the Theory of Subresultants," *J. ACM* **18** (October 1971), pp. 505-514.
154. E. R. Berlekamp, "Factoring Polynomials Over Large Finite Fields," *Math. Comput.* **24** (July 1970), pp. 713-735.

Chapter 10

Digital Communications

By the early 1980s, digital communications was taken for granted. Virtually all new transmission and switching systems were digital, and the telephone plant was in the midst of an evolution that promised to provide all users of telecommunications facilities with flexible, end-to-end digital connectivity. The story of the turnabout from the analog transmission facilities of the 1940s to the first digital transmission system—the T-1 carrier—installed in 1962 is a fascinating one, and one on which pivots the entire philosophy of communications in the modern era. The path from analog to digital was not an obvious one, and the turnings to and fro in response to progress and circumstance illuminate the nature of telecommunications research in one of its most fertile periods. This far-reaching advance and the further innovations that followed illustrate some of the great successes of the combination and coordination of research and development at Bell Laboratories.

I. PULSE-CODE MODULATION (PCM)

It is ironic that before Alexander Graham Bell's invention of the telephone in 1875, the existing communications facilities—i.e., telegraph systems—were digital. Inventors during the 40 years preceding Bell's invention had attempted unsuccessfully to "telegraph" music and speech using simple openings and closings of electrical circuits. Bell focused the world's attention on the intrinsic advantages of analog transmission. His aim was " . . . by means of the undulation of pressure of sound on a membrane, to produce an electric current the strength of which should at every instant vary directly as the pressure varied."[1] Analog transmission of speech was ideally suited to the needs, media, and technology of the first half of the 20th century, and it was only during the period immediately preceding World War II that some researchers turned their attention toward the consideration of the possibilities of digital methodologies for speech transmission. There was no foreshadowing at that time of the digital electronics and computer revolution yet to come, which would provide such a natural environment for the evolution to a digital plant.

The history of pulse-code modulation (PCM) in the Bell System parallels

Principal author: R. W. Lucky. Portions of this chapter have been adapted from an unpublished manuscript on pulse-code modulation by W. R. Bennett.

that of the microwave radio systems discussed in Chapter 5 of this volume. Both had their antecedents in the years before World War II, and each grew to commercial application during the period from 1950 to 1965. Ironically, PCM was invented for possible application to microwave radio links and, instead, became the dominant technique for short-haul cable systems. In 1938, the extra bandwidth needed for PCM on radio links seemed economical and easily obtainable, but the following decades showed that the more important application was time-multiplexing of many (24) channels on a single cable pair, thereby increasing the utilization of existing conduit facilities. It was only in the early 1980s that once again PCM and radio technologies came together in the form of high-capacity digital radio systems. In the interim, PCM had a rich history of its own, changing the face of modern communications technology and emerging as one of the principal themes of change in the telecommunications plant during the second half of the 20th century.

1.1 Mathematical Foundations of PCM

PCM is based on two concepts: first, a continuous signal wave can be reconstructed from isolated samples, and, second, the samples can be adequately approximated by discrete numbers. Of these concepts, the first is the more revolutionary. Once the notion of reproducing a wave from samples is accepted, the idea of measuring the samples in terms of a discrete scale of numbers with sufficiently close spacing to make roundoff negligible presents few difficulties.

Determination of a complete waveform from a set of samples is an interpolation problem, and as such was touched on by various mathematicians in the 19th century and earlier. Some of the history of this problem, and the central contribution of H. Nyquist [Fig. 10-1], have been recounted in Chapter 1, section 2.3 of this volume. Although E. T. Whittaker had shown a complete demonstration of the sampling theorem in the Proceedings of the Royal Society of Edinburgh in 1915,[2] communications engineers remained unaware that a band-limited function could be uniquely reconstructed from a set of samples taken at a rate exceeding twice the highest frequency of its components. The first need for the notion of sampling in communications came when multiplexing of telephone channels by time division was proposed. Some patents were issued on methods of time-sharing for independent speech waves in the early 1900s, but because of the relatively slow rotating switches available at that time, time-sharing did not come close to a useful realization.

A serious suggestion reviving the idea of time-division multiplexing for voice channels was made by G. Valensi of France in 1920. Valensi offered his idea to the United States as a gift expressing his gratitude for aid in World War I. The method was brought to the attention of the American

Fig. 10-1. H. Nyquist, who originated many fundamental concepts of communications, including the criterion for stability of negative feedback amplifiers and sampling theory as applied to digital systems.

Telephone and Telegraph Company (in an unpublished memorandum transmitted to J. J. Carty in 1920), and J. R. Carson was given the assignment to analyze its merit. Carson, in an unpublished memorandum of 1920, calculated the response that would be observed in the output of the typical segment of a receiving distributor from a contact rotating in synchronism with that of a similar distributor at the transmitting end of a line when independent signals were impressed on the different segments at the transmitter. His calculations showed that a low-pass filter in the output circuit with cutoff at the highest frequency in the signal band reproduced the original signal correctly when the sampling rate exceeded twice the highest signal frequency. This was, in effect, the sampling theorem, but Carson did not emphasize this result. He was more interested in the crosstalk between the channels assigned to adjacent commutator segments. It appeared that the amount of bandwidth required to reduce the crosstalk below tolerable limits was far too great to make the plan attractive. Carson's well-founded objections of that time laid time-division multiplex telephony to rest for many years, just as his evaluation of frequency modulation in the same era properly dampened the enthusiasm of early FM adherents. (See Chapter 1, section 2.2 in this volume.)

The next appearance of the sampling theorem was in the classic paper by Nyquist in 1928.[3] Nyquist's problem at that time was telegraph transmission over a limited bandwidth. He showed how many independent samples could be received over a channel with specified bandwidth in the absence of noise. Although the sampling theorem was not explicitly stated, the result was implicit in Nyquist's work, and communications engineers in succeeding years came again and again to refer to the insight in Nyquist's landmark contribution.

The feasibility of time-division multiplex telephony became a subject of further examination in the late 1930s when the Bell System began the development of a truly wideband facility using a coaxial cable as the transmission medium. Nyquist and W. R. Bennett [Fig. 10-2] looked at the problem, and both naturally began by studying Carson's 1920 memorandum. Nyquist thought that Carson was too pessimistic about bandwidth requirements and suggested that the principles enunciated in his 1928 paper could be applied to use bandwidth more efficiently. Nyquist's proposal consisted of the use of linear networks to rearrange the spectrum

Fig. 10-2. W. R. Bennett, who pioneered in digital communications and wrote several books on the field.

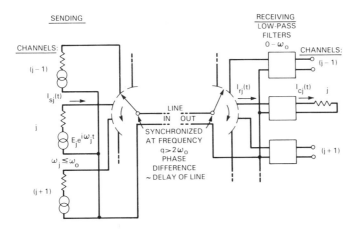

Fig. 10-3. W. R. Bennett's 1941 representation of a time-division multiplex system. Samples from three channels at left are delivered to three receiving channels at right.

of the signal samples before transmission to the line. It became clear to Bennett from a study of Nyquist's algebra that what Nyquist was trying to do was equivalent to taking samples with infinitesimal contact time. Bennett's paper on time-division multiplex telephony, published in 1941, expounded this idea and again exhibited the sampling theorem.[4] The conclusion reached was that time-division multiplex was not a good method to apply to the coaxial cable. [Fig. 10-3] Although the available bandwidth would have been sufficient, the variations in attenuation and delay as functions of frequency over a long multirepeatered coaxial cable system were large enough to produce intolerable crosstalk between channels. The knowledge gained by these studies remained a part of the communications art and was available when new problems arose with different constraints.

1.2 The Invention of PCM

PCM was first disclosed in a patent issued to P. M. Rainey of the Western Electric Company in 1926.[5] Rainey gave a complete description of how the method could be applied to picture and facsimile signals. [Fig. 10-4] His invention aroused little interest at the time and was, in fact, forgotten by Bell System engineers. The existence of his patent was only discovered after many other PCM patents had been issued. The second patent on PCM, and the one that became associated with its invention, was obtained by A. H. Reeves, who conceived the idea in 1937 while working at the Paris laboratories of the International Telephone and Telegraph Corporation.[6,7] Reeves's patent, issued in the United States in 1942, expressed the three steps in succession that were necessary in a PCM

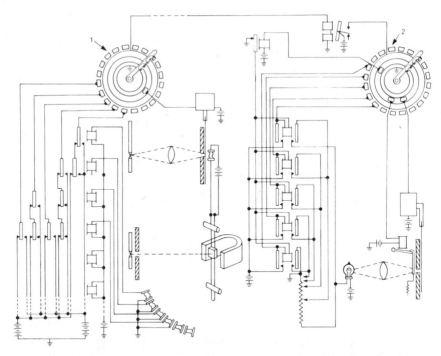

Fig. 10-4.   Drawing adapted from a diagram in P. M. Rainey's patent, filed in 1921
and issued in 1926, showing how code could be transmitted from the distributor (1) to
the receiving distributor (2). The application here was for sending photographs or other
graphic information over telegraph lines.

system. The first, not new, was to scan the speech at a suitable rate and
measure the amplitude of the speech wave at each time interval. The
second was to quantize the amplitudes thus measured to a nearest integer.
The third was to code such integers in ordinary telegraph code.

Reeves conducted shortwave transmission experiments across the English
Channel in the years immediately preceding World War II. He successfully
transmitted speech by pulse-amplitude modulation, pulse-duration modulation, and pulse-position modulation. His work on PCM was apparently
restricted to disclosure on paper as to how it could be done. Engineers at
Bell Laboratories saw copies of Reeves's circuit descriptions furnished as
a part of the cross-licensing arrangements with the International Telephone
and Telegraph Corporation. The significance of the PCM invention was
not readily apparent at that time. For one thing, the interest at Bell Laboratories was in media with narrow bandwidth. Also the complexity of
the PCM process called for components that, at the time, were not well
adapted. In consequence, although during and after World War II pulse-
time modulation was used to a fairly large extent, the use of PCM had
hardly begun.

1.3 PCM Technology During World War II

Somewhat before the entry of the United States into World War II, a group of circuit research engineers at Bell Laboratories was presented with a problem that, in effect, made PCM mandatory. The problem was that of developing effective systems for the secret transmission of speech. In World War I, the secrecy problem for telegraphy had been solved by using a method consisting of adding a random binary key modulo 2 to a synchronous binary message. If the key was completely random, then all decoded messages became equally probable. Recovery of the original message could be performed only if the random key was known. This method had not been applied to voice transmission because it necessitated transmission of voice waves by digitized samples, which would have expanded the bandwidth required.

The need at that time was for a secure enciphering of speech on an ordinary voice channel. Means for facilitating this were at hand in the form of the vocoder invented by H. Dudley in 1935. (See Chapter 2, section 1.2.1, of this volume.)[8,9] The vocoder provided a bandwidth reduction of speech by a factor of ten if preservation of intelligibility but not necessarily speech quality were considered satisfactory. If the vocoder signal could be transmitted by digitized samples over an ordinary voice channel, an encrypted speech system could be furnished for wide usage.

Details of a vocoder secrecy system were worked out by R. K. Potter and R. C. Mathes in 1941. A laboratory study of the project was initiated by engineers of the circuit research group. There was no government contract at first, and the early investigations had no classified status. The scheme that was evolved transmitted ten spectrum channels and a pitch channel. The bandwidth of each of these 11 channels was restricted to the range of 0 to 25 hertz, and hence each required sampling at the rate of 50 times per second. It was found by trial that the spectrum channels could be represented adequately by a voltage scale with six steps and that the pitch values required a further subdivision of each of the six primary steps into six smaller steps.

The complete transmission requirement could be expressed as that of sending twelve 6-valued pulses, 50 times per second. The total number of pulses per second was 600, which appeared to be within the capability of voice channels at that time. Since a principal application was to be on transoceanic radio circuits plagued by multipath transmission, it seemed best to send the 12 pulses simultaneously in separate frequency subbands of the voice channel, with the six possible levels being distinguished in each subband by a choice among six discrete frequencies. The system, which later became known as Project X, could be described as 12-channel hexary PCM-FM-FDM (frequency-division multiplex). It represented the first successful realization of a PCM system for transmission of speech. (For more detail on this system, see Chapter 5, section 4.3 in a companion volume in this series, subtitled *National Service in War and Peace (1925-1975)*, pp. 296-317.)

Before the end of the war, several research groups at Bell Laboratories were engaged in studying PCM. A secrecy system using PCM applied to the complete voice band was developed by H. S. Black and J. O. Edson.[10] This was an 8-channel system known as the AN/TRC-16, operating at a sampling rate of 8000 samples per second and quantizing the samples in 32 steps corresponding to five binary digits (bits). It was designed for use on high-quality microwave radio circuits that could accommodate the high pulse rate, which was 320 kilobits per second. The AN/TRC-16 required a bandwidth of 420 kilohertz (kHz). Although built for the United States government, it was not used during World War II because no satisfactory keying equipment was provided. The Project X system used an encryption key obtained by recording samples of uniformly distributed random noise and playing copies of the record at the transmitter and receiver. The technology of recording and reproducing was not sufficiently advanced at that time for a similar operation at the higher AN/TRC-16 pulse rate. Recourse was therefore taken to pseudorandom keying systems obtained by mixing multivibrator cycles, but skilled government cryptanalysts showed that the apparently secure key generated in this fashion could be broken with ridiculous ease.

Another proposed military use of PCM was being studied at that time in the radio research department at the Holmdel, New Jersey location of Bell Labs under W. M. Goodall. Working in conjunction with R. L. Carbrey and D. M. Black, then at the Murray Hill, New Jersey location, Goodall's group was building a 4-channel PCM system to be submitted to the Navy for encrypted voice transmission. One of the difficulties in the design was the necessity of keeping proper synchronism in spite of the roll of the ship, which could keep the directive antennas out of contact for many seconds at a time. Carbrey developed an arrangement using a voltage-controlled crystal oscillator with the feedback voltage stored on a large capacitor, which was able to hold the 8-kHz timing wave in synchronism during outages of up to one minute. Unfortunately, the project was rejected by the Navy on the grounds that the ships then had so many radar antennas installed that there was not room or time to reconfigure for yet another antenna. In spite of the lack of military interest, some fundamentally important results on coding methodologies grew out of this project.

Before the end of World War II, Bell Labs scientists and engineers began an exploration of PCM for ordinary telephone use, apart from the aspect of secrecy. This work was security classified at that time because of the sensitivity of the subject with regard to military applications. The classification was later removed, but many of the earlier results remain unpublished to the time of this writing (1984). Other wartime communications projects at Bell Laboratories have been described in *National Service in War and Peace (1925-1975)*.

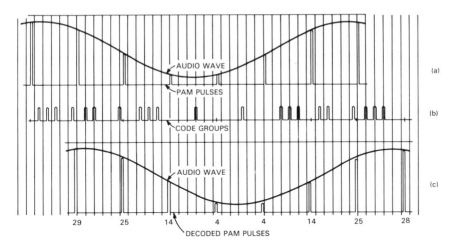

1.4 Early Nonmilitary PCM Experimental Systems

The period from 1944 to 1948 was the most fruitful in the history of PCM. The wartime projects had provided a stimulus immediately after the invention of PCM, at a time when there was no apparent commercial need for such a system. Research groups were intrigued with the concept of PCM and were engaged in building experimental PCM systems by the end of the war. At Deal, New Jersey (near Holmdel), Goodall sent a single voice channel by a PCM radio link, with a sampling rate of 8 kHz and 5-bit (32-level) quantization.[11] [Fig. 10-5] At Murray Hill, New Jersey, H. S. Black and Edson continued their experimental work with the 8-channel PCM multiplex system. One of their notable inventions was the notion of companding—i.e., compressing the signal at the transmitter and expanding it at the receiver. A logarithmic relation was used in the quantization of the speech waveform, so that low-amplitude speech amplitudes were finely quantized, whereas high-amplitude speech amplitudes were more coarsely quantized. This resulted in a subjectively higher signal-to-noise ratio in the decoded speech. Companding has been in universal use in PCM systems.

Fig. 10-5. Analog-to-digital-to-analog conversion in W. M. Goodall's single-voice channel of 1947. Diagram shows (a) Original, sampled wave. (b) Code groups corresponding to the samples. (c) Reconstructed waveform.

The early experimental systems showed such promise that a skeletonized 96-channel system was constructed by a group led by C. B. Feldman at Murray Hill. [Fig. 10-6] This system represented the fruition of an extensive series of experimental and analytical investigations of PCM, and was reported in a number of published papers during 1948 and early 1949.[12-20] The 96-channel system utilized a 4-gigahertz (GHz) radio link between laboratory locations at Murray Hill and New York City. [Fig. 10-7] Speech

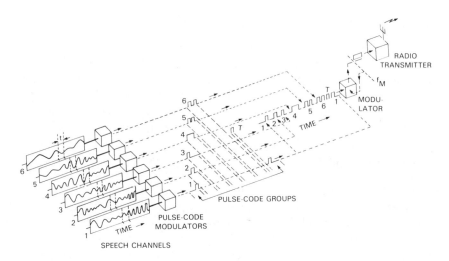

Fig. 10-6.   Schematic of a time-multiplexed transmission system for six speech channels. This is taken from a 1948 description of C. B. Feldman's experimental 96-channel system.

Fig. 10-7.   Experimental 96-channel PCM system, demonstrated by Bell Laboratories in 1947. Photo shows a front view of the terminal equipment with covers removed from a 12-channel group bay.

signals were sampled at an 8-kHz rate and quantized in 7-bit samples. Twelve such channels were combined at a time-division multiplex signal, which modulated an intermediate frequency carrier. Several such carriers, separated by 1.5 megahertz (MHz), could drive the up-converter of a microwave system. Two such 12-channel groups were transmitted from one location, regenerated at the other location, and transmitted back to the first location. The first phase of this notable trial system was completed in 1946.

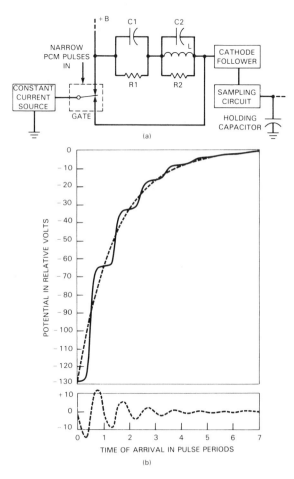

Fig. 10-8. Principles of Shannon-Rack decoder. (a) The decoder uses two capacitor discharging circuits in series. In the left-hand circuit, a capacitor is shunted by a resistor and discharges exponentially. In the right-hand circuit, the capacitor is shunted by a resistor and a resonating inductor; it discharges as an exponential sinusoid. (b) Curves in dashed lines represent the discharge of the left and right circuits of (a); their combination is shown by the solid-line curve.

1.4.1 PCM Codecs

During this postwar period, perhaps the key technical problem was the implementation of coding and decoding circuits for PCM. One of the earliest effective coders was invented by C. E. Shannon, who is best known for his later work on information theory (see Chapter 1, section VIII). The Shannon coder generated binary-weighted values by sampling an exponentially decaying waveform. The decay was set to decrease by one-half for each digit period. The resulting binary-weighted values were then used to generate the quantized approximation to the voice signal by subtracting proportional charge from a capacitor. This circuit suffered significantly if there was the slightest jitter in the sampling wave, because the exponential signal was decaying so rapidly for the high-order digits. A. J. Rack later improved on this by adding a sine wave of the bit frequency of appropriate magnitude to the decaying waveform. When properly phased, this provided a relatively flat step during the time the samples were taken. The resulting coder/decoder (codec) was termed the "Shannon-Rack" codec. [Fig. 10-8] In designing the early PCM system intended for Navy use, Carbrey had encountered difficulty in sampling the decaying waveform of the Shannon circuit and invented and demonstrated sequential approximation codecs using binary-weighted divider networks in 1947.[21] Although this invention was passed by because of other codec developments at that time, a similar technique evolved from later work and became the chief method of codec implementation in large-scale integrated circuits.

1.4.2 The Beam Coding Tube

The 1948 Murray Hill PCM system quantized with an electron-beam coding tube invented by R. W. Sears.[22] [Fig. 10-9] This tube used a focused-point beam that passed through a code-masking plate with a pattern of square holes, such that the current reaching the collector behind the plate was a series of binary-coded pulses corresponding to the proper code for

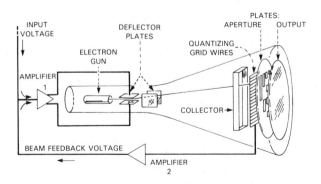

Fig. 10-9.   Diagram of R. W. Sears's PCM coding tube.

DECIMAL	CONVENTIONAL BINARY	GRAY CODE
0	0000	0000
1	0001	0001
2	0010	0011
3	0011	0010
4	0100	0110
5	0101	0111
6	0110	0101
7	0111	0100
8	1000	1100
9	1001	1101
10	1010	1111
11	1011	1110
12	1100	1010
13	1101	1011
14	1110	1001
15	1111	1000

Fig. 10-10. Gray code. This form of Gray code (right column) illustrates that from any number to any adjacent number in a Gray code, only one change from one to zero or zero to one is required. By contrast, note that the change from 7 to 8 requires, in conventional binary notation, a change in all four digits.

the amplitude of the deflection in the x-direction. The first beam coding tube utilized a 7-digit, 128-level code plate. Quantization of the signal was provided by quantizing grid wires. These were very fine wires stretched in front of the code plate at each of the 128 levels. A feedback arrangement caused the input sample to pull down until part of the beam rested on the wire. This part of the beam was then held in contact with that wire as the beam was swept across the plate. To allow for sample drift, the beam was swept from the least significant bit to the most significant bit. The result was a form of the Shannon-Rack decoder that worked the least significant bit first.

Unfortunately, in the beam coder tube, the beam current passing through the grid wires caused those very fine wires to sag. If the sag was sufficient, the beam would then home on the next lower grid wire and generate an error. F. Gray looked into this problem and invented what he called the Reflected Binary Code, in which adjacent numbers differ in only one digit.[23] [Fig. 10-10] With the Gray code, even if the grid wires in the beam coder tube sagged, the coded level of the output would differ by no more than one step. The Gray code has been in universal use for analog-to-digital conversion.

1.4.3 Flash Coding

The invention of the Gray code led to the realization of the first flash coder, in which all of the bits corresponding to a given level of quantization could be generated simultaneously. Gray and Sears recognized that the quantizing grid wires in the beam coder tube could be eliminated because one of the two adjacent codes would be developed even if the beam fell halfway across the edge of the one aperture hole between the two levels. In the Gray code, only one bit could be in doubt when the sample was midway between adjacent numbers, and it did not matter, in this case, which decision was made. F. W. Kammerer and Sears collaborated on creating a ribbon-beam flash coder with separate collector plates behind each digit column. The plates were placed at an angle with respect to the beam to provide increased collector current as a result of grazing incidence. The ribbon beam illuminated simultaneously all windows of a given row and produced directly the corresponding Gray-code value. With the flash coder, the speed restriction was set by the sampling rate and the time required to make a single-bit decision, rather than by the time required to make N-bit decisions as in the earlier beam coder tube. In addition, the problem of decay of the held sample was alleviated because the sample was held for only one bit interval. Once encoded, higher-speed logic could be used to convert the parallel bits to serial for transmission over a single path. Beam coding tubes with both 8 and 9 digits were built during the next few years.

The increased speed of the flash coder was used by Goodall in the first demonstration of PCM transmission of television signals.[24] Goodall's system, constructed at Holmdel in 1950, used a 10-MHz sampling rate and a 5-bit code. Microwave radio provided the wide bandwidth needed for such a high-rate digital signal.

1.5 Experimental and Theoretical Advances of PCM Concepts

There appears to be general agreement that the year 1948 brought to a close the first phase of the development of PCM. By then most of the main factors required for efficient long-distance PCM were well realized, together with an impressive body of basic theory and philosophy. In that year, L. A. Meacham and E. Peterson published the account of the experimental multichannel system constructed at Murray Hill.[25] This is the first account of an experimental PCM multichannel system intended for toll quality. In the same year, the beam coder tube work was published, and P. A. Reiling described for the first time the principle of companding. Perhaps all these contributions were overshadowed by a landmark publication by B. M. Oliver, J. R. Pierce, and Shannon entitled "The Philosophy of PCM."[26] This paper explained the basic philosophy of PCM in terms of the previous work by Nyquist, but in a more usable form. It lucidly and compellingly presented the case for PCM and, as a result, influenced a generation of communications engineers. There were other significant conceptual contributions during 1948. Two papers by Bennett entitled

"Spectra of Quantized Signals" and "Noise in PCM Systems,"[27] together with Bennett's 1941 paper on time-division multiplex, became classics that were still referenced in the early 1980s.

Considering that in 1948 Shannon also pioneered information theory and that the transistor had just been invented, it is doubtful that there has ever been a more fruitful year in the history of Bell Laboratories. But with the end of 1948 came a lull in the explosive pace of PCM development. Although work on PCM continued at Bell Laboratories, it was on a somewhat more modest scale. An impressive amount of communication skills had been developed with no immediate matching need in the telephone plant.

With the successful demonstrations of PCM, it had to be decided what application PCM would have in the plans of the Bell System for expansion of their communications facilities. A committee was formed to study the pros and cons. The recommendation was adverse, with some difference of opinion as to the relative importance of the various factors affecting the decision. Probably the most important consideration was that FM was available and simple. Furthermore, FM could almost meet requirements for L1 coaxial carrier coast-to-coast for both voice and television. PCM had indeed excellent properties, but it did require complicated instrumentation, and its capability for television signals had not yet been demonstrated in the laboratory. (Goodall's experimental television system was reported in 1951.) The decision not to pursue PCM for immediate use in the Bell System naturally led to a temporary subsiding of the activity related to PCM in Bell Laboratories.

As seen in retrospect, the committee decision against PCM was technically well-founded. It was 35 more years before PCM was to be used for long-haul radio system applications. It was just that the committee was looking at the wrong application for this new technology. There appeared to be three situations in which PCM had future possibilities for commercial application. One was the microwave radio relay, for which it had been rejected on the first round. Simplification and speeding up of the coding and decoding operations to handle huge blocks of channels with great economy were investigated as factors that might change the verdict. Also attractive was the possibility of realizing a regenerative microwave pulse repeater that did not require translating the pulses to baseband.[28,29] The second future application was the use of PCM in long distance transmission by waveguide, using the circular electric TE_{01} mode. (See Chapter 6, section IV in this volume.) It seemed that this application would materialize because the wide band of the waveguide was contaminated with mode-changing reflections that could be overridden only by regenerated digital signals. Such an application, however, was bypassed by subsequent technological alternatives.

The third vision at that time, and the one that led to commercial application, was that of deriving multiplex speech channels by PCM over exchange-area cable pairs or over toll cable pairs not suitable for the existing carrier techniques. While a pair of wires has an inherently large bandwidth, analog transmission methods have difficulty in using the available bandwidth because they cannot tolerate the accumulation of noise and distortion that occurs in a long repeatered system. Digital channels can secure immunity from accumulated defects by the use of closely spaced regenerators. Each regenerative repeater delivers clean retimed pulses, and no degradation accrues unless the disturbance in an individual link is great enough to cause an error. Practical realization of this philosophy of "regenerative payoff" required the development of a satisfactory repeater that could be used in large numbers at low cost.

1.6 Repeaters in PCM

The invention of the transistor offered a possible solution to the quest for a practical regenerative repeater. The attractive potentialities for small size, low cost, low power, long life, and stable operation seemed the answer to the communications engineer's prayer. Unfortunately, the first transistors, which were of the point-contact type, did not fulfill all of these promises. It is not generally remembered that the initial excitement over the transistor was followed by a period of gloom and frustration on the part of those who tried to find uses for the wonderful new device. What perhaps seems now a reactionary step in PCM research was taken by seriously considering a regenerative repeater equipped with vacuum tubes for use on cable circuits. The vacuum tube department agreed that no one had ever tried to make a tube having the required properties. They proceeded to make some, concentrating on the goals of low power consumption and long life at the expense of linearity and gain. Good regenerative repeaters using these tubes were actually constructed, and a reasonable version of PCM on cable emerged from the work.

The project as seen from modern perspective was, of course, only one of marking time, but some basic problems in circuit design were solved for later use in a more promising environment. One problem was how to make efficient use of a cable pair between repeaters. For a number of reasons, the very low frequencies, including zero, are not very attractive. There are considerable variations in the response of a wire circuit in the low-frequency region, as well as an undue contamination by extraneous noise sources. Also it is a great advantage to be able to use transformers and blocking capacitors in the design of repeaters. To send pulses over a system that does not pass dc and that severely attenuates low-frequency components opens the door to the problem of zero wander. This was an age-old problem in telegraphy that had in fact been solved by J. W. Milnor when vacuum-tube repeaters were inserted in the New York-Azores submarine telegraph cable.[30] The method was to feed back to the input a part of the outgoing regenerated pulse through a low-pass network complementary to the high-pass characteristic that had caused the distortion. This is not linear equalization but is a replacement of the suppressed components by clean new ones generated by the repeater. In later years, this approach came to be known as decision feedback equalization.

Other solutions to the low-frequency transmission problem were proposed. Meacham proposed the so-called "dicode" pulse in which the dc is removed by delaying the pulse train one bit interval and subtracting the delayed wave from the original pulse train.[31] Subsequently, it was learned that British engineers had a simpler way of achieving the same result; they merely reversed the polarity of alternate pulses. The disadvantage in both cases is that positive and negative pulses must be distinguished as well as the value zero, and margin over noise is lost relative to straight binary decisions. It is of interest that what was then called "British dicode" was in fact the same as the alternate bipolar pulse train used in the T-1 carrier system.[32]

The work on the vacuum-tube regenerative repeater for PCM on cable was quite well in hand in 1952. At that time, junction-type transistors began to be available in sufficient quantities and of satisfactory quality to cast a cloud on the future of tubes for regeneration. L. R. Wrathall[33] built

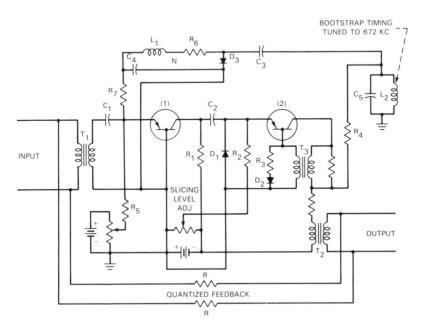

Fig. 10-11. Circuit diagram of L. R. Wrathall's transistorized regenerative repeater. The repeater demonstrated the feasibility of PCM in the cable plant.

a transistorized regenerative repeater that incorporated a new twist suggested by Rack to compensate the zero wander in on-off signaling. [Fig. 10-11] The scheme was similar to the earlier submarine telegraph method except that the complementary low-pass network in the feedback path was replaced by a high-pass structure with the same cutoff properties that caused the low-frequency defect in the first place. This solution strongly underscored the principle of quantized feedback, rather than equalization. What was accomplished was the canceling out of the pulse tails at the subsequent sampling times, and it did not matter what the wave did between samples. Rack's solution matched time constants rather than frequency characteristics and obtained the advantage of an ac-coupled feedback path. The repeater designed by Wrathall was demonstrated on an experimental cable system, using repeater spacings of 2.3 miles on 19-gauge cable, and 0.56 mile on 32-gauge cable. At about the same time, O. E. DeLange built a repeater operating at 4 GHz, with regeneration carried out directly at microwave frequencies, greatly simplifying the repeater.[34] Wrathall's repeater eventually achieved widespread recognition and became the cornerstone upon which a strong case was made for a PCM system to increase the number of voice channels available on existing cables.

1.6.1 *Timing Jitter in Regenerative Repeaters*

Before PCM systems could become commercial realities, a series of engineering problems had to be solved. One of the problems that drew most attention was that of the accumulation of jitter in the timing of the regenerative repeaters. This problem was not only one of inventive circuit design and experimentation, but one of conceptual interest and importance. Bennett had set forth the mathematical foundation for consideration of this problem in his 1958 paper on statistics of regenerative repeaters.[35] DeLange contributed early experimental results this same year, but many more results were obtained by a series of authors over the next decade before the problem was considered solved.

A regenerative repeater has three functions—the so-called three Rs: reshaping, retiming, and regeneration. On the simplest level, the repeater detects the incoming pulses and recreates new, clean pulses to pass down the line to the next repeater. So long as the digital error rate is small, the signal remains uncontaminated by any accumulation of noise and distortion as happens with analog transmission. However, it is inconvenient for remote repeaters to have a source of absolute timing information to use in the recreation of the pulses. Therefore, self-timed repeaters are used in which the timing signal is extracted from the incoming signal itself—usually by means of a high-Q (low-loss) tank circuit, which derives a source of stable clock from the transitions in the input signal. Such self-timed repeaters are subject to five sources of error, which can have the effect of introducing a random (or pattern-dependent) jitter into the outgoing pulse train. The sources of jitter are random noise, mistuning of the tank circuit, finite width of the pulses, amplitude-to-phase conversion by nonlinear devices, and crosstalk between channels. Studies by M. R. Aaron and Gray,[36] C. J. Byrne, B. J. Karafin, and D. B. Robinson, Jr.,[37] DeLange,[38,39] M. Pustelnyk,[39] B. K. Kinariwala,[40] J. M. Manley,[41] H. E. Rowe,[42] and E. D. Sunde[43] gradually shed light on this problem. It was shown that the accumulation of jitter due to noise was small and did not grow indefinitely in a long string of repeaters. Surprisingly, the most important sources of jitter were the pattern-dependent effects related to the pulse shape.

1.7 The T-1 PCM Carrier System

The research contribution to PCM—a period of 10 years of discovery and incubation—ended with Wrathall's transistorized repeater. It was clear at that time (1956) that PCM could be used to increase the number of voice channels available on existing cables. Many of the pairs in cables were then being used for single voice channels and were equipped with loading coils at a spacing of 1.8 kilometers (km) to improve their response in the voice band. What could be more natural than to replace the loading coils with matchbox-sized, unattended repeaters that would extend the capability from 1 to 24 channels? The economics of the proposal was favored by the filled state of cable conduits in the metropolitan areas. It was not only the cost of providing more cable to be used for single-channel voice circuits that made up the competition, but the more serious cost of digging up the streets to install new conduits.

A decision was made to develop a PCM carrier system, and the project was undertaken by a group headed by E. E. Sumner. A prototype 24-channel PCM carrier system was constructed and tested during 1958 and 1959 on a link between Summit, New Jersey and South Orange, New Jersey. The T-1 system transmitted the 24 voice channels using a 1.544-MHz pulse train in a bipolar code. A 7-bit logarithmic encoding with 26 dB of companding was decided on, with later expansion to 8-bit coding. The solid-state repeaters were intended for use at the 1.8-km spacing coinciding with the usual loading coil placements. By this time, the Wrathall repeater had been rejected because its timing circuit had been found to be unduly vulnerable to crosstalk. Nevertheless, this and the other contributions of research had focused attention on this new approach to more efficient use of the existing telephone plant.

The story of the development of the T-1 carrier system is reserved for a projected future volume of this series, subtitled *Transmission Technology*. Taken together, the research inventions and conceptual contributions, and the subsequent systems design of the development area, represent one of the great success stories of the Bell System. The Bell System pioneered the introduction of PCM transmission systems in the world with the first T-1 operating link that went into service in Skokie, Illinois in 1962. In 1984, there were more than 200 million circuit-kilometers of T-1 carrier in the United States. The postwar research effort was put into perspective by PCM-inventor Reeves when he wrote "Although suitably cheap, long-life components were not still available, the U. S. Bell System took a long shot, that eventually proved correct, in deciding that PCM-steered efforts would be justified at that date as a reasonable bet for future civilian networks."

II. DIFFERENTIAL PCM AND TIME ASSIGNMENT SPEECH INTERPOLATION

During the early development of PCM, there were several significant advances in communications technology that took place as by-products of PCM research. One of these was the invention of differential PCM (DPCM) by C. C. Cutler in 1950.[44] DPCM is a coded form of delta modulation in which the differences between successive samples are coded in a binary form. The difference samples are quantized using a nonuniform compression to take advantage of the redundancy inherent in speech. Thus, fewer levels are required to obtain a given fidelity of speech. This technique has also found application in the coding of television signals. In the early 1980s, a DPCM algorithm using adaptive quantization and prediction was being considered for an international standard for speech encoding.

The other contribution of research worthy of note was the invention of time assignment speech interpolation (TASI). The earliest mention of the concept of sharing a speech channel during quiet intervals is apparently due to A. C. Dickieson in a 1945 internal memorandum entitled "Radio Telephone Systems—Voice Operated Control." In 1947, the group under C. B. Feldman at Murray Hill was pursuing time-multiplexing systems for PCM for as many as 2304 channels. A. E. Melhose designed a speech interpolation system using relays for use on the experimental PCM system. His results were encouraging, but the switching system he employed was cumbersome, and there were problems with speech clipping and hangover. In early 1949, Rack and Carbrey became involved with the problem and evolved a speech interpolation system essentially like the one finally employed in the transatlantic cable application. The only public disclosure of research on TASI-related work at that time was the patent application for TASI filed for Carbrey in 1954.[45] In the same year, a program for the development of TASI for the undersea cable program was undertaken in the Bell Labs transmission development area.

Concurrently with the work on TASI, Carbrey and Feldman investigated another means of speech interpolation known as elastic speech interpolation (ESI).[46] In ESI, the sampling rate for speech was lowered according to the demand for channels. As more and more users demanded service, the overload resulted in channels being sampled at less than optimum rates. The ESI system was tested and appeared to provide reasonable quality. Significant development of TASI-like systems took place during the 1970s, and the combination of technology with new algorithms had a major impact on digital speech interpolation systems.

III. DATA COMMUNICATIONS AND THE COMPUTER

Data communications in the two decades following the introduction of the T-1 PCM carrier system can be divided into two distinct eras. The first represented the period in which the primary aim of communications research was to develop efficient modems (modulators/demodulators) to transmit data in a speech-like form over traditional analog voice channels. In this era the research problems concerned modulation and detection techniques to combat noise and intersymbol interference. The second era was devoted to the conception of computer networks built on the inherently digital capability of systems like T-1 and its progeny in which the native transmission mode handles data directly. Here the concerns turned towards network configurations, queueing, and protocols. Obviously, the emergence of such high-level considerations had to await the growth of significant digital capability in the telecommunications system.

3.1 Data Transmission on Analog Channels

When the first T-1 facilities went into service in 1962, the need for computer-to-computer and terminal-to-computer communication was just beginning to be felt. The evolution of PCM had proceeded on the basis of voice transmission, and the need for a native digital mode of transmission in the telephone plant for computer communications had played no role in the development of the T-1 system. By 1960, however, it was obvious that there would be a growing demand for data traffic on the telephone network, and a data communications laboratory had been formed at Murray Hill (later at Holmdel) under W. O. Fleckenstein to provide a means for carrying data on the existing voice-oriented telephone facilities. Bennett, who had contributed so much to the evolution of PCM, was appointed head of a research department in this new laboratory to study the question of data communications over voice channels.

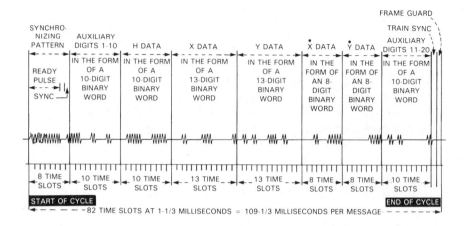

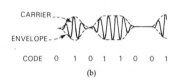

Fig. 10-12. Transmission of radar data with AN/TSQ-7 transmitter over ordinary telephone lines. The transmitter accepted voltages in analog form, converted these to binary digit form, and used the binary digits to control spurts of a carrier frequency applied to the telephone lines; the binary ones denoted the presence of spurts, and the zeros, the absence of spurts. (a) Typical transmitted message; *X* and *Y* data represent east-west and north-south location information, respectively, of detected aircraft, *H* its height, and $\dot{X}$ and $\dot{Y}$ its motin. (b) The line waveform for eight digits.

The art and practice of transmitting data on analog facilities were already quite old in 1960, since the history of telegraphy went back more than 100 years. It is interesting to note that Thomas Edison had transmitted about 500 bits per second on an open-wire telegraph line in 1874—about the same time as the invention of the telephone by Bell. The early data modems were derived directly from these years of telegraph experience. One of the first such modems was the military AN/TSQ data system, which was designed for operation at 750 bits per second using full-carrier double-sideband AM. It was put into service in 1957.[47] [Fig. 10-12] About this same time, the Bell System had developed a modem for the semiautomatic ground environment (SAGE) continental air defense system.[48] The SAGE modem used vestigial-sideband (VSB) AM to transmit data at 2000 bits per second. The first commercial modems developed at Bell Laboratories in the early 1960s were the 103, 202, and 201 modems transmitting respectively at 300, 1200, and 2400 bits per second using full-duplex FM, FM, and phase-shift keyed (PSK) methods of modulation.[49,50] [Fig. 10-13]

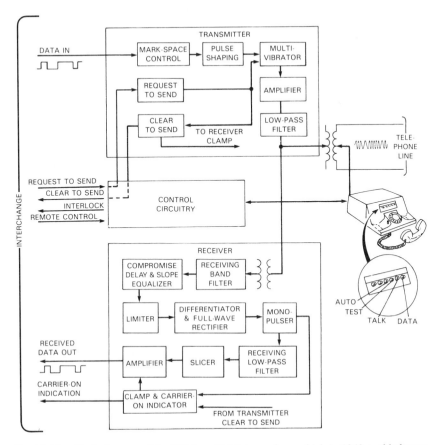

Fig. 10-13.   Block diagram of the 202-type FM data modem, which in 1962 enabled transmission over the switched telephone network at 1200 bits per second.

Twenty years later, in the early 1980s, these modems were worldwide standards, and many hundreds of thousands were put into service. However, none of them represented a significant improvement in communication efficiency over the telegraph art, and, against this backdrop, researchers went to work to study the limitations of the existing analog facilities for digital transmission, and to develop more efficient modulation and detection techniques.

3.2 The Shannon Equation for the Capacity of a Communication Channel

In 1948, Shannon had derived his famous equation for the capacity of a communications channel.[51] (See Chapter 1, section 8.2 in this volume.) In this equation, the capacity of the channel in bits per second is equal to the product of the bandwidth and the logarithm (base 2) of the signal-to-noise ratio plus one. When crudely applied to a voice telephone channel, it indicated that transmission at speeds of about 20,000 bits per second was possible at vanishingly small error rates. This was an order of magnitude greater than the existing modems were capable of operating, so the challenge was well defined. Shannon's proof of the capacity equation was an existence proof, based on an ingenious random-coding bound, but it held no clue as to how higher speeds were to be obtained. Nevertheless, such a bound provided a unique and forceful stimulus for invention, a measure against which the threshold of diminishing returns could be judged, and a means of rejection for the steady stream of ill-considered schemes for higher-rate transmission. Shannon's equation was truly one of the greatest achievements in communications science of Bell Laboratories, and it cast its light across the decades of research in digital communications.

3.3 Channel Dispersion of Pulses—Equalization and Error-Correction Techniques

Although the theoretically limiting factor in voice-band data transmission was the background noise level (about 20 to 30 dB below signal levels), the practical constraint was determined by the channel dispersion. Well-formed pulses transmitted through typical voice channels suffered from distortion caused by the arrival at the receiver of various frequency components at differing times. Because of this dispersion, pulses spread over a greater duration and overlap with adjacent pulses—a phenomenon known as intersymbol interference. Intersymbol interference limited data transmission speeds to less than 2400 bits per second on typical telephone channels. The origin and effects of intersymbol interference as related to measurement of the phase characteristic of the channel were studied by Sunde.[52] Unlike random background noise, intersymbol interference is in theory correctable, and finding an automatic correction technique was one of three goals of a project originated in 1963 to obtain the highest possible data speeds on voice telephone channels. The other two goals were determining the most efficient modulation and deciding on an efficient error-correction coding technique.

In 1964, R. W. Lucky invented the first automatic equalizer for correction of pulse dispersion in data transmission.[53] Lucky's automatic equalizer was based on the use of a tapped delay line (transversal filter), whose successive gain coefficients were automatically set during a training period preceding actual transmission using a steepest-descent algorithm for the minimization of intersymbol interference. [Fig. 10-14] The first model of this automatic equalizer was designed by E. Port and F. K. Becker using 13 adjustable taps controlled by relay-driven ladder attenuator networks. Shortly thereafter, Lucky [Fig. 10-15] conceived of a technique to make the equalizer continuously adaptive during actual data transmission.[54] In

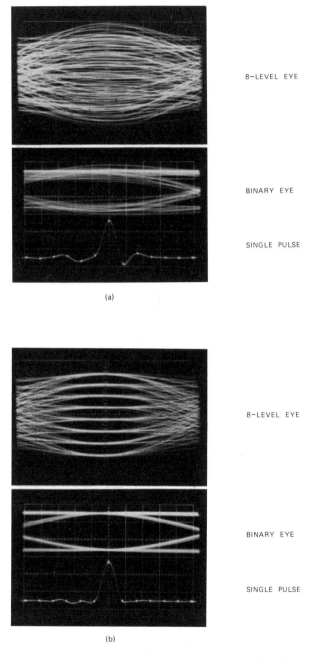

8–LEVEL EYE

BINARY EYE

SINGLE PULSE

(a)

8–LEVEL EYE

BINARY EYE

SINGLE PULSE

(b)

Fig. 10-14. Oscilloscope sweeps of received data voltage for a horizontal sweep rate of $1/T$, where T is the sampling period. The display is known as an eye pattern for binary data. (a) Before equalization, and (b) after equalization with R. W. Lucky's automatic equalizer.

Fig. 10-15.   R. W. Lucky, who invented the automatic equalizer for PCM. The equalizer corrected
effects of pulse dispersion in data transmission.

the adaptive equalizer, the feedback control information was obtained by
comparing decided bits against the receiver's incoming, distorted analog
pulse train in order to ascertain an error component. This technique of
using prior decisions to determine an ideal upon which to base adaptation
became known as decision direction; it subsequently became the basis not
only for equalization but for the recovery of timing and other necessary
receiver parameters. [Fig. 10-16]

The automatic equalizer was implemented in an exploratory high-speed
modem designed by a group under Becker.[55] It had been determined that
VSB modulation was the most efficient technique, so the exploratory modem
used this method in conjunction with a multilevel alphabet which transmitted 4 bits per pulse as a choice among 16 possible amplitude levels.
The transmission of as many as 16 levels of pulse amplitude was made
possible by the combination of the precision of the adaptive equalization
combined with the intrinsically low level of the background noise on the
typical telephone channel.

The third goal of the exploratory project was centered around the inclusion of a powerful error-control system for the correction of the inevitable
errors in any digital communications system. A valuable study of the

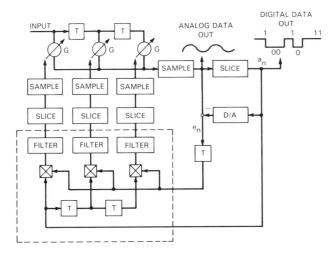

Fig. 10-16. Block diagram of the periodically sampled adaptive equalizer. The circuitry within the dashed rectangle cross-correlates the error signal, e_n, with the (time-shifted) output, a_n, and adjusts the tap gains, G, to eventually reduce this cross-correlation to a value close to zero. D/A is a digital-to-analog converter, and T is the sampling period; e_n is the difference between the distorted analog signal and the reconstructed digital equivalent.

characteristics of error occurrence in voice-band data transmission had been made by A. A. Alexander, R. M. Gryb, and D. W. Nast in 1960.[56] Their study showed a superposition of two error-causing phenomena, one due largely to background noise that caused random errors to be sprinkled throughout the received data, and the other due to burst noise that caused clumps of errors to be clustered in the received data. An error-control system designed by H. O. Burton and E. J. Weldon, Jr., intended to correct both of these characteristic patterns was incorporated in the exploratory modem.[57] The error-control system used an interleaved (for burst-error protection) random error-correcting code. Bell Laboratories researchers R. W. Hamming, D. Slepian, and D. W. Hagelbarger had pioneered such coding techniques earlier (see Chapter 1, section 8.6 in this volume), but this was the first realization of an error-correction system intended for data transmission. In subsequent years as the data communications field matured, it became apparent that error-control systems were more properly incorporated in the sources and nodes of a computer network, rather than within the modems themselves, and this line of research was discontinued.

The exploratory high-speed modem, termed the X203 modem, was used to transmit data in the range of 7200 to 10,800 bits per second on conditioned, leased lines. The X203 modem became the forerunner of the standard 209 modem (9600 bits per second). Studies by D. D. Falconer showed that quadrature amplitude modulation (QAM), in which two quadrature carriers are each amplitude modulated, was somewhat more efficient than the original VSB modulation. The 209 modem used 16-ary QAM (4 amplitudes on each quadrature carrier) and a pulse rate of 2400 pulses per second to obtain a speed of 9600 bits per second. A new passband adaptive equalizer was developed, and timing and carrier phasing were obtained at the receiver using decision-directed feedback loops. The recovery of equalizer and timing information was enhanced by ensuring randomness of the transmitted data by means of self-synchronizing scramblers and descramblers, a technique that had been invented years earlier by R. D. Fracassi[58] but had been classified secret for many years because of its significance to encryption techniques. By this time, about 1970, the high-speed modem was indeed a complicated communications system, and further improvements in communications efficiency suffered from diminishing returns. The eyes of the communications research world turned towards digitally oriented computer communications networks.

3.4 Computer Networks

Interest in the design of networks for digital communications gradually built up during the 1960s. The earliest problem that captured the interest of researchers was that of synchronization of a number of geographically diverse digital links. There were at least two distinct approaches. In one method, a master clock was distributed to all necessary links, while a different philosophy permitted the network to operate without a master clock by averaging the incoming clocks at each network node. G. P. Darwin and R. C. Prim invented a useful network synchronization technique,[59] and considerable analytical work was accomplished by a number of

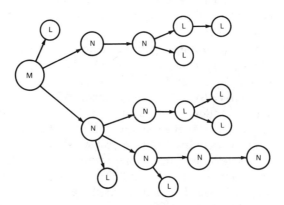

Fig. 10-17.   Synchronization hierarchy of the Digital Data System. The master clock, *M*, derived from an atomic standard, is passed down the hierarchy to nodal, *N*, and local, *L*, timing sources that are phase-locked to the standard.

contributors[60-70] to evaluate the efficacies of proposed synchronization schemes. When the first all-digital network, the Digital Data System (DDS), was designed in the early 1970s, it was decided to use a master clock to synchronize the entire network. The clock distribution formed a hierarchy, with the most accurate clock (an atomic standard) at the top of the hierarchy. [Fig. 10-17] At the bottom of the hierarchy, the links were served by phase-locked loops and could only maintain synchronization in a free-running mode for a period of seconds. Of course, if a branch of the network were cut off, communication within the branch using the local clock as a standard was still possible. This DDS synchronization system was described by B. R. Saltzberg and H. M. Zydney.[71]

In 1968, W. D. Farmer and E. E. Newhall stimulated a renaissance in computer network thought when they demonstrated an experimental network in which nodes were connected onto a closed transmission loop, and the order and priority for use of the common transmission facility was controlled by a protocol enforced on the system by a central controller.[72] Subsequently, Pierce generalized the loop system into a hierarchy of interconnected loops without central control. [Fig. 10-18] In Pierce's system, each node waited for an opening in traffic on its loop to insert blocks of preaddressed data.[73] The early systems concepts of Farmer and Newhall and Pierce were the forerunners of an enormous effort that grew into the

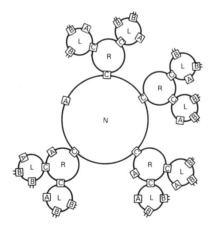

Fig. 10-18. The loop transmission hierarchy proposed by J. R. Pierce in 1972 for data transmission of blocks of data. L, R, and N represent local, regional, and national loops. Three types of boxes appear in the loops. In general, A times and closes the loop; B puts blocks of data on and takes blocks of data off the loop; C transfers blocks of data from one loop to another.

study of local area networks. Some of the Bell Laboratories contributions to this field are detailed in Chapter 8, section 4.4 and in Chapter 9, section 8.1.

By the early 1980s, much of the effort in computer communications was concentrated on protocols to control the entry and flow of packets of data in computer networks. By this time, digital transmission was taken for granted. The philosophy of PCM, which had taken so long to be understood, was the cornerstone of communications thought. With the rapid development of relevant technology, digital switches had been installed in both toll and local serving area applications. The emerging optical transmission facilities were inherently digital. The growth in computer traffic was exponential, and, indeed, the vision of the early researchers of the role of digital communications has certainly been fulfilled.

REFERENCES

1. T. A. Watson, "The Birth and Babyhood of the Telephone," *Ann. Conf. Telephone Pioneers,* Chicago (October 17, 1913), p. 8 in booklet published by AT&T in 1971.
2. E. T. Whittaker, "On the Functions which are represented by the Expansions of the Interpolation-Theory," *Proc. Royal Soc. Edinburgh* **18** (June 7, 1915), pp. 181-194.
3. H. Nyquist, "Certain Topics in Telegraph Transmission Theory," *Trans. Amer. Inst. Elec. Eng.* **47** (April 1928), pp. 617-644.
4. W. R. Bennett, "Time Division Multiplex Systems," *Bell Syst. Tech. J.* **20** (April 1941), pp. 199-221.
5. P. M. Rainey, U.S. Patent No. 1,608,527; filed July 20, 1921; issued November 30, 1926.
6. A. H. Reeves, French Patent No. 852,183; filed October 3, 1938; issued October 23, 1939.
7. A. H. Reeves, U.S. Patent No. 2,272,070; filed November 22, 1939; issued February 3, 1942.
8. H. Dudley, "Remaking Speech," *J. Acoust. Soc. Amer.* **11** (October 1939), pp. 169-177.
9. H. Dudley, U.S. Patent No. 2,151,091; filed October 30, 1935; issued March 21, 1939.
10. H. S. Black and J. O. Edson, "Pulse Code Modulation," *Trans. Amer. Inst. Elec. Eng.* **66** (1947), pp. 895-899.
11. W. M. Goodall, "Telephony By Pulse Code Modulation," *Bell Syst. Tech. J.* **26** (July 1947), pp. 395-409.
12. L. A. Meacham and E. Peterson, "An Experimental Multichannel Pulse Code Modulation System of Toll Quality," *Bell Syst. Tech. J.* **27** (January 1948), pp. 1-43.
13. W. R. Bennett, "Spectra of Quantized Signals," *Bell Syst. Tech. J.* **27** (July 1948), pp. 446-472.
14. C. B. Feldman, "A 96-Channel Pulse Code Modulation System," *Bell Lab. Rec.* **26** (September 1948), pp. 364-370.
15. R. W. Sears, "Beam Deflection Tube for Coding in PCM," *Bell Lab. Rec.* **26** (October 1948), pp. 411-415.
16. R. L. Carbrey, "Decoding in PCM," *Bell Lab. Rec.* **26** (November 1948), pp. 451-456.
17. P. A. Reiling, "Companding in PCM," *Bell Lab. Rec.* **26** (December 1948), pp. 487-490.
18. W. R. Bennett, "Noise in PCM Systems," *Bell Lab. Rec.* **26** (December 1948), pp. 495-499.
19. A. E. Johanson, "Timing Control for PCM," *Bell Lab. Rec.* **27** (January 1949), pp. 10-15.
20. J. M. Manley, "Synchronization for the PCM Receiver," *Bell Lab. Rec.* **27** (February 1949), pp. 62-66.
21. R. L. Carbrey, U.S. Patent No. 2,610,295; filed October 30, 1947; issued September 9, 1952.

22. See reference 15.
23. F. Gray, "Pulse Code Communication," U.S. Patent No. 2,632,058; filed November 13, 1947; issued March 17, 1953.
24. W. M. Goodall, "Television by Pulse Code Modulation," *Bell Syst. Tech. J.* 30 (January 1951), pp. 33-49.
25. See reference 12.
26. B. M. Oliver, J. R. Pierce, and C. E. Shannon, "Philosophy of PCM," *Proc. IRE* 36 (November 1948), pp. 1324-1331.
27. See references 13 and 18.
28. P. A. Reiling, "Waveguide Filters for Pulse Transmission Studies," *Bell Lab. Rec.* 29 (April 1951), pp. 164-168.
29. W. A. Klute, "Pulse Generation and Shaping at Microwave Frequencies," *Bell Lab. Rec.* 29 (May 1951), pp. 216-220.
30. J. W. Milnor, U.S. Patent No. 1,717,116; filed November 9, 1927; issued June 11, 1929.
31. L. A. Meacham, U.S. Patent No. 2,759,047; filed December 27, 1950; issued August 14, 1956.
32. M. R. Aaron, "PCM Transmission in the Exchange Plant," *Bell Syst. Tech. J.* 41 (January 1962), pp. 99-141.
33. L. R. Wrathall, "Transistorized Binary Pulse Regenerator," *Bell Syst. Tech. J.* 35 (September 1956), pp. 1059-1084.
34. O. E. DeLange, "Experiments on the Regeneration of Binary Microwave Pulses," *Bell Syst. Tech. J.* 35 (January 1956), pp. 67-90.
35. W. R. Bennett, "Statistics of Regenerative Digital Transmission," *Bell Syst. Tech. J.* 37 (November 1958), pp. 1501-1542.
36. M. R. Aaron and J. R. Gray, "Probability Distributions for the Phase Jitter in Self-Timed Reconstructive Repeaters for PCM," *Bell Syst. Tech. J.* 41 (March 1962), pp. 503-558.
37. C. J. Byrne, B. J. Karafin, and D. B. Robinson, Jr., "Systematic Jitter in a Chain of Digital Regenerators," *Bell Syst. Tech. J.* 42 (November 1963), pp. 2679-2714.
38. O. E. DeLange, "The Timing of High-Speed Regenerative Repeaters," *Bell Syst. Tech. J.* 37 (November 1958), pp. 1455-1486.
39. O. E. DeLange and M. Pustelnyk, "Experiments on the Timing of Regenerative Repeaters," *Bell Syst. Tech. J.* 37 (November 1958), pp. 1487-1500.
40. B. K. Kinariwala, "Timing Errors in a Chain of Regenerative Repeaters, I," *Bell Syst. Tech. J.* 41 (November 1962), pp. 1769-1780; B. K. Kinariwala, "Timing Errors in a Chain of Regenerative Repeaters, II," *Bell Syst. Tech. J.* 41 (November 1962), pp. 1781-1797; B. K. Kinariwala, "Timing Errors in a Chain of Regenerative Repeaters, III," *Bell Syst. Tech. J.* 43 (July 1964), pp. 1481-1504.
41. J. M. Manley, "The Generation and Accumulation of Timing Noise in PCM Systems— An Experimental and Theoretical Study," *Bell Syst. Tech. J.* 48 (March 1969), pp. 541-613.
42. H. E. Rowe, "Timing in a Long Chain of Regenerative Binary Repeaters," *Bell Syst. Tech. J.* 37 (November 1958), pp. 1543-1598.
43. E. D. Sunde, "Self-Timing Regenerative Repeaters," *Bell Syst. Tech. J.* 36 (July 1957), pp. 891-937.
44. C. C. Cutler, U.S. Patent No. 2,605,361; filed June 29, 1950; issued July 29, 1952.
45. R. L. Carbrey, U.S. Patent No. 2,907,829; filed May 17, 1954; issued October 6, 1959.
46. R. L. Carbrey and C. B. H. Feldman, U.S. Patent No. 2,961,492; filed September 26, 1957; issued November 22, 1960.
47. W. Koenig, "Coordinate Data Sets for Military Use," *Bell Lab. Rec.* 36 (May 1958), pp. 166-170.
48. R. O. Soffel and E. G. Spack, "SAGE Data Terminals," *Trans. Amer. Inst. Elec. Eng., Pt. 1—Commun. Electron.* 77 (January 1959), pp. 872-879.
49. S. T. Meyers, "An FM Data Set for Voiceband Data Transmission," *Bell Lab. Rec.* 41 (January 1963), pp. 2-7.

50. P. A. Baker, "Phase-Modulation Data Sets for Serial Transmission at 2,000 and 2,400 Bits per Second," *Trans. Amer. Inst. Elec. Eng., Pt. 1—Commun. Electron.* **61** (July 1962), pp. 166-171.

51. C. E. Shannon, "A Mathematical Theory of Communication," *Bell Syst. Tech. J.* **27** (July 1948), pp. 379-423, and (October 1948), pp. 623-656.

52. E. D. Sunde, "Theoretical Fundamentals of Pulse Transmission," *Bell Syst. Tech. J.* **33** (May 1954), pp. 721-788, and (July 1954), pp. 987-1010.

53. R. W. Lucky, "Automatic Equalization for Digital Communication," *Bell Syst. Tech. J.* **44** (April 1965), pp. 547-588.

54. R. W. Lucky, "Techniques for Adaptive Equalization of Digital Communication Systems," *Bell Syst. Tech. J.* **45** (February 1966), pp. 255-286.

55. F. K. Becker, "An Exploratory, Multi-level Vestigial Sideband Data Terminal for Use on High Grade Voice Facilities," *Proc. 1st IEEE Ann. Commun. Conf.*, Boulder, Colorado (June 7-9, 1965), pp. 481-484.

56. A. A. Alexander, R. M. Gryb, and D. W. Nast, "Capabilities of the Telephone Network for Data Transmission," *Bell Syst. Tech. J.* **39** (May 1960), pp. 431-476.

57. H. O. Burton and E. J. Weldon, Jr., "An Error Control System for Use with a High Speed Voiceband Data Set," *Proc. 1st IEEE Ann. Commun. Conf.*, Boulder, Colorado (June 7-9, 1965), pp. 489-490.

58. R. D. Fracassi and T. Tammaru, U.S. Patent No. 4,304,962; filed August 25, 1965; issued December 8, 1981.

59. G. P. Darwin and R. C. Prim, "Synchronization in a System of Interconnected Units," U.S. Patent No. 2,986,723; filed February 26, 1960; issued May 30, 1961.

60. J. V. Scattaglia, "A Self-Reorganizing Synchronization Network," *Bell Syst. Tech. J.* **42** (September 1963), pp. 2493-2496.

61. A. Gersho and B. J. Karafin, "Mutual Synchronization of Geographically Separated Oscillators," *Bell Syst. Tech. J.* **45** (December 1966), pp. 1689-1704.

62. M. Karnaugh, "A Model for the Organic Synchronization of Communications Systems," *Bell Syst. Tech. J.* **45** (December 1966), pp. 1705-1735.

63. M. B. Brilliant, "The Determination of Frequency in Systems of Mutually Synchronized Oscillators," *Bell Syst. Tech. J.* **45** (December 1966), pp. 1737-1748.

64. M. B. Brilliant, "Dynamic Response of Systems of Mutually Synchronized Oscillators," *Bell Syst. Tech. J.* **46** (February 1967), pp. 319-356.

65. J. C. Candy and M. Karnaugh, "Organic Synchronization: Design of the Controls and Some Simulation Results," *Bell Syst. Tech. J.* **47** (February 1968), pp. 227-259.

66. R. H. Bosworth, F. W. Kammerer, D. E. Rowlinson, and J. V. Scattagilia, "Design of a Simulator for Investigating Organic Synchronization Systems," *Bell Syst. Tech. J.* **47** (February 1968), pp. 209-226.

67. J. R. Pierce, "Synchronizing Digital Networks," *Bell Syst. Tech. J.* **48** (March 1969), pp. 615-636.

68. I. W. Sandberg, "On Conditions Under Which It is Possible To Synchronize Digital Transmission Systems," *Bell Syst. Tech. J.* **48** (July/August 1969), pp. 1999-2022.

69. I. W. Sandberg, "Some Properties of a Nonlinear Model of a System for Synchronizing Digital Transmission Networks," *Bell Syst. Tech. J.* **48** (November 1969), pp. 2975-2997.

70. M. M. Buchner, Jr., "An Asymmetric Encoding Scheme for Word Stuffing," *Bell Syst. Tech. J.* **49** (March 1970), pp. 379-398.

71. B. R. Saltzberg and H. M. Zydney, "Digital Data System: Network Synchronization," *Bell Syst. Tech. J.* **54** (May/June 1975), pp. 879-892.

72. W. D. Farmer and E. E. Newhall, "An Experimental Distributed Switching System to Handle Bursty Computer Traffic," *Proc. ACM Symp. Problems in Optimization of Data Commun. Syst.*, Pine Mountain, Georgia (October 13-16, 1969), pp. 1-33.

73. J. R. Pierce, "Network for Block Switching of Data," *Bell Syst. Tech. J.* **51** (July/August 1972), pp. 1133-1145.

Chapter 11

Behavioral Science

The importance of human vision and audition was recognized early at Bell Labs, in the 1920s and 1930s; however, behavioral science as an organized research center started in 1955 with a study of instructional technology and learning and led to the development of a highly successful course on the fundamentals of basic electricity for communication technicians and to the spread of programmed instruction more generally throughout the Bell System. Starting in the early 1960s as a theory of mental representations, the technique of multidimensional scaling developed into a powerful tool for analysis of behavioral science data, with applications in the study of interpersonal relations and market research, for example. In vision research the novel technique of random-dot stereograms proved to be quite useful in the study of binocular vision and texture discrimination. Research in human information processing resulted in better understanding of short-term and long-term memory, visual information storage, word recognition, and language comprehension. New techniques were also developed for analyzing mental processes in the control of actions, such as speech production and finger movements in typing. Scientific contributions in social psychology and decision making also emerged from these and related efforts.

I. ORIGINS OF BEHAVIORAL RESEARCH

Behavioral research at Bell Laboratories began in a technical sense in 1956 with the recruitment of A. Bavelas, a social psychologist who was concerned with human motivation,[1] to the newly established social science research group. The group grew during the next six years to nine members of technical staff with PhDs mainly in experimental and social psychology and nine assistants who also had substantial technical training in these areas. This group continued with some changes in management and the addition in the early 1960s of new fields of research such as speech quality and visual perception. In 1971, the group was combined with the Acoustical

---

Principal authors: J. D. Carroll, B. Julesz, M. V. Mathews, E. Z. Rothkopf, S. Sternberg, and M. Wish.

Research Department, from which one branch of its psychologists had come, to form the Acoustical and Behavioral Research Center.

How does a new area of research begin? The part of behavioral research that concerns social psychology was strongly affected by a well-known series of industrial psychological experiments, often called the Hawthorne Studies, conducted at the Western Electric manufacturing plant in Hawthorne, Illinois between 1927 and 1932.[2] In these studies, the effect on productivity of changing working conditions was examined. To the surprise of the experimenters, productivity increased if one made a change; but it also increased if one made the opposite change. The immediate conclusion was that people like to be subjects of experiments and often work harder, at least for a while, as a result of a novel condition. The more general conclusion was that far too little was known about job motivation and the interaction of people in organizations. This conclusion led R. K. Greenleaf of the AT&T Personnel Department to suggest that a department of social research be set up inside the Bell System. Bell Labs with its scientific environment seemed a good place for this new organization, which was established in 1955 under the name Communications Social Science Research Center; in 1958, the name of the center was changed to Behavioral Research Center. In response to Greenleaf's suggestion, the Bell Labs group engaged the Yale University psychologist C. I. Hovland as a consultant; he contributed much toward the guidance of the center in its early days.[3]

Hovland was also instrumental in attracting good people to the group and contributed to its growth. He recruited scientists who reflected his interests in both social psychology and the psychology of learning. Among the earliest members of the center were R. N. Shepard from Hovland's PhD program in psychology, H. M. Jenkins from Harvard, the social psychologists M. Deutsch from the Massachusetts Institute of Technology (MIT) and H. Gerard from the University of Michigan, as well as two educational psychologists who had recently worked in military training research programs, H. O. Holt and E. Z. Rothkopf. Shepard stayed eight years, long enough to attract G. Sperling from Harvard, S. Sternberg from the University of Pennsylvania, and J. D. Carroll from Princeton. Sternberg, in turn, attracted D. E. Meyer from the University of Michigan, C. S. Harris from the University of Pennsylvania, and T. K. Landauer from Stanford University. Sternberg, Carroll, Landauer, Meyer, Sperling, and Harris formed the nucleus of one part of the center. Holt and Rothkopf, together with E. U. Coke (New York University) and L. T. Frase (University of Illinois) formed another part.

II. INSTRUCTIONAL TECHNOLOGY AND LEARNING

In 1958, Holt was appointed director of the Behavioral Research Center. About that time, the Harvard psychologist B. F. Skinner proposed a radically new teaching technique, called programmed instruction.[4] Among the central principles of this method was that learning was fostered through active participation by the student and by immediate rewards for correct responses. These principles and other aspects of the new instructional technique were supported largely by the results from animal learning experiments. Except for a single course in elementary psychology at Harvard, very little human data were available about programmed learning.

2.1 Programmed Course on Fundamentals of Basic Electricity

Holt [Fig. 11-1] asked the vital question, "Would the Skinner programmed techniques be practically effective for Bell System training?" To study this question, he programmed an existing course on the fundamentals of basic electricity and made a careful comparison of the performance of the new course with that of the existing one. The performance of a group of students after taking the programmed course was compared with that of a group taking the standard course. Not only was the average performance better for the programmed material, but also the lower tail of the performance curve was eliminated. In other words, with the programmed material everyone learned a significant amount of information; with the standard class presentations some of the students learned almost nothing.

Fig. 11-1.   H. O. Holt, who pioneered in the development of programmed instruction material for training Bell System employees.

This result is typical of present-day, self-paced instructional techniques, which are more adaptable to the individual student's abilities.

The times required to complete the two compared courses were about the same. The class students, being locked together by the lecture schedule, all took the same amount of time. In the programmed course, the students who needed more time were able to take more, and those who needed less time could finish sooner, but their average time was the same as the class time. In other courses, programmed techniques have resulted in a significant saving of average time. These and other results demonstrated the practical importance of programmed techniques and were factors that led to the widespread use of these methods in the Bell System.[5,6] [Fig. 11-2]

Beginning in the early 1960s, training technology spread throughout the Bell System. The process by which technical information about learning and training was disseminated in the Bell System is also of historical interest. In the educational world, research, development, and application

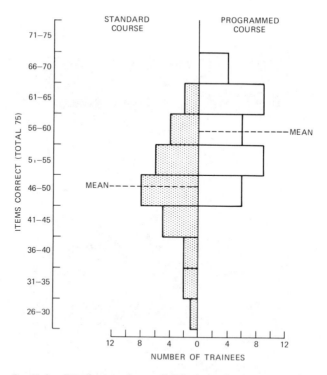

Fig. 11-2.   Distribution of scores for final examinations given after a standard and a programmed course in basic electricity. The programmed course produced a higher average performance and produced no students with low scores. [Holt, in *Programed Learning: A Critical Evaluation* (1963): 31.]

seldom occur within the same organization. The Bell System was an important exception in this respect. Two departments in behavioral research—Human Information Processing and Learning and Instruction—worked on fundamental questions about learning. Another Bell Laboratories organization—the Human Performance Technology Center—was created to deal both with the design of the human component in computerized systems and with training for jobs operating these systems. This was done because in computerizing Bell System operations, training and job design were found to be at least as important as equipment design and computer programming. This center became a useful testing ground for new ideas originating in instructional research.

In 1962, Holt transferred from Bell Laboratories to AT&T, and the Office of Training Research was formed at AT&T. This office interacted with the two Bell Laboratories departments in behavioral research as well as with Bell Operating Companies' schools and became an important conduit for training technology. It provided professional advice and standards and monitored the quality of training material. The function of the Office of Training Research was subsequently aided by the creation of training advisory boards in various special areas; the boards coordinated the creation of training materials among operating companies.

Bell Laboratories work on instructional technology had an enormous impact on training practices in the Bell System. In about 15 years, between 1960 and 1975, the number of programmed self-instructional courses grew from zero to over 2000. These courses were more effective than traditional training methods and provided, with substantial savings in time and effort, a reliable supply of superbly trained technicians and managers.

Programmed instruction is a good example of a practical technique that worked, even though it did not start with well-founded theory. Further research, as well as practical experience, contributed to the development of an appropriate theoretical foundation.

2.2 Studies of Basic Mechanisms of Learning

2.2.1 Effect of Quizzing, Method of Presentation, and Context on Human Learning

About the same time as the field trials of the basic electricity program were initiated, more fundamental research on human learning was started. This work changed our conceptions of programmed learning and also provided new ideas about the use of written language in teaching. For example, Rothkopf [Fig. 11-3] and his coworkers were able to show that frequent quizzing of learners, a common maneuver in programmed instruction, not only improved memory for tested knowledge but also strongly focused and maintained attention in subsequent instruction.[7-9] Thus, questions requiring numerical answers or proper names resulted not only in

Fig. 11-3.   E. Z. Rothkopf, who made fundamental contributions to human learning mechanisms.

better recall of the material about which students had been questioned
but also in improved learning from later passages of numerical information
or information about proper names. The observed changes in learning
occurred because the questions shaped selective attention; this took place
even when students were unaware of the biased nature of the questions.
These and other related studies led to experiments on the use of questions
and verbal descriptions of learning goals to aid students in learning from
text.[10] Adjunct aids, a simple and effective method for improving learning
from suboptimal written material, was subsequently widely adopted in
the Bell System and elsewhere.

Concern with programmed instruction led to the analysis of the se-
quencing of instructional experiences. In the early 1960s, Rothkopf and
Coke[11] were able to establish that the interval between repeated presentations had an important effect on what was learned and remembered.
Longer intervals were much more effective than shorter intervals, a finding
that has direct implication for the design of drill sequences. Other research
in this field was carried out by Landauer, who devised a coherent, theoretical
interpretation of repetition phenomena.[12]

In the 1970s, Landauer made several studies of the importance of the
retention of learned material, of events that follow learning, and of the
timing of those events. For example, he found that the rate at which critical

information is forgotten over a 20-minute period depends on the order in which it is followed by additional easy and hard material: forgetting is faster when the additional hard material is presented first.[13] Together with other findings, this "backward" effect supports the existence of a consolidation process in human memory with a time constant of several minutes. On a larger time scale, Landauer showed that people's retention of information one year after taking a course was substantially improved by administering a review examination after six months, but not after six weeks.[14]

Studies in this area during the 1960s and early 1970s aroused substantial interest in many other psychological laboratories both in the United States and abroad. They resulted in widespread recognition of the importance in instruction of shaping and sustaining internal processes involved in learning.

General interest in improving the effectiveness of written material led to experimental studies of the effect of surface structure and organization on learning from written language. This work led to the first automated computer-based readability index, developed by Coke and Rothkopf in 1968.[15] The readability index, a version of the Standard Flesch Score,[16] predicted difficulty by regression techniques from average word length and sentence length of text samples. Together with L. Landgraf's pioneering development of the automatic parsing program (described in an internal computer science memorandum), the readability index provided the first step toward the system of computerized writing aids known as the WRITER'S WORKBENCH* software.

In the mid-1970s, D. E. Egan analyzed the characteristics of learners in order to understand how the conditions of learning might be adapted to individuals. He showed that people differed in how they mentally represented simple reasoning problems.[17] These representations affected the nature of the reasoning errors people made. Given suitable instruction, people could change the way they reasoned and alter the number and pattern of reasoning errors.[18] Egan also developed procedures for analyzing tasks, such as computer text editing, so as to determine which learner characteristics were important in training. These studies led to suggestions for the design of human/computer interfaces and instructional approaches tailored to individual computer users.

In the late 1970s, the role of context (i.e., background) in learning and recall was studied extensively. Using instructional television, controlled classroom studies, and computer-controlled information presentations, Rothkopf and his coworkers demonstrated that background elements played a subtle but pervasive role in remembering. For example, they were able to show that the place in which information is seen is coded in memory.

---

* Trademark of AT&T Technologies, Inc.

Learners remembered more about speakers appearing in diverse places than they did about speakers appearing in the same place.[19] Similar effects were obtained for a statistics course taught in several classrooms rather than in only one and for verbal information presented on several computer terminals rather than one.

2.2.2 Research With Animals

Guided by the belief that analysis of learning in lower organisms might shed light on mechanisms that transcend particular species, several fundamental questions about learning were attacked in research with animals. Thus, to investigate the role of reward in learning, H. M. Jenkins carried out experiments with pigeons in the early 1960s. It was already well known that persistence of responding when all reward is discontinued is increased by training with a mixture of reward and nonreward as compared with consistent reward. His experiments showed that a mixture increases persistence even when it is followed by extensive training with consistent reward.[20] In a related study, Jenkins investigated the learning of discrimination between positive and negative signals of reward. He showed that unrewarded responses resulting from errors early in the course of learning also increased persistence in the absence of reward, even though errors ceased well before the test for persistence began.[21] These experiments showed a surprising degree of permanence of the effect of an early exposure to intermittent reward on the persistence of nonrewarded response.

The use of animals to investigate fundamental learning mechanisms was revived at Bell Laboratories in 1981 by A. Gelperin in research on the neural basis of associative learning in the giant garden slug, *Limax maximus*. This work has already provided insight into cellular mechanisms of learning and memory storage.[22]

III. MULTIDIMENSIONAL SCALING

Work on multidimensional scaling (MDS) at Bell Laboratories was originally motivated by R. N. Shepard's [Fig. 11-4] interest in understanding how people perceive various qualities, or "subjective dimensions," of the world around them. Shepard suggested that relations among mental concepts can often be described by their separations in a mental space— separations that could be captured by their locations on a mental "map." He proposed that conceptual relations could be constructed from subjective judgments or other measures of similarity or dissimilarity, for which he used the general term "proximities." Proximities may be viewed as measures of the subjective distances between objects. Unlike physical measures of distance, however, many measures of proximity used in psychology and other behavioral sciences at best measure only the ordering of these distances, not their precise numerical values. Thus Shepard invented the first "nonmetric" method of MDS, which he called "analysis of proximities."

Fig. 11-4. R. N. Shepard, who pioneered in developing computer methods for constructing multidimensional "maps" of mental concepts from judged proximities among them.

In this, as in other nonmetric MDS procedures, it is possible, by using sophisticated numerical methods implemented by a computer, to construct these mental maps—given proximities that indicate only the rank order of distances.

Basically, MDS procedures spatially represent the hidden structure in a matrix of "distance-like" numbers. For a matrix of geographical distances between cities, an MDS analysis would provide a reconstruction of the two-dimensional map of cities. Other simpler geometric techniques (e.g., triangulation) could be used for the errorless objective data in a table of city distances. However, since there is generally considerable uncertainty in subjective judgments or perceptions (e.g., nonlinear relations between proximities and distances in the mental map, uncertainty about dimensionality of the map, and error or "noise" in such subjective data), it takes powerful mathematical data analysis and statistical techniques to find the map that best fits the data.

3.1 Metric MDS

The earliest form of MDS, the so-called classical method of "metric" MDS, was devised by a group working at Princeton University in the early 1950s; it was based on some earlier theoretical work (going back to about

1938) by the mathematicians G. Young and A. S. Householder.[23] The approach used by W. S. Torgerson, a mathematical psychologist of the Princeton group, involved a very time-consuming and complicated data collection and analysis procedure, called the method of triads, designed to get highly accurate numerical, or "ratio scale," measures of subjective distances among all pairs of stimuli. The number of judgments required of subjects went up roughly as the cube of the number of stimuli and severely limited the number of stimuli that could be used. After ratio scale estimates of distances were derived from these triads data (in which all triples of stimuli were presented, and each subject was asked to judge which of two was more similar to a third), these estimated subjective distances were further processed to derive "scalar product" measures for all pairs of stimuli (which are analogous to covariances among pairs of variables). These derived scalar products were then subjected to a procedure very much like principal components analysis to produce the mental maps of stimuli.

3.2 Nonmetric MDS

Shepard's development of proximity analysis, the first computer-implemented version of nonmetric MDS, in the early 1960s, constituted a major breakthrough; it allowed use of proximities data (similarities or dissimilarities) assumed to be related to distances in an underlying multidimensional space only by a very general monotonic, or order-preserving, function.[24,25] This allowed application of MDS to a much broader range of data than the earlier metric method of Torgerson and others, which required much stronger and more restrictive assumptions about the relation between the data and the interpoint distances.[26] Soon after Shepard's pioneering work, the mathematician J. B. Kruskal [Fig. 11-5] introduced significant conceptual, algorithmic, and practical improvements to Shepard's earlier approach, leading to the computer program MDSCAL, which was more sophisticated than earlier methods for performing multidimensional scaling, and later to KYST (for the initials of Kruskal, Young, Shepard, and Torgerson) computer-based algorithms for nonmetric MDS.[27,28] These algorithms have become the most widely used procedures for what has often been called "two-way" MDS. Since these nonmetric procedures allowed researchers to use a much broader variety of proximity measures, many requiring considerably less arduous tasks of human judges, these methods also allowed use of a much larger number of stimuli. A number of people at universities and other institutions have carried out programs on MDS research. A summary of this work up to 1980 is provided in a review paper by J. D. Carroll and P. Arabie.[29]

To get an idea of how two-way nonmetric MDS works, let us consider an example of data from a study by Rothkopf in which many people unfamiliar with Morse code listened to pairs of Morse-code signals and then indicated whether they were the same or different.[30] The data were

Fig. 11-5.   J. B. Kruskal, who made fundamental contributions to the mathematics and computer methods of constructing multidimensional "maps" from numerical proximities.

the percentage of "same" responses for all pairs of signals. This produced a 36 × 36 matrix of what are often called "confusions" data for all pairs of the 36 Morse-code signals.

Using Kruskal's MDS computer program, Shepard analyzed these data, which he interpreted as measures of psychological proximity of the signals, to produce a multidimensional scaling map where distances between signals are (as nearly as possible) monotonically related to the probability of their being confused. In other words, the more often two signals were confused with each other, the closer, generally speaking, the points representing them were in the map. This map showed much more clearly and simply the pattern underlying the confusabilities of different Morse-code signals than did the original 36 × 36 table of confusions data. [Fig. 11-6]

Although the computer produced the map, Shepard had to furnish the interpretation. Interpretation of a dimension generally involves distinguishing how stimulus objects at one extreme differ from those at the other. He observed that the number of components in the signals increased from bottom to top and that the relative number of dashes increased from

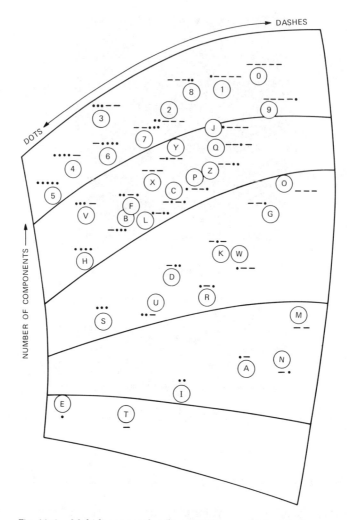

Fig. 11-6. Multidimensional scaling (MDS) map obtained by a computer analyzing data on confusability between Morse-code signals. The distance between any two signals on the map is monotonically and inversely related to the degree of confusion experienced by the listener (i.e., believing that two signals are the same). The confusability between two Morse-code signals appears to depend on the difference in the number of components (dots or dashes) in the two signals and on the relative proportions of dots and dashes. The curved lines, arbitrarily drawn to divide the map into regions where the signals have the same total number of components, facilitate the interpretation of the results. [Shepard, *Human Factors* **5** (1963): 39.]

left to right.[31] He therefore interpreted the two dimensions as "number of components" and "dots versus dashes."

The MDS program also determined the monotonic function relating confusion probabilities to distances in the map. The shape of this function approximated an exponential decay function, which is very consistent with the widely supported theory of stimulus generalization in psychology. (In fact, part of Shepard's early interest in proximity analysis was in determining the nature of such functions, which often bear on important theoretical issues in psychology or other behavioral sciences.) Of course, the points scattered quite considerably about the curve, as is typical of most psychological data. [Fig. 11-7]

The application of MDS methods also shed new light on issues in learning. Thus Shepard and coworkers explored the distinction between "analyzable" stimuli, for which people can selectively attend to one attribute (such as size, shape, or color), and "unitary" stimuli (e.g., homogeneous colors), for which they can not. They contributed support to the conclusion that for unitary stimuli the Euclidean metric is appropriate for multidimensional scaling, and the difficulty of learning different classifications of the stimuli can be predicted solely from their pairwise similarities; whereas for analyzable stimuli, a non-Euclidean metric and more complicated principles of classification learning are indicated.[32]

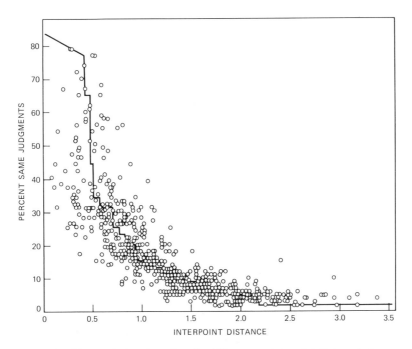

Fig. 11-7. Monotonic function of confusability versus interpoint distance between any pair of points of Fig. 11-6. The abscissa is the interpoint distance, and the ordinate is a measure of confusability. The confusability function, computed by MDS analysis, is shown as a solid line that is the best fitting monotonic curve to these data points. [Shepard, *Human Factors* **5** (1963): 41.]

To summarize, Shepard's interest in understanding mental representations of objects or maps led him to his pioneering work in nonmetric
MDS, while Kruskal's fascination with the mathematical structure of this
problem led to the improved algorithms represented by the MDSCAL and
later KYST computer programs. Kruskal's involvement in MDS work also
illustrates important long-term interactions of members of the Acoustical
and Behavioral Research Center with scientists of other research centers
at Bell Labs.

3.3 Three-Way MDS

In the late 1960s and early 1970s, J. D. Carroll [Fig. 11-8] and J. J.
Chang developed the next major breakthrough in MDS methodology[33]—
the "three-way" MDS model and method known as INdividual Differences
multidimensional SCALing (INDSCAL). INDSCAL is called a three-way
MDS approach because it uses a three-way array of data, consisting of a
number of (two-way) proximities matrices—one for each of a number of
different human subjects or other data sources. It represents these data by
a generalized Euclidean distance model in which each subject (or other

Fig. 11-8. J. D. Carroll, who made fundamental contributions to
MDS by showing how to use a three-way array of proximities to
get an improved multidimensional "map."

data source) corresponding to the third dimension of the data array has a different pattern of weights for a common set of dimensions. These "subject weights" define the relative saliences or perceptual importances of the stimulus dimensions for the different subjects or other entities, and they often serve as extremely useful parameters to characterize, discriminate among, or predict other characteristics of the subjects. An additional highly useful aspect of the INDSCAL approach is that the stimulus dimensions are uniquely determined. In the two-way MDS methods, dimensions are determined only up to a rigid, or orthogonal, rotation, which often made interpretations of MDS solutions in more than two dimensions extremely difficult.

As an illustration of the INDSCAL procedure, let us turn to a completely different subject for mental maps—relationships between people. One of the psychologists, M. Wish (who came to the Behavioral Research Center in 1967 to exploit Shepard's, Kruskal's, and Carroll's original work in

IN MAKING THESE JUDGMENTS OF SIMILARITIES PLEASE TAKE INTO ACCOUNT THE WAYS THE TWO INDIVIDUALS IN A RELATIONSHIP THINK AND FEEL ABOUT EACH OTHER, ACT AND REACT TOWARD EACH OTHER, TALK AND LISTEN TO EACH OTHER, AND ANY OTHER CHARACTERISTICS RELEVANT TO THESE RELATIONSHIPS.	VERY DIFFERENT								VERY SIMILAR
A. BETWEEN PARENT AND TEENAGER B. BETWEEN INTERVIEWER AND JOB APPLICANT	1	2	3	4	5	6	7	8	9
A. BETWEEN SALESMAN AND REGULAR CUSTOMER B. BETWEEN HUSBAND AND WIFE	1	2	3	4	5	6	7	8	9
A. BETWEEN BUSINESS RIVALS B. BETWEEN TEACHER AND YOUNG PUPIL	1	2	3	4	5	6	7	8	9
A. BETWEEN PARENT AND TEENAGER B. BETWEEN CASUAL ACQUAINTANCES	1	2	3	4	5	6	7	8	9
A. BETWEEN SECOND COUSINS B. BETWEEN SUPERVISOR AND EMPLOYEE	1	2	3	4	5	6	7	8	9
A. BETWEEN MOTHER-IN-LAW AND SON-IN-LAW B. BETWEEN SUPERVISOR AND EMPLOYEE	1	2	3	4	5	6	7	8	9
A. BETWEEN NURSE AND INVALID B. BETWEEN PSYCHOTHERAPIST AND PATIENT	1	2	3	4	5	6	7	8	9
A. BETWEEN CHILDREN IN A FAMILY B. BETWEEN TEAMMATES (DURING A GAME)	1	2	3	4	5	6	7	8	9

Fig. 11-9. Sample questions from a questionnaire designed to determine how people rate the similarity or dissimilarity of different relationships among individuals. [Wish, *Ind. Res.* **17** (1975): 28.]

multidimensional scaling), thought that the scaling techniques could be
used to better understand people's conceptions of interpersonal relationships. He devised a questionnaire in which he asked a number of subjects
to rate the similarity between 25 pairs of relationships.[34,35] [Fig. 11-9]

When these data were analyzed, using the INDSCAL procedure, which
had been devised by Carroll and Chang, the results came out not in a
two-dimensional map but, rather, in a four-dimensional map. [Fig. 11-10]
It is probably largely due to what is called the "dimensional uniqueness"
property of INSDCAL—i.e., the fact that the stimulus dimensions do not
have to be rotated to attain an interpretable structure—that Wish was able
to uncover a highly stable and meaningful MDS solution in as high as
four dimensions. (Shepard had to rotate the two-dimensional coordinate
system originally given by the two-way MDS computer program he was
using to find the two interpretable dimensions described earlier for Rothkopf's Morse-code data.)

Upon examining the position of the objects in this conceptual map,
Wish labeled the dimensions of the mental space. The labels were only
Wish's interpretations of the dimensions, but there is considerable statistical
evidence, based on multiple regression analysis, supporting these interpretations. The primary understanding obtained from this study is that

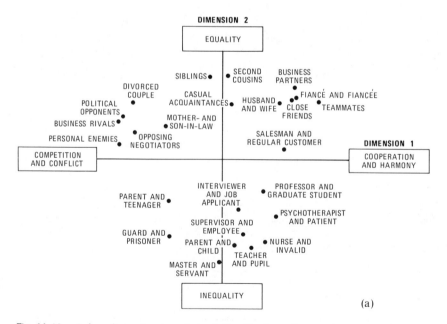

Fig. 11-10.   A four-dimensional analysis of the data from the questionnaire in Fig. 11-9.
The MDS program produced a four-dimensional map. The four dimensions that characterize
these interpersonal relationships can be interpreted as (a) competition versus cooperation
(dimension 1) and equality versus inequality (dimension 2), and (b) task-oriented versus

people view social relationships according to four different qualities that can be called cooperation, equality, formality, and intensity. If we know these four factors for a particular relationship, then we will be in a good position to predict people's expectations of this relationship and perhaps be better able to understand how people who have different relationships communicate and interact with each other. In addition to the information this INDSCAL analysis provided about the important subjective dimensions underlying perception of these interpersonal relationships, the dimension weights for subjects, which could be portrayed graphically in what is called the "subject space," exhibited important and meaningful correlations with various demographic variables, attitude measures, and other attributes of the subjects. Thus, the INDSCAL approach to three-way MDS provides two important extensions of the two-way MDS methods. One is the use of individual differences among subjects or other data sources to orient the coordinate system uniquely—the dimensional uniqueness property— which makes feasible easily interpretable solutions in more than two or three dimensions. The second is that the subject weights provide very

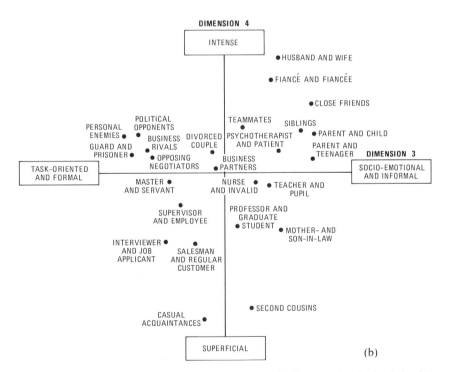

socially oriented (dimension 3) and intense versus superficial (dimension 4). A relationship can be characterized by its perceived coordinates in these four dimensions. [Wish, *Ind. Res.* **17** (1975): 28.]

useful parameters for measuring individual differences in subjects or other data sources.

3.4 An Application of MDS to Preference Analysis—PICTUREPHONE* Visual Telephone Service

In addition to methods of MDS for proximities data, there has been a considerable amount of research at Bell Labs and elsewhere on MDS methods for representing subjects' preferences. These methods are particularly applicable to market research, where having an accurate appraisal of both people's perceptions and preferences is vital. In an effort to understand better why PICTUREPHONE visual telephone service had not been an initial market success, Wish devised an extensive questionnaire. Business executives used this questionnaire to rate PICTUREPHONE visual telephone service, the telephone, and a face-to-face visit in terms of their effectiveness in accomplishing various tasks. Because of the power of the scaling techniques, the questions posed to the subject in a very simple and easily answerable form were sufficient for this purpose. [Fig. 11-11]

A scaling program, called MDPREF (for MultiDimensional PREFerence analysis), developed by Carroll and Chang, was used for these data.[36] MDPREF produces a map that displays information both about people's perceptions of the relationships between the stimuli under study (the business tasks in this case) and their preferences for these stimuli. The stimuli are represented as points in the map, and each subject filling out this questionnaire is represented by a vector that indicates that person's preferred direction with respect to the three services. The projections of the stimuli on a subject's vector recover as well as possible (in a statistically well-defined sense) that subject's preference ordering of the stimuli for these services.

An MDPREF analysis of the PICTUREPHONE visual telephone service data showed that most of the business executives in the study thought that face-to-face visits were more useful than either PICTUREPHONE service or telephone for all the tasks;[37] this was expected. However, the map produced by the analysis revealed additional information about the respondents. [Fig. 11-12] First, there was a group of people biased toward the PICTUREPHONE visual service and a group biased toward the telephone. In addition, some people favored the telephone for some tasks, such as "business discussions within the same company," whereas the PICTUREPHONE visual telephone service was considered more useful for such tasks as getting an idea across.

---

* Registered service mark of AT&T.

BUSINESS SITUATION CHECK LIST

P = PICTUREPHONE visual telephone service
T = Telephone
V = Visit

	NOT AT ALL USEFUL									EXTREMELY USEFUL
A. Discussing business with someone in your own company.		*P*							*T*	*V*
B. Selling a product.						*T*		*P*		*V*
C. Getting an idea across.					*P*	*T*		*V*		
D. Finding out other people's ideas.				*T*				*P*		*V*
E. Establishing good relations with a new customer.		*T*		*P*						*V*
F. Maintaining good relations with a regular customer.				*T*	*P*			*V*		
G. Negotiating a business deal.			*P*		*T*				*V*	
H. Interviewing a potential employee.		*T*							*P*	*V*
I. Conference involving three or four people.			*T*			*P*			*V*	
J. Conference involving five to ten people.	*T*	*P*								*V*
K. Discussion with someone at about the same level as yourself.							*P*	*T*	*V*	
L. Discussion with someone at a higher level than yourself.			*P*				*T*			*V*
M. Discussion with someone at a lower level than yourself.					*P*		*T*	*V*		

Fig. 11-11. Sample questions (with answers from a typical respondent) from a questionnaire designed to determine how business executives rate PICTUREPHONE visual telephone service compared with telephone calls and face-to-face visits.

Multidimensional scaling became one of the standard tools of market research by the late 1960s and early 1970s. It has become increasingly important as a methodological tool in psychology, marketing, and many other behavioral sciences; it has even been used in some branches of engineering, computer science, and the biological and physical sciences. New models and methods, particularly for individual differences analysis of both perceptual and preference data, have been devised by Carroll, S. Pruzansky, and W. S. DeSarbo.[38] These new models and methods have

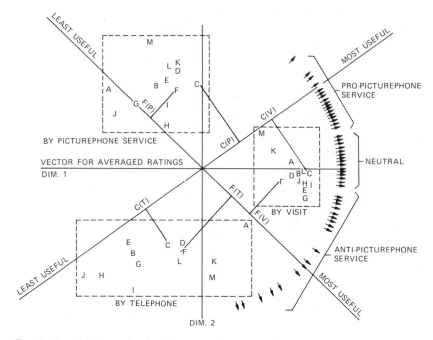

Fig. 11-12.   Multidimensional preference analysis (MDPREF) based on ratings of usefulness of three different communication conditions—telephone (T), face-to-face visit (V), and PICTUREPHONE service (P) for the 13 different business tasks listed in Fig. 11-11. Each letter (A through M) refers to a different task; each task is represented three times, one for each communication condition. An arrowhead indicates the end of a vector through the origin that reflects a respondent's rating. A letter representing a task that received a high usefulness rating by someone projects highly on that person's vector. Positions of arrowheads and letters were determined directly by the MDPREF computer program. The rectangles around each of the services are inserted as an aid in interpreting the data. Generally, a visit was judged to be more useful for every business situation—i.e., all letters for visit project highest on most of the vectors. An interesting feature of this map is that two dimensions are required to account for all of the respondents' ratings. The second dimension separates PICTUREPHONE visual telephone service from the telephone.

greatly expanded the areas of applications of this powerful methodology for measurement and data analysis in the behavioral (and other) sciences.

In contrast to programmed instruction discussed in section II in this chapter, MDS started from purely theoretical notions about similarity and mental processes and gradually developed into techniques of great practical importance.

IV. VISION RESEARCH

Although the first studies in physiological optics at Bell Labs go back to H. E. Ives, a major early figure in optics, who in the early part of the

Fig. 11-13.   B. Julesz, who invented the technique of random-dot stereograms for the study of binocular vision.

20th century developed flicker color photometry, modern interest in basic research on vision began in 1960 with the introduction by B. Julesz [Fig. 11-13] of computer-generated random-dot stereograms. Julesz was originally interested in bandwidth compression when transmitting information in television pictures; this led him to the problem of object separation in binocular depth perception.

4.1 Random-Dot Stereograms

Julesz studied an arrangement of two matrices of dots, the first of which is generated randomly (e.g., by a computer) and the second copied from the first, except for some small area where all the dots in that area are slightly displaced from the respective positions in the first matrix by the same amount. When these two arrays are binocularly fused, they can give rise to vivid depth percepts as the central nervous system finds correlated areas of certain binocular disparities, in spite of the fact that the left and right images of the stereopair by themselves are just aggregates of random dots.[39,40] [Fig. 11-14] Many such random-dot stereograms, printed as red-

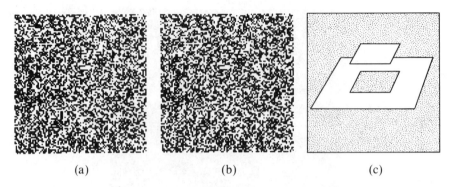

(a)   (b)   (c)

Fig. 11-14.   Random-dot stereogram prepared by a program of B. Julesz. (a) and (b) Images seen by the left and right eyes are shown side-by-side in the figure. No patterns are perceptible in these separate images. (c) However, if the two images are fused, then a vivid pattern of depth variation can be seen in the fused image. [Julesz, *Sci. Amer.* **212** (1965): 43.]

green anaglyphs to help fusion, are shown in Julesz's book *Foundations of Cyclopean Perception.*[41]

The invention of the random-dot stereogram, one of the early applications of computers in psychology, solved several problems in experimental psychology and neurophysiology:

1. It provided a robust test for stereopsis. In the next two decades, Julesz and his coworkers combined the technique of random-dot stereograms with evoked potentials measured on the scalp of human infants and showed the onset of functional binocularity in 3-1/2 month-old infants. Early diagnosis of stereodeficiencies might help to prevent stereoblindness that afflicts 2 percent of mankind.[42]

2. It showed that, contrary to prevailing belief, binocular depth perception does not depend on monocular form recognition. This realization had an impact on neurophysiological research, and much of the work shifted from monocular pattern-recognition problems to the search for binocular, disparity-tuned neurons in the cortex of monkeys.

3. The random-dot stereogram provided a tractable problem to model: How does the brain find (match) areas of the same binocular disparity (parallax) amidst look-alike false matches? The models developed by Julesz and his coworkers were the simplest cooperative systems known in brain research[43] and had great impact on both psychology and artificial intelligence.[44,45,46]

4. Random-dot stereograms could portray and elicit most of the known perceptual aftereffects and optical illusions. Because the information coming from the left and right eyes is combined only in the visual cortex, optical illusions or aftereffects produced by random-dot ste-

reograms are not generated by any processing stages in the brain (retina, geniculate, etc.) prior to the binocular combination. Julesz called this technique "psychoanatomy."[47]

An outgrowth of random-dot stereograms was random-dot cinematograms, for which the correlated random-dot arrays were presented in temporal succession. The correlated areas appear to move, thus permitting the study of a movement perception.[48,49]

In 1964, the Sensory and Perceptual Processes Department, headed by Julesz, was established at Bell Labs. In 1966, J. Krauskopf joined the department and together with Julesz initiated a postdoctoral fellow program in which a dozen talented young scientists have thus far participated. This resulted in several important findings, some of which are noted below.

4.2 Texture Discrimination

Besides random-dot stereograms and cinematograms (to study movement perception), Julesz explored spatial-frequency-tuned channels in vision.[50] He also initiated a study of preattentive texture discrimination using random textures with constrained stochastic parameters.[51] With the help of Bell Laboratories mathematicians, particularly D. Slepian, E. N. Gilbert, and L. A. Shepp, he studied the discrimination of random textures with identical second-order statistics.[52] That led him to a texton theory of human vision, where the textons are local conspicuous features, the basic elements of preattentive vision.[53,54] Much of the later work of Julesz required very fast computer graphics that were developed by W. Kropfl.[55] From the 1970s on, Chang collaborated with Julesz in many perceptual studies.[56,57]

4.3 Color Vision

Since 1966, J. Krauskopf's main line of research has been the basic mechanisms of color vision. He demonstrated that each of the primary-color mechanisms independently controls its own time constants. This was demonstrated by psychophysical, electrophysiological, and reaction-time experiments.[58] He showed that what is experienced with very weak stimuli can reveal the nature of fundamental sensory mechanisms. Using this principle, he determined the spectral sensitivity of fundamental cone mechanisms in the human eye from the appearance of small brief spots of monochromatic light.[59] Applying methods based on the same fundamental assumptions, he demonstrated the existence of separate mechanisms for the detection of increments and decrements of light.[60]

In 1982, Krauskopf demonstrated the existence of two mechanisms that signal the color of stimuli and a third that signals brightness by using a new psychophysical method of selective habituation. These experiments were closely followed by electrophysiological studies that showed that single cells in the lateral geniculate nucleus of a monkey had precisely the same signaling properties.

4.4 Mathematical and Neural Models of Visual Function

During the late 1960s, Bell Labs researchers developed mathematical and neural models that accounted for a wide range of visual phenomena and provided new understanding of the visual system. Examples are the studies of temporal phenomena, such as flicker fusion by J. Z. Levinson,[61] and flicker detection and masking by G. Sperling and M. M. Sondhi.[62,63] They were able to show, for example, that many phenomena of luminance discrimination and flicker detection can be explained by a neurally plausible model that contains a series of resistance-capacitance circuits of which only three have adjustable time constants. Other theoretical work by Sperling concerned spatial phenomena of contrast detection, and the accommodation, vergence, and fusion phenomena of binocular vision.[64,65]

In research on mechanisms of pattern recognition, Harris and A. R. Gibson showed that orientation-specific color adaptation cannot be due to ordinary afterimages but can be explained by hypothetical sensory units less highly structured than edge detectors. Harris also found that such adaptation depends on spatial frequency of the pattern.[66,67] Later, with N. Weisstein and others, Harris found that detection of a line segment is markedly easier in a perceptually meaningful context, especially if the context appears to be three-dimensional. This "object-superiority" effect is hard to reconcile with pattern-recognition models in which elementary features are detected first, and overall structure then ascertained from the features.[68,69] With Weisstein and others, Harris demonstrated that spatial patterns can interact over large retinal separations, supporting the idea of a spatially distributed (perhaps Fourier-like) visual representation.[70,71]

V. HUMAN INFORMATION PROCESSING

In all human communication, information is transferred from one person's memory to another. Regardless of how a message is sent, it must eventually arrive in a form that can be encoded, preserved, and retrieved by the brain. As technology provides more alternatives for transmitting information, the choice among alternative possibilities depends on an understanding of the mental processes that underlie people's performance in communication situations. Research on human information processing includes studies of perception, learning, memory, thinking, and action that view the person as an information-processing system having speed and capacity limits.

Starting about 1950, there was a revolution in psychological research on mental processes, partly inspired by such technological advances as electronic signal detection, the information theory developed in 1948 by C. E. Shannon (see Chapter 1, section VIII in this volume), and the field of computer science. Information theory led psychologists to explore more precisely the way that information is mentally coded, classified, and transformed. One of the earliest examples of such research was the set of experiments by J. R. Pierce and J. E. Karlin in 1957 using oral reading to estimate human channel capacities.[72] Signal-detection devices stimulated Bell Labs researchers to regard retrieval from memory as involving statistical decisions based on noisy signals. Computer science raised questions about serial versus parallel processes in the brain, fostered ideas about simple search mechanisms, and encouraged a quest for data on basic mental operations.

The new interest in the constituents rather than merely the consequences of mental activity led to a revival of reaction-time methods. (In reaction-time studies, one measures the amount of time a task requires when it is performed with relatively high accuracy.) In turn, these methods provide some of the strongest supporting data for a flowchart concept of the mind by showing that the time between stimulus and response can be a sum, composed of the durations of a series of separate stages of processing.[73]

Fig. 11-15.   S. Sternberg, who developed new ways of using reaction-time data to analyze mental information processes.

Bell Labs scientists participated in this revolution in human information processing in large measure through the use of two powerful new methods described below and developed by Sperling, S. Sternberg [Fig. 11-15], and others, one making use of information sampling, and the other exploiting reaction-time measurements. In the 1960s and 1970s, the research on human information processing was concentrated, first, on memory (including short-term memory storage and retrieval, long-term memory storage and retrieval, visual information storage, and categorization based on stored knowledge) and, second, on word recognition and language comprehension.

5.1 Human Memory

In the late 1960s, Bell Labs psychologists pioneered a new way to study both short-term and long-term memory. Most research on memory had been based on the number and pattern of errors people make when they attempt to remember something under conditions that produce frequent failures. The Bell Labs technique allowed memory processes to be studied under conditions in which people were able to perform rapidly and to make almost no errors. Instead of measuring errors, investigators measured how long a person took to remember correctly selected kinds and amounts of information.

5.1.1 Short-Term Memory

Human short-term memory can be regarded as a temporary buffer memory that can hold from five to ten pieces of information. Unless a person repeats the information to himself, it is typically forgotten in less than a minute. This type of storage is used, for example, when we look up and dial a new telephone number, or when we recall what someone said a moment ago. It probably also serves as a small-capacity "working memory" that plays a critical role in reasoning and comprehension.

In one study of short-term memory, a subject was asked to memorize from a display a list of one to six digits, for example, 2, 9, 6, 1, 7. After the list was memorized, a test digit, for example, 9 or 5, was displayed and the subject pressed a key to indicate that the digit was or was not in the memorized list—one key for yes, another key for no.[74,75,76] Reaction time was measured from the moment the test digit appeared on the display until a key was pressed. This procedure was repeated on several hundred trials with different memorized lists and test digits. [Fig. 11-16]

The tests showed that reaction time increased by approximately the same amount for each digit added to the memorized list, with the rate of increase about 40 milliseconds for each additional digit.

This result indicated a high-speed internal search process that people use to retrieve information from memory, analogous to one a computer

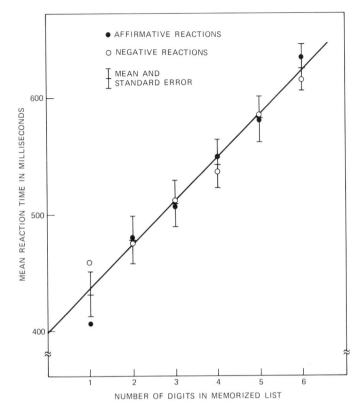

Fig. 11-16. Time to retrieve information from short-term memory as a function of number of digits memorized. A person was first asked to memorize a list of from one to six different digits, selected randomly from the ten digits that were displayed visually, one after another, in a random order (e.g., 2, 9, 6, 1, 7). The person was then shown a test digit and asked whether it was contained in the list (e.g., 9) or was not (e.g., 5). This procedure was repeated on several hundred trials, with different lists and test digits, and with eight participants. Note the linear increase in retrieval time (about 40 milliseconds per digit) with digit added. [Sternberg, *Science* **153** (1966): 653.]

might use. The finding also demonstrated that a task that seems automatic, effortless, and instantaneous to the person performing it requires time that varies according to the experimental conditions. Analysis of these variations revealed the structure of internal mental processes that could not be observed directly.

Using other techniques to study short-term memory, Sperling and R. G. Speelman demonstrated mental auditory recoding of visually presented letters by exploring the dramatic effects on recall of the acoustic similarity of letter names.[77] They also showed the importance of subvocal rehearsal and demonstrated that the capacity of human short-term memory is greater for item information than for order information.

5.1.2 Long-Term Memory

In contrast to short-term memory, the capacity of human long-term memory is extremely large for both facts and experiences. Information can be preserved in this memory for many years, with no conscious effort to retain it. Long-term memory is used, for example, when we remember our own telephone number, understand the meaning of a word, or recognize a face.

Reaction-time methods similar to those mentioned above were applied by D. E. Meyer to investigate the organization and retrieval of word meanings in long-term memory and led him to discover mechanisms quite unlike those of digital computers.[78,79] In one experiment, a person was shown three rows of letters, one after the other, with words and nonwords intermixed randomly. For example, the words might be *nurse, bread,* or *doctor;* nonwords might be *smuke, pable, reab.* The person to whom these words were presented had to decide whether each row was a word or a nonword, indicating yes or no decisions by pressing different keys. Reaction time was measured separately for each row, and the procedure was repeated with hundreds of different words and nonwords.

The significant findings from this experiment come from those trials in which all three rows of letters were words rather than nonwords. Such trials included the following sequences: (1) adjacent and related words, like *smoke, nurse, doctor,* in which the second and third words had related meanings; (2) separated and related words, like *nurse, smoke, doctor,* in which the first and third words had related meanings; and (3) unrelated words, like *bread, smoke, doctor,* in which the words all had unrelated meanings. People recognized the third word of a sequence more rapidly if it was related in meaning to one of the preceding words than if the words were unrelated. This happened whether the related words were adjacent or separated in the sequence, although the effect was larger for adjacent related words. [Fig. 11-17]

Through this study and others, Meyer arrived at a plausible explanation of how the memory retrieves information. Retrieving a word from long-term memory, he found, temporarily increases neural activity at the locations of other nearby related words in the memory structure. This "spreading activation" reduces the amount of additional activity needed to recognize a related word and, therefore, speeds the reaction if the word is presented soon enough. While Meyer's experiments implied that the activation decays over time, they showed that it persists for at least a few seconds and outlasts the decision about an intervening unrelated word.

Thus, unlike short-term memory, long-term memory seems to involve

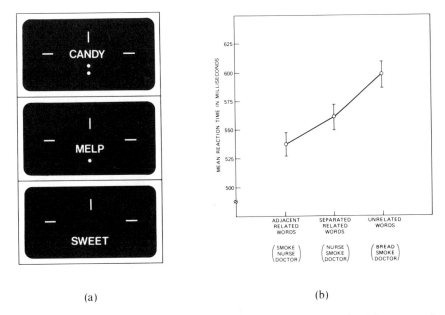

(a)   (b)

Fig. 11-17. Information retrieval time in long-term memory. (a) Sample of three rows of letters shown, one after another, to a person with words and nonwords mixed randomly. The person had to decide for each row of letters whether it was a word or nonword; reaction time was measured for each row. The procedure was repeated with hundreds of different words and nonwords and with 20 participants. (b) Results of measured reaction time for the third row of letters only for those trials where all three rows were words and where the words were either adjacent related, separated related, or unrelated. The data show that people recognized the third row word faster if it was related to one of the preceding words— particularly if it is adjacent related (e.g., *smoke, nurse, doctor*).

mechanisms quite different in character from those of digital computers. Of course, it is not too surprising that the two memories function in essentially different ways. Even the search rate of 30 items per second that was observed for short-term memory is much too slow for finding a particular word among the thousands a person has learned. Reading, writing, or speaking a single sentence would take several minutes! So either (1) there is some useful way to limit the number of words that are searched for in long-term memory, or (2) the search rate in long-term memory is much faster, or (3) many words are searched for at the same time. Of these alternatives, the findings about memory organization supported the first possibility.

Three other findings about long-term memory storage and retrieval should be mentioned here. In 1967, Shepard demonstrated the remarkably large capacity of human memory in distinguishing previously seen pictures from others.[80] In 1973, K. H. Smith showed that people use rules in retrieving learned sequences, especially rules about positional regularities. He found that, as a consequence, structured material is recalled more accurately.[81] In 1975, T. K. Landauer showed that many phenomena of human learning, forgetting, and retrieval can be explained by a memory in which neither storage location nor search organization depends on content.[82]

5.1.3 Short-Term Visual Information Storage

Around 1960, Sperling [Fig. 11-18] and E. Averbach and A. S. Coriell discovered that visual information from a large display of alphanumeric characters remains available for a brief period after the display is turned off, and they investigated the characteristics of the underlying visual memory. Information representation in this memory is similar to the visual input itself. The memory has a large capacity, but is short-lived. They measured its decay time (about 0.25 second) and capacity (as much as 12 letters—much more than can be read out accurately) and showed that old information is erased by new.[83,84]

Fig. 11-18. G. Sperling, who made fundamental contributions in research on vision and visual memory.

5.1.4 *Categorization Based on Stored Knowledge*

Meyer showed that two successive operations are used in retrieving information from memory about category inclusion: the first determines whether two categories intersect and involves self-terminating comparisons of category names; the second determines whether one category is wholly contained in the other and involves self-terminating comparison of category attributes. This work showed that at least two kinds of information about a semantic category are stored in human memory and do not require "computation": the attributes of the semantic category and the other categories it intersects.[85,86] Meyer also showed that one decision about category membership can facilitate a second such decision, insofar as the categories are semantically related.

Landauer and Meyer showed that the effect of category size on the time taken by decisions about category membership is due to size *per se* and not merely to the correlated variation in degree of semantic relatedness, supporting a category-search model of categorizing performance.[87]

5.2 Language Comprehension and Word Recognition

During the 1960s, Bell Labs psychologists began to investigate language comprehension at both the sentence and word levels. For example, Smith and L. E. McMahon conducted a series of studies on the process of sentence comprehension and on the way people extract information from the memory representation of a sentence, again using reaction-time methods. They demonstrated that more processing time was needed for passive than active sentences, and showed how syntactic structure controls the relative accessibility of different items of information in the sentence.[88] J. S. Sachs showed that while attempting to comprehend connected discourse, a listener stores the original form of a sentence only for the short time necessary for comprehension to occur.[89] When a semantic interpretation has been made, the meaning is stored more permanently. Memory of the meaning, therefore, does not depend on memory of the original form of the sentence.

Bell Labs psychologists investigating word recognition in the 1970s found that close relations between the meanings of words help people to recognize and pronounce the words faster, especially when the words are hard to see because of visual distortions. Close relations between word meanings also facilitate the comprehension of some sentences, as indicated by how long a person takes to decide whether the sentences are true or false. The facilitation is not universal, however. When the relation between the meanings of two words must be analyzed carefully, their semantic proximity may actually inhibit mental processing.

These results, along with additional findings, support the hypothesis that human memory includes a semantic network that represents various categories of objects at distinct locations that are linked so as to specify their relations with each other. The memory structure probably influences a number of different mental processes that use it. One possible access route to the network is through a set of detectors designed to accumulate sensory information in the brain and signal the presence of particular words. There also appear to be processes for searching and comparing pieces of knowledge after a person finds the memory locations of designated categories.[90]

J. C. Johnston showed that the perceptual advantage of words over strings of unrelated letters is due not to the constraining influence of context but to the formation in the brain of higher-level (word-level) perceptual codes, in addition to letter codes.[91] Evidence that he collected showed that identification of a word is mediated by identification of its component letters; it also showed the existence of word-level detectors. Johnston used variations in a phenomenon in which recognition of a letter in a word is more accurate than recognition of the letter in isolation.[92]

Meyer and coworkers investigated the mechanism of how context aids the recognition of ambiguous words, supporting a selective-access hypothesis (only the context-appropriate meaning is activated) as opposed to the hypothesis that all meanings are activated and only one used.[93] They also showed that the recognition of visually displayed words is mediated by phonemic as well as visual codes.[94] Landauer and L. A. Streeter discovered that the structural properties of common and rare words differ in several respects important in understanding the well-known effects of word frequency on recognition.[95]

5.3 New Methods of Analyzing Mental Processes

Two examples of influential techniques developed and used by Bell Labs scientists investigating human information processing are the partial-report method, or information sampling, and the additive-factor method.

5.3.1 Partial-Report Method

The partial-report or information-sampling method was developed by Sperling and by Averbach and Coriell in their studies of visual information storage[96] (see section 5.1.3 in this chapter). Because the amount that can be stored is much greater than the amount that can be recalled about a visual display, only these information-sampling methods could reveal its large initial capacity and its rapid decay. After its development, the partial-report method was used in hundreds of studies in other laboratories.

5.3.2 Additive-Factor Method

In 1969, Sternberg introduced an additive-factor method that could be used to decompose mental actions into successive information-processing stages, study their properties, and localize new phenomena among the stages already identified. The method's main feature was the search for noninteracting effects of experimental factors on mean reaction time. Much other Bell Labs work using reaction-time measurements made use of the method, which also had considerable impact on researchers elsewhere who were concerned with such topics as word perception, visual search, retrieval from short-term and long-term memory, sentence comprehension, mental arithmetic, imagery, and the control of physical movements.[97]

5.4 Control of Action

In the late 1970s, a new area of research was initiated on how people control the movements of their arms, fingers, and articulatory organs of speech. For example, Sternberg and coworkers showed, in studies of both finger movements in typing and in articulator movements in speech, that the execution of a memorized action sequence involves the retrieval of subprograms for action units from a motor program for the whole sequence prepared in advance.[98,99] By analyzing the autocovariance of the sequence of inter-response intervals, A. M. Wing showed that control of the timing of repetitive movements is based on separate time-keeping and movement-generation processes, that successive movement delays are correlated, and that the variability of movement delays is strongly influenced by which muscles are used to generate the movement.[100] In investigating how people control the time interval between a pair of successive movements, D. A. Rosenbaum and O. Patashnik discovered a time-consuming process of "clock-setting" that must be delayed until just before execution of the first response.[101]

5.5 Reasoning, Decision Making, and Selective Attention

In the late 1970s, Bell Labs psychologists expanded their research on reasoning, decision making, and selective attention. One area of interest was decision making under conditions of uncertainty. Earlier, Jenkins and W. C. Ward had discovered systematic errors in people's judgment of the contingency, or degree of correlation, between two streams of events.[102,103] Later, in collaboration with psychologists at the University of Michigan, D. H. Krantz discovered that decision making under uncertainty is a train-able skill in the sense that small amounts of training can make the application of statistical heuristics to everyday problems both more likely and more effective.[104]

M. L. Shaw showed that when a binary decision must be based on information from several stimulus sources (as in the division of perceptual attention) or on information about more than one attribute or variable, people evaluate the sources or attributes separately and independently, making covert binary decisions about each, and then combine these covert decisions.[105,106] Although not optimal, this approach appears to reduce the complexity of mental "computations."

5.6 Impact on Telephone Operating Procedures and Research Experiments in Other Fields

Results of Bell Laboratories research suggested ways to improve communication by increasing a person's rate of processing information and by reducing errors. For example, the fact that information in short-term memory may be stored or retrieved in an acoustic form, as shown by G. Sperling and R. G. Speelman,[107] suggested that the jobs of telephone operators and craftspeople should be designed to minimize listening and talking when information is being held in short-term memory, since these activities interfere more with the memory than looking and writing do. For the same reason, the symbols in alphanumeric sequences should be selected to minimize similarities among their sounds.

Another implication of such experiments was that if the order of symbols is not important, then sequences of numbers or letters in short-term memory can be processed faster (as shown by Sternberg[108]) and more accurately (as shown by Sperling and Speelman[109]). When this is not so, as with phone numbers, the seriousness of errors can still be reduced. For example, frequently called telephones can be assigned numbers that do not turn into other working numbers when adjacent digits are interchanged.

Bell Laboratories discoveries about human information processing influenced research far removed from the topics originally investigated. Scientists outside Bell Labs used some of the experimental procedures and theories developed at Bell Labs to study child development and aging, the effects of acceleration in space and of hallucinogenic drugs, and the nature of aphasia, schizophrenia, and mental retardation.[110] New questions about the nature of visual memory were explored in numerous studies using partial-report methods,[111,112] and reaction-time methods were employed to attack a growing variety of other questions about mental processes, both fundamental and applied.[113]

VI. SOCIAL PSYCHOLOGY

Topics in social psychology, especially several concerned with interpersonal communication, were the focus of active research in the 1960s and 1970s. M. Deutsch and R. M. Krauss used two-person experimental bargaining games to study factors causing interpersonal conflict and influencing its outcome. They found that bargainers who possessed a means of retaliation were less likely to reach mutually satisfactory agreements. Communication between the bargaining parties was helpful in conflict resolution only when the parties were oriented toward reaching agreement; otherwise, it tended to make the conflict worse.[114]

S. Rosenberg and B. D. Cohen developed a laboratory communication task to investigate the processes by which a speaker selects an utterance that distinguishes one object (the referent) from another and the processes by which a listener uses the utterance to identify the referent. Experimental data were well described by a stochastic model with two processes (sampling and comparison) for the speaker and one process (comparison) for the listener.[115,116]

Krauss, P. D. Bricker, and others developed a two-person communication task to investigate the conditions under which communicators could converge on a language for encoding unfamiliar objects. They found that the efficiency of encoding was critically dependent on feedback the sender got from the receiver. When feedback was missing, distorted, or temporally delayed, senders encoded messages that were both longer and less effective.[117]

The use of multidimensional scaling of questionnaire responses by Wish, Deutsch, and S. J. Kaplan to discover four dimensions that underlie people's judgments of interpersonal relationships was discussed above[118] (see section 3.3 in this chapter). Later a similar set of dimensions was also found to underlie judgments about episodes of actual interpersonal communication.[119] These findings provided a useful framework for other research on interpersonal relations and communication.

VII. CONCLUDING COMMENT

The overall success of the Behavioral Research Center was due in considerable measure to its effective coupling to the larger environment in which it was situated. With the growth of the center from two members of staff in 1955 to over 25 members in the early 1980s, it acquired the ability to tackle important questions in the Bell System, it achieved a reputation in the scientific world, and it established an important resource in Bell Laboratories.

REFERENCES

1. A. Bavelas, "Communication Patterns in Task-oriented Groups," in *Group Dynamics: Research and Theory*, ed. D. Cartwright and A. Zander (Evanston, Illinois: Row, Peterson, 1953), pp. 493-506.
2. F. J. Roethlisberger and W. J. Dickson, *The Hawthorne Studies, 1924-1974: A Synopsis* (New York: Western Electric Co., 1974).
3. C. I. Hovland, "Two New Social Science Research Units in Industrial Settings," *Amer. Psychol.* 16 (February 1961), pp. 87-91.
4. B. F. Skinner, *Technology of Teaching* (New York: Appelton, 1968).
5. H. O. Holt and J. Hammock, "Books as Teaching Machines: Some Data," in *Applied*

Programed Instruction, ed. S. Margulies and L. D. Eigen (New York: John Wiley, 1962), pp. 50-56.

6. H. O. Holt, *A Programmed Learning Course in Basic Electricity* (AT&T Operations Department, 1962).

7. E. Z. Rothkopf, "Some Conjectures about Inspection Behavior in Learning from Written Sentences and the Response Mode Problem in Programmed Self-Instruction," *J. Programmed Instruction* **2** (Winter 1963), pp. 31-45; E. Z. Rothkopf, "Some Theoretical and Experimental Approaches to Problems in Written Instruction," in *Learning and the Educational Process,* ed. J. D. Krumboltz (Chicago: Rand McNally Company, 1965), pp. 193-221; E. Z. Rothkopf and E. E. Bisbicos, "Selective Facilitative Effects of Interspersed Questions on Learning from Written Material," *J. Educ. Psychol.* **58** (February 1967), pp. 56-61; E. Z. Rothkopf, "Two Scientific Approaches to the Management of Instruction," in *Learning Research and School Subjects,* ed. R. M. Gagné and W. J. Gephart (Itasca, Illinois: Peacock Publishers, 1968), pp. 107-132.

8. E. Z. Rothkopf and E. U. Coke, "Repetition Interval and Rehearsal Method in Learning Equivalences from Written Sentences," *J. Verb. Learn. Verb. Behav.* **2** (December 1963), pp. 406-416.

9. E. Z. Rothkopf and E. U. Coke, "Variations in Phrasing, Repetition Intervals, and the Recall of Sentence Material," *J. Verb. Learn. Verb. Behav.* **5** (February 1966), pp. 86-91.

10. E. Z. Rothkopf and E. U. Coke, "Learning about Added Sentence Fragments Following Repeated Inspection of Written Discourse," *J. Exp. Psychol.* **78** (October 1968), pp. 191-199; E. Z. Rothkopf, "Experiments on Mathemagenic Behavior and the Technology of Written Instruction," in *Verbal Learning Research and the Technology of Written Instruction,* ed. E. Z. Rothkopf and P. E. Johnson (New York: Columbia University Teachers College Press, 1971), pp. 284-303; E. Z. Rothkopf and R. Kaplan, "An Exploration of the Effect of Density and Specificity of Instructional Objectives on Learning from Text," *J. Educ. Psychol.* **63** (August 1972), pp. 295-302.

11. See references 8 and 9.

12. T. K. Landauer, "Memory Without Organization: Properties of a Model with Random Storage and Undirected Retrieval," *Cog. Psychol.* **7** (October 1975), pp. 495-531.

13. T. K. Landauer, "Consolidation in Human Memory: Retrograde Amnestic Effects of Confusable Items in Paired-Associate Learning," *J. Verb. Learn. Verb. Behav.* **13** (February 1974), pp. 45-53.

14. T. K. Landauer, "Quantity and Quality in Knowledge," in *Structural/Process Models of Complex Human Behavior,* ed. J. M. Scandura and C. J. Brainerd (Netherlands: Sijthoff & Noordhoff, 1978), pp. 177-206.

15. E. U. Coke and E. Z. Rothkopf, "Note on a Simple Algorithm for a Computer-Produced Reading Ease Score," *J. Appl. Psychol.* **54** (June 1970), pp. 208-210.

16. R. Flesch, "A New Readability Yardstick," *J. Appl. Psychol.* **32** (June 1948), pp. 221-233.

17. D. E. Egan and D. D. Grimes-Farrow, "Differences in Mental Representations Spontaneously Adopted for Reasoning," *Memory Cog.* **10** (July 1982), pp. 297-307.

18. D. E. Egan, "Retrospective Reports Reveal Differences in People's Reasoning," *Bell Syst. Tech. J.* **62** (July/August 1983), pp. 1675-1697.

19. E. Z. Rothkopf, D. G. Fisher, and M. J. Billington, "Effects of Spatial Context During Acquisition on the Recall of Attributive Information," *J. Exp. Psychol.: Learn., Memory, Cog.* **8** (March 1982), pp. 126-138.

20. H. M. Jenkins, "Resistance to Extinction when Partial Reinforcement is Followed by Regular Reinforcement," *J. Exp. Psychol.* **64** (November 1962), pp. 441-450.

21. H. M. Jenkins, "The Effect of Discriminative Training on Extinction," *J. Exp. Psychol.* **61** (February 1961), pp. 111-121.

22. A. Gelperin, "Neuroethological Studies of Associative Learning in Feeding Control

Systems," in *Neuroethology and Behavioral Physiology*, ed. F. Huber and H. Mark (Berlin: Springer-Verlag, 1983), pp. 189-205

23. G. Young and A. S. Householder, "Discussion of a Set of Points in Terms of Their Mutual Distances," *Psychometrika* **3** (March 1938), pp. 19-22.

24. R. N. Shepard, "The Analysis of Proximities: Multidimensional Scaling with an Unknown Distance Function," *Psychometrika* **27** (June 1962), pp. 125-140, and (September 1962), pp. 219-246.

25. R. N. Shepard, "Metric Structures in Ordinal Data," *J. Math. Psychol.* **3** (July 1966), pp. 287-315.

26. W. S. Torgeson, *Theory and Methods of Scaling* (New York: John Wiley, 1958).

27. J. B. Kruskal, "Multidimensional Scaling by Optimizing Goodness of Fit to a Nonmetric Hypothesis," *Psychometrika* **29** (March 1964), pp. 1-27.

28. J. B. Kruskal, "Nonmetric Multidimensional Scaling: A Numerical Method," *Psychometrika* **29** (June 1964), pp. 115-129.

29. J. D. Carroll and P. Arabie, "Multidimensional Scaling," in *Annual Review of Psychology* **31**, ed. M. R. Rosenzweig and L. W. Porter (Palo Alto, California: Annual Reviews Inc., 1980), pp. 607-649.

30. E. Z. Rothkopf, "Signal Similarity and Reception Errors in Early Morse Code Training," in *Symposium on Air Force Human Engineering, Personnel, and Training Research*, Publ. No. 455, ed. G. Finch and F. Cameron (Washington, D.C.: National Academy of Sciences-National Research Council, 1956), pp. 229-235.

31. R. N. Shepard, "Analysis of Proximities as a Technique for the Study of Information Processing in Man," *Human Factors* **5** (February 1963), pp. 33-48.

32. R. N. Shepard, C. I. Hovland, and H. M. Jenkins, "Learning and Memorization of Classifications," *Psychol. Monogr.* **75**, Whole No. 517 (1961), pp. 1-42; R. N. Shepard and J. J. Chang, "Stimulus Generalization in the Learning of Classifications," *J. Exp. Psychol.* **65** (January 1963), pp. 94-102; R. N. Shepard, "Attention and the Metric Structure of the Stimulus Space," *J. Math. Psychol.* **1** (January 1964), pp. 54-87.

33. J. D. Carroll and J. J. Chang, "Analysis of Individual Differences in Multidimensional Scaling via an N-way Generalization of 'Eckart-Young' Decomposition," *Psychometrika* **35** (September 1970), pp. 283-319.

34. M. Wish, "The Structure of Interpersonal Communication," *Ind. Res.* **17** (November 15, 1975), pp. 24-31.

35. M. Wish, M. Deutsch, and S. J. Kaplan, "Perceived Dimensions of Interpersonal Relations," *J. Pers. Soc. Psychol.* **33** (April 1976), pp. 409-420.

36. J. D. Carroll, "Individual Differences and Multidimensional Scaling," in *Multidimensional Scaling: Theory and Applications in the Behavioral Sciences*, Vol. 1, ed. R. N. Shepard, A. K. Romney, and S. B. Nerlove (New York and London: Seminar Press, 1972), pp. 105-155.

37. J. D. Carroll, "Models and Methods for Multidimensional Analysis of Preferential Choice (or Other Dominance) Data," in *Similarity and Choice*, ed. E. D. Lantermann and H. Feger (Bern, Stuttgart, Vienna: Hans Huber Publishers, 1980), pp. 234-289.

38. M. Wish, "User and Non-user Conceptions of PICTUREPHONE Service," *Proc. Human Factors Soc. 19th Ann. Meeting*, Dallas (October 14-16, 1975), pp. 81-86; J. D. Carroll and S. Pruzansky, "Discrete and Hybrid Scaling Models," in *Similarity and Choice*, ed. E. D. Lantermann and H. Feger (Bern, Stuttgart, Vienna: Hans Huber Publishers, 1980), pp. 108-139; W. S. DeSarbo and J. D. Carroll, "Three-way Metric Unfolding," *Proc. 3rd ORSA/TIMS Special Interest Conf. Market Measurements Anal.* (March 1981), pp. 157-183.

39. B. Julesz, "Binocular Depth Perception of Computer-Generated Patterns," *Bell Syst. Tech. J.* **39** (September 1960), pp. 1125-1162.

40. B. Julesz, "Binocular Depth Perception Without Familiarity Cues," *Science* 145 (July 24, 1964), pp. 356-362.

41. B. Julesz, *Foundations of Cyclopean Perception* (Chicago: University of Chicago Press, 1971).

42. B. Julesz and W. Kropfl, "Binocular Neurons and Cyclopean Visually Evoked Potentials in Monkey and Man," *Annals of the New York Academy of Sciences* 388 (June 1982), pp. 37-44.

43. D. Fender and B. Julesz, "Extension of Panum's Fusional Area in Binocularly Stabilized Vision," *J. Opt. Soc. Amer.* 57 (June 1967), pp. 819-830.

44. B. Julesz and S. C. Johnson, " 'Mental Holography': Stereograms Portraying Ambiguously Perceivable Surfaces," *Bell Syst. Tech. J.* 47 (December 1968), pp. 2075-2093.

45. B. Julesz and R. A. Schumer, "Early Visual Perception," in *Annual Review of Psychology* 9, ed. M. R. Rosenzweig and L. W. Porter (Palo Alto, California: Annual Reviews Inc., 1981), pp. 575-627.

46. D. Marr, *Vision: A Computational Investigation into the Human Representation and Processing of Visual Information* (San Francisco: W. H. Freeman, 1982).

47. See reference 41.

48. B. Julesz and R. A. Payne, "Differences Between Monocular and Binocular Stroboscopic Movement Perception," *Vision Res.* 8 (April 1968), pp. 433-444.

49. B. Julesz and R. I. Hesse, "Inability to Perceive the Direction of Rotational Movement of Line Segments," *Nature* 225 (January 17, 1970), pp. 243-244.

50. C. F. Stromeyer, III and B. Julesz, "Spatial-Frequency Masking in Vision: Critical Bands and Spread of Masking," *J. Opt. Soc. Amer.* 62 (October 1972), pp. 1221-1232.

51. B. Julesz, "Visual Pattern Discrimination," *IRE Trans. Inform. Theory* IT-8 (February 1962), pp. 84-92.

52. M. Rosenblatt and D. Slepian, "Nth Order Markov Chains with Every N Variables Independent," *J. Soc. Ind. Appl. Math.* 10 (1962), pp. 537-549; B. Julesz, E. N. Gilbert, L. A. Shepp, and H. L. Frisch, "Inability of Humans to Discriminate Between Visual Textures that Agree in Second-Order Statistics—Revisited," *Perception* 2 (1973), pp. 391-405; B. Julesz, E. N. Gilbert, and J. D. Victor, "Visual Discrimination of Textures with Identical Third-Order Statistics," *Biol. Cybern.* 31 (1978), pp. 137-140.

53. B. Julesz, "Textons: The Elements of Texture Perception, and Their Interactions," *Nature* 290 (March 12, 1981), pp. 91-97.

54. B. Julesz and J. R. Bergen, "Textons, The Fundamental Elements in Preattentive Vision and Perception of Textures," *Bell Syst. Tech. J.* 62 (July/August 1983), pp. 1619-1645.

55. See reference 42.

56. B. Julesz and J. J. Chang, "Interaction Between Pools of Binocular Disparity Detectors Tuned to Different Disparities," *Biol. Cybern.* 22 (1976), pp. 107-119.

57. J. J. Chang and B. Julesz, "Displacement Limits, Directional Anisotropy and Direction versus Form Discrimination in Random-dot Cinematograms," *Vision Res.* 23 (1983), pp. 639-646.

58. J. Krauskopf and J. D. Mollon, "The Independence of the Temporal Integration Properties of Individual Chromatic Mechanisms in the Human Eye," *J. Physiol.* 219 (1971), pp. 611-623; J. D. Mollon and J. Krauskopf, "Reaction Time as a Measure of the Temporal Response Properties of Individual Colour Mechanisms," *Vision Res.* 13 (January 1973), pp. 27-40; J. Krauskopf, "Contributions of the Primary Chromatic Mechanisms to the Generation of Visual Evoked Potentials," *Vision Res.* 13 (December 1973), pp. 2289-2298.

59. J. Krauskopf, "On Identifying Detectors," in *Visual Psychophysics and Physiology*, ed. J. C. Armington, J. Krauskopf, and B. R. Wooten (New York: Acadmic Press, 1978), pp. 283-295.

60. J. Krauskopf, "Discrimination and Detection of Changes in Luminance," *Vision Res.* 20 (1980), pp. 671-677.

61. J. Z. Levinson, "Flicker Fusion Phenomena," *Science* **160** (April 5, 1968), pp. 21-28.
62. G. Sperling and M. M. Sondhi, "Model for Visual Luminance Discrimination and Flicker Detection," *J. Opt. Soc. Amer.* **58** (August 1968), pp. 1133-1145.
63. G. Sperling, "Temporal and Spatial Visual Masking. I. Masking by Impulse Flashes," *J. Opt. Soc. Amer.* **55** (May 1965), pp. 541-559.
64. G. Sperling, "Model of Visual Adaptation and Contrast Detection," *Perception Psychophys.* **8** (September 1970), pp. 143-157.
65. G. Sperling, "Binocular Vision: A Physical and Neural Theory," *Amer. J. Psychol.* **83** (December 1970), pp. 461-534.
66. C. S. Harris and A. R. Gibson, "Is Orientation-Specific Color Adaptation in Human Vision Due to Edge Detectors, After Images, or 'Dipoles'?" *Science* **162** (December 1968), pp. 1506-1507.
67. C. S. Harris, "Insight or Out of Sight?: Two Examples of Perceptual Plasticity in the Human Adult," in *Visual Coding and Adaptability*, ed. C. S. Harris (Hillsdale, New Jersey: Lawrence Erlbaum Associates, 1980), pp. 95-149.
68. N. Weisstein and C. S. Harris, "Visual Detection of Line Segments: An Object-Superiority Effect," *Science* **186** (November 1974), pp. 752-755.
69. N. Weisstein, M. C. Williams, and C. S. Harris, "Depth, Connectedness, and Structural Relevance in the Object-Superiority Effect: Line Segments are Harder to See in Flatter Patterns," *Perception* **11** (1982), pp. 5-17.
70. N. Weisstein and C. S. Harris, "Masking and the Unmasking of Distributed Representations in the Visual System," in *Visual Coding and Adaptability*, ed. C. S. Harris (Hillsdale, New Jersey: Lawrence Erlbaum Associates, 1980), pp. 317-364.
71. N. Weisstein, C. S. Harris, K. Berbaum, J. Tangney, and A. Williams, "Contrast Reduction by Small Localized Stimuli: Extensive Spatial Spread of Above-Threshold Orientation-Selective Masking," *Vision Res.* **17** (March 1977), pp. 341-350.
72. J. R. Pierce and J. E. Karlin, "Reading Rates and the Information Rate of a Human Channel," *Bell Syst. Tech. J.* **36** (March 1957), pp. 497-516.
73. S. Sternberg, "The Discovery of Processing Stages: Extensions of Donders' Method," in *Attention and Performance II*, ed. W. G. Koster (Amsterdam: North-Holland, 1969), pp. 276-314.
74. S. Sternberg, "High-speed Scanning in Human Memory," *Science* **153** (August 5, 1966), pp. 652-654.
75. S. Sternberg, "Memory Scanning: Mental Processes Revealed by Reaction-Time Experiments," *Amer. Sci.* **57** (Winter 1969), pp. 421-457.
76. S. Sternberg, "Memory Scanning: New Findings and Current Controversies," *Quart. J. Exp. Psychol.* **27** (February 1975), pp. 1-32.
77. G. Sperling and R. G. Speelman, "Acoustic Similarity and Auditory Short-Term Memory: Experiments and a Model," in *Models of Human Memory*, ed. D. A. Norman (New York: Academic Press, 1970), pp. 151-202.
78. R. W. Schvaneveldt and D. E. Meyer, "Retrieval and Comparison Processes in Semantic Memory," in *Attention and Performance IV*, ed. S. Kornblum (New York: Academic Press, 1973), pp. 395-409.
79. D. E. Meyer and R. W. Schvaneveldt, "Meaning, Memory Structure, and Mental Processes," *Science* **192** (April 1976), pp. 27-33.
80. R. N. Shepard, "Recognition Memory for Words, Sentences, and Pictures," *J. Verb. Learn. Verb. Behav.* **6** (February 1967), pp. 156-163.
81. K. H. Smith, "Effect of Exceptions on Verbal Reconstructive Memory," *J. Exp. Psychol.* **97** (January 1973), pp. 119-139.
82. See reference 12.
83. G. Sperling, "A Model for Visual Memory Tasks," *Human Factors* **5** (February 1963), pp. 19-31.

84. E. Averbach and A. S. Coriell, "Short-Term Memory in Vision," *Bell Syst. Tech. J.* **40** (January 1961), pp. 309-328.

85. D. E. Meyer, "On the Representation and Retrieval of Stored Semantic Information," *Cog. Psychol.* **1** (August 1970), pp. 242-300.

86. D. E. Meyer, "Correlated Operations in Searching Stored Semantic Categories," *J. Exp. Psychol.* **99** (June 1973), pp. 124-133.

87. T. K. Landauer and D. E. Meyer, "Category Size and Semantic-Memory Retrieval," *J. Verb. Learn. Verb. Behav.* **11** (October 1972), pp. 539-549.

88. K. H. Smith and L. E. McMahon, "Understanding Order Information in Sentences: Some Recent Work at Bell Laboratories," in *Advances in Psycholinguistics*, ed. G. Flores d'Arcais and W. J. M. Levelt (Amsterdam: North-Holland, 1970), pp. 253-274.

89. J. S. Sachs, "Recognition Memory for Syntactic and Semantic Aspects of Connected Discourse," *Perception Psychophys.* **2** (September 1967), pp. 437-442.

90. See reference 78.

91. J. C. Johnston, "A Test of the Sophisticated Guessing Theory of Word Perception," *Cog. Psychol.* **10** (April 1978), pp. 123-153.

92. J. C. Johnston and J. L. McClelland, "Experimental Tests of a Hierarchical Model of Word Identification," *J. Verb. Learn. Verb. Behav.* **19** (October 1980), pp. 503-524.

93. R. W. Schvaneveldt, D. E. Meyer, and C. A. Becker, "Lexical Ambiguity, Semantic Context, and Visual Word Recognition," *J. Exp. Psychol.: Hum. Perception Perform.* **2** (May 1976), pp. 243-256.

94. D. E. Meyer, R. W. Schvaneveldt, and M. G. Ruddy, "Functions of Graphemic and Phonemic Codes in Visual Word-Recognition," *Memory Cog.* **2** (April 1974), pp. 309-321.

95. T. K. Landauer and L. A. Streeter, "Structural Differences Between Common and Rare Words: Failure of Equivalence Assumptions for Theories of Word Recognition," *J. Verb. Learn. Verb. Behav.* **12** (April 1973), pp. 119-131.

96. See references 83 and 84.

97. See reference 73.

98. S. Sternberg, S. Monsell, R. L. Knoll, and C. E. Wright, "The Latency and Duration of Rapid Movement Sequences: Comparisons of Speech and Typewriting," in *Information Processing in Motor Control and Learning*, ed. G. E. Stelmach (New York: Academic Press, 1978), pp. 117-152.

99. S. Sternberg, C. E. Wright, R. L. Knoll, and S. Monsell, "Motor Programs in Rapid Speech: Additional Evidence," in *Perception and Production of Fluent Speech*, ed. R. A. Cole (Hillsdale, New Jersey: Lawrence Erlbaum Associates, 1980), pp. 507-534.

100. A. M. Wing, "Effects of Type of Movement on the Temporal Precision of Response Sequences," *Brit. J. Math. Statist. Psychol.* **30** (May 1977), pp. 60-72.

101. D. A. Rosenbaum and O. Patashnik, "Time to Time in the Human Motor System," in *Attention and Performance VIII*, ed. R. S. Nickerson (Hillsdale, New Jersey: Lawrence Erlbaum Associates, 1980), pp. 93-106.

102. H. M. Jenkins and W. C. Ward, "Judgment of Contingency Between Responses and Outcomes," *Psychol. Monogr.* **79,** Whole No. 594 (1965), pp. 1-17.

103. W. C. Ward and H. M. Jenkins, "The Display of Information and Judgment of Contingency," *Can. J. Psychol.* **19** (September 1965), pp. 231-241.

104. R. E. Nisbett, D. H. Krantz, C. Jepson, and G. T. Fong, "Improving Inductive Inference," in *Judgment Under Uncertainty: Heuristics and Biases*, ed. D. Kahneman, P. Slovic, and A. Tversky (Cambridge, England: Cambridge University Press, 1982), pp. 445-449.

105. M. L. Shaw, "Division of Attention among Spatial Locations: A Fundamental Difference between Detection of Letters and Detection of Luminance Increments," in *Attention and Performance X*, ed. H. Bouma and D. G. Bouwhuis (Hillsdale, New Jersey: Lawrence Erlbaum Associates, 1984), pp. 109-121.

106. M. L. Shaw, "Attending to Multiple Sources of Information: I. The Integration of Information in Decision Making," *Cog. Psychol.* **14** (July 1982), pp. 353-409.

107. See reference 77.

108. See reference 74.

109. See reference 77.

110. See reference 76.

111. M. Coltheart, "Iconic Memory and Visible Persistence," *Perception Psychophys.* **27** (March 1980), pp. 183-228.

112. M. T. Turvey, "Visual Processing and Short-Term Memory," in *Handbook of Learning and Cognitive Processes: Volume 5, Human Information Processing,* ed. W. K. Estes (Hillsdale, New Jersey: Lawrence Erlbaum Associates, 1978), pp. 91-142.

113. W. G. Chase, "Elementary Information Processes," in *Handbook of Learning and Cognitive Processes: Volume 5, Human Information Processing,* ed. W. K. Estes (Hillsdale, New Jersey: Lawrence Erlbaum Associates, 1978), pp. 19-90.

114. M. Deutsch and R. M. Krauss, "The Effect of Threat Upon Interpersonal Bargaining," *J. Abnorm. Soc. Psychol.* **61** (September 1960), pp. 181-189; M. Deutsch and R. M. Krauss, "Studies of Interpersonal Bargaining," *J. Conflict Resolution* **6** (March 1962), pp. 52-76; R. M. Krauss and M. Deutsch, "Communication in Interpersonal Bargaining," *J. Pers. Soc. Psych.* **4** (November 1966), pp. 572-577.

115. S. Rosenberg and B. D. Cohen, "Referential Processes of Speakers and Listeners," *Psychol. Rev.* **73** (May 1966), pp. 208-231.

116. S. Rosenberg and B. D. Cohen, "Speakers' and Listeners' Processes in a Word-Communication Task," *Science* **145** (September 11, 1964), pp. 1201-1203.

117. R. M. Krauss and S. Weinheimer, "Concurrent Feedback, Confirmation and the Encoding of Referents in Verbal Communication," *J. Pers. Soc. Psych.* **4** (September 1966), pp. 343-346; R. M. Krauss and P. D. Bricker, "Effects of Transmission Delay and Access Delay on the Efficiency of Verbal Communication," *J. Acoust. Soc. Amer.* **41** (February 1967), pp. 286-292; R. M. Krauss, P. S. Vivekananthan, and S. Weinheimer, " 'Inner Speech' and 'External Speech': Characteristics and Communication Effectiveness of Socially and Nonsocially Encoded Messages," *J. Pers. Soc. Psych.* **9** (August 1968), pp. 295-300.

118. See reference 35.

119. M. Wish, R. G. D'Andrade, and J. E. Goodnow II, "Dimensions of Interpersonal Communication: Correspondences Between Structures for Speech Acts and Bipolar Scales," *J. Pers. Soc. Psych.* **39** (November 1980), pp. 848-860.

Chapter 12

Economics Research in the Communications Industry

This chapter describes the first steps taken in establishing an economics research center at Bell Laboratories. This effort paralleled several events at AT&T—the founding of a new journal, the "Bell Journal of Economics and Management Science," the establishment of a Council of Economic Advisers of eminent economists, and the creation of a Regulatory Research Section. In addition to recruitment, which started with the acquisition of outstanding new PhDs in economics, seminars and self-study programs were set up. Early research was undertaken on such topics as financial modeling and the cost of capital, the possibility of rate-base regulation leading to the wasting of capital resources, and peak-load pricing. One of the group's major accomplishments was the creation of a new theory of natural monopoly for the multiproduct firm. The theory established both the cost and demand bases of natural monopoly and showed that, in spite of lower costs, a multiproduct natural monopoly is not necessarily invulnerable to attack by rivals. A by-product of this work was the first coherent theory of cross subsidization. Along with the development of theory, the group did extensive empirical studies of both the cost of and demand for Bell System products and services. Later work contributed significantly to a number of fundamental areas of economics that were not specific to regulation, including the application of the concept of stochastic dominance to unify and extend financial theory, the development of the notion of estimation risk, the theoretical study of equilibria in which supply and demand are unequal and may result in unemployment, and theoretical studies of labor markets.

I. ESTABLISHMENT OF AN ECONOMICS RESEARCH CENTER AT BELL LABORATORIES

Economics research at Bell Laboratories historically dealt with economies in the design and engineering of new telephone equipment and plant. To

---

Principal author: E. E. Zajac.

cope with rapidly growing technical innovation and with its relations to legal and political questions of regulation, competition, and monopoly that confronted the Bell System in the 1960s, Bell Laboratories organized for the first time a formal economics research group. An intense effort was made to create a group that could analyze all aspects of the Bell System's economic environment and assess and develop new economic theory and practices. The group became responsible for the analysis of such crucial issues for government-regulated businesses as the relationship among prices, demands for service, revenues, and costs. For example, it was soon realized that the existing economic theory of natural monopoly was extremely simple, confined almost entirely to a firm producing a single product. One of the group's major accomplishments was the creation of a new theory of natural monopoly for the multiproduct firm. This theory established both the cost and demand bases of natural monopoly and showed that, in spite of lower costs, a multiproduct natural monopoly is not necessarily invulnerable to attack by rivals. To further the understanding of the economics of the regulated firm and the economic environment in which it finds itself, the Bell System also founded the *Bell Journal of Economics and Management Science* in 1970.

1.1 Genesis and Early Research in Economic and Financial Modeling

Since its beginning, Bell Laboratories has evaluated in economic terms alternative ways of engineering new telephone plant. However, organized, systematic economics research as an aid to Bell System policymakers was not begun until the mid-1960s. The impetus for such policy-directed research, in addition to stimulus from accelerated technical opportunities, came from two major sources. First, from the mid-1960s to the early 1980s, regulatory activity was intense, both at the federal and state levels. This activity encompassed the determination of rates of return, prices, and the conditions for allowing new firms to enter the telecommunications industry, as well as a host of questions not previously addressed. Second, with the advent of digital computers, quantitative and analytical techniques and simulation models of economic activities began to play an increasing role in guiding business management decisions. Thus, by the mid-1960s, it was apparent that policy-directed economics research could help not only in regulatory activities but in internal management as well.

The initial exposure at Bell Laboratories to these economic problems was through the consulting activities of mathematicians and statisticians, principally F. W. Sinden, M. E. Terry, M. B. Wilk, and E. E. Zajac. These consultations began in late 1965 in connection with the investigation by the Federal Communications Commission (FCC) of the Bell System, FCC Docket 16258, and revealed that many economic issues were far reaching, important, and not clearly defined. To understand better and cope with these issues, AT&T established a Council of Economic Advisers, composed of distinguished outside economists, as well as a Regulatory Research Section and began publishing the *Bell Journal of Economics and Management Science.* In March 1968, Bell Labs established a formal economics research effort with Sinden and Zajac as the nucleus. The economics effort was combined with computer graphics—which in 1968 was still a research interest of both Sinden and Zajac—and became the Economic Analysis and Graphics Research Department.

In 1968, P. B. Linhart of the Analytical Support Center of AT&T, who had transferred in 1967 from the Bell Labs switching study center, set up an informal committee to study financial modeling. Linhart's effort was motivated in part by the important role played by an econometric financial model introduced by Professor M. J. Gordon of the University of Rochester in the FCC investigation of the Bell System.[1] In addition to Sinden and Zajac, Linhart invited, among others, J. H. Weber and G. R. Faulhaber to serve on his financial modeling committee. As a result, in March 1968, Faulhaber and E. E. Bailey (then a member of Faulhaber's supervisory group working on telephone traffic problems) also turned their attention to economics. This effort evolved in 1970 into the Economic Modeling Group under V. O. Mowery. Subsequently, the group grew and formed two departments that were part of the Bell Labs Operations Research Center: Economics Research under Bailey and Economic Modeling and Financial Research under Faulhaber. Although located in two different centers in two different locations, Sinden and Zajac at the Murray Hill, New Jersey labs and Bailey and Faulhaber at the Holmdel, New Jersey labs, they maintained close contact, influenced each other's work, and frequently collaborated. [Fig. 12-1]

From the outset, research in economics was patterned after research in other disciplines at Bell Labs: it stressed the development of fundamental understanding and methodology. Thus, on issues involving the Bell System and the nation, the researchers' hope was that the knowledge developed would help both industry and government policymakers. In this regard, publication of research by Bell Labs scientists in scholarly journals was especially important, not only to assure high-quality research and to disseminate the findings, but also to benefit from exposure to viewpoints of scholars outside of the Bell System.

1.2 Introduction of Study Seminars

Although the goals of policy-directed economics research were obvious from the outset, how to achieve these goals was less clear. For example, there was the problem of obtaining a sufficiently strong nucleus of high-caliber economists. Research economists who could do high-quality work would be best attracted by other high-quality research economists. But

Fig. 12-1.   Bell Laboratories economists in the Holmdel and Murray Hill, New Jersey locations confer by video link. From left: F. W. Sinden, E. E. Zajac, and J. H. Rohlfs. On the monitor: G. R. Faulhaber and E. E. Bailey.

how were the first such economists to be obtained? Second, although Bailey, Faulhaber, Sinden, and Zajac were experienced applied mathematicians and engineers, and Bailey had her undergraduate degree in economics, none had a PhD in economics.

Several measures were adopted to cope with these start-up problems. Sinden and Zajac organized a self-study seminar at Murray Hill. Typically, when a new book aroused interest, a seminar was set up to analyze the book—individual members taking turns lecturing on the book's contents. In such a manner, about ten mathematicians worked through a number of standard texts on micro- and macroeconomics in 1968 and 1969. In addition, both Faulhaber and Bailey obtained PhDs in economics at Princeton under the Bell Labs Doctoral Support Plan. To supplement the group's self-education, established economists were invited to spend summers at Bell Labs. Finally, and most importantly, the Bell Labs group embarked on a program of learning by doing, i.e., by formulating and analyzing economic problems and publishing the results.

1.3 Recruitment and Consolidation

These educational efforts were paralleled by a vigorous recruiting program. The growth of the staff was slow; only a few candidates met the high standards required, and these were typically the most sought after by leading universities. But by the end of 1975, in addition to the nucleus, the recruiting effort had added seven members of staff at Murray Hill and five at Holmdel.

At the end of the 1970s, two eminent economists joined the economic research staff: P. Fishburn, Research Professor of Management Science at Pennsylvania State University, an authority on voting, decision, and choice theory, and R. Radner, member of the National Academy of Sciences and former chairman of the Economics Department of the University of California at Berkeley, and an expert on the economics of information and internal organization.

In 1978, roughly ten years after the formal beginning of economics research at Bell Laboratories, the Murray Hill and Holmdel economics groups were consolidated to form the Economics Research Center, with Zajac as its director.

II. EFFECT OF RATE-OF-RETURN REGULATION ON RESOURCE ALLOCATION

In a seminal paper published in 1962, H. Averch and L. L. Johnson of the Rand Corporation pointed out that rate-of-return regulation might cause a firm to allocate resources improperly.[2] The two researchers constructed a static, theoretical model in which a profit-maximizing, regulated firm was allowed a rate of return that exceeded the firm's cost of capital. Their model indicated that the firm would be driven to operate inefficiently with an overintensive use of capital. [Fig. 12-2]

The issue raised by the Averch-Johnson model was important, and was analyzed by several Bell Labs economists. One of the earliest Bell Labs contributions in this area was Zajac's 1970 paper that appeared in the *American Economic Review*, which recast the model into a simple geometric framework that could be understood without the use of advanced mathematics.[3] In 1970, Bailey and J. C. Malone published a study in the *Bell Journal of Economics* on the consequences of alternative objectives for the firm, such as maximizing output instead of profit.[4] Later, both Bailey, in her PhD dissertation (published as a book in 1973), and Zajac extended the basic Averch-Johnson model to study the possibility of the firm's acquiring unproductive capital to increase its potential profits by increasing its rate base. (This type of activity was sometimes called wasting, padding the rate base, or gold plating.)[5,6] Bailey and Zajac found that, within the framework of the basic, static Averch-Johnson model, unproductive use of capital could be profitable, but only under special circumstances—essentially when the firm had exhausted all productive outlets for capital. Still further extensions of the model were developed by Bailey in her book.

The assumptions of perfect information and a static world were obvious problems of the basic Averch-Johnson model. Bailey, R. D. Coleman,[7] and E. G. Davis[8] formulated dynamic models to encompass regulatory lag.

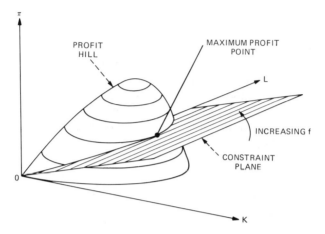

Fig. 12-2. A geometric exposition of the Averch-Johnson Theory. The regulated firm's profit (π) is assumed to depend on the amount of capital (K) and labor (L) it uses and can be depicted as a profit hill. Regulation imposes the constraint: $\pi \leq (f - i)K$, where f is the fair rate of return on capital (decided by the regulators) and i is the cost of capital (determined by the capital markets). The firm must operate on the profit hill on or below the constraint plane ($\pi = (f - i)$). If $f > i$, the constraint plane is swung upward like a door hinged on the L axis. Clearly, *the maximum profit point occurs at the point of maximum K along the intersection of the constraint plane and the profit hill* (unless regulation is ineffective, i.e., f is so large that the constraint plane is above the top of the profit hill). It also can be shown by simple geometric arguments that at the level of output corresponding to the maximum profit point, the firm uses more capital and less labor than if it were minimizing cost, and thus supports the Averch-Johnson thesis: if regulators allow $f > i$, the firm will be driven to non-cost-minimizing behavior. [Zajac, *Amer. Econ. Rev.* **60** (1970): 119.]

This work was further extended by V. S. Bawa and D. S. Sibley, who allowed for rate-setting based on the firm's average cost in a previous test period and with the probability of rate review in one period dependent on the firm's profitability in previous periods.[9] In the Bawa-Sibley model, the firm tends to exercise cost minimization even if the allowed rate of return exceeds the cost of capital.

III. THE THEORY OF MULTIPRODUCT NATURAL MONOPOLY

While the term natural monopoly had been known and used by economists for a long time, a formal theory of natural monopoly was largely the work of Bell Laboratories economists in the early 1970s. The theory produced a number of surprising insights.

Two papers in 1972, one by Zajac[10] and the other by Faulhaber,[11] laid the groundwork for the development of the theory. Both dealt with the problem of cross subsidization in the pricing structure of a multiproduct firm. Zajac showed that in the presence of cross elasticities of demand, cross subsidization is an elusive concept, and under some seemingly reasonable definitions of the term, subsidy-free prices may fail to exist. Faulhaber considered general cost functions and showed that game theory could be a useful tool for addressing cross subsidization. In particular, a cooperative-solution concept, referred to as the core, satisfied the intuitive notion of subsidy-free prices. Furthermore, Faulhaber pointed out that the phenomenon of no subsidy-free prices, illustrated by Zajac with a special, somewhat artificial example, appeared to be a general possibility, even when a natural monopoly could produce its output at less cost than two or more firms. The use of the core was further developed in Faulhaber's 1975 paper.[12] Also, the basic game theoretic approach was extended by W. W. Sharkey to include benefit as well as cost considerations.[13]

Soon after publication of the Faulhaber and Zajac papers in 1972, I. W. Sandberg studied the properties of multiproduct demand functions and subadditive cost structures and their use in the formulation of conditions under which a single, regulated, multiproduct firm could produce larger outputs of higher-quality products at lower prices than could a multifirm alternative.[14,15] This study was followed by the development by W. J. Baumol of Princeton and New York Universities, together with Bailey and R. D. Willig of Bell Labs, of the theory of sustainable prices for a multiproduct natural monopoly.[16] Sustainable prices are those that satisfy a profit constraint and deter competitive entry. The most surprising result of the work of Baumol, Bailey, and Willig was that, under certain conditions, Ramsey prices satisfied the conditions for sustainability. (Ramsey prices are those that maximize consumer welfare while giving the firm's shareholders a fair return on their investment.) The theory of sustainability was extended in the work of J. C. Panzar and Willig.[17]

Panzar and Willig also contributed to the theory of natural monopoly by defining and showing the importance of economies of scope, which are economies of joint production. They also showed that the usual definition of economies of scale could be usefully modified when considering questions involving natural monopoly.

The work of Bell Labs economists in creating a modern theory of natural monopoly was later summarized in a book by Sharkey.[18] It led to the development by Baumol, Panzar, and Willig of the theory of contestable markets (an extension of the classical competitive model to incorporate increasing returns to scale).[19]

IV. REGULATORY PRICING THEORY

In 1970, a paper by Baumol and D. F. Bradford directed the attention of regulatory economists to the pricing decisions of multiproduct regulated firms subject to a budget constraint (revenue requirement).[20] Building on the 1927 work of F. Ramsey, they stated the now-famous, inverse elasticity rule: to maximize economic welfare, the percentage deviation of a product price above marginal cost should be inversely related to its elasticity of demand.[21] The fundamental research of Willig on consumers' surplus provided a methodology that made this approach intuitive and accessible, yet precise; i.e., it maximized economic welfare (surplus) subject to the constraint that the firm retain financial viability.[22]

The first type of multiproduct model analyzed at Bell Labs arose naturally from the fact that most utilities must serve periodically fluctuating demand with a given level of capacity; i.e., utilities characteristically face a peak-load problem. This model fits into the above framework when it is realized that day and night output can be viewed as different products. Bailey first combined the peak-load and Averch-Johnson models and demonstrated that only peak-period users benefit from regulation and that a level of capacity greater than the welfare-maximizing level may result. Bailey and L. J. White (then of Princeton University) analyzed additional models that could result in the optimal peak-period price being lower than that in the off-peak period. Panzar and R. E. Dansby also developed additional insights into the theory of peak-load pricing by relaxing some of the fundamental assumptions employed in the traditional literature. Bell Labs peak-load-pricing research was summarized by Bailey and E. B. Lindenberg in a paper published in 1976.[23]

Still another approach to the welfare-pricing problem was J. H. Rohlfs' economy-wide or general equilibrium model, which had a constrained (regulated) sector and an unconstrained (competitive) sector. The result, published in 1976, was a generalized economic surplus inequality that signaled price changes that improved welfare.[24] An elementary summary of modern regulatory pricing theory, aimed at lawyers, engineers, and other noneconomists, was published by Zajac in 1978.[25]

V. EMPIRICAL STUDIES OF COMMUNICATIONS SERVICES AND PRICING

Good economic decisions require facts as well as theory, and the Economics Research Group undertook a wide variety of empirical studies. The empirical work also aided in testing and strengthening economic theories. In addition, it provided prototypes for larger-scale studies done outside of the Economics Research Center.

5.1 Full Additional Cost Study

One of the earliest empirical studies in economics at Bell Labs was an analysis of the cost of telephone service. In the late 1960s, a task force at

Bell Laboratories under Wilk, working with people in R. L. Breedlove's Management Science Section at AT&T, constructed a model of the Bell System toll services that related prices, demands for service, revenues, and costs. Known as the Full Additional Cost Model, it made it possible for planners to estimate both the incremental costs and revenues that would result from price changes in Message Toll Service (MTS) or Wide Area Telephone Service (WATS) and was used for simulation studies to provide insights for MTS and WATS rate schedule design.

5.2 Demand for PICTUREPHONE* Visual Telephone Service

In the late 1960s, PICTUREPHONE visual telephone service (see Chapter 3, section 2.2.2) was offered in Pittsburgh and Chicago, but customer response was disappointing. Rohlfs, an economist, and M. Wish, a psychologist, collaborated to analyze this problem. They designed an interview study and supervised its administration to business executives in Chicago and to users of PICTUREPHONE visual telephone service within the Bell System. They then analyzed the responses from the perspectives of economics and psychology. (See Chapter 11, section 3.4.)

Their principal conclusion from the perspective of economics was that the weak sales of PICTUREPHONE visual telephone service were not caused solely by the start-up problem. Rohlfs and Wish suggested that the PICTUREPHONE visual telephone service might have expanded its sales under a different tariff structure: a low, fixed, monthly charge in conjunction with a high usage charge. Although the Rohlfs-Wish proposed tariff structure was not tried, the project led to Rohlfs' theory of the evolution of a communications service, when an individual subscriber's demand depends on who else subscribes.[26] It also led to Wish's research on the factors that influence the way people communicate with each other and on procedures for measuring verbal and nonverbal aspects of communication.[27]

5.3 Economically Efficient Pricing

The first study to estimate economically efficient prices† was begun in 1974 by Willig and Bailey and published in 1977. They analyzed interstate traffic and argued that increasing short-haul rates and decreasing long-haul rates would improve economic efficiency.[28] Another study was undertaken by Rohlfs in late 1975. He concluded that economic efficiency

---

* Registered service mark of AT&T.

† Economic efficiency takes account of consumption as well as production. Briefly, an economy is economically efficient when goods and services are produced at minimum cost and respond to consumers' desires.

would be increased if local rates were substantially increased and long-distance rates were cut in half. Moreover, he argued that this restructuring of rates might be essential, given the competitive environment in telecommunications. Rohlfs' completed study was submitted to Congress by AT&T in the fall of 1978 and was issued as a Bell Laboratories Discussion Paper in 1979.[29]

5.4 Demographic Determinants of Local Residence Demand

An important part of policy research is to determine the significance of a proposed policy change for some groups in the population. In 1972, this issue arose with respect to the possible initiation of more usage-sensitive rates for residential service, and was initially considered by Sinden and W. H. Williams. Subsequently, B. B. Brandon initiated a major empirical study of a sample of residential customers in Chicago. She was later helped by P. S. Brandon and a number of other economists and statisticians in an extensive analysis of the calling patterns of groups classified by demographic variables, such as age of head of household and income.[30]

VI. FINANCIAL ECONOMICS RESEARCH

Bell Labs research in the application of modern quantitative methods to corporate financial problems was triggered by testimony in 1967 by Gordon, who was first to use quantitative modeling techniques in FCC regulatory proceedings. One of the first efforts was Sinden's study of financial flows, which grew directly out of his critical analysis of the Gordon model. The work took two main paths: computer simulation of the financial flows, including interactive graphic output, and characterization of the flows by a set of differential equations whose properties could be studied. Among other things, Sinden's work showed that regulatory decisions that appear to favor one party often produce contrary effects in the future, so that the net effect in the present-worth sense is nearly neutral. In particular, Linhart, J. L. Lebowitz, and Sinden showed such effects in connection with the choice between capitalizing and expensing of costs.[31]

This early work by Sinden and others provided an incentive to study the nature and measurement of risk and the explicit analysis of risk-return tradeoffs in determining optimal financial decisions of individuals and corporations. Contributions to the theory of portfolio management, capital market equilibrium analysis, and pricing of financial assets were made possible by two early developments: the application of theoretical methods to the study of risk and return in the financial markets and the study of the impact of estimation risk on these markets.

6.1 Development and Application of New Financial Theory

Subsequent to Gordon's 1967 FCC docket testimony, attempts were made to introduce concepts of modern financial economics into regulatory proceedings to estimate the return on equity required by investors. At the same time, these concepts were being applied to the Bell System pension funds by those in AT&T responsible for its management, to the measurement of portfolio performance, the evaluation of money managers, and the asset mix decisions, as well as to financial planning at AT&T Treasury, typified by W. M. Boyce's 1970 development of rules for the optimal timing of the issuance of bonds.[32] However, the development and application of these ideas were hindered by the dependence on two crucial assumptions of the new theory: (1) that the probability distribution of rates of return was normal, or Gaussian, and (2) that this probability distribution was known and agreed upon by participants in the capital market. In 1974, Bawa developed mathematical techniques to surmount these problems.[33]

This research extended the concept of risk used heretofore in the financial literature. For a wide class of probability distributions, optimal choices could be characterized by the expected return and this new measure of risk. This led Bawa and Lindenberg[34] to show that if all investors in the capital market chose portfolios on this basis, expected return on investment in the capital market is a linear function of the (appropriately specified) measure of risk.

6.2 Estimation Risk

The development of these ideas did not resolve the problem that the theory required the investors to know and agree on the probability distribution of asset returns. However, Bawa, S. J. Brown, and R. W. Klein were able to surmount this problem by further theory developed in their 1979 book, *Estimation Risk and Optimal Portfolio Choice*.[35]

This research in financial economics was applied to the design of practical and fruitful tools for Bell System financial operations. For example, in 1975, Bawa and Lindenberg developed computer software for an asset allocation planning model for the Bell System pension fund. The model used principles of modern financial economics to simplify the problem of allocating periodic corporation pension fund contributions to alternative investment vehicles. Bawa and Brown also developed pension fund performance measures using these principles and developed guidelines for the evaluation of money managers. K. Ramaswamy together with Professor R. Litzenberger of Stanford developed rate-of-return testimony based on the capital asset pricing model of modern financial economics. Ramaswamy also developed training materials to familiarize required earnings staff at AT&T and lawyers with the model and concepts of financial theory.

VII. OTHER ISSUES IN ECONOMIC THEORY

The earliest research by Bell Labs economists was devoted to understanding the consequences of rate-of-return regulation, investigating appropriate modes of public utility pricing, and studying financial questions of importance to the Bell System. As economics research expanded, other questions of interest to the Bell System began to receive attention. In papers published in 1973 and 1974, Sandberg considered a nonlinear input-output economic model and derived theorems that facilitated perturbation analyses of equilibria.[36] C. A. Futia studied the possible existence of equilibria in which supply does not necessarily equal demand in all of the economy's markets.[37] The work suggested possible explanations of long-term unemployment. Finally, D. S. Sibley studied the effect of wage uncertainties on consumption.[38]

Other areas explored were the theoretical underpinnings of the much-used consumer-surplus methodology (started by Willig in his PhD dissertation of 1973, and further pursued by Zajac),[39] the economics of innovation in a regulated industry (Bailey),[40] and the effect on the demand for labor of a firm's uncertain future profits (Sibley).[41]

By the beginning of the 1980s the Economics Research Center at Bell Laboratories had evolved into a center for the study of diverse economics problems of interest to the Bell System.

REFERENCES

1. M. J. Gordon testimony in Federal Communications Commission Docket 16258, Exhibits 17 and 17a, 1967.
2. H. Averch and L. L. Johnson, "Behavior of the Firm Under Regulatory Constraint," *Amer. Econ. Rev.* **52** (December 1962), pp. 1053-1069.
3. E. E. Zajac, "A Geometric Treatment of Averch-Johnson's Behavior of the Firm Model," *Amer. Econ. Rev.* **60** (March 1970), pp. 117-125.
4. E. E. Bailey and J. C. Malone, "Resource Allocation and the Regulated Firm," *Bell J. Econ. Manage. Sci.* **1** (Spring 1970), pp. 129-142.
5. E. E. Bailey, *Economic Theory of Regulatory Constraint* (Lexington, Massachusetts: Lexington Books, 1973).
6. E. E. Zajac, "Note on 'Gold Plating' or 'Rate Base Padding,' " *Bell J. Econ. Manage. Sci.* **3** (Spring 1972), pp. 311-315.
7. E. E. Bailey and R. D. Coleman, "The Effect of Lagged Regulation in an Averch-Johnson Model," *Bell J. Econ. Manage. Sci.* **2** (Spring 1971), pp. 278-292.
8. E. G. Davis, "A Dynamic Model of the Regulated Firm with a Price Adjustment Mechanism," *Bell J. Econ. Manage. Sci.* **4** (Spring 1973), pp. 270-282.
9. V. S. Bawa and D. S. Sibley, "Dynamic Behavior of a Firm Subject to Stochastic Regulatory Review," Bell Laboratories Discussion Paper No. 38, September 1975 (Murray Hill, New Jersey: Bell Laboratories Economics Research Center).

10. E. E. Zajac, "Some Preliminary Thoughts on Subsidization," *Proc. Conf. Commun. Policy Res.*, Washington, D.C. (November 17-18, 1972), pp. 1-16.

11. G. R. Faulhaber, "On Subsidization: Some Observations and Tentative Conclusions," *Proc. Conf. Commun. Policy Res.*, Washington, D.C. (November 17-18, 1972), pp. 17-47.

12. G. R. Faulhaber, "Cross-Subsidization: Pricing in Public Enterprises," *Amer. Econ. Rev.* **65** (December 1975), pp. 966-977.

13. W. W. Sharkey, "Suggestions for a Game-Theoretic Approach to Public Utility Pricing and Cost Allocation," *Bell J. Econ.* **13** (Spring 1982), pp. 57-68.

14. I. W. Sandberg, "Some Theorems Concerning Multifirm Alternatives to the Single Regulated Multiservice Firm," *IEEE Trans. Syst. Man Cybern.* **5** (March 1975), pp. 201-208.

15. I. W. Sandberg, "Two Theorems on Justification of the Multiservice Regulated Company," *Bell J. Econ.* **6** (Spring 1975), pp. 346-356.

16. W. J. Baumol, E. E. Bailey, and R. D. Willig, "Weak Invisible Hand Theorems on the Sustainability of Multiproduct Natural Monopoly," *Amer. Econ. Rev.* **67** (June 1977), pp. 350-365.

17. J. C. Panzar and R. D. Willig, "Economies of Scale in Multi-output Production," *Quart. J. Econ.* **91** (August 1977), pp. 481-493.

18. W. W. Sharkey, *The Theory of Natural Monopoly* (New York: Cambridge University Press, 1982).

19. W. J. Baumol, J. C. Panzar, and R. D. Willig, *Contestable Markets and The Theory of Industry Structure* (New York: Harcourt, Brace, Jovanovich, 1982).

20. W. J. Baumol and D. F. Bradford, "Optimal Departures from Marginal Cost Pricing," *Amer. Econ. Rev.* **60** (June 1970), pp. 265-283.

21. F. Ramsey, "A Contribution to the Theory of Taxation," *Econ. J.* **37** (March 1927), pp. 47-61.

22. R. D. Willig, "Consumer's Surplus Without Apology," *Amer. Econ. Rev.* **66** (September 1976), pp. 589-597.

23. E. E. Bailey and E. B. Lindenberg, "Peak Load Pricing Principles: Past and Present," in *New Dimensions in Public Utility Pricing,* ed. H. M. Trebing (East Lansing, Michigan: Michigan State University Press, 1976), pp. 9-31.

24. J. H. Rohlfs, "Evaluation of Changes in a Suboptimal Economy," *Rev. Econ. Stud.* **43** (June 1976), pp. 359-362.

25. E. E. Zajac, *Fairness or Efficiency, An Introduction to Public Utility Pricing* (Cambridge, Massachusetts: Ballinger, 1978).

26. J. H. Rohlfs, "A Theory of Interdependent Demand for a Communications Service," *Bell J. Econ. Manage. Sci.* **5** (Spring 1974), pp. 16-37.

27. M. Wish, "The Structure of Interpersonal Communication," *Ind. Res.* **17** (November 1975), pp. 24-31.

28. R. D. Willig and E. E. Bailey, "Ramsey-Optimal Pricing of Long Distance Telephone Services," in *Pricing in Regulated Industries, Theory and Application,* ed. J. T. Wenders (Denver, Colorado: Mountain States Telephone and Telegraph Co., 1977), pp. 68-97.

29. J. H. Rohlfs, "Economically-Efficient Bell-System Pricing," Bell Laboratories Discussion Paper No. 138, January 1979 (Murray Hill, New Jersey: Bell Laboratories Economics Research Center).

30. B. B. Brandon, ed., *The Effect of the Demographics of Individual Households on Their Telephone Usage* (Cambridge, Massachusetts: Ballinger, 1981).

31. P. B. Linhart, J. L. Lebowitz, and F. W. Sinden, "The Choice Between Capitalizing and Expensing Under Rate Regulation," *Bell J. Econ. Manage. Sci.* **5** (Autumn 1974), pp. 406-419.

32. W. M. Boyce, "Stopping Rules for Selling Bonds," *Bell J. Econ. Manage. Sci.* **1** (Spring 1970), pp. 27-53.

33. V. S. Bawa, "Optimal Rules for Ordering Uncertain Prospects," *J. Fin. Econ.* **2** (March 1975), pp. 95-121; V. S. Bawa, "Admissible Portfolios for All Individuals," *J. Finan.* **31**

(September 1976), pp. 1169-1183; V. S. Bawa, "Mathematical Programming of Admissible Portfolios," *Manage. Sci.* **23** (March 1977), pp. 779-785.

34. V. S. Bawa and E. B. Lindenberg, "Capital Market Equilibrium in a Mean-Lower Partial Moment Model," *J. Fin. Econ.* **5** (November 1977), pp. 189-200.

35. V. S. Bawa, S. J. Brown, and R. W. Klein, *Estimation Risk and Optimal Portfolio Choice* (New York: North Holland, 1979).

36. I. W. Sandberg, "A Nonlinear Input-Output Model of a Multisectored Economy," *Econometrica* **41** (November 1973), pp. 1167-1182; I. W. Sandberg, "A Global Non-linear Extension of the LeChatelier-Samuelson Principle for Linear Leontief Models," *J. Econ. Theory* **7** (January 1974), pp. 40-52; I. W. Sandberg, "Some Comparative-Statics Results for Nonlinear Input-Output Models of a Multisectored Economy, and Related Results for Nonlinear Price-Demand Relations," *J. Econ. Theory* **8** (June 1974), pp. 248-258.

37. C. A. Futia, "The Existence of Non-Walrasian Equilibria," Bell Laboratories Discussion Paper No. 36, August 1975 (Murray Hill, New Jersey: Bell Laboratories Economics Research Center).

38. D. S. Sibley, "Permanent and Transitory Income Effects in a Model of Optimal Consumption with Wage Income Uncertainty," *J. Econ. Theory* **11** (August 1975), pp. 68-82.

39. E. E. Zajac, "An Elementary Road Map of Integrability and Consumer's Surplus," Bell Laboratories Discussion Paper No. 51, January 1976 (Murray Hill, New Jersey: Bell Laboratories Economics Research Center).

40. E. E. Bailey, "Innovation and Regulation," *J. Public Econ.* **3** (August 1974), pp. 285-295.

41. D. S. Sibley, "The Demand for Labor in a Dynamic Model of the Firm," *J. Econ. Theory* **15** (August 1977), pp. 252-265.

Credits

Credits

Figure 1-4 photo by Charles Nacke, Seattle, Washington.

Figure 1-10 from R. M. Foster, *Trans. Amer. Inst. Elec. Eng.* **51** (June 1932), p. 315. Copyright 1932 by the American Institute of Electrical Engineers.

Figure 1-13 adapted from C. A. Wright and A. F. Puchstein, *Telephone Communication* (1925), p. 402. Copyright 1925 by McGraw-Hill, New York.

Figure 1-19 from L. A. MacColl, *Fundamental Theory of Servomechanisms* (1945), p. 6. Copyright 1945 by D. Van Nostrand Co., New York.

Figure 1-21 from H. W. Bode, *Network Analysis and Feedback Amplifier Design* (1945), p. 316. Copyright 1945 by D. Van Nostrand Co., New York.

Figure 1-22 from K. S. Johnson, *Transmission Circuits for Telephone Communication* (1924), p. 144. Copyright 1924 by Western Electric Co., Lancaster, Pennsylvania.

Figure 1-27 from W. Keister, A. E. Ritchie, and S. H. Washburn, *The Design of Switching Circuits* (1951), p. 69. Copyright 1951 by D. Van Nostrand Co., New York.

Figure 1-29 from E. F. Moore, *Sci. Amer.* **195** (October 1956), pp. 118-119. Copyright 1956 by Scientific American, Inc.

Figure 2-2 from L. J. Sivian and S. D. White, *J. Acoust. Soc. Amer.* **4** (April 1933), p. 313. Copyright 1933 by the American Institute of Physics.

Figure 2-4 from H. Fletcher and W. A. Munson, *J. Acoust. Soc. Amer.* **5** (October 1933), p. 91. Copyright 1933 by the American Institute of Physics.

Figure 2-6 from H. K. Dunn and D. W. Farnsworth, *J. Acoust. Soc. Amer.* **10** (January 1939), p. 186. Copyright 1939 by the American Institute of Physics.

Figure 2-8 from H. Dudley, R. R. Riesz, and S. S. A. Watkins, *J. Franklin Inst.* **227** (June 1939), p. 748. Copyright 1939 by the Franklin Institute.

Figure 2-10a from H. Dudley, *J. Audio Eng. Soc.* **3** (1955), p. 179. Copyright 1955 by the Audio Engineering Society, Inc.

Figure 2-15 from J. L. Flanagan, *J. Acoust. Soc. Amer.* **51** (May 1972), p. 1385. Copyright 1972 by the American Institute of Physics. Reprinted with permission.

Figure 2-20b from J. L. Flanagan, *J. Acoust. Soc. Amer.* **51** (May 1972), p. 1380. Copyright 1972 by the American Institute of Physics. Reprinted with permission.

489

Transmission (1950), p. 127. Copyright 1950 by D. Van Nostrand Co., New York.

Figure 6-6 from G. C. Southworth, *Principles and Applications of Waveguide Transmission* (1950), pp. 338 and 341. Copyright 1950 by D. Van Nostrand Co., New York.

Figure 6-7 from G. C. Southworth, *Principles and Applications of Waveguide Transmission* (1950), p. 321. Copyright 1950 by D. Van Nostrand Co., New York.

Figure 6-8 from A. G. Fox, *Proc. IRE* **35** (December 1947), p. 1496. Copyright 1947 by the Institute of Radio Engineers, Inc.

Figure 6-10 from G. C. Southworth, *Principles and Applications of Waveguide Transmission* (1950), p. 346. Copyright 1950 by D. Van Nostrand Co., New York.

Figure 7-2 from J. Stone and C. A. Burrus, *Fiber Integrated Opt.* **2** (1979), p. 36. Copyright 1979 by Crane, Russak & Co., Inc. Reprinted with permission.

Figure 7-3 from C. A. Burrus and R. W. Dawson, *Appl. Phys. Lett.* **17** (August 1, 1970), p. 97. Copyright 1970 by the American Institute of Physics. Reprinted with permission.

Figure 7-6 from W. M. Muska, T. Li, and A. G. Dentai, *Electron. Lett.* **13** (September 1977), p. 606. Copyright 1977 by the Institution of Electrical Engineers, London. Reprinted with permission.

Figure 7-7 from D. L. Bisbee, *Appl. Opt.* **15** (March 1976), p. 797. Copyright 1976 by the Optical Society of America. Reprinted with permission.

Figure 7-9 from I. P. Kaminow, *Phys. Rev. Lett.* **6** (May 15, 1961), p. 528. Copyright 1961 by the American Physical Society. Reprinted with permission.

Figure 7-15 from J. C. Campbell, A. G. Dentai, T. P. Lee, and C. A. Burrus, *IEEE J. Quantum Electron.* **QE-16** (June 1980), pp. 601 and 602. Copyright 1980 by the Institute of Electrical and Electronics Engineers, Inc. Reprinted with permission.

Figure 7-16 from T. P. Lee, C. A. Burrus, and A. G. Dentai, *Electron. Lett.* **16** (October 23, 1980), pp. 845 and 846. Copyright 1980 by the Institution of Electrical Engineers, London. Reprinted with permission.

Figure 8-7 from J. H. McGuigan, *Proc. IRE* **41** (October 1953), p. 1439. Copyright 1953 by the Institute of Radio Engineers, Inc.

Figure 8-9 from W. A. Malthaner and H. E. Vaughan, *IRE Trans.* **4** (March 1955), p. 25. Copyright 1955 by the Institute of Radio Engineers, Inc.

Figure 8-10 photo supplied by Lehigh University Office of Public Information, Bethlehem, Pennsylvania.

Index

Index